FLORIDA
CHEMISTRY
MATTER & CHANGE

SCIENCE
NOTEBOOK

About the Consultant

Douglas Fisher, Ph.D. is a Professor in the Department of Teacher Education at San Diego State University. He is the recipient of an International Reading Association Celebrate Literacy Award, as well as a Christa McAuliffe Award for Excellence in Teacher Education. He has published numerous articles on reading and literacy, differentiated instruction, and curriculum design as well as books, such as *Improving Adolescent Literacy: Strategies at Work* and *Responsive Curriculum Design in Secondary Schools: Meeting the Diverse Needs of Students.* He has taught a variety of courses in SDSU's teacher credentialing program as well as graduate-level courses on English language development and literacy. He also has taught classes in English, writing, and literacy development to secondary school students.

mheducation.com/prek-12

Send all inquiries to:
McGraw-Hill Education
8787 Orion Place
Columbus, OH 43240

ISBN: 978-0-07-904385-6
MHID: 0-07-904385-2

Printed in the United States of America.

3 4 5 6 7 8 9 10 QSX 22 21 20 19 18

Table of Contents

Table of Contents

Note-Taking Tips

Your notes are a reminder of what you learned in class. Taking good notes can help you succeed in science. The following tips will help you take better classroom notes.

- Before class, ask what your teacher will be discussing in class. Review mentally what you already know about the concept.
- Be an active listener. Focus on what your teacher is saying. Listen for important concepts. Pay attention to words, examples, and/or diagrams your teacher emphasizes.
- Write your notes as clearly and concisely as possible. The following symbols and abbreviations may be helpful in your note-taking.

Word or Phrase	Symbol or Abbreviation	Word or Phrase	Symbol or Abbreviation
for example	e.g.	and	+
such as	i.e.	approximately	≈
with	w/	therefore	∴
without	w/o	versus	vs

- Use a symbol such as a star (★) or an asterisk (*) to emphasize important concepts. Place a question mark (?) next to anything that you do not understand.
- Ask questions and participate in class discussion.
- Draw and label pictures or diagrams to help clarify a concept.
- When working out an example, write what you are doing to solve the problem next to each step. Be sure to use your own words.
- Review your notes as soon as possible after class. During this time, organize and summarize new concepts and clarify misunderstandings.

Note-Taking Don'ts

- **Don't** write every word. Concentrate on the main ideas and concepts.
- **Don't** use someone else's notes. They may not make sense.
- **Don't** doodle. It distracts you from listening actively.
- **Don't** lose focus or you will become lost in your note-taking.

1 The Central Science

ESSENTIAL QUESTION

Write the Essential Question for this chapter.

_____

_____

_____

Use the "What I Know" column to list the things you know about the Essential Question. Then list the questions you have about the Essential Question in the "What I Want to Find Out" column. As you read the chapter, fill in the "What I Learned" column.

K *What I Know*	W *What I Want to Find Out*	L *What I Learned*

1 The Central Science

1 What is chemistry?

BUILD TO THE ESSENTIAL QUESTION

Read the items under Build to the Essential Question at the beginning of the lesson. Restate each in your own words.

_____

_____

REVIEW VOCABULARY

matter

Recall the definition of the Review Vocabulary term.

matter _____

_____

NEW VOCABULARY

chemistry

science

hypothesis

theory

scientific law

pure research

applied research

substance

mass

weight

model

Define each New Vocabulary term.

chemistry _____

_____

science _____

_____

hypothesis _____

_____

theory _____

_____

scientific law _____

_____

pure research _____

_____

applied research _____

_____

substance _____

_____

mass _____

_____

weight _____

_____

model _____

_____

Compare and contrast mass and weight using the Venn diagram below.

• does not reflect gravitational pull on matter
• a measure of the effect of gravitational pull on matter
• a measurement that reflects the amount of matter in an object

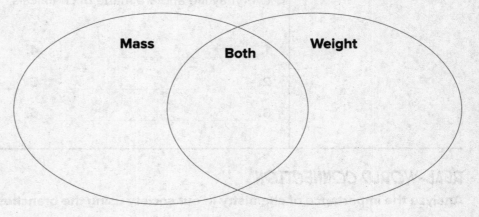

Organize the following terms by arranging them from largest to smallest.

macroscopic, submicroscopic, microscopic

_____

Explain a chemical model by completing the following sentences.

The _____, composition, and _____ of all matter can

be explained on a _____ level. All that we observe

depends on _____ and the _____ they undergo.

_____ seeks to explain the submicroscopic events that lead to

_____. One way to do this is by making a chemical

model, which is a _____ of a

_____.

GET IT? **Identify** two additional types of models that are used by scientists.

_____

_____

Describe scientific investigations by completing the following sentences. Pure research becomes _____ when scientists develop a hypothesis based on the data and try to solve a specific problem.

Identify six substances mentioned in the book that are important in everyday life and are made of chemicals.

1. _____   4. _____

2. _____   5. _____

3. _____   6. _____

REAL-WORLD CONNECTION
Analyze the importance of chemistry in our society using the branches of chemistry as examples.

_____

_____

_____

_____

_____

_____

_____

1 What is chemistry? (continued)

REVIEW IT!

1. **Explain** why the study of chemistry should be important to everyone.

_____

_____

_____

2. **Define** *substance* and give two examples of things that are substances.

_____

_____

_____

3. **Explain** why there are different branches of chemistry.

_____

_____

_____

4. **Explain** why scientists use mass instead of weight for their measurements.

_____

_____

_____

5. **Summarize** why it is important for chemists to study changes in the world at a submicroscopic level.

_____

_____

_____

6. **Infer** why chemists use models to study submicroscopic matter.

_____

_____

_____

1 What is chemistry? (continued)

7. Identify three models that scientists use, and explain why each model is useful.

_____

_____

_____

_____

8. Evaluate How would your mass and weight differ on the Moon? The gravitational force of the Moon is one-sixth the gravitational force on Earth.

_____

9. Evaluate If you put a scale in an elevator and weigh yourself as you ascend and then descend, does the scale have the same reading in both instances? Explain your answer.

_____

_____

_____

_____

10. Distinguish Jacques Charles described the direct relationship between temperature and volume of all gases at constant pressure. Should this be called Charles's law or Charles's theory? Explain.

_____

_____

1 The Central Science

2 Measurement

BUILD TO THE ESSENTIAL QUESTION

Read the items under Build to the Essential Question at the beginning of the lesson. Restate each in your own words.

_____

_____

REVIEW VOCABULARY

mass

Recall the definition of the Review Vocabulary term.

mass

_____

NEW VOCABULARY

base unit

second

meter

kilogram

kelvin

derived unit

liter

density

scientific notation

dimensional analysis

conversion factor

Define each New Vocabulary term.

base unit

_____

derived unit

_____

density

_____

scientific notation

_____

dimensional analysis

_____

conversion factor

_____

Match the SI base units below with their functions.

second	distance
meter	temperature
kilogram	time
kelvin	mass
liter	volume

2 Measurement (continued)

Units

Identify five items around your home that use SI units of measurement.

1. _____
2. _____
3. _____
4. _____
5. _____

Base Units and SI Prefixes

Sequence these prefixes from smallest to largest.

_____ pico		_____ giga	
_____ micro		_____ nano	
_____ deci		_____ milli	
_____ kilo		_____ centi	
_____ mega			

Compare and contrast the Kelvin scale and the Celsius scale.

_____

_____

_____

GET IT? **Infer** Which is warmer, 25°F or 25°C?

_____

Derived Units

Explain density by completing the following statement and equation.

Density is a _____ that _____ the _____ of an object to its _____.

density = ————

GET IT? **State** the quantities that must be known in order to calculate density.

_____

2 Measurement (continued)

Solve Read Example Problem 1 in your text.

YOU TRY IT

Problem

Determine the mass of an object that, when placed in a 25-mL graduated cylinder containing 14 mL of water, causes the level of the water to rise to 19 mL. The object has a density of 3.2 g/mL.

1. Analyze the Problem

Known: _____

Unknown: _____

You know the density and the volume of an object and must determine its mass; therefore, you will calculate the answer using the density equation.

2. Solve for the Unknown

Write the density equation.

_____ = _____

Rearrange the density equation to solve for mass.

_____

Substitute the known values for _____ and _____ into the equation.

_____

Multiply the values and units. The mL units will cancel out.

mass = _____ × _____ = _____

3. Evaluate the Answer

The two sides of the equation should be _____

density = _____

If you divide 16 g by 5.0 mL, you get _____

2 Measurement (continued)

Scientific Notation

Solve Read Example Problem 2 in your text.

YOU TRY IT

Problem
Change the following data into scientific notation:

a. The distance between Pluto and the Sun is 5,913,000 km.

b. The density of nitrogen gas, a major component of Pluto's atmosphere, is 0.0012506 g/cm^3.

1. Analyze the Problem

Known: _____

Unknown: _____

You are given two measurements. In both cases, the answers will be factors between 1 and 10 that are multiplied by a power of ten.

2. Solve for the Unknown

Move the decimal point to produce a factor between 1 and 10. Count the number of places the decimal point moved and the direction.

a.

The decimal point moved

_____ places to the _____.

b.

The decimal point moved

_____ places to the _____.

Remove the extra zeros at the end or beginning of the factor.

Multiply the result by 10^n where n equals the _____.

_____. When the decimal point moves to the left, n is a

_____ number. When the decimal point moves to the right,

n is a _____ number. Remember to add units to the answers.

a. _____

b. _____

3. Evaluate the Answer

The answers have _____ factors. The first factor is a number

between _____ and _____. In answer a, because the distance

to Pluto is a large number, 10 has a _____ exponent. In answer b,

because the density of nitrogen gas is a very small number, the

exponent is _____.

2 Measurement (continued)

GET IT? **Restate** the process used to add two numbers that are expressed in scientific notation.

_____

_____

Using Conversion Factors

Solve Read Example Problem 4 in your text.

YOU TRY IT

Problem

The Cassini probe heading toward Saturn reached speeds of 5.2 kilometers per second. How many meters per minute did it travel at this speed?

1. Analyze the Problem

Known: _____

Unknown: _____

You need conversion factors that relate kilometers to meters and

seconds to minutes. A conversion factor is a _____ of

_____ used to express _____ in

_____ .

2. Solve for the Unknown

First convert kilometers to meters. Set up the conversion factor so that the kilometer units will cancel out.

$$\frac{5.2 \text{ km}}{\text{s}} \times \frac{1000 \text{ m}}{1 \text{ km}} = \underline{\quad\quad} \frac{\text{m}}{\text{s}}$$

Next convert seconds to minutes. Set up the conversion factor so that the seconds will cancel out.

$$\frac{5200 \text{ m}}{\text{s}} \times \frac{60 \text{ s}}{1 \text{ min}} = \underline{\quad\quad} \frac{\text{m}}{\text{min}}$$

3. Evaluate the Answer

To check your answer, you can do the steps in reverse order.

$$\frac{5.2 \text{ km}}{\text{s}} \times \frac{60 \text{ s}}{1 \text{ min}} = \frac{312 \text{ km}}{\text{min}} \times \frac{1000 \text{ m}}{\text{km}} = \underline{\quad\quad} \frac{\text{m}}{\text{min}}$$

2 Measurement (continued)

REVIEW IT!

27. **Define** the SI units for length, mass, time, and temperature.

_____

28. **Describe** how adding the prefix mega- to a unit affects the quantity being described.

_____

29. **Compare** a base unit and a derived unit, and list the derived units used for density and volume.

_____

_____

30. **Calculate** Samples A, B, and C have masses of 80 g, 12 g, and 33 g, and volumes of 20 mL, 4 cm^3, and 11 mL, respectively. Which of the samples have the same density?

_____

_____

31. **Design** a concept map that shows the relationships among the following terms: _volume, derived unit, mass, base unit, time,_ and _length_.

32. **Describe** how scientific notation makes it easier to work with very large or very small numbers.

_____

_____

_____

33. **Write** a conversion factor relating cubic centimeters and milliliters.

_____

34. **Explain** how dimensional analysis is used to solve problems.

_____

_____

35. **Apply Concepts** A classmate converts 68 km to meters and gets 0.068 m as the answer. Explain why this answer is incorrect, and identify the likely source of the error.

_____

_____

36. **Organize** Create a flowchart that outlines when to use dimensional analysis and when to use scientific notation.

1 The Central Science

3 Uncertainty in Data

BUILD TO THE ESSENTIAL QUESTION

Read the items under Build to the Essential Question at the beginning of the lesson. Restate each in your own words.

_____

_____

_____

REVIEW VOCABULARY

dimensional analysis

Recall the definition of the Review Vocabulary term.

dimensional analysis

_____

_____

NEW VOCABULARY

accuracy

precision

error

percent error

significant figure

Define each New Vocabulary term.

accuracy

_____

_____

precision

_____

_____

error

_____

_____

percent error

_____

_____

significant figure

_____

_____

3 Uncertainty in Data (continued)

Accuracy and Precision

Explain percent error by completing the statement and equation below.

Percent error is the _____ of an _____ to an _____.

$$\text{Percent error} = \underline{\hspace{3cm}} \times 100$$

GET IT? **Summarize** why error is important.

_____

_____

Solve Read Example Problem 5 in your text.

YOU TRY IT

Problem

Calculating Percent Error

Calculate the percent errors. Report your answers to two places after the decimal point. The table below summarizes Student B's data.

Trial	Density (g/cm^3)	Error (g/cm^3)
1	1.40	−0.19
2	1.68	0.09
3	1.45	−0.14

1. Analyze the Problem

Known: _____

_____

Unknown: _____

Use the accepted value for density and the errors to calculate percent error.

2. Solve for the Unknown

Substitute each error into the percent error equation.

$$\text{percent error} = \frac{\underline{\hspace{2cm}}}{\text{accepted value}} \times 100$$

$$\text{percent error} = \frac{\underline{\hspace{2cm}}}{1.59 \text{ g/cm}^3} \times 100 = \boxed{}$$

$$\text{percent error} = \frac{\underline{\hspace{2cm}}}{1.59 \text{ g/cm}^3} \times 100 = \boxed{}$$

$$\text{percent error} = \frac{\underline{\hspace{2cm}}}{1.59 \text{ g/cm}^3} \times 100 = \boxed{}$$

3. Evaluate the Answer

The percent error is greatest for trial _____ which had the largest error, and smallest for trial _____, which was closest to the accepted value.

Significant Figures

Identify the significant numbers below by drawing a circle around them. Use the five rules for recognizing significant digits for reference.

0.025   325,078   5600

Rounding Numbers

Explain the rules for rounding numbers by completing the following sentences. Then complete the example of each rule for rounding numbers by rounding to three significant figures.

1. If the digit to the immediate right of the last significant figure is less than five, _____

   3.751 _____

2. If the digit to the immediate right of the last significant figure is greater than five, _____

   4.127 _____

3. If the digit to the immediate right of the last significant figure is equal to five and is followed by a nonzero digit, _____

   _____

   8.3253 _____

4. If the digit to the immediate right of the last significant figure is equal to five and is not followed by a nonzero digit, look at the last significant figure. _____

   _____

   1.4750 = _____ ; 1.4650 = _____

REVIEW IT!

50. State how a measured value is reported in terms of known and estimated digits.

_____

_____

51. **Define** *accuracy* and *precision*.

_____

_____

52. **Identify** the number of significant figures in each of these measurements of an object's length: 76.48 cm, 76.47 cm, and 76.59 cm.

_____

53. **Apply** The object in Question 52 has an actual length of 76.49 cm. Are the measurements in Question 52 accurate? Are they precise?

_____

_____

54. **Calculate** the error and percent error for each measurement in Question 52.

_____

_____

55. **Apply** Write an expression for the quantity 506,000 cm in which it is clear that all the zeros are significant.

_____

56. **Analyze Data** Students collected mass data for a group of coins. The mass of a single coin is 5.00 g. Determine the accuracy and precision of the measurements.

Number of coins	5	10	20	30	50
Mass (g)	23.2	54.5	105.9	154.5	246.2

_____

_____

_____

_____

1 The Central Science

4 Representing Data

BUILD TO THE ESSENTIAL QUESTION

Read the items under Build to the Essential Question at the beginning of the lesson. Restate each in your own words.

_____

_____

_____

REVIEW VOCABULARY

base unit

Recall the definition of the Review Vocabulary term.

base unit

_____

_____

NEW VOCABULARY

graph

independent variable

dependent variable

Define each New Vocabulary term.

graph

_____

independent variable

_____

dependent variable

_____

_____

4 Representing Data (continued)

Graphing

Draw and label (a) a circle graph and (b) a bar graph using the information in the table below.

Student Budget	
Budget items	**Percent**
Car insurance	45
Movies	6
Books	5
Clothing	30
Miscellaneous	4
Gas	10

Student Budget bar graph   Student Budget circle graph

The _____ best displays the data in the Student Budget

table because _____

_____ .

4 Representing Data (continued)

Graphing

GET IT? **Interpret** Which two food servings provide equal amounts of magnesium?

_____

Identify each of the following slopes.

_____ slope   _____ slope

Analyze whether the following sequences will likely plot as linear or nonlinear relationships.

Sequence A: **Sequence B:**

Result 1: 2   Result A: 31

Result 2: 4   Result B: 27

Result 3: 7   Result C: 49

Result 4: 10   Result D: 45

Answer: _____   Answer: _____

GET IT? Identify the graph that shows a direct relationship.

_____

4 Representing Data (continued)

Interpreting Graphs

Organize information about interpreting graphs by completing the sentences below.

Information on a graph typically consists of _____ types of

variables: _____ variables and _____ variables.

The relationship between the variables may reflect either a _____

or a _____ slope.

When reading the graph, you use either interpolation for _____

_____ or _____ for estimated

values beyond the plotted points.

GET IT? **Explain** why extrapolation might be less reliable than interpolation.

_____

_____

GET IT? **Interpret** By how much did the total ozone vary during the 9-month period shown for 1979–2010?

_____

_____

REVIEW IT!

57. Explain why graphing can be an important tool for analyzing data.

_____

_____

_____

4 Representing Data (continued)

58. Infer What type of data must be plotted on a graph for the slope of the line to represent density?

_____

_____

59. Relate If a linear graph has a negative slope, what can you say about the dependent variable?

_____

60. Summarize What data are best displayed on a circle graph? On a bar graph?

_____

61. Construct a circle graph for the composition of air: 78.08% N_2, 20.95% O_2, 0.93% Ar, and 0.04% CO_2 and other gases.

_____

62. Infer from Figure 22 how long the ozone hole lasts.

_____

63. Apply Graph mass versus volume for the data given in the table. What is the slope of the line?

Volume (cm³)	7.5	12	15	22
Mass (g)	24.1	38.5	48.0	70.1

_____

_____

2 Matter—Properties and Changes

ESSENTIAL QUESTION

Write the Essential Question for this chapter.

_____

_____

_____

Use the "What I Know" column to list the things you know about the Essential Question. Then list the questions you have about the Essential Question in the "What I Want to Find Out" column. As you read the chapter, fill in the "What I Learned" column.

K _What I Know_	W _What I Want to Find Out_	L _What I Learned_

Copyright © McGraw-Hill Education

2 Matter—Properties and Changes

1 Properties of Matter

Read the items under Build to the Essential Question at the beginning of the lesson. Restate each in your own words.

_____

REVIEW VOCABULARY

density

Recall the definition of the Review Vocabulary term.

density

_____

NEW VOCABULARY

states of matter

solid

liquid

gas

vapor

physical property

extensive property

intensive property

chemical property

Define each New Vocabulary term.

states of matter

_____

solid

_____

liquid

_____

gas

_____

vapor

_____

physical property

_____

extensive property

_____

intensive property

_____

chemical property

_____

Match each of the following states of matter with its physical description

solid	flows and fills the entire volume of its container
liquid	has definite shape and volume
gas	flows and has a constant volume

1 Properties of Matter (continued)

GET IT? **Name** four states of matter.

_____

GET IT? **Compare** the properties of solids and liquids in terms of their particle arrangements.

_____

_____

_____

_____

Compare the way the three common states of matter fill a container.

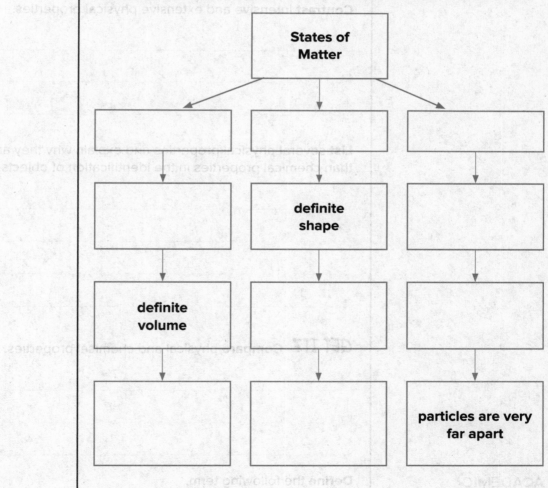

States of Matter

definite shape

definite volume

particles are very far apart

GET IT? **Differentiate** between gas and vapor.

_____

_____

_____

GET IT? **Define** *physical property* and provide examples.

_____

_____

_____

Contrast intensive and extensive physical properties.

_____

_____

_____

List several physical properties and explain why they are used more than chemical properties in the identification of objects.

_____

_____

_____

_____

GET IT? **Compare** physical and chemical properties.

_____

_____

_____

Define the following term.

resource

_____

ACADEMIC VOCABULARY

resource

2 Matter—Properties and Changes

2 Changes in Matter

1 Properties of Matter (continued)

REVIEW IT!

1. **Create** a table that describes four states of matter in terms of their properties.

2. **Describe** the characteristics that identify a sample of matter as a substance.

3. **Classify** each of the following as a physical or a chemical property.

    a. Iron and oxygen form rust.

    b. Iron is more dense than aluminum.

    c. Magnesium burns brightly when ignited.

    d. Oil and water do not mix.

    e. Mercury melts at −39°C.

4. **Organize** Create a chart that compares physical and chemical properties. Give two examples for each type of property.

2 Matter—Properties and Changes

2 Changes in Matter

BUILD TO THE ESSENTIAL QUESTION

Read the items under Build to the Essential Question at the beginning of the lesson. Restate each in your own words.

_____

_____

_____

REVIEW VOCABULARY

observation

Recall the definition of the Review Vocabulary term.

observation

_____

_____

NEW VOCABULARY

physical change

phase change

chemical change

law of conservation of mass

Define each New Vocabulary term.

physical change

_____

phase change

_____

chemical change

_____

law of conservation of mass

_____

2 Changes in Matter (continued)

Determine which type of change each statement represents. Use P for physical change and C for chemical change. Explain your answers.

silver spoon tarnishes _____

Explanation: _____

crushing an aluminum can _____

Explanation: _____

freezing water _____

Explanation: _____

burning wood _____

Explanation: _____

copper turns a greenish color _____

Explanation: _____

grind coffee beans _____

Explanation: _____

Describe how iron turns into a brownish-red powder. Name the reactants and product that are involved.

_____

_____

_____

_____

GET IT? **Define** *chemical change.*

_____

_____

2 Changes in Matter (continued)

Summarize Fill in the blanks to help you take notes while you read Example Problem 1.

Problem

The total _____ of the products must _____ the total mass of the

_____. This shows the law of _____.

1. Analyze the Problem

Known: _____

_____

Unknown: _____

2. Solve for the Unknown

Write an equation showing conservation of mass of reactants and products.

mass of _____ = mass of _____ + mass of _____

Write an equation to solve for the mass of oxygen.

mass of _____ = mass of _____ — mass of _____

Substitute known values and solve.

Mass of oxygen = _____ g — _____ g

Mass oxygen = _____ g

3. Evaluate the Answer

Write an equation that shows mass of the two products equals the mass of the reactant.

_____ g mercury + _____ g oxygen = _____ g mercury(II) oxide

2 Changes in Matter (continued)

REVIEW IT!

10. **Classify** each change as physical or chemical.
    a. crushing an aluminum can
    b. recycling used aluminum cans to make new ones
    c. aluminum combining with oxygen to form aluminum oxide

    _____

11. **Describe** the results of a physical change and list three examples of physical change.

    _____

    _____

12. **Describe** the results of a chemical change. List four indicators of chemical change.

    _____

    _____

13. **Calculate** Solve each of the following.
    a. If 22.99 g of sodium and 35.45 g of chlorine fully react, how much sodium chloride forms?
    b. A 12.2-g sample of X reacts with a sample of Y to form 78.9 g of XY. What mass of Y reacted?

    _____

    _____

    _____

    _____

14. **Evaluate** A friend tells you, "Because composition does not change during a physical change, the appearance of a substance does not change." Is your friend correct? Explain.

    _____

    _____

2 Matter—Properties and Changes

3 Elements and Compounds

BUILD TO THE ESSENTIAL QUESTION

Read the items under Build to the Essential Question at the beginning of the lesson. Restate each in your own words.

_____

_____

REVIEW VOCABULARY

proportion

Recall the definition of the Review Vocabulary term.

proportion _____

_____

NEW VOCABULARY

element

periodic table

compound

law of definite proportions

percent by mass

law of multiple proportions

Define each New Vocabulary term.

element _____

_____

periodic table _____

_____

compound _____

_____

law of definite proportions _____

_____

percent by mass _____

_____

law of multiple proportions _____

_____

_____

_____

3 Elements and Compounds (continued)

Discuss elements and compounds by completing the following paragraph.

There are more than _____ naturally occurring elements. Seventy-five

percent of the universe is _____. The Earth's crust and the human

body are made of different elements. But _____ is an element that

is abundant in both. Most objects are made of _____ with

approximately ten million known and over _____ being developed

and discovered every _____.

Describe how the periodic table organizes elements.

_____

_____

_____

GET IT? **Define** *element* and *compound*.

_____

_____

Explain how Figure 16 illustrates the fact that the properties of a
compound are different from the properties of its component elements.

_____

_____

_____

GET IT? **Explain** the process of electrolysis.

_____

_____

_____

_____

3 Elements and Compounds (continued)

GET IT? **Summarize** how the properties of a compound and the properties of its component elements compare.

_____

_____

_____

Describe how to do percent by mass by completing the following paragraph.

The _____ of a compound is _____ to the _____ of the masses of the _____ that make up the compound. This demonstrates the law of _____.

GET IT? **State** the law of definite proportions.

_____

_____

_____

Analyze the law of definite proportions by indicating whether the following examples are for identical or different compounds.

Description	Analysis
Compound 1 consists of 24g of Na, and 36g of Cl. Compound 2 has 36g of Na and 54g of Cl.	
Compound 3 has 10.00g of lead and 1.55g of sulfur. Compound 4 has 10.00 g of lead, 1.55g of sulfur, and 1.55g of carbon.	

3 Elements and Compounds (continued)

Describe the law of multiple proportions by completing the following statement.

When different _____ are formed by combining the same _____, different masses of one element combine with the same _____ of the other element in a ratio of _____.

GET IT? **State** the law of multiple proportions in your own words.

_____

_____

_____

GET IT? **Explain** why the ratio of the relative masses of copper in both compounds is 2:1.

SYNTHESIZE

Carbon combines with oxygen to form two compounds, carbon monoxide and carbon dioxide. Based on the law of multiple proportions, describe how the proportions of oxygen in the two compounds relate to each other.

_____

_____

REVIEW IT!

20. **Compare** and contrast elements and compounds.

_____

_____

21. **Describe** the basic organizational feature of the periodic table of the elements.

_____

_____

_____

3 Elements and Compounds (continued)

22. Explain how the law of definite proportions applies to compounds.

_____

_____

23. State the type of compounds that are compared in the law of multiple proportions.

_____

_____

24. Complete the table. Then analyze the data to determine if Compounds I and II are the same compound. If the compounds are different, use the law of multiple proportions to show the relationship between them.

Analysis Data of Two Iron Compounds					
Compound	Total Mass (g)	Mass Fe (g)	Mass O (g)	Mass Percent Fe	Mass Percent O
I	75.00	52.46	22.54		
II	56.00	43.53	12.47		

_____

_____

_____

25. Calculate the mass percent of each element in water.

_____

_____

26. Graph Create a graph that illustrates the law of multiple proportions.

2 Matter—Properties and Changes

4 Mixtures of Matter

Read the items under Build to the Essential Question at the beginning of the lesson. Restate each in your own words.

_____

_____

REVIEW VOCABULARY

substance

Recall the definition of the Review Vocabulary term.

substance _____

_____

NEW VOCABULARY

mixture

heterogeneous mixture

homogeneous mixture

solution

filtration

distillation

sublimation

chromatography

crystallization

Define each New Vocabulary term.

mixture _____

_____

heterogeneous mixture _____

_____

homogeneous mixture _____

_____

solution _____

filtration _____

_____

distillation _____

_____

sublimation _____

chromatography _____

_____

_____

crystallization _____

_____

4 Mixtures of Matter (continued)

Describe how mixtures relate to substances.

_____

_____

GET IT? **Compare and contrast** heterogeneous and homogeneous mixtures. Give examples of each.

_____

_____

_____

_____

Describe what an alloy is and why alloys are used.

_____

_____

Identify five techniques that take advantage of different physical properties in order to separate mixtures and describe how each is done.

Technique 1: _____

How it is done: _____

Technique 2: _____

How it is done: _____

_____

_____

Technique 3: _____

How it is done: _____

_____

Technique 4: _____

How it is done: _____

_____

Technique 5: _____

How it is done: _____

_____

_____

Sequence the steps of separating a mixture of sand, salt, and iron filings. Identify which physical property you were using in each step.

_____ Mix the sand and salt mixture with water.

Physical property used: _____

_____

_____ Boil the salt and water mixture, leaving the salt behind.

Physical property used: _____

_____

_____ Separate the iron filings from the sand and salt by using a magnet.

Physical property used: _____

_____

_____ Use filtration to separate the sand from the salt and water.

Physical property used: _____

_____

4 Mixtures of Matter (continued)

REVIEW IT!

27. **Classify** each of the following as either a heterogeneous or a homogeneous mixture.

   a. tap water   **b.** air   **c.** raisin muffin

   _____

28. **Compare** mixtures and substances.

   _____

   _____

   _____

29. **Describe** the separation technique that could be used to separate each of the following mixtures.

   a. two colorless liquids

   b. a nondissolving solid mixed with a liquid

   c. red and blue marbles of the same size and mass.

   _____

30. **Design** a concept map that summarizes the relationships among matter, elements, mixtures, compounds, pure substances, and homogeneous and heterogeneous mixtures.

Copyright © McGraw-Hill Education

3 The Structure of the Atom

ESSENTIAL QUESTION

Write the Essential Question for this chapter.

_____

_____

_____

Use the "What I Know" column to list the things you know about the Essential Question. Then list the questions you have about the Essential Question in the "What I Want to Find Out" column. As you read the chapter, fill in the "What I Learned" column.

K _What I Know_	W _What I Want to Find Out_	L _What I Learned_

3 The Structure of the Atom

1 Early Ideas About Matter

BUILD TO THE ESSENTIAL QUESTION

Read the items under Build to the Essential Question at the beginning of the lesson. Restate each in your own words.

_____

_____

Use the "What I Know" column to list the things you know about the Essential Question.
List the questions
As you read the chapter, fill in the "What I Learned" column.

REVIEW VOCABULARY

theory

Recall the definition of the Review Vocabulary term.

theory

_____

_____

_____

NEW VOCABULARY

Dalton's atomic theory

Define each New Vocabulary term.

Dalton's atomic theory

_____

_____

_____

1 Early Ideas About Matter (continued)

Summarize the effect that Aristotle had on the atomic theory proposed by Democritus.

_____

_____

_____

_____

_____

GET IT? **Infer** why it was hard for Democritus to defend his ideas.

_____

_____

List the main points of Dalton's atomic theory.

1. _____

2. _____

   _____

3. _____

4. _____

   _____

5. _____

GET IT? **Compare and contrast** Democritus' and Dalton's ideas.

_____

_____

_____

_____

_____

_____

VOCABULARY

Word Origin

Atom

_____

_____

_____

1 Early Ideas About Matter (continued)

Discuss Dalton's ideas by completing the following paragraph.

After years of studying _____, Dalton was able to

accurately determine the _____ of the elements involved in the

reactions. His conclusions resulted in the _____, which helped to

explain that _____ in chemical reactions separate, _____, or

_____, but are not created, _____, or_____.

Compare and contrast the atomic theories of Democritus and Dalton. Mark an X under each name if a statement applies to that person's theory.

Statement	Democritus	Dalton
All matter is made of tiny pieces.		
Matter is made of empty space through which atoms move.		
Atoms cannot be divided.		
Atoms cannot be created.		
Atoms cannot be destroyed.		
Different atoms combine in whole-number ratios to form compounds.		
The properties of atoms vary based on shape, size, and movement.		
Different kinds of atoms come in different sizes and shapes.		

1 Early Ideas About Matter (continued)

REVIEW IT!

1. **Contrast** the methods used by the Greek philosophers and Dalton to study the atom.

_____

_____

2. **Define** *atom* using your own words.

_____

_____

3. **Summarize** Dalton's atomic theory.

_____

_____

_____

4. **Explain** how Dalton's theory of the atom and the conservation of mass are related.

_____

_____

5. **Apply** Six atoms of Element A combine with eight atoms of Element B to produce six compound particles. How many atoms of Elements A and B does each particle contain? Are all of the atoms used to form compounds?

_____

_____

6. **Design** a concept map that compares and contrasts the atomic ideas proposed by Democritus and John Dalton.

3 The Structure of the Atom

2 Defining the Atom

BUILD TO THE ESSENTIAL QUESTION

Read the items under Build to the Essential Question at the beginning of the lesson. Restate each in your own words.

_____

_____

REVIEW VOCABULARY

model

Recall the definition of the Review Vocabulary term.

model _____

_____

NEW VOCABULARY

atom

cathode ray

electron

nucleus

proton

neutron

Define each New Vocabulary term.

atom _____

cathode ray _____

_____

electron _____

_____

nucleus _____

_____

proton _____

_____

neutron _____

_____

Explain an atom by completing the following statements.

The atom is the _____

_____.

When a group of atoms _____ and act as a

_____, the result is known as a _____.

2 Defining the Atom (continued)

Summarize the information you learned about cathode ray experiments. Use Figure 7 for reference.

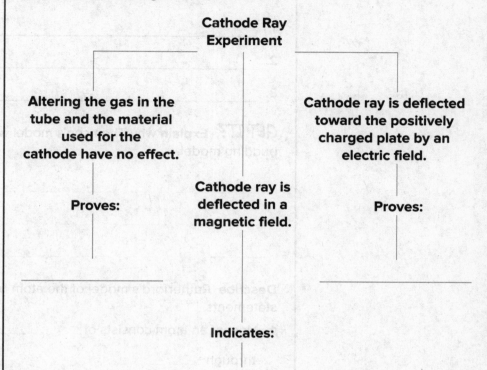

Cathode Ray Experiment

Altering the gas in the tube and the material used for the cathode have no effect.

Cathode ray is deflected in a magnetic field.

Cathode ray is deflected toward the positively charged plate by an electric field.

Proves:

Proves:

Indicates:

GET IT? **Explain** how the cathode ray was discovered.

_____

_____

GET IT? **Summarize** how Thomson discovered the electron.

_____

_____

_____

_____

2 Defining the Atom (continued)

Identify the major discoveries about subatomic particles made by the 19th century.

1. _____

2. _____

3. _____

GET IT? **Explain** why Thomson's model was called the plum pudding model.

_____

_____

_____

Describe Rutherford's model of the atom by completing the following statements.

1. Most of an atom consists of _____ moving _____ through _____ .

2. The electrons are _____ within the atom by their _____ to the positively charged _____ .

3. The volume of _____ through which the electrons move is many times _____ than the volume of the _____ .

GET IT? **Describe** Rutherford's model of the atom.

_____

_____

_____

VOCABULARY

Science usage v. Common Usage

Neutral

Science usage: to have no electric charge. *Neutrons have a charge of zero. They are neutral particles.*

Common usage: not engaged in either side. *Switzerland remained neutral during World War II.*

2 Defining the Atom (continued)

Organize the properties of subatomic particles by completing the table below. Use Table 3 for reference.

	Electron	Proton	Neutron
Symbol			
Location			in nucleus
Relative electrical charge		1+	

Summarize what you have learned about subatomic particles by completing the following paragraph.

Atoms have a _____ shape. The _____ of an atom is made up

of _____ that have a positive charge and _____ that have no

_____. The nucleus makes up _____ of the mass of an atom.

Most of the area of an _____ is made up of negatively charged

_____ traveling around the _____ charged nucleus. The

_____ are held in place by their _____ to the positive charge of

the _____. The _____ of the protons and neutrons are almost

_____ to each other while the _____ of the electrons is

_____.

2 Defining the Atom (continued)

REVIEW IT!

7. **Describe** the structure of a typical atom. Identify where each subatomic particle is located.

_____

_____

8. **Compare and contrast** Thomson's plum pudding atomic model with Rutherford's nuclear atomic model.

_____

_____

_____

_____

_____

9. **Evaluate** the experiments that led to the conclusion that electrons are negatively charged particles found in all matter.

_____

_____

_____

10. **Compare** the relative charge and mass of each of the subatomic particles.

11. **Calculate** What is the difference expressed in kilograms between the mass of a proton and the mass of an electron?

_____

3 The Structure of the Atom

3 How Atoms Differ

BUILD TO THE ESSENTIAL QUESTION

Read the items under Build to the Essential Question at the beginning of the lesson. Restate each in your own words.

_____

_____

_____

REVIEW VOCABULARY

periodic table

Recall the definition of the Review Vocabulary term.

periodic table _____

_____

_____

_____

NEW VOCABULARY

atomic number

isotope

mass number

atomic mass unit (amu)

atomic mass

Define each New Vocabulary term.

atomic number _____

_____

isotope _____

_____

mass number _____

_____

_____

atomic mass unit (amu) _____

_____

atomic mass _____

_____

ACADEMIC VOCABULARY

specific

Define the following term.

specific _____

_____

Explain how to use an atomic number to identify an element by completing the paragraph below.

Each _____ of an element has a unique number of _____. Since the overall charge of an atom is _____ the number of _____ equals the number of _____. Atomic number = number of _____ = number of _____. If you know how many one of the three an atom contains, you also know the other _____. Once you know the _____, the _____ can be used to find the name of the _____.

Solve Read Example Problem 1 in your text.

YOU TRY IT

Problem

Given the following information about atoms, determine the name of each atom's element and its atomic number.

a. Atom 1 has 11 protons   **b. Atom 2 has 20 electrons**

1. Analyze the Problem

Apply the relationship among atomic number, number of protons, and number of electrons to determine the name and atomic number of each element.

2. Solve for the Unknown

a. Atom 1

Atomic number = number of protons = number of electrons

Atomic number = _____ = number of electrons

The element with an atomic number of 11 is _____

b. Atom 2

Atomic number = number of protons = number of electrons

Atomic number = number of protons = _____

The element with an atomic number of _____ is _____.

3. Evaluate the Answer

The answers agree with _____ and element _____ given in the periodic table.

3 How Atoms Differ (continued)

Review your understanding of isotopes and mass number by completing the following paragraph.

Isotopes are elements with _____ but with

_____ . The number of neutrons can be

determined by _____ the atomic number from the

_____ . The mass number is

_____ .

Solve Read Example Problem 2 in your text.

YOU TRY IT

Problem

You are given two samples of carbon. The first sample, carbon-12, has a mass number of 12, the second sample, carbon-13, has a mass number of 13. Both samples have an atomic number of 6. Determine the number of protons, electrons, and neutrons in each sample.

1. **Analyze the Problem**
   Known:

   Carbon-12

   Mass number is _____

   Atomic number is _____

   Unknown:

   Carbon-13

   Mass number is _____

   Atomic number is _____

   The number of protons, electrons, and neutrons in each sample.

2. **Solve for the Unknown**

   Number of protons = number of electrons = atomic number = _____

   Number of neutrons = mass number − atomic number

   The number of neutrons for carbon-12 = 12 − 6 = _____

   The number of neutrons for carbon-13 = 13 − 6 = _____

3. **Evaluate the Answer**

   The number of neutrons does equal the _____

   minus the _____ , or the number of protons.

GET IT? **Explain** how to calculate atomic mass.

_____

_____

Summarize Fill in the blanks to help you take notes while you read Example Problem 3.

Problem

Given the _____ in the table in the left margin, _____ the _____ of unknown element X. Then, _____ the unknown _____, which is used _____ to treat some _____.

Isotope Abundance for Element X		
Isotope	**Mass (amu)**	**Percent abundance**
^{6}X	6.015	7.59%
^{7}X	7.016	92.41%

1. Analyze the problem

Known: Unknown:

For isotope ^{6}X: _____ of X = ? amu

mass = _____   _____ of element X = ?

abundance = _____

For isotope ^{7}X:

mass = _____

abundance = _____

2. Solve for the unknown

Mass contribution = (_____) (_____)

For ^{6}X: Mass contribution = _____ = _____

For ^{7}X: Mass contribution = _____ = _____

Sum the mass contributions to find the atomic mass.

_____ of X = _____ = _____

Use the _____ to identify the element.

The element with an atomic mass of 6.939 amu is _____.

3. Evaluate the answer

The number of neutrons does equal the _____ minus the _____, or number of _____.

3 The Structure of the Atom

4 Unstable Nuclei and Radioactive Decay

BUILD TO THE ESSENTIAL QUESTION

3 How Atoms Differ (continued)

REVIEW IT!

20. Explain how the type of an atom is defined.

_____

21. Recall Which subatomic particle identifies an atom as that of a particular element?

_____

22. Explain how the existence of isotopes is related to the fact that atomic masses are not whole numbers.

_____

_____

23. Calculate Copper has two isotopes: Cu-63 (abundance = 69.2%, mass = 62.930 amu) and Cu-65 (abundance = 30.8%, mass = 64.928 amu). Calculate the atomic mass of copper.

_____

_____

_____

24. Calculate Three magnesium isotopes have atomic masses and relative abundances of 23.985 amu (78.99%), 24.986 amu (10.00%), and 25.982 amu (11.01%). Calculate the atomic mass of magnesium.

_____

_____

_____

3 The Structure of the Atom

4 Unstable Nuclei and Radioactive Decay

BUILD TO THE ESSENTIAL QUESTION

Read the items under Build to the Essential Question at the beginning of the lesson. Restate each in your own words.

_____

_____

_____

REVIEW VOCABULARY

element

Recall the definition of the Review Vocabulary term.

element

_____

_____

NEW VOCABULARY

radioactivity

radiation

nuclear reaction

radioactive decay

alpha radiation

alpha particle

nuclear equation

beta radiation

beta particle

gamma ray

Define each New Vocabulary term.

radioactivity

_____

radiation

_____

nuclear reaction

_____

_____

radioactive decay

_____

_____

alpha radiation

_____

_____

alpha particle

_____

_____

nuclear equation

_____

_____

beta radiation

_____

beta particle

_____

_____

gamma ray

_____

4 Unstable Nuclei and Radioactive Decay (continued)

Explain radioactivity by completing the paragraph below.

In chemical reactions, atoms may be _____, but their

_____ do not change. The rearrangement _____ only

the _____ of the atoms, not the _____.

_____ reactions are different. In nuclear reactions,

_____ gain stability by emitting _____. As a result of

_____ in the nuclei, the atoms' _____ change.

_____ will continue emitting _____, in a process

called _____, until stable nuclei, often of a

_____, are formed.

Sequence the steps of a nuclear reaction.

_____ A stable, nonradioactive atom is formed.

_____ Radiation is emitted.

_____ The process of radioactive decay continues until the nucleus is stable.

_____ An atom has an unstable nucleus.

Distinguish between alpha, beta, and gamma radiation by completing the table below.

Radiation Type			
	Alpha	**Beta**	**Gamma**
Symbol	$\alpha \left({}^{4}_{2}\text{He} \right)$		
Mass (amu)		1/1840	
Charge			0

Discuss why some elements are radioactive while most elements are not.

_____

_____

4 Unstable Nuclei and Radioactive Decay (continued)

REVIEW IT!

25. Explain how unstable atoms gain stability.

_____

26. State what quantities are conserved when balancing a nuclear reaction.

_____

27. Classify each of the following as a chemical reaction, a nuclear reaction, or neither.
   a. Thorium emits a beta particle.
   b. Two atoms share electrons to form a bond.
   c. A sample of pure sulfur emits heat energy as it slowly cools.
   d. A piece of iron rusts.

_____

28. Calculate How much heavier is an alpha particle than an electron?

_____

_____

_____

29. Create a table showing how each type of radiation affects the atomic number and the mass number of an atom.

4 Electrons in Atoms

ESSENTIAL QUESTION

Write the Essential Question for this chapter.

_____

_____

_____

Use the "What I Know" column to list the things you know about the Essential Question. Then list the questions you have about the Essential Question in the "What I Want to Find Out" column. As you read the chapter, fill in the "What I Learned" column.

K _What I Know_	W _What I Want to Find Out_	L _What I Learned_

4 Electrons in Atoms

1 Light and Quantized Energy

BUILD TO THE ESSENTIAL QUESTION

Read the items under Build to the Essential Question at the beginning of the lesson. Restate each in your own words.

_____

_____

REVIEW VOCABULARY

radiation

Recall the definition of the Review Vocabulary term.

radiation

_____

NEW VOCABULARY

electromagnetic radiation

wavelength

frequency

amplitude

electromagnetic spectrum

quantum

Planck's constant

photoelectric effect

photon

atomic emission spectrum

Define each New Vocabulary term.

electromagnetic radiation

_____

wavelength

_____

frequency

amplitude

electromagnetic spectrum

quantum

_____

Planck's constant

photoelectric effect

_____

photon

_____

atomic emission spectrum

_____

1 Light and Quantized Energy (continued)

List the three reasons scientists found Rutherford's nuclear atomic model to be fundamentally incomplete.

1. _____

_____

2. _____

_____

3. _____

Explain the relationship shown by the figure below. Use the following terms: wavelength, frequency, amplitude, and speed.

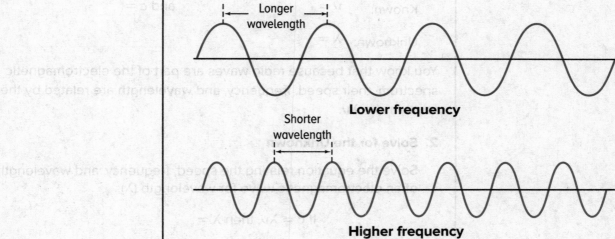

Longer wavelength

Lower frequency

Shorter wavelength

Higher frequency

_____

_____

_____

GET IT? **State** the relationship between the energy and the frequency of electromagnetic radiation.

_____

_____

Solve Read Example Problem 1 in your text.

YOU TRY IT

Problem

Radio waves are used to transmit information on various channels. What is the wavelength of a radio wave having the frequency of 5.40×10^{10} Hz?

1. Analyze the Problem

Known: $\nu =$ _____ and $c =$ _____

Unknown: $\lambda =$ _____

You know that because radio waves are part of the electromagnetic spectrum, their speed, frequency, and wavelength are related by the formula $c = \lambda \nu$.

2. Solve for the Unknown

Solve the equation relating the speed, frequency, and wavelength of an electromagnetic wave for wavelength (λ).

If $c = \lambda\nu$, then $\lambda =$ _____

Substitute c and the frequency of the radio wave, ν, into the equation. Note that hertz is equivalent to 1/s or s^{-1}.

$\lambda =$

Divide the values to determine wavelength, λ and cancel units as required.

$\lambda =$

1 Light and Quantized Energy (continued)

3. Evaluate the Answer

The answer is correctly expressed in a unit of _____.

Both of the known values in the problem are expressed with _____

significant figures, so the answer must have _____ significant

figures.

Identify two facts the wave model of light failed to explain.

1. _____

_____

2. _____

_____

Describe Planck's quantum concept by completing the following
statement.

The quantum concept concludes that matter can gain or lose _____

only in small, specific amounts called _____. A quantum is the

minimum amount of energy that can be _____ or _____

by an atom.

GET IT? Explain why the color of heated objects changes with temperature.

_____

_____

_____

GET IT? Describe the photoelectric effect.

_____

_____

1 Light and Quantized Energy (continued)

Compare and contrast Einstein's equation with Planck's equation by completing the following sentence.

Planck's equation, _____, demonstrates mathematically that the energy of a quantum is related to the _____ of the emitted radiation. Einstein went further by explaining that, in addition to its wavelike characteristics, a beam of light can be thought of as a stream of _____ called _____.

Contrast the continuous electromagnetic spectra and the atomic emission spectra.

_____

_____

_____

_____

GET IT? **Explain** how an emission spectrum is produced.

_____

_____

_____

1 Light and Quantized Energy (continued)

REVIEW IT!

8. **Describe** the phenomena that can be explained only by the particle model of light.

_____

_____

9. **Compare and contrast** continuous spectrum and emission spectrum.

_____

_____

10. **Discuss** the way in which Einstein utilized Planck's quantum concept to explain the photoelectric effect.

_____

_____

_____

11. **Calculate** Heating 235 g of water from 22.6°C to 94.4°C in a microwave oven requires 7.06×10^4 J of energy. If the microwave frequency is 2.88×10^{10} s^{-1}, how many quanta are required to supply the 7.06×10^4 J?

_____

_____

12. **Interpret Scientific Illustrations** Use Figure 5 and your knowledge of electromagnetic radiation to match the numbered items with the lettered items. The numbered items may be used more than once or not at all.

   a. longest wavelength   **1.** gamma ray

   b. highest frequency   **2.** infrared wave

   c. greatest energy   **3.** radio waves

_____

_____

4 Electrons in Atoms

2 Quantum Theory and the Atom

BUILD TO THE ESSENTIAL QUESTION

Read the items under Build to the Essential Question at the beginning of the lesson. Restate each in your own words.

_____

_____

_____

REVIEW VOCABULARY

atom

Recall the definition of the Review Vocabulary term.

atom _____

_____

NEW VOCABULARY

ground state

quantum number

de Broglie equation

Heisenberg uncertainty principle

quantum mechanical model of the atom

atomic orbital

principal quantum number

principal energy level

energy sublevel

Define each New Vocabulary term.

ground state _____

quantum number _____

de Broglie equation _____

_____

Heisenberg uncertainty principle _____

_____

_____

quantum mechanical model of the atom ____

_____

_____

atomic orbital _____

principal quantum number _____

_____

_____

principal energy level _____

energy sublevel _____

_____

Classify the characteristics of each series in hydrogen's line spectrum. Include the following information.

1. Beginning orbit(s) and ending orbit

2. Description of the spectral line

Balmer	Paschen	Lyman
1.	1.	1.
2.	2.	2.

GET IT? **Explain** why different colors of light result from electron behavior in the atom.

_____

_____

_____

_____

Sequence de Broglie's process in developing his equation by completing the following sentences.

1. Whole _____ of _____ are allowed in a circular orbit of fixed _____.

2. Light has both _____ and _____ characteristics.

3. Can particles of matter, including electrons, behave like _____?

4. If an electron has _____ and is restricted to circular orbits of fixed radius, the _____ is allowed only certain possible wavelengths, _____, and _____.

2 Quantum Theory and the Atom (continued)

Discuss how Heisenberg's principle influenced Schrödinger to develop his wave equation.

_____

_____

_____

_____

_____

GET IT? **Explain** the Heisenberg uncertainty principle.

_____

_____

_____

GET IT? **Compare and contrast** Bohr's model and the quantum mechanical model.

_____

_____

_____

_____

GET IT? **Describe** where electrons are located in an atom.

_____

_____

_____

Identify four facts about atomic orbitals by completing the following statements.

1. _____ indicate the relative sizes and

   energies of atomic orbitals.

2. The atom's major energy levels are called

3. Principal energy levels contain _____.

4. The number of _____ in a principal

   energy level _____ as *n* increases.

GET IT? **Explain** the relationship between energy levels and sublevels.

_____

GET IT? **Describe** the shapes of *s* and *p* orbitals.

_____

SUMMARIZE
Compare and contrast the Bohr and quantum mechanical models of the atom.

_____

_____

_____

_____

_____

REVIEW IT!
13. **Explain** the reason, according to Bohr's atomic model, why atomic emission spectra contain only certain frequencies of light.

_____

_____

2 Quantum Theory and the Atom (continued)

14. **Differentiate** between the wavelength of visible light and the wavelength of a moving soccer ball.

_____

_____

15. **Explain** why the location of an electron in an atom is uncertain using the Heisenberg uncertainty principle and de Broglie's wave-particle duality. How is the location of electrons in atoms defined?

_____

_____

_____

16. **Compare and contrast** Bohr's model and the quantum mechanical model of the atom.

_____

_____

_____

_____

17. **Enumerate** the sublevels contained in the hydrogen atom's first four energy levels. What orbitals are related to each s sublevel and each p sublevel?

_____

_____

_____

18. **Calculate** Use the information in Table 1 to calculate how many times larger the hydrogen atom's seventh Bohr radius is than its first Bohr radius.

_____

_____

_____

4 Electrons in Atoms

3 Electron Configuration

BUILD TO THE ESSENTIAL QUESTION

Read the items under Build to the Essential Question at the beginning of the lesson. Restate each in your own words.

_____

_____

_____

REVIEW VOCABULARY

electron

Recall the definition of the Review Vocabulary term.

electron

_____

_____

_____

NEW VOCABULARY

electron configuration

aufbau principle

Pauli exclusion principle

Hund's rule

valence electron

electron-dot structure

Define each New Vocabulary term.

electron configuration

_____

aufbau principle

_____

Pauli exclusion principle

_____

Hund's rule

_____

valence electron

_____

electron-dot structure

_____

_____

Organize information about electron configurations by completing the following outline.

Electron configuration is _____.

1. Ground–state electron configurations

   A. Three rules define how electrons can be arranged in an atom's orbitals:

      1. _____
      2. _____
      3. _____

   GET IT? **State** the three rules that define how electrons are arranged in atoms.

   _____

   _____

   _____

   _____

   B. The _____ methods for representing an atom's electron configuration

      1. Orbital diagrams

         a. An empty box represents an _____.

         b. A box containing a single up arrow represents an orbital with _____.

         c. A box containing both up and down arrows represents a _____.

         d. Each box is labeled with the _____ and _____ associated with the orbital.

   GET IT? **Explain** how to write the noble-gas notation for an element. What is the noble-gas notation for calcium?

   _____

   _____

Solve Read Example Problem 3 in your text.

YOU TRY IT

Problem

Ruthenium (Ru) is commonly used in the manufacture of platinum alloys. What is the ground-state electron configuration for an atom of ruthenium?

1. Analyze the Problem

Known: _____

Unknown: _____

Determine the number of additional electrons a ruthenium atom has compared to the nearest preceding noble gas, and then write out ruthenium's electron configuration.

2. Solve for the Unknown

From the periodic table, ruthenium's atomic number is determined to be ☐. Thus a ruthenium atom contains ☐ electrons. The noble gas preceding ruthenium is krypton (Kr), which has an atomic number of 36. Represent ruthenium's first 36 electrons using the chemical symbol for krypton written inside brackets. _____

The first 36 electrons have filled out the 1s, 2s, 2p, 3s, 3p, 4s, 3d and 4p sublevels. The remaining ☐ electrons of ruthenium's configuration need to be written out. Thus, the remaining ☐ electrons fill the _____ orbitals.

Using the maximum number of electrons that can fill each orbital, write out the electron configuration. _____

3. Evaluate the Answer

All ☐ electrons in a ruthenium atom have been accounted for. The correct preceding noble gas _____ has been used in the notation, and the order of orbital filling for the _____ is correct.

3 Electron Configuration (continued)

REVIEW IT!

27. **Apply** the Pauli exclusion principle, the aufbau principle, and Hund's rule to write out the electron configuration and draw the orbital diagram for each of the following elements.

    a. silicon   **b.** fluorine   **c.** calcium   **d.** krypton

28. **Define** *valence electron.*

29. **Illustrate** and describe the sequence in which ten electrons occupy the five orbitals related to an atom's d sublevel.

30. **Extend** the aufbau sequence through an element that has not yet been identified, but whose atoms would completely fill 7p orbitals. How many electrons would such an atom have? Write its electron configuration using noble-gas notation for the previous noble gas, radon.

31. **Interpret Scientific Illustrations** Which is the correct electron-dot structure for an atom of selenium? Explain.

    a. ·S̈e: **b.** ·S̈e·   **c.** ·S̈e·   **d.** ·S̈·

5 The Periodic Table and Periodic Law

ESSENTIAL QUESTION

Write the Essential Question for this chapter.

_____

_____

_____

Use the "What I Know" column to list the things you know about the Essential Question. Then list the questions you have about the Essential Question in the "What I Want to Find Out" column. As you read the chapter, fill in the "What I Learned" column.

K _What I Know_	W _What I Want to Find Out_	L _What I Learned_

5 The Periodic Table and Periodic Law

1 Development of the Modern Periodic Table

BUILD TO THE ESSENTIAL QUESTION

Read the items under Build to the Essential Question at the beginning of the lesson. Restate each in your own words.

_____

_____

_____

REVIEW VOCABULARY

atomic number

Recall the definition of the Review Vocabulary term.

atomic number

_____

NEW VOCABULARY

periodic law

group

period

representative element

transition element

metal

alkali metal

alkaline earth metal

transition metal

inner transition metal

lanthanide series

actinide series

nonmetal

halogen

noble gas

metalloid

Define each New Vocabulary term.

periodic law

_____

group

_____

period

_____

representative element

transition element

metal

alkali metal

alkaline earth metal

transition metal

_____

inner transition metal

lanthanide series

_____

actinide series

_____

nonmetal

_____

halogen

noble gas

metalloid

1 Development of the Modern Periodic Table (continued)

Sequence the events that helped develop the periodic table.

1. In 1864, _____

and saw the properties of elements _____.

2. In 1869, _____

_____. He left blank spaces

_____

3. In 1913, _____

_____. He arranged

elements by _____.

GET IT? Compare and contrast the ways in which Mendeleev and Moseley organized the elements.

_____

_____

Locate each of the following groups of elements on the periodic table.

alkali metals	nonmetals	halogens
alkaline earth metals	representative elements	transition metals
inner transition metals	transition elements	noble gases

PERIODIC TABLE OF THE ELEMENTS

Key:
- Metal
- Metalloid
- Nonmetal
- Recently observed
- Synthetic

Atomic number: 1
Symbol: H
Element: Hydrogen
Atomic mass: 1.008

1																	18
1 H Hydrogen 1.008	2											13	14	15	16	17	2 He Helium 4.003
3 Li Lithium 6.941	4 Be Beryllium 9.012											5 B Boron 10.811	6 C Carbon 12.011	7 N Nitrogen 14.007	8 O Oxygen 15.999	9 F Fluorine 18.998	10 Ne Neon 20.180
11 Na Sodium 22.990	12 Mg Magnesium 24.305	3	4	5	6	7	8	9	10	11	12	13 Al Aluminum 26.982	14 Si Silicon 28.086	15 P Phosphorus 30.974	16 S Sulfur 32.066	17 Cl Chlorine 35.453	18 Ar Argon 39.948
19 K Potassium 39.098	20 Ca Calcium 40.078	21 Sc Scandium 44.956	22 Ti Titanium 47.867	23 V Vanadium 50.942	24 Cr Chromium 51.996	25 Mn Manganese 54.938	26 Fe Iron 55.847	27 Co Cobalt 58.933	28 Ni Nickel 58.693	29 Cu Copper 63.546	30 Zn Zinc 65.39	31 Ga Gallium 69.723	32 Ge Germanium 72.61	33 As Arsenic 74.922	34 Se Selenium 78.96	35 Br Bromine 79.904	36 Kr Krypton 83.80
37 Rb Rubidium 85.468	38 Sr Strontium 87.62	39 Y Yttrium 88.905	40 Zr Zirconium 91.224	41 Nb Niobium 92.906	42 Mo Molybdenum 95.94	43 Tc Technetium (98)	44 Ru Ruthenium 101.07	45 Rh Rhodium 102.906	46 Pd Palladium 106.42	47 Ag Silver 107.868	48 Cd Cadmium 112.411	49 In Indium 114.82	50 Sn Tin 118.710	51 Sb Antimony 121.757	52 Te Tellurium 127.60	53 I Iodine 126.904	54 Xe Xenon 131.290
55 Cs Cesium 132.905	56 Ba Barium 137.327	57 La Lanthanum 138.905	72 Hf Hafnium 178.49	73 Ta Tantalum 180.948	74 W Tungsten 183.84	75 Re Rhenium 186.207	76 Os Osmium 190.23	77 Ir Iridium 192.217	78 Pt Platinum 195.08	79 Au Gold 196.967	80 Hg Mercury 200.59	81 Tl Thallium 204.383	82 Pb Lead 207.2	83 Bi Bismuth 208.980	84 Po Polonium 208.982	85 At Astatine 209.987	86 Rn Radon 222.018
87 Fr Francium (223)	88 Ra Radium (226)	89 Ac Actinium (227)	104 Rf Rutherfordium (261)	105 Db Dubnium (262)	106 Sg Seaborgium (266)	107 Bh Bohrium (264)	108 Hs Hassium (277)	109 Mt Meitnerium (268)	110 Ds Darmstadtium (281)	111 Rg Roentgenium (272)	112 Cn Copernicium (285)	113 Uut Ununtrium (284)	114 Fl Flerovium (289)	115 Uup Ununpentium (288)	116 Lv Livermorium (293)	117 Uus Ununseptium (294)	118 Uuo Ununoctium (295)

The number in parentheses is the mass number of the longest-lived isotope for that element.

* The names and symbols for elements 113, 115, 117, and 118 are temporary. Final names will be approved by IUPAC (International Union of Pure and Applied Chemistry).

Lanthanide series	58 Ce Cerium 140.115	59 Pr Praseodymium 140.908	60 Nd Neodymium 144.242	61 Pm Promethium (145)	62 Sm Samarium 150.36	63 Eu Europium 151.965	64 Gd Gadolinium 157.25	65 Tb Terbium 158.925	66 Dy Dysprosium 162.50	67 Ho Holmium 164.930	68 Er Erbium 167.259	69 Tm Thulium 168.934	70 Yb Ytterbium 173.04	71 Lu Lutetium 174.967
Actinide series	90 Th Thorium 232.038	91 Pa Protactinium 231.036	92 U Uranium 238.029	93 Np Neptunium (237)	94 Pu Plutonium (244)	95 Am Americium (243)	96 Cm Curium (247)	97 Bk Berkelium (247)	98 Cf Californium (251)	99 Es Einsteinium (252)	100 Fm Fermium (257)	101 Md Mendelevium (258)	102 No Nobelium (259)	103 Lr Lawrencium (262)

1 Development of the Modern Periodic Table (continued)

GET IT? **Define** *groups* and *periods.*

_____

_____

Organize information about the periodic table by completing the concept map below.

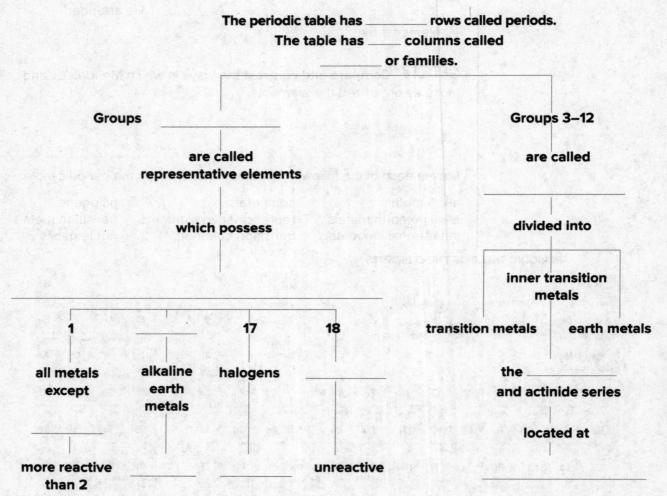

The periodic table has _____ rows called periods. The table has _____ columns called _____ or families.

Groups _____

are called
representative elements

which possess

Groups 3–12

are called
_____

divided into

inner transition metals

transition metals **earth metals**

| 1 | | 17 | 18 |

all metals except

alkaline earth metals

halogens

_____

the _____ **and actinide series**

located at

_____

more reactive than 2

_____ _____

unreactive

_____

1 Development of the Modern Periodic Table (continued)

Identify the information that is given on a typical box from the periodic table.

1. _____   3. _____

2. _____   4. _____

Match the box color on the periodic table in Figure 5 with the class of element the box describes.

blue   nonmetal

green   recently discovered

yellow   metalloid

gray   metal

REVIEW IT!

1. **Describe** the development of the modern periodic table. Include contributions made by Lavoisier, Newlands, Mendeleev, and Moseley.

_____

_____

_____

_____

2. **Sketch** a simplified version of the periodic table, and indicate the location of metals, nonmetals, and metalloids.

1 Development of the Modern Periodic Table (continued)

3. Describe the general characteristics of metals, nonmetals, and metalloids.

_____

_____

_____

4. Identify each of the following as a representative element or a transition element.

    a. lithium (Li)

    b. platinum (Pt)

    c. promethium (Pm)

    d. carbon (C)

_____

5. Compare For each of the given elements, list two other elements with similar chemical properties.

    a. iodine (I)

    b. barium (Ba)

    c. iron (Fe)

_____

_____

6. Interpret Data A company plans to make an electronic device. They need to use an element that has chemical behavior similar to that of silicon (Si) and lead (Pb). The element must have an atomic mass greater than that of sulfur (S), but less than that of cadmium (Cd). Use the periodic table to determine which element the company could use.

_____

5 The Periodic Table and Periodic Law

2 Classification of the Elements

BUILD TO THE ESSENTIAL QUESTION

Read the items under Build to the Essential Question at the beginning of the lesson. Restate each in your own words.

_____

_____

REVIEW VOCABULARY

valence electron

Recall the definition of the Review Vocabulary term.

valence electron

_____

_____

ACADEMIC VOCABULARY

structure

Define the following term.

structure

_____

_____

2 Classification of the Elements (continued)

Organize information about electron configurations by completing the outline below.

I. Electrons

    A. Valence electrons

        1. electrons in _____

        2. atoms in the _____ have _____

        _____.

    B. Valence electrons and period

        1. The _____ of an element's valence electrons

        indicates _____.

            a. Elements with valence electrons in energy level 2 are found

            in _____.

            b. Elements with _____

            are found in the fourth period.

    C. Valence electrons and group number

        1. Representative elements.

            a. All elements in group 1 have _____.

            b. All elements in group 2 have _____.

            c. Group 13 elements have _____,

            group 14 elements have _____, and so on.

        2. Helium, in group 18, is an _____.

Describe the relationship between the number of valence electrons and the chemical properties of atoms.

_____

_____

_____

2 Classification of the Elements (continued)

Distinguish between s-, p-, d-, and f-block elements by completing the table below.

	Periodic Table Groups	Orbitals	Type of Occupied Element
s-block			representative elements
p-block		p	
d-block	3 through 12		
f-block			

Summarize Fill in the blanks while you read Example Problem 1.

PROBLEM

Without using the periodic table, determine the group, period, and block in which strontium is located on the periodic table.

1. Analyze the Problem

Known: Unknown:

_____   _____

2. Solve for the unknown

Group: Strontium has a valence configuration of _____.

All group _____ elements have the _____ configuration.

Period: The _____ in $5s^2$ indicates that strontium is in _____.

Block: The _____ indicates that strontium's valence

electrons _____. Therefore, strontium is in the _____.

3. Evaluate the answer

The relationships among _____ and

_____ have been correctly applied.

2 Classification of the Elements (continued)

REVIEW IT!

11. **Explain** what determines the blocks in the periodic table.

_____

_____

12. **Determine** in which block of the periodic table the elements having the following valence electron configurations are located.
    a. s^2p^4 **b.** s^1 **c.** s^2d^1 **d.** s^2p^1

_____

_____

13. **Infer** Xenon, a nonreactive gas used in strobe lights, is a poor conductor of heat and electricity. Would you expect xenon to be a metal, a nonmetal, or a metalloid? Where would you expect it to be on the periodic table? Explain.

_____

_____

_____

14. **Explain** why elements within a group have similar chemical properties.

_____

_____

15. **Model** Make a simplified sketch of the periodic table, and label the s-, p-, d-, and f-blocks.

5 The Periodic Table and Periodic Law

3 Periodic Trends

BUILD TO THE ESSENTIAL QUESTION

Read the items under Build to the Essential Question at the beginning of the lesson. Restate each in your own words.

_____

_____

REVIEW VOCABULARY

principal energy level

Recall the definition of the Review Vocabulary term.

principal energy level

_____

NEW VOCABULARY

ion

ionization energy

octet rule

electronegativity

Define each New Vocabulary term.

ion

_____

ionization energy

_____

_____

octet rule

_____

electronegativity

_____

_____

Analyze any trends that you observe in Figure 12 and how the trends relate to atomic mass.

_____

_____

_____

GET IT? **Discuss** how the fact that the principal energy level remains the same within a period explains the decrease in the atomic radii across a period.

_____

_____

_____

Summarize Fill in the blanks to help you take notes while you read Example Problem 2.

PROBLEM

Which has the largest atomic radius: carbon (C), fluorine (F), beryllium (Be), or lithium (Li)? Explain your answer in terms of trends in atomic radii.

1. **Analyze the Problem**

   Known: periodic table information for four elements

   Unknown: which of the four has the _____

2. **Solve for the unknown**

   Use the _____ to determine if the elements are in the

   same group or period. All four elements are in _____.

   Order the elements from _____ across the period.

   _____

   Determine the largest based on trends of _____.

   _____

3. **Evaluate the answer**

   The _____ in atomic radii have been correctly applied.

Describe atomic size and ionic change by completing the table below.

Ionic Change	Ion Charge	Size of Atom
Atom _____ electrons	becomes positive	
_____ gains _____	becomes _____	increases

Identify two reasons why the relative size of an atom becomes smaller due to the loss of electrons.

1. _____

2. _____

   _____

Describe ionization energy trends on the periodic table by completing the paragraphs below.

Ionization energies generally _____ as you move left-to-right

across a _____. Increased nuclear charge leads to an _____

on valance electrons. Ionization energy generally _____ when you

move down a _____. Less energy is required to remove

_____ because they are _____ from the nucleus.

The octet rule states that atoms tend to gain, lose, or share _____

in order to acquire a full set of _____. First period

elements are the _____ to this rule.

GET IT? **Define** *ionization energy.*

_____

_____

_____

GET IT? **Infer** how many electrons carbon is likely to lose.

_____

3 Periodic Trends (continued)

20. Explain how the period and group trends in atomic radii are related to electron configuration.

_____

_____

_____

_____

21. Indicate whether fluorine or bromine has a larger value for each of the following properties.

    a. electronegativity   **c.** atomic radius

    b. ionic radius   **d.** ionization energy

_____

_____

22. Explain why it takes more energy to remove the second electron from a lithium atom than it does to remove the fourth electron from a carbon atom.

_____

_____

23. Calculate Determine the differences in electronegativity, ionic radius, atomic radius, and first ionization energy for oxygen and beryllium.

_____

_____

24. Make and Use Graphs On a separate sheet of paper, graph the atomic radii of the representative elements in periods 2, 3, and 4 versus their atomic numbers. Connect the points of elements in each period, so that there are three separate curves on the graph. Summarize the trends in atomic radii shown on your graph. Explain.

_____

_____

_____

6 Ionic Compounds and Metals

ESSENTIAL QUESTION

Write the Essential Question for this chapter.

_____

_____

_____

Use the "What I Know" column to list the things you know about the Essential Question. Then list the questions you have about the Essential Question in the "What I Want to Find Out" column. As you read the chapter, fill in the "What I Learned" column.

K _What I Know_	W _What I Want to Find Out_	L _What I Learned_

6 Ionic Compounds and Metals

1 Ion Formation

BUILD TO THE ESSENTIAL QUESTION

Read the items under Build to the Essential Question at the beginning of the lesson. Restate each in your own words.

_____

_____

REVIEW VOCABULARY

octet rule

Recall the definition of the Review Vocabulary term.

octet rule _____

_____

NEW VOCABULARY

chemical bond

cation

anion

Define each New Vocabulary term.

chemical bond _____

_____

cation _____

_____

anion _____

_____

1 Ion Formation (continued)

Organize information about forming chemical bonds by completing the concept map below.

As the number of
_____

in an atom increases,

_____, or
the atom's ability to attract

electrons, _____.

reactivity _____.

Electron affinity is smallest for

_____,

which in general have eight

_____ in their outermost

s and p orbitals.

_____, which

is the energy needed to

remove electrons from

the outer orbitals,

_____.

Write the electron configuration of the most likely ion and the charge that is lost or gained by each of the following atoms. Indicate what the overall charge of the ion is, and whether it is a cation or an anion.

Cs: [Xe]6s^1

_____
_____

O: [He]2s^{2}2p^4

_____
_____

Ga: [Ar]4s^{2}3d^{10}4p^1

_____
_____

Br: [Ar]4s^{2}3d^{10}4p^5

_____
_____

Ag: [Kr]5s^{1}4d^{10}

_____
_____

Sc: [Ar]4s^{2}3d^1

_____
_____

1 Ion Formation (continued)

GET IT? **Identify** the number of electrons in the outermost energy level that are associated with maximum stability.

_____

_____

Sequence the first group of elements in order of increasing ionization energy. Sequence the second group of elements in order of increasing electron affinity.

First Group	Second Group

First Group

_____ $K \rightarrow K^+$

_____ $Ne \rightarrow Ne^+$

_____ $P \rightarrow P^{5+}$

_____ $Fe \rightarrow Fe^{2+}$

_____ $Rb \rightarrow Rb^+$

_____ $Mg \rightarrow Mg^{2+}$

Second Group

_____ $P \rightarrow P^{3-}$

_____ $O \rightarrow O^{2-}$

_____ $Xe \rightarrow Xe^-$

_____ $S \rightarrow S^{2-}$

_____ $I \rightarrow I^-$

_____ $F \rightarrow F^-$

Identify the following ions.

Ag^+ _____

Li^+ _____

Br^- _____

Ca^{2+} _____

S^{2-} _____

B^{3+} _____

As^{3-} _____

H^- _____

Cd^{2+} _____

Se^{2-} _____

REVIEW IT!

1. **Compare** the stability of a lithium atom with that of its ion, Li^+.

_____

2. **Describe** two different causes of the force of attraction in a chemical bond.

_____

_____

3. **Apply** Why are all of the elements in group 18 relatively unreactive, whereas those in group 17 are very reactive?

_____

_____

_____

4. **Summarize** ionic bond formation by correctly pairing these terms: _cation, anion, electron gain,_ and _electron loss._

_____

5. **Apply** Write out the electron configuration for each atom. Then, predict the change that must occur in each to achieve a noble-gas configuration.
   a. nitrogen   **b.** sulfur   **c.** barium   **d.** lithium

_____

6. **Model** Draw models to represent the formation of the positive calcium ion and the negative bromide ion.

6 Ionic Compounds and Metals

2 Ionic Bonds and Ionic Compounds

BUILD TO THE ESSENTIAL QUESTION

Read the items under Build to the Essential Question at the beginning of the lesson. Restate each in your own words.

_____

_____

_____

REVIEW VOCABULARY

compound

Recall the definition of the Review Vocabulary term.

compound _____

_____

Define each New Vocabulary term.

NEW VOCABULARY

ionic bond

ionic compound

crystal lattice

electrolyte

lattice energy

ionic bond _____

_____

ionic compound _____

_____

crystal lattice _____

_____

_____

electrolyte _____

_____

lattice energy _____

_____

_____

2 Ionic Bonds and Ionic Compounds (continued)

Solve

YOU TRY IT

Problem

Describe the formation of an ionic compound from the elements boron and selenium.

1. Analyze the Problem

Known: the electron configurations of the given elements

_____

_____

Unknown: the number of valence electrons for each neutral atom

_____

_____

2. Solve for the Unknown

Determine how many electrons need to be removed from boron and how many electrons need to be added to selenium to form noble gas configurations.

_____

_____

_____

Determine how many boron atoms and how many selenium atoms must be present for the total number of electrons exchanged between the two elements to be equal.

_____

_____

3. Evaluate the Answer

The overall charge on one unit of this compound is zero.

☐ boron ions (3+/boron ion) + ☐ selenide ions (☐/selenide ion) = ☐ (3+) + ☐ (☐) = 0

2 Ionic Bonds and Ionic Compounds (continued)

Analyze the relationship between the lattice energy of an ionic compound and the force of attraction.

_____

_____

_____

Describe the relationship between the size of the ions in a compound and the compound's lattice energy.

_____

_____

_____

Explain the relationship between lattice energy and the charge of the ion.

_____

_____

GET IT? **Explain** what determines the ratio of positive ions to negative ions in an ionic crystal.

_____

_____

GET IT? **Identify** the mineral shown in Figure 8 that is a silicate. Identify the mineral that is a carbonate.

_____

_____

GET IT? **Summarize** the charges on each ion in the following ionic compounds: MgO, NaF, SrCl$_2$.

_____

2 Ionic Bonds and Ionic Compounds (continued)

REVIEW IT!

12. **Explain** how an ionic compound made up of charged particles can be electrically neutral.

_____

_____

13. **Describe** the energy change associated with ionic bond formation, and relate it to stability.

_____

_____

14. **Identify** three physical properties of ionic compounds that are associated with ionic bonds, and relate them to bond strength.

_____

_____

_____

15. **Explain** how ions form bonds, and describe the structure of the resulting compound.

_____

_____

_____

16. **Relate** lattice energy to ionic-bond strength.

_____

_____

2 Ionic Bonds and Ionic Compounds (continued)

17. **Apply** Use electron configurations, orbital notation, and electron-dot structures to represent the formation of an ionic compound from the metal strontium and the nonmetal chlorine.

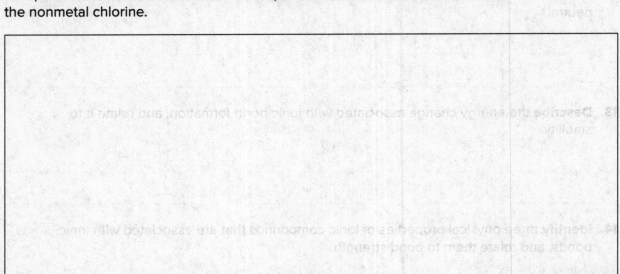

18. **Design** a concept map that shows the relationships among ionic bond strength, physical properties of ionic compounds, lattice energy, and stability.

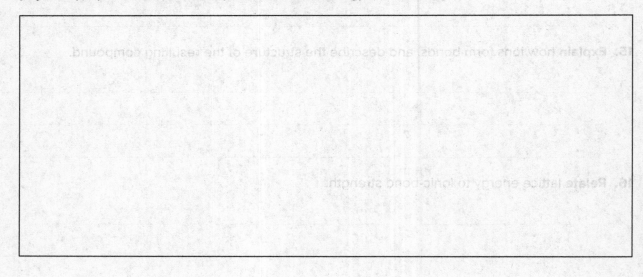

6 Ionic Compounds and Metals

3 Names and Formulas for Ionic Compounds

BUILD TO THE ESSENTIAL QUESTION

Read the items under Build to the Essential Question at the beginning of the lesson. Restate each in your own words.

REVIEW VOCABULARY

nonmetal

Recall the definition of the Review Vocabulary term.

nonmetal

NEW VOCABULARY

formula unit

monoatomic ion

polyatomic ion

oxyanion

Define each New Vocabulary term.

formula unit

monoatomic ion

polyatomic ion

oxyanion

ACADEMIC VOCABULARY

transfer

Define the following term.

transfer

GET IT? **Relate** the charge of an ion to its oxidation number.

_____

Solve Read Example Problem 1 in your text.

YOU TRY IT
Problem

Calcium can form a cation with a 2+ charge. Write the formula for the ionic compound formed from calcium ions and chloride ions.

1. **Analyze the Problem**

   Known: the ionic forms of the component elements

                    and _____

   Unknown: _____

2. **Solve for the Unknown**

   The smallest number that is divisible by both ionic charges is

   _____, so the compound contains _____ calcium ion(s) and _____

   chloride ion(s). The formula for the ionic compound formed is

   _____.

3. **Evaluate the Answer**

   The overall charge on one formula unit of this compound is zero.

   ☐ Ca ion(s) (2+/Ca ion) + ☐ Cl ions (1− /Cl ion) = 0

Solve Read Example Problem 3 in your text.

YOU TRY IT
Problem

Write the formula for the ionic compound formed from the calcium ion and the bromate ion.

1. **Analyze the Problem**

   Known: the ionic forms of the component elements

                    _____ and _____

   Unknown: _____

3 Names and Formulas for Ionic Compounds (continued)

2. Solve for the Unknown

The smallest number that is divisible by both ionic charges is _____, so _____ bromate ions combine with _____ calcium ion. The formula for the ionic compound formed is _____.

3. Evaluate the Answer

The overall charge on one formula unit of this compound is zero.

1 Ca ion (2+/Ca ion) + ☐ BrO_3 ions (1–/BrO_3 ion) = 0

Classify the ions listed below as monatomic or polyatomic cations or anions. If the ion is a polyatomic anion, indicate whether it is an oxyanion.

CN^- _____

MnO_4^- _____

Ba^{2+} _____

$Fe(CN)_6^{4-}$ _____

NH_4^+ _____

N^{3-} _____

Hg_2^{2+} _____

$S_2O_3^{2-}$ _____

O^{2-} _____

Identify the ionic compounds listed below.

CaO _____

$KMnO_4$ _____

$Sr(IO_3)_2$ _____

NH_4OH _____

Fe_2S_3 _____

$Sn(NO_3)_4$ _____

$Pb_3(PO_4)_2$ _____

Hg_2SO_4 _____

$PtCl_4$ _____

REVIEW IT!

34. State the order in which the ions associated with a compound composed of potassium and bromine would be written in the chemical formula and the compound name.

_____

_____

35. Describe the difference between a monatomic ion and a polyatomic ion, and give an example of each.

_____

_____

_____

36. Apply Ion X has a charge of 2+, and ion Y has a charge of 1−. Write the formula unit of the compound formed from the ions.

_____

_____

37. State the name and formula for the compound formed from Mg and Cl.

_____

_____

38. Write the name and formula for the base formed from rubidium ions and hydroxide ions.

_____

_____

39. Analyze What subscripts would you most likely use if the following substances formed an ionic compound?
   a. an alkali metal and a halogen
   b. an alkali metal and a nonmetal from group 16
   c. an alkaline earth metal and a halogen
   d. an alkaline earth metal and a nonmetal from group 16

_____

6 Ionic Compounds and Metals

4 Metallic Bonds and the Properties of Metals

BUILD TO THE ESSENTIAL QUESTION
Read the items under Build to the Essential Question at the beginning of the lesson. Restate each in your own words.

_____

_____

REVIEW VOCABULARY

physical property

Recall the definition of the Review Vocabulary term.

physical property _____

_____

NEW VOCABULARY

electron sea model

delocalized electrons

metallic bond

alloy

Define each New Vocabulary term.

electron sea model _____

_____

_____

delocalized electrons _____

_____

_____

metallic bond _____

_____

alloy _____

_____

Summarize how the electron sea model accounts for the malleability, high thermal conductivity, and high electrical conductivity of metals.

_____

_____

_____

_____

_____

Explain the properties of metals by completing the following sentences.

The _____ of transition metals increases as the

number of delocalized electrons _____.

Because the _____ in metals are strongly attracted to the delocalized

electrons in the metal, they are not easily _____ from the metal,

causing the metal to be very _____.

Alkali metals are _____ than transition metals because they have only

_____ per atom.

The _____ of metals vary greatly. The melting points are not as

extreme as the _____. It does not take an extreme amount of

energy for _____ to be able to move past each other.

However, during _____, atoms must be separated from a group of

_____, which requires a lot of _____.

Light absorbed and released by the _____ in a metal

accounts for the _____ of the metal.

GET IT? **Contrast** the behavior of metals and ionic compounds when each is struck by a hammer.

_____

4 Metallic Bonds and the Properties of Metals (continued)

Match the alloy composition given in the first column with the common name of the alloy in the second column and the alloy's uses in the third column. Draw lines between the appropriate items. Use Table 13 as a reference.

45% Cu, 15% Ag, 42% Au	cast iron	tableware, jewelry
75% Fe, 17% Cr, 8% Ni	10-carat gold	dental fillings
97% Fe, 3% C	sterling silver	casting
92.5% Ag, 7.5% Cu	dental amalgam	medals, bells
80% Cu, 15% Zn, 5% Sn	brass	instruments, sinks
85% Cu, 15% Zn	bronze	jewelry
50% Hg, 35% Ag,15% Sn	stainless steel	hardware, lighting

Contrast a substitutional alloy with an interstitial alloy. Give an example of each.

_____

_____

_____

_____

_____

_____

_____

_____

4 Metallic Bonds and the Properties of Metals (continued)

REVIEW IT!

40. Contrast the structures of ionic compounds and metals.

_____

_____

41. Explain how the conductivity of electricity and the high boiling points of metals are explained by metallic bonding.

_____

_____

42. Contrast the cause of the attraction in ionic bonds and metallic bonds.

_____

_____

43. Summarize alloy types by correctly pairing these terms and phrases: *substitutional, interstitial, replaced,* and *filled in.*

_____

_____

44. Design an experiment that could be used to distinguish between a metallic solid and an ionic solid. Include at least two different methods for comparing the solids. Explain your reasoning.

_____

_____

_____

45. Model Draw a model to represent the physical property of metals known as ductility, or the ability to be drawn into a wire. Base your drawing on the electron sea model shown in Figure 11.

7 Covalent Bonding

ESSENTIAL QUESTION

Write the Essential Question for this chapter.

_____

_____

_____

Use the "What I Know" column to list the things you know about the Essential Question. Then list the questions you have about the Essential Question in the "What I Want to Find Out" column. As you read the chapter, fill in the "What I Learned" column.

K _What I Know_	W _What I Want to Find Out_	L _What I Learned_

7 Covalent Bonding

1 The Covalent Bond

Read the items under Build to the Essential Question at the beginning of the lesson. Restate each in your own words.

_____

_____

REVIEW VOCABULARY

chemical bond

Recall the definition of the Review Vocabulary term.

chemical bond _____

NEW VOCABULARY

covalent bond

molecule

Lewis structure

sigma bond

pi bond

endothermic reaction

exothermic reaction

Define each New Vocabulary term.

covalent bond _____

molecule _____

Lewis structure _____

_____

sigma bond _____

_____

pi bond _____

_____

endothermic reaction _____

_____

exothermic reaction _____

_____

1 The Covalent Bond (continued)

Explain the octet rule by completing the following sentences.

The _____ rule states that _____

_____ .

Although exceptions exist, the rule provides a useful framework for

understanding _____ .

Complete the octet rule by completing the following sentences.

The force between two atoms is the result of _____

repulsion, nucleus-nucleus _____ , and nucleus-electron

_____ . At the point of _____ , the

_____ forces balance the _____ forces. The most

stable arrangement of atoms exists at the point of _____ ,

when the atoms bond covalently and a _____ forms.

GET IT? Describe how a Lewis structure shows a covalent bond.

_____

_____

Solve Read Example Problem 1 in your text.

YOU TRY IT
Problem

Draw the Lewis structure for hydrogen chloride, HCl.

1. **Analyze the Problem**
   Write the electron-dot structures of each of the two
   component atoms.

   Known: H· and ·C̈l:

   Unknown: _____ of HCl

   Hydrogen, H, has only one valence electron. Chlorine, Cl, has
   seven valence electrons. Cl needs one electron to complete
   its octet.

2. Solve for the Unknown

Draw the electron-dot structure for each of the component atoms. Then show the sharing of the pairs of electrons.

$$H\cdot \qquad + \qquad \ddot{\underset{\cdot\cdot}{C}}l\!: \quad \rightarrow \qquad H\!-\!\ddot{\underset{\cdot\cdot}{C}}l\!:$$

_____ _____ _____

_____ _____ _____

3. Evaluate the Answer

Each atom in the molecule has achieved a _____

configuration and thus is _____.

GET IT? **List** the orbitals that can form sigma bonds in a covalent compound.

_____

_____

_____

Identify each bond between the component atoms as sigma bonds (single bonds), one sigma bond and one pi bond (double bonds), or one sigma bond and two pi bonds (triple bonds).

$H - C \equiv C - H$ _____

_____

_____

$H - C = O$
$\quad\;\; |$
$\quad\;\; H$

_____

_____

_____

GET IT? **Relate** covalent bond type to bond length.

_____

_____

1 The Covalent Bond (continued)

REVIEW IT!

7. **Identify** the type of atom that generally forms covalent bonds.

_____

8. **Describe** how the octet rule applies to covalent bonds.

_____

9. **Illustrate** the formation of single, double, and triple covalent bonds using Lewis structures.

10. **Compare and contrast** ionic bonds and covalent bonds.

_____

_____

11. **Contrast** sigma bonds and pi bonds.

_____

_____

12. **Apply** Create a graph on a separate sheet of paper using the bond-dissociation energy data and bond-length data in **Table 1**. Describe the relationship between bond length and bond-dissociation energy.

_____

_____

13. **Predict** the relative bond-dissociation energies needed to break the bonds in the structures below.

a. $H - C \equiv C - H$ **b.**

7 Covalent Bonding

2 Naming Molecules

BUILD TO THE ESSENTIAL QUESTION

Read the items under Build to the Essential Question at the beginning of the lesson. Restate each in your own words.

_____

_____

_____

REVIEW VOCABULARY

oxyanion

Recall the definition of the Review Vocabulary term.

oxyanion _____

_____

_____

NEW VOCABULARY

oxyacid

Define the New Vocabulary term.

oxyacid _____

_____

Identify the prefixes for these two binary molecular compounds.

Ge_3N_2 _____ -germanium _____ -nitride

C_2Cl_4 _____ -carbon _____ -chloride

2 Naming Molecules (continued)

Solve **Read** Example Problem 2 in your text.

YOU TRY IT

Problem

Name the compound N_2O_3.

1. Analyze the Problem

Known: _____

Unknown: _____

The formula reveals the elements present and the number of atoms for each element. Only two elements are present, and both are nonmetals, so the compound can be named according to the rules for binary molecular compounds.

2. Solve for the Unknown

The first element present in the compound is _____, _____.

The second element is _____, _____. The root of this

name is _____, so the second part of the name is _____.

From the formula, two _____ atoms and three _____

atoms make up a molecule of the compound. The prefix for two

is _____ and prefix for three is _____. The complete name for

the compound is _____.

3. Evaluate the Answer

The name _____ shows that a molecule of the

compound contains _____ atoms and _____

atoms, which agrees with the chemical formula for the

compound, N_2O_3.

GET IT? **Apply** What are the scientific names for ammonia, hydrazine, and nitric oxide?

_____

_____

2 Naming Molecules (continued)

Match the chemical formulas listed below with the correct acids.

HF   sulfurous acid

HIO_4 hydrofluoric acid

H_2SO_3 phosphoric acid

H_3PO_4 hypochlorous acid

$HC_2H_3O_2$ periodic acid

H_2CO_3 permanganic acid

HClO   acetic acid

$HMnO_4$ carbonic acid

Write the chemical formula for the molecular compound names given below. Use the flow chart in Figure 12 to help you determine the correct formulas.

_____ dicarbon tetrabromide   _____ tetrasulfur tetranitride

_____ arsenic pentafluoride   _____ arsenic acid

_____ perchloric acid   _____ hydrocyanic acid

SYNTHESIZE

Create questions and answers about naming molecules for your own original quiz game. Include topics such as: prefixes and number of atoms; formulas, common names, and molecular names for covalent binary compounds; and formulas, common names, and molecular names for binary acids and oxyacids.

_____

_____

_____

2 Naming Molecules (continued)

REVIEW IT!

31. Summarize the rules for naming binary molecular compounds.

_____

_____

_____

32. Define a binary molecular compound.

_____

_____

33. Describe the difference between a binary acid and an oxyacid.

_____

_____

34. Apply Using the system of rules for naming binary molecular compounds, describe how you would name the molecule N_2O_4.

_____

_____

_____

35. Apply Write the molecular formula for each of these compounds: _iodic acid, disulfur trioxide, dinitrogen monoxide,_ and _hydrofluoric acid._

_____

_____

36. State the molecular formula for each compound listed below.

　a. dinitrogen trioxide　　**b.** nitrogen monoxide　　**c.** hydrochloric acid

　d. chloric acid　　**e.** sulfuric acid　　**f.** sulfurous acid

_____

_____

7 Covalent Bonding

3 Molecular Structures

BUILD TO THE ESSENTIAL QUESTION

Read the items under Build to the Essential Question at the beginning of the lesson. Restate each in your own words.

_____

_____

REVIEW
VOCABULARY

ionic bond

Recall the definition of the Review Vocabulary term.

ionic bond _____

_____

NEW VOCABULARY

structural formula

resonance

coordinate covalent bond

Define each New Vocabulary term.

structural formula _____

_____

resonance _____

_____

coordinate covalent bond _____

_____

List the steps that should be used to determine Lewis structures.

1. _____

2. _____

3. _____

_____

4. _____

_____

Solve Read Example Problem 4 in your text.

YOU TRY IT

Problem

Draw the Lewis structure for FCHO.

1. Analyze the Problem

Known: the compound formula: _____

Unknown: _____

Carbon has less attraction for shared electrons, so it is the
central atom.

2. Solve for the Unknown

Find the total number of valence electrons and the number
of bonding pairs.

[⬚] valence electrons/C atom + [⬚] valence electrons/F atom

+ 1 valence electron/H atom + [⬚] valence electrons/O atom

= [⬚] valence electrons

[⬚] available valence electrons/(2 electrons/pair) = [⬚]
available pairs

Draw single bonds, which each represent _____, from the carbon atom to each terminal atom, and place electron pairs around the _____ and _____ atoms to give them stable _____.

_____ available pairs − _____ pairs used = 0; Carbon does not have an octet, so one of the lone pairs on the _____ atom must be used to form a _____ bond.

3. **Evaluate the Answer**

Both carbon and _____ now have an octet, which satisfies the octet rule.

Solve Read Example Problem 5 in your text.

YOU TRY IT

Problem

Draw the Lewis structure for the permanganate ion (MnO_4^-).

1. **Analyze the Problem**

Known: the compound formula: _____

Unknown: _____

Manganese has less attraction for shared electrons, so it is the central atom.

2. **Solve for the Unknown**

Find the total number of valence electrons and the number of bonding pairs.

1 Mn atom × (⬚ valence electrons/Mn atom) + ⬚ O atoms × (6 valence electrons/O atom + ⬚ electron(s) from the negative charge = ⬚ valence electrons

3 Molecular Structures (continued)

[ ] available valence electrons/(2 electrons/pair) = [ ] available pairs

Draw single bonds, which represent an _____,

from the Mn atom to each O atom, and place electron pairs around the O atoms to give them stable _____.

[ ] available pairs − [ ] pairs used = 0

No electron pairs remain available for the Mn atom, so the Lewis structure for the permanganate ion is:

3. Evaluate the Answer

All atoms now have an octet, and the group of atoms has a net charge of _____.

Explain resonance structures by completing the following sentences.

Each actual molecule or ion that undergoes _____ behaves as if it has only _____ structure. Experimentally measured bond lengths show that the bonds are _____ to each other.

GET IT? **Summarize** three reasons why some molecules do not conform to the octet rule.

_____

_____

_____

3 Molecular Structures (continued)

REVIEW IT!

50. Describe the information contained in a structural formula.

_____

_____

51. State the steps used to draw Lewis structures.

_____

_____

_____

_____

52. Summarize exceptions to the octet rule by correctly pairing these molecules and phrases: odd number of valence electrons, PCl_5, ClO_2, BH_3, expanded octet, less than an octet.

_____

53. Evaluate A classmate states that a binary compound having only sigma bonds displays resonance. Could the classmate's statement be true?

_____

_____

54. Draw the resonance structures for the dinitrogen oxide (N_2O) molecule.

55. Draw the Lewis structures for CN^-, SiF_4, HCO_3^-, and, AsF_6^-.

7 Covalent Bonding

4 Molecular Shapes

REVIEW VOCABULARY

atomic orbital

NEW VOCABULARY

VSEPR model

hybridization

BUILD TO THE ESSENTIAL QUESTION

Read the items under Build to the Essential Question at the beginning of the lesson. Restate each in your own words.

_____

_____

Recall the definition of the Review Vocabulary term.

atomic orbital _____

_____

Define each New Vocabulary term.

VSEPR model _____

_____

_____

_____

hybridization _____

_____

4 Molecular Shapes (continued)

Match the molecular shapes listed below with their corresponding bond angles.

trigonal planar	180°
trigonal pyramidal	120°
bent	109.5°
linear	107.3°
octahedral	104.5°
tetrahedral	90° (out of plane); 120° (in plane)
trigonal bipyramidal	90°

Label the hybrid orbitals in the figures below as sp, sp^2, sp^3 sp^3d, or sp^3d^2.

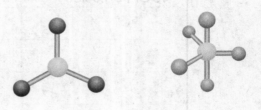

GET IT? **State** the number of electrons that are available for bonding in a hybrid sp^3 orbital.

_____

_____

Solve Read Example Problem 7 in your text.

YOU TRY IT

Problem

What is the shape of a SbI_5 molecule? Determine the bond angles, and identify the type of hybrid orbitals that form the molecule's bonds.

1. **Analyze the Problem**

Known: the compound formula: _____

Unknown: _____

_____

The molecule contains one central antimony atom bonded to

_____ iodine atoms.

2. **Solve for the Unknown**

Find the number of valence electrons and the number of electron pairs.

1 Sb atom × (☐ valence electrons/Sb atom) + ☐ I atoms ×

(☐ valence electrons/I atom) = ☐ valence electrons

Three electron pairs exist on each iodine atom. This leaves ☐

available valence electrons for bonding. ☐ available valence

electrons/(2 electrons/pair) = ☐ available pairs

Draw the molecule's Lewis structure. From this Lewis structure, determine the molecular shape.

Lewis structure   Molecular shape

The molecule's shape is _____, with a bond

angle of _____ in the horizontal plane, and a bond angle of _____

between the vertical and horizontal bonds. The bonds are made

up of _____ hybrid orbitals.

3. **Evaluate the Answer**

Each iodine atom has an octet. The antimony atom has _____

electrons, which is allowed when a d orbital is hybridized.

4 Molecular Shapes (continued)

REVIEW IT!

61. Summarize the VSEPR bonding theory.

_____

_____

62. Define the term _bond angle_.

_____

_____

63. Describe how the presence of a lone electron pair affects the spacing of shared bonding orbitals.

_____

_____

64. Compare the size of an orbital that has a shared electron pair with one that has a lone pair.

_____

_____

65. Identify the type of hybrid orbitals present and bond angles for a molecule with a tetrahedral shape.

_____

66. Compare the molecular shapes and hybrid orbitals of PF_3 and PF_5 molecules. Explain why their shapes differ.

_____

_____

_____

67. List in a table, the Lewis structure, molecular shape, bond angle, and hybrid orbitals for molecules of CS_2, CH_2O, H_2Se, CCl_2F_2, and NCl_3.

7 Covalent Bonding

5 Electronegativity and Polarity

BUILD TO THE ESSENTIAL QUESTION

Read the items under Build to the Essential Question at the beginning of the lesson. Restate each in your own words.

_____

_____

Recall the definition of the Review Vocabulary term.

electronegativity _____

_____

Define the following New Vocabulary term.

polar covalent bond _____

_____

_____

_____

Sequence the following elements from the least electronegative to the most electronegative. Use Figure 20 for reference.

———— Au

———— Y

———— Ba

———— P

———— H

———— Te

———— O

———— I

———— Co

GET IT? **Analyze** What is the percent ionic character of a pure covalent bond?

_____

GET IT? **Determine** the percent ionic character of calcium oxide.

_____

Draw the Lewis structure for each of the molecular compounds listed below. Analyze the symmetry of the structure to determine whether or not the compound is polar covalent or nonpolar covalent.

N_2 _____ _____

CO_2 _____ _____

CH_3Cl _____

_____

5 Electronegativity and Polarity (continued)

Determine whether each of the properties listed below is characteristic of ionic compounds, covalent compounds, nonpolar covalent compounds, or polar covalent compounds.

low melting point _____

very soft solid _____

high boiling point _____

weak interaction between
formula units _____

solubility in oil _____

very hard solid _____

high melting point _____

solubility in water _____

easily vaporized _____

strong interaction between
formula units _____

Describe what the network solid for quartz (SiO_2) molecules is like and how it has a tetrahedral structure similar to diamond structure.

_____

_____

_____

_____

_____

_____

_____

_____

_____

_____

5 Electronegativity and Polarity (continued)

REVIEW IT!

68. Summarize how electronegativity difference is related to bond character.

_____

_____

_____

69. Describe a polar covalent bond.

_____

_____

_____

70. Describe a polar molecule.

_____

_____

_____

71. List three properties of a covalent compound in the solid phase.

_____

_____

_____

72. Categorize bond types using electronegativity difference.

_____

_____

_____

73. Generalize Describe the general characteristics of covalent network solids.

_____

_____

_____

74. Predict the type of bond that will form between the following pair of atoms:

a. H and S   b. C and H   c. Na and S

_____

75. Identify each molecule as polar or nonpolar: SCl_2, CS_2, and CF_4.

_____

_____

5 Electronegativity and Polarity (continued)

76. Determine whether a compound made of hydrogen and sulfur atoms is polar or nonpolar.

_____

_____

77. Draw the Lewis structures for the molecules SF_4 and SF_6. Analyze each structure to determine whether the molecule is polar or nonpolar.

8 Chemical Reactions

ESSENTIAL QUESTION

Write the Essential Question for this chapter.

_____

_____

_____

Use the "What I Know" column to list the things you know about the Essential Question. Then list the questions you have about the Essential Question in the "What I Want to Find Out" column. As you read the chapter, fill in the "What I Learned" column.

K _What I Know_	W _What I Want to Find Out_	L _What I Learned_

8 Chemical Reactions

1 Reactions and Equations

8 Chemical Reactions

ESSENTIAL QUESTION

Write the Essential Que

BUILD TO THE ESSENTIAL QUESTION

Read the items under Build to the Essential Question at the beginning of the lesson. Restate each in your own words.

_____

_____

_____

REVIEW VOCABULARY

chemical change

Recall the definition of the Review Vocabulary term.

chemical change

_____

NEW VOCABULARY

chemical reaction

reactant

product

chemical equation

coefficient

Define each New Vocabulary term.

chemical reaction

_____

reactant

_____

product

_____

chemical equation

_____

_____

coefficient

_____

_____

ACADEMIC VOCABULARY

formula

Define the following term.

formula

_____

_____

1 Reactions and Equations (continued)

Identify three examples of chemical reactions you have seen, heard, or smelled in the last 24 hours. Think about activities at home, at school, or outside. Include any evidence you had that a chemical reaction was occurring.

Reaction	Evidence
1.	
2.	
3.	

Organize types of equations that can express a chemical reaction. In the second column, list the elements (words, coefficients, etc.) that are used to create each equation. In the third column, rank each equation from 1 to 3, giving a 3 to the equation that provides the most information, and a 1 to the equation that provides the least information.

Type	Elements	Ranking
Word equations		
Chemical equations		
Skeleton equations		

Label the chemical state each symbol below identifies in a chemical equation

(s) _____

(g) _____

(aq) _____

(l) _____

GET IT? **Compare** What information do skeleton equations provide that word equations lack?

_____

_____

_____

Science Notebook • Chemical Reactions
133

1 Reactions and Equations (continued)

Solve Read Example Problem 1 in your text.

YOU TRY IT

Problem

Balance the chemical equation for the reaction in which fluorine reacts with water to produce hydrofluoric acid and oxygen.

1. Analyze the Problem

Known: _____

Unknown: _____

2. Solve for the Unknown

Use the space below to write the skeleton equation:

_____

Count the atoms of each element in the reactants.

_____ F, _____ H, _____ O

Count the atoms of each element in the products.

_____ F, _____ H, _____ O

Insert the coefficient _____ in front of _____ to balance the oxygen atoms.

Insert the coefficient _____ in front of _____ to balance the _____.

Insert the coefficient _____ in front of _____ to balance the _____.

Write the equation after adding the coefficients.

_____

Check that the coefficients are at their lowest possible ratio. The ratio of the coefficients is _____.

Write the number of atoms in the balanced equation below:

Reactants: _____

Products: _____

3. Evaluate the Answer

The _____ of each element is _____ on both sides of the equation. The _____ are written to the _____ ratio.

Copyright © McGraw-Hill Education

1 Reactions and Equations (continued)

REVIEW IT!

7. **Explain** why it is important that a chemical equation be balanced.

_____

_____

8. **List** three types of physical evidence that indicate a chemical reaction has occurred.

_____

_____

9. **Compare and contrast** a skeleton equation and a chemical equation.

_____

_____

10. **Explain** why it is important to reduce coefficients in a balanced equation to the lowest-possible whole-number ratio.

_____

_____

11. **Analyze** When balancing a chemical equation, can you adjust the subscript in a formula? Explain.

_____

_____

12. **Assess** Is the following equation balanced? If not, correct the coefficients to balance the equation.

$$2K_2CrO_4(aq) + Pb(NO_3)_2(aq) \rightarrow 2KNO_3(aq) + PbCrO_4(s)$$

_____

13. **Evaluate** Aqueous phosphoric acid and aqueous calcium hydroxide react to form solid calcium phosphate and water. Write a balanced chemical equation for this reaction.

_____

_____

8 Chemical Reactions

2 Classifying Chemical Reactions

BUILD TO THE ESSENTIAL QUESTION

Read the items under Build to the Essential Question at the beginning of the lesson. Restate each in your own words.

_____

_____

_____

REVIEW VOCABULARY

metal

Recall the definition of the Review Vocabulary term.

metal _____

_____

NEW VOCABULARY

synthesis reaction

combustion reaction

decomposition reaction

single-replacement reaction

double-replacement reaction

precipitate

Define each New Vocabulary term.

synthesis reaction _____

_____

combustion reaction _____

_____

_____

decomposition reaction _____

_____

_____

single-replacement reaction _____

_____

_____

double-replacement reaction _____

_____

precipitate _____

_____

2 Classifying Chemical Reactions (continued)

Complete the following diagrams illustrating each classification of chemical reaction. The first one has been completed for you.

Synthesis reaction

Substance
Substance ──────────→ New compound

A + B → _____

Combustion reactions

Metal, nonmetal, or compound substance

_____ ──────→ _____

Decomposition reactions

Element or _____

Compound ──────→ Element or _____

AB → _____ or _____

Single-replacement reactions

Metal or nonmetal

Compound ──────→ _____

A + BX → _____

Double-replacement reactions

Compound with anion ──────→ _____

AX + BY → _____

GET IT? Analyze In the reaction between lithium and water, which element replaces hydrogen in water?

_____

_____

2 Classifying Chemical Reactions (continued)

GET IT? **Explain** how a single-replacement reaction works.

_____

_____

GET IT? **Describe** what happens to the anions in a double-replacement reaction.

_____

_____

_____

Organize types of chemical reactions. The first column in the chart below lists some possible products in a chemical reaction. In the second column, write the type of chemical reaction that is likely to generate each product.

Products	Possible Chemical Reaction
two different compounds, one of which is often a solid, a gas, or water	
oxide of the metal or a nonmetal or two or more oxides	
two or more elements or compounds	
a new compound and a replaced metal or nonmetal	
one compound	

ANALOGY

Consider the list of metals and halogens and their relative reactivity in Figure 13. Using your own experiences, identify people or things that could be ranked according to how they react in a certain situation.

1. (Example) Rank baseball bats by how likely they are to break.

2. _____

3. _____

4. _____

2 Classifying Chemical Reactions (continued)

REVIEW IT!

29. Describe the four types of chemical reactions and their characteristics.

_____

_____

_____

_____

_____

30. Explain how an activity series of metals is organized.

_____

_____

_____

31. Compare and contrast single-replacement reactions and double-replacement reactions.

_____

_____

_____

_____

32. Describe the result of a double-replacement reaction.

_____

_____

33. Classify What type of reaction is most likely to occur when barium reacts with fluorine? Write the chemical equation for the reaction.

_____

_____

34. Interpret Data Could the following reaction occur? Explain your answer.
$$3Ni + 2AuBr_3 \rightarrow 3NiBr_2 + 2Au$$

_____

_____

8 Chemical Reactions

3 Reactions in Aqueous Solutions

BUILD TO THE ESSENTIAL QUESTION

Read the items under Build to the Essential Question at the beginning of the lesson. Restate each in your own words.

_____

_____

REVIEW VOCABULARY

solution

Recall the definition of the Review Vocabulary term.

solution _____

_____

NEW VOCABULARY

aqueous solution

solute

solvent

complete ionic equation

spectator ion

net ionic equation

Define each New Vocabulary term.

aqueous solution _____

_____

solute _____

_____

solvent _____

_____

complete ionic equation _____

_____

spectator ion _____

_____

net ionic equation _____

_____

3 Reactions in Aqueous Solutions (continued)

Connect English words to their Latin roots. The term *aqueous* comes from the Latin word for water, *aqua*. Use a dictionary to find three words that also come from *aqua,* and list them in the box below together with a brief definition that explains their connection to water.

Word	Definition

Compare a complete ionic equation and a chemical equation.

_____

_____

_____

_____

_____

_____

Draw a circle around the spectator ions in the following equation.

$$2A^+(aq) + 2B^-(aq) + C^{2+}(aq) + 2D^-(aq) \longrightarrow 2A^+(aq) + 2D^-(aq) + CB_2$$

Identify whether each of the equations below is a complete ionic equation or a net ionic equation.

$$A^+(aq) + B^-(aq) + C^+(aq) + D^-(aq) \longrightarrow AD + B^-(aq) + C^+(aq)$$

_____

$$E^+(aq) + F^-(aq) \longrightarrow EF$$

_____

$$G^+(aq) + HI^-(aq) \longrightarrow GI + H(g)$$

_____

3 Reactions in Aqueous Solutions (continued)

GET IT? **Compare** How are complete ionic equations and net ionic equations different from chemical equations?

_____

_____

_____

Compare reactions that form a precipitate with reactions that form water. Put each of the following characteristics in the appropriate category.

- can be described with ionic equations
- generates a solid product

- double-replacement reaction
- has no observable evidence

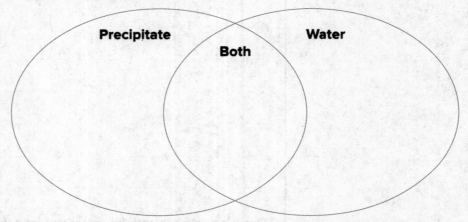

GET IT? **Analyze** In the reaction between hydrobromic acid and sodium hydroxide, why are the sodium ions and bromine ions called spectator ions?

_____

_____

Identify three gases produced by reactions in aqueous solutions.

_____

_____

_____

State the evidence that would indicate that carbon dioxide gas is escaping from the solution containing sodium hydrogen carbonate shown in Figure 19.

_____

3 Reactions in Aqueous Solutions (continued)

List the two reactions that occur when any acidic solution is mixed with sodium hydrogen carbonate.

_____

_____

GET IT? **Describe** What is an overall equation?

_____

_____

GET IT? **Infer** Why is a mechanism needed to remove carbon dioxide gas from your cells?

_____

_____

SYNTHESIZE

Sequence the steps in writing an overall equation.

1. _____

2. _____

3. _____

4. _____

What if ten years from now, you are a chemist working for a government agency that investigates chemical reactions. Read each of the case studies below, and in the space provided, list the type of chemical reaction that you think is involved and any products or effects that you would expect to discover during or after the chemical reaction.

1. Owners of an industrial plant plan to mix oxygen with existing chemical substances in order to create a new product.

Type of Reaction	Product or Effect

2. Two vats of chemicals have spilled into a river and created a gelatinous ooze.

Type of Reaction	Product or Effect

REVIEW IT!

50. List three common types of products produced by reactions that occur in aqueous solutions.

_____

_____

51. Describe solvents and solutes in an aqueous solution.

_____

_____

_____

52. Distinguish between a complete ionic equation and a net ionic equation.

_____

_____

_____

53. Write complete ionic and net ionic equations for the reaction between sulfuric acid (H_2SO_4) and calcium carbonate $(CaCO_3)$.

$$H_2SO_4(aq) + CaCO_3(s) \rightarrow H_2O(l) + CO_2(g) + CaSO_4(aq)$$

_____

_____

_____

54. Analyze Complete and balance the following equation: $CO_2(g) + HCl(aq) \rightarrow$

_____

_____

55. Predict What type of product would the following reaction be most likely to produce? Explain your reasoning.

$$Ba(OH)_2(aq) + 2HCl(aq) \rightarrow$$

_____

_____

_____

56. Formulate Equations A reaction occurs when nitric acid (HNO_3) is mixed with an aqueous solution of potassium hydrogen carbonate. Aqueous potassium nitrate is produced. Write the chemical and net ionic equations for the reaction.

_____

_____

_____

9 The Mole

ESSENTIAL QUESTION

Write the Essential Question for this chapter.

_____

_____

_____

Use the "What I Know" column to list the things you know about the Essential Question. Then list the questions you have about the Essential Question in the "What I Want to Find Out" column. As you read the chapter, fill in the "What I Learned" column.

K _What I Know_	W _What I Want to Find Out_	L _What I Learned_

9 The Mole

1 Measuring Matter

BUILD TO THE ESSENTIAL QUESTION

Read the items under Build to the Essential Question at the beginning of the lesson. Restate each in your own words.

_____

_____

REVIEW VOCABULARY

molecule

Recall the definition of the Review Vocabulary term.

molecule _____

_____

NEW VOCABULARY

mole

Avogadro's number

Define each New Vocabulary term.

mole _____

_____

Avogadro's number _____

_____

List three common counting units and their values.

1. _____

2. _____

3. _____

1 Measuring Matter (continued)

Describe why chemists needed to invent a new counting unit.

_____

_____

List three representative particles that can be measured using moles.

1. _____

2. _____

3. _____

Analyze the usefulness of a conversion factor.

_____

_____

_____

Write the equation for finding the number of representative particles in a number of moles.

Explain how you would find the number of moles that are represented by a certain number of representative particles.

GET IT? **Describe** how you can tell if the wrong conversion factor has been used.

_____

_____

GET IT? **List** the two conversion factors that can be written from Avogadro's number.

_____

Summarize Fill in the blanks to help you take notes as you read Example Problem 1.

Problem

Convert 4.50×10^{24} atoms of Zn to find the number of mol of Zn.

1. **Analyze the Problem**

   Known: number of atoms = _____

   1 mole Zn = _____ atoms of Zn

   Unknown: mole Zn = _____

2. **Solve for the Unknown**

   the number of atoms × conversion factor = number of moles

   _____ atoms Zn ×

   _____ = number of moles

   = _____

3. **Evaluate the Answer**

   The answer has _____ significant digits and is less than _____.

REVIEW IT!

7. **Explain** why chemists use the mole.

_____

_____

1 Measuring Matter (continued)

8. State the mathematical relationship between Avogadro's number and 1 mol.

_____

9. List the conversion factors used to convert between particles and moles.

_____

_____

10. Explain how a mole is similar to a dozen.

_____

_____

11. Apply How does a chemist count the number of particles in a given number of moles of a substance?

_____

12. Calculate the mass in atomic mass units of 0.25 mol of carbon-12 atoms.

_____

_____

13. Calculate the number of representative particles of each substance.

   a. 11.5 mol Ag   **c.** 0.150 mol NaCl

   b. 18.0 mol H_2O **d.** 1.35×10^{-2} mol CH_4

_____

_____

_____

_____

14. Arrange these three samples from smallest to largest in terms of number of representative particles: 1.25×10^{25} atoms of zinc (Zn), 3.56 mol of iron (Fe), and 6.78×10^{22} molecules of glucose ($C_6H_{12}O_6$).

_____

_____

9 The Mole

2 Mass and the Mole

Read the items under Build to the Essential Question at the beginning of the lesson. Restate each in your own words.

_____

_____

_____

REVIEW VOCABULARY

conversion factor

Recall the definition of the Review Vocabulary term.

conversion factor _____

_____

_____

NEW VOCABULARY

molar mass

Define the New Vocabulary term.

molar mass _____

_____

_____

2 Mass and the Mole (continued)

Analyze molar mass by completing the following statements.

The mass of one mole of carbon-12 atoms is _____ grams.

The mass of one mole of hydrogen is ___ gram and is _____ the mass of one mole of _____.

The mass of one mole of helium-4 is _____ the mass of one mole of _____ and is equal to _____ grams.

One mole of manganese is equal to _____ atoms of Mn.

Organize the following equations by drawing a line from type of conversion to the correct equation.

mole to mass
$$mass \times \frac{1\ mole}{number\ of\ grams}$$

mass to mole
$$mass \times \frac{1\ mole}{number\ of\ grams},$$
$$moles \times \frac{6.02 \times 10^{23}}{1\ mole}$$

mass to atoms
$$number\ of\ moles \times \frac{number\ or\ grams}{1\ mole}$$

atoms to mass
$$atoms \times \frac{1\ mole}{6.02 \times 10^{23}},$$
$$moles \times \frac{number\ or\ grams}{1\ mole}$$

GET IT? **Compare** How are the jelly bean conversion factors used above similar to the molar mass of a compound?

_____

_____

2 Mass and the Mole (continued)

Solve Read Example Problem 4.

YOU TRY IT

Problem

Determine how many atoms are in 10 g of pure copper (Cu).

1. Analyze the Problem

Known: mass = _____

Unknown: molar mass

               number of atoms

2. Solve for the Unknown

Use the periodic table to find the atomic mass of copper and convert it to g/mol.

_____

Complete the conversion equations.

mass Cu × conversion factor = moles Cu

_____ × _____ g Cu = _____ moles Cu

moles Cu × conversion factor = atoms Cu

_____ mol Cu × _____

atoms Cu

3. Evaluate the Answer

Restate the answer with correct significant digits.

_____

2 Mass and the Mole (continued)

REVIEW IT!

22. Summarize in terms of particles and mass, one-mole quantities of two different monatomic elements.

_____

23. State the conversion factor needed to convert between mass and moles of the atom fluorine.

_____

24. Explain how molar mass relates the mass of an atom to the mass of a mole of atoms.

_____

25. Describe the steps used to convert the mass of an element to the number of atoms of the element.

_____

26. Arrange these quantities from smallest to largest in terms of mass: 1.0 mol of Ar, 3.0×10^{24} atoms of Ne, and 20g of Kr.

_____

27. Identify the quantity that is calculated by dividing the molar mass of an element by Avogadro's number.

_____

_____

28. Design a concept map that shows the conversion factors needed to convert between mass, moles, and number of particles.

9 The Mole

3 Moles of Compounds

BUILD TO THE ESSENTIAL QUESTION

Read the items under Build to the Essential Question at the beginning of the lesson. Restate each in your own words.

_____

_____

_____

REVIEW VOCABULARY

representative particle

Recall the definition of the Review Vocabulary term.

representative particle _____

_____

Describe the relationship between the mole information of a substance and its chemical formula.

_____

_____

_____

Summarize Fill in the blanks to help you take notes as you read Problem 6.

Problem

Determine the number of moles of Al^{3+} ions in 1.25 moles of Al_2O_3.

1. Analyze the Problem

Known: number of moles of alumina = _____

Unknown: number of moles = _____

2. Solve for the unknown

Write the conversion factor: ☐ mol Al^{3+} ions / ☐ mol Al_2O_3

Multiply the known number of moles by the conversion factor.

☐ mol Al_2O_3 × ☐ mol Al^{3+} ions/ ☐ mol Al_2O_3

= ☐ mol Al^{3+} ions

3. Evaluate the Answer

Restate the answer with correct significant digits:

_____

3 Moles of Compounds (continued)

Describe the molar mass of a compound.

_____

_____

Investigate the process of finding molar mass by completing the table below.

Number of Moles	Molar Mass	=	Number of Grams
mol K	g K/ 1 mol K	=	g
mol Cr	g Cr/ 1 mol Cr	=	g
mol O	g O/ 1 mol O	=	g
molar mass of K_2CrO_4		=	g

Analyze the process of converting moles of a compound to molar mass by completing the table below. Refer to Example Problem 7.

Number of Moles	Molar Mass	=	Number of Grams
2 × 3 mol C	g C/ 1 mol C	=	g
2 × 5 mol H	g H/ 1 mol H	=	g
1 mol S	g S/ 1 mol S	=	g
molar mass of $(C_3H_5)_2S$		=	g

3 Moles of Compounds (continued)

Investigate the process of converting the mass of a compound to moles by completing the following. Refer to Example Problem 8.

Number of Moles	Molar Mass	=	Number of Grams
1 mol Ca	g Ca/ 1 mol Ca	=	g
2 × 1 mol O	g O/ 1 mol O	=	g
2 × 1 mol H	g H/ mol H	=	g
molar mass of Ca(OH)$_2$		=	g

Conversion factor: _____ g of Ca(OH)$_2$/1 mol Ca(OH)$_2$

g Ca(OH)$_2$ × conversion factor = mol Ca(OH)$_2$

_____ × _____ / _____ = _____ mol Ca(OH)$_2$

Explain the steps in converting the mass of a compound to number of particles.

1. Determine the _____.

2. Multiply by the _____ of the molar mass to convert to _____.

3. Multiply by _____ to calculate the number of _____.

4. Use the ratios from the _____ to calculate the number of _____.

5. Calculate the _____ per formula unit.

REVIEW IT!

47. Describe how to determine the molar mass of a compound.

_____

_____

48. Identify the conversion factors needed to convert between the number of moles and the mass of a compound.

_____

3 Moles of Compounds (continued)

49. Explain how you can determine the number of atoms or ions in a given mass of a compound.

_____

_____

50. Apply How many moles of K, C, and O atoms are there in 1 mol of $K_2C_2O_4$?

_____

51. Calculate the molar mass of $MgBr_2$.

_____

_____

52. Calculate Calcium carbonate is the calcium source for many vitamin tablets. The recommended daily allowance of calcium is 1000 mg of Ca^{2+} ions. How many moles of Ca^{2+} does 1000 mg represent?

_____

_____

53. Design a bar graph that will show the number of moles of each element present in 500 g of a particular form of dioxin ($C_{12}H_4Cl_4O_2$), a powerful poison.

9 The Mole

4 Empirical and Molecular Formulas

BUILD TO THE ESSENTIAL QUESTION

Read the items under Build to the Essential Question at the beginning of the lesson. Restate each in your own words.

_____

_____

_____

REVIEW VOCABULARY

percent by mass

Recall the definition of the Review Vocabulary term.

percent by mass
_____

_____

NEW VOCABULARY

percent composition

empirical formula

molecular formula

Define each New Vocabulary term.

percent composition
_____

_____

empirical formula
_____

_____

molecular formula
_____

_____

4 Empirical and Molecular Formulas (continued)

Write the equation for determining the percent by mass for any element in a compound.

Describe the general equation for calculating the percent by mass of any element in a compound.

Explain empirical formulas by completing the following statements.

To determine the empirical _____ for a compound, you must first determine the smallest _____ of the moles of the elements in the compound. This ratio provides the _____ in the empirical formula. If the empirical formula differs from the molecular formula, the molecular formula will be a _____ multiple of the empirical formula. The data used to determine the chemical formula may be in the form of _____ or it may be the actual masses. When the percent composition is given, you can assume that the total mass of the compound is 100.0 g to simplify calculations. The _____ of elements in a compound must be _____ to whole numbers to be used as _____ in the chemical formula.

GET IT? **List** the steps needed to calculate the empirical formula from percent composition data.

_____

_____

_____

_____

_____

_____

4 Empirical and Molecular Formulas (continued)

Explain how a molecular formula distinguishes two distinct substances sharing the same empirical formula.

_____

_____

Investigate molecular formulas by completing the steps below. Refer to Example Problem 12 in your text.

empirical formula = $C_2H_3O_2$
molar mass = 118.1 g/mol

Identify the molar mass of the compound.

Moles of Element	Mass of Element / 1 Mol of Element	=	Mass of Element
2 mol C	____ g C/ mol C	=	____ g C
3 mol H	____ g H/ mol H	=	____ g H
2 mol O	____ g O/ mol O	=	____ g O
empirical molar mass of $C_2H_3O_2$		=	____ g

Divide the molar mass of the substance by the molar mass of the compound to determine n.

$$n = \frac{\text{molar mass of substance}}{\text{molar mass of compound}} = $$

Multiply the subscripts in the empirical formula by _n_. Write the molecular formula.

_____

4 Empirical and Molecular Formulas (continued)

Examine the flow chart below. Write the steps in determining empirical and molecular formulas from percent composition or mass data next to the relevant boxes in the flow chart.

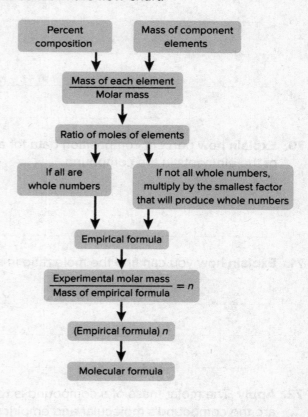

REVIEW IT!

67. Assess A classmate tells you that experimental data shows a compound's molecular formula to be 2.5 times its empirical formula. Is he correct? Explain.

_____

_____

68. Calculate Analysis of a compound composed of iron and oxygen yields 174.86 g of Fe and 75.14 g of O. What is the empirical formula for this compound?

_____

_____

_____

_____

69. Calculate An oxide of aluminum contains 0.545 g of Al and 0.485 g of O. Find the empirical formula for the oxide.

_____

_____

_____

_____

70. Explain how percent composition data for a compound are related to the masses of the elements in the compound.

_____

_____

_____

71. Explain how you can find the mole ratio in a chemical compound.

_____

_____

_____

72. Apply The molar mass of a compound is twice that of its empirical formula. How are the compound's molecular and empirical formulas related?

_____

_____

73. Analyze Hematite (Fe_2O_3) and magnetite (Fe_3O_4) are two ores used as sources of iron. Which ore provides the greater percent of iron per kilogram?

_____

_____

_____

_____

9 The Mole

5 Formulas of Hydrates

BUILD TO THE ESSENTIAL QUESTION

Read the items under Build to the Essential Question at the beginning of the lesson. Restate each in your own words.

_____

_____

Recall the definition of the Review Vocabulary term.

crystal lattice
_____

_____

NEW VOCABULARY

hydrate

Define the New Vocabulary term.

hydrate
_____

_____

Explain how hydrates are named by completing the table below.

Prefix	Molecules of Water
mono-	1
	2
	3
	4
	5
	6
	7
	8
nona-	9
	10

5 Formulas of Hydrates (continued)

Describe an anyhydrate.

_____

_____

GET IT? **Explain** why a dot is used in writing the formula of a hydrate.

_____

_____

Solve **Read** Example Problem 14 in your text.

YOU TRY IT

Problem

A 5.00 g sample of barium chloride hydrate was heated in a crucible. After the experiment, the mass of the solid weighed 4.26 g. Determine the number of moles of water that must be attached to $BaCl_2$.

1. **Analyze the Problem**

   Known: mass of hydrated compound = _____ g $BaCl_2 \cdot x\, H_2O$

   mass of anhydrous compound = _____ g $BaCl_2$

   molar mass of H_2O = _____ g/mol

   molar mass of $BaCl_2$ = 208.23 g/mol

   Unknown: formula for hydrate

   name of hydrate

5 Formulas of Hydrates (continued)

2. Solve for the Unknown

Subtract the mass of the anhydrous compound from the hydrated compound.

_____

Calculate the number of moles of H_2O and anhydrous $BaCl_2$ using the conversion factor that relates moles and mass based on the molar mass.

4.26 g $BaCl_2$ × _____ = _____

0.74 g H_2O × _____ = _____

Determine the value of x.

$$x = \frac{\text{moles } H_2O}{\text{moles } BaCl_2} =$$

3. Evaluate the Answer

The ratio of H_2O to $BaCl_2$ is _____, so the formula for the hydrate is

_____, and the name of the hydrate is _____

_____.

5 Formulas of Hydrates (continued)

REVIEW IT!

76. Summarize the composition of a hydrate.

_____

77. Name the compound that has the formula $SrCl_2 \cdot 6H_2O$.

_____

78. Describe the experimental procedure for determining the formula of a hydrate. Explain the reason for each step.

_____

_____

_____

_____

_____

79. Apply A hydrate contains 0.050 mol of H_2O to every 0.00998 mol of ionic compound. Write a generalized formula of the hydrate.

_____

80. Calculate the mass of the water of hydration if a hydrate loses 0.025 mol of H_2O when heated.

_____

81. Arrange these hydrates in order of increasing percent water content: $MgSO_4 \cdot 7H_2O$, $Ba(OH)_2 \cdot 8H_2O$, and $CoCl_2 \cdot 6H_2O$.

_____

_____

82. Apply Explain how the hydrate in **Figure 17** might be used as a means of roughly determining the probability of rain.

_____

_____

10 Stoichiometry

ESSENTIAL QUESTION

Write the Essential Question for this chapter.

_____

_____

_____

Use the "What I Know" column to list the things you know about the Essential Question. Then list the questions you have about the Essential Question in the "What I Want to Find Out" column. As you read the chapter, fill in the "What I Learned" column.

K _What I Know_	W _What I Want to Find Out_	L _What I Learned_

10 Stoichiometry

1 Defining Stoichiometry

Read the items under Build to the Essential Question at the beginning of the lesson. Restate each in your own words.

_____

_____

REVIEW VOCABULARY

reactant

Recall the definition of the Review Vocabulary term.

reactant

_____

Define each New Vocabulary term.

NEW VOCABULARY

stoichiometry

mole ratio

stoichiometry

_____

_____

mole ratio

_____

Explain the importance of the law of conservation of mass in chemical reactions.

_____

_____

_____

_____

_____

GET IT? **List** the types of relationships that can be derived from the coefficients in a balanced chemical equation.

_____

_____

_____

Summarize Fill in the blanks to help you take notes while you read Example Problem 1.

Problem

Interpret the equation in terms of _____,

and _____ . Show that the law of conservation of mass is _____ .

1. Analyze the Problem

Known: _____

Unknown: _____

_____

_____

2. Solve for the Unknown

The coefficients indicate the number of _____ .

The coefficients indicate the number of _____ .

Use the space below to calculate the mass of each reactant and each product. Multiply the number of moles by the conversion factor molar mass.

$$\text{moles of reactant} \times \frac{\text{grams of reactant}}{\text{1 mole of reactant}} = \text{grams of} \underline{\hspace{2cm}}$$

$$\text{moles of product} \times \frac{\text{grams of product}}{\text{1 mole of product}} = \text{grams of} \underline{\hspace{2cm}}$$

Add the masses of the reactants.

$\boxed{}$ **g C$_3$H$_8$ +** $\boxed{}$ **g O$_2$ =** $\boxed{}$ **g reactants**

Add the masses of the products.

$\boxed{}$ **g CO$_2$ +** $\boxed{}$ **g H$_2$O =** $\boxed{}$ **g products**

Determine if the _____ is observed.

Does the mass of the reactants equal the mass of the products?

_____ .

3. Evaluate the Answer

Each product or reactant has $\boxed{}$ significant figures. Your answer must have $\boxed{}$ significant figures.

1 Defining Stoichiometry (continued)

Examine Relationships between coefficients can be used to write conversion factors called _____.

Example

Given the equation $2KClO_3(s) \longrightarrow 2KCl(s) + 3O_2(g)$

Each substance forms a _____ with the other substances in the reaction.

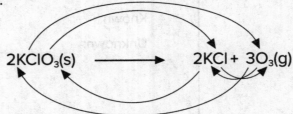

$$2KClO_3(s) \longrightarrow 2KCl + 3O_3(g)$$

Write the mole ratios that define the mole relationships in this equation. (Hint: Relate each reactant and each product to each of the other substances.)

Write the mole ratios for the equation
$C_2H_4(g) + 3O_2(g) \longrightarrow 2CO_2(g) + 2H_2O(l)$.

GET IT? **Identify** the source from which a chemical reaction's mole ratios are derived.

_____

_____

_____

1 Defining Stoichiometry (continued)

REVIEW IT!

5. **Compare** the mass of the reactants and the mass of the products in a chemical reaction, and explain how these masses are related.

_____

_____

6. **State** how many mole ratios can be written for a chemical reaction involving three substances.

_____

7. **Categorize** the ways in which a balanced chemical equation can be interpreted.

_____

8. **Apply** The general form of a chemical reaction is $xA + yB \rightarrow zAB$. In the equation, A and B are elements, and x, y, and z are coefficients. State the mole ratios for this reaction.

_____

9. **Apply** Hydrogen peroxide (H_2O_2) decomposes to produce water and oxygen. Write a balanced chemical equation for this reaction, and determine the possible mole ratios.

_____

_____

10. **Model** Write the mole ratios for the reaction of hydrogen gas and oxygen gas, $2H_2(g) + O_2(g) \rightarrow 2H_2O$. Make a sketch of six hydrogen molecules reacting with the correct number of oxygen molecules. Show the water molecules produced.

10 Stoichiometry

2 Stoichiometric Calculations

BUILD TO THE ESSENTIAL QUESTION

Read the items under Build to the Essential Question at the beginning of the lesson. Restate each in your own words.

_____

_____

Recall the definition of the Review Vocabulary term.

chemical reaction _____

_____

_____

Identify the tools needed for stoichiometric calculations.

All stoichiometric calculations start with _____ based on a _____. Finally, _____ are required.

2 Stoichiometric Calculations (continued)

Sequence the steps needed to convert from the balanced equation to the mass of the unknown.

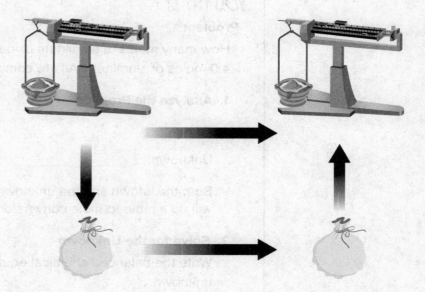

Identify the steps in stoichiometric calculations by completing the summary below.

1. _____. Interpret the

   equation in terms of _____.

2. _____

   _____. Use the _____

   _____ as the conversion factor.

3. _____

   _____ Use the appropriate mole ratio from

   the _____ as the conversion factor.

4. _____

   _____

   Use _____ as the conversion factor.

2 Stoichiometric Calculations (continued)

Solve Read Example Problem 2 in your text.

YOU TRY IT

Problem

How many moles of aluminum oxide (Al_2O_3) are produced when 4.0 moles of aluminum (Al) are combined with oxygen gas (O_2)?

1. Analyze the Problem

Known: _____

Unknown: _____

Both the known and the unknown are in moles, therefore, you will do a mole-to-mole conversion.

2. Solve for the Unknown

Write the balanced chemical equation. Label the known and unknown.

$$\boxed{} \; Al(s) + \boxed{} \; O_2 = \boxed{} \; Al_2O_3(s)$$

List the mole ratios for this equation. (Hint: *Draw arrows that show the relationships of the substances in this equation.*)

Circle the mole ratio that converts moles of Al to mol of Al_2O_3.

Multiply the known number of moles Al by the mole ratio to find the moles of unknown Al_2O_3.

$$\boxed{} \; \text{moles Al} + \frac{\boxed{} \text{moles } Al_2O_3}{\boxed{} \text{moles of Al}} = \boxed{} \; \text{moles of } Al_2O_3$$

3. Evaluate the Answer

The given number of moles has $\boxed{}$ significant figures. Therefore, the answer must have $\boxed{}$ significant figures.

2 Stoichiometric Calculations (continued)

Solve Read Example Problem 3 in your text.

YOU TRY IT

Problem

How many grams of solid iron(III) chloride ($FeCl_3$) are produced when 2.00 moles of solid iron (Fe) are combined with chlorine gas (Cl_2)?

1. Analyze the Problem

Known: _____

Unknown: _____

You are given the moles of the reactant, Fe, and must determine the mass of the product, $FeCl_3$; therefore, you will do a mole to mass conversion.

2. Solve for the Unknown

Write the balanced chemical equation. Identify the known and unknown substances.

$\boxed{}$ Fe(s) + $\boxed{}$ Cl_2(g) = $\boxed{}$ $FeCl_3$(s)

List the mole ratios for this equation. (Hint: *Draw arrows that show the relationships of the substances in this equation.*) Circle the mole ratio that relates moles of Fe to $FeCl_3$.

Multiply the number of moles of Fe by the mole ratio.

$\boxed{}$ mol Fe + $\dfrac{\boxed{}\ \text{mol } FeCl_3}{\boxed{}\ \text{mol Fe}}$ = $\boxed{}$ mol of $FeCl_3$

Multiply the moles of $FeCl_3$ by the molar mass of $FeCl_3$.

$\boxed{}$ mol $FeCl_3$ + $\dfrac{\boxed{}\ \text{mol g } FeCl_3}{1\ \text{mol } FeCl_3}$ = $\boxed{}$ g $FeCl_3$

3. Evaluate the Answer

The given number of moles has $\boxed{}$ digits, so the mass of $FeCl_3$ must have $\boxed{}$ digits.

2 Stoichiometric Calculations (continued)

Solve Read Example Problem 4 in your text.

YOU TRY IT

Problem

Determine the mass of ammonia (NH_3) produced when 3.75 g of nitrogen gas (N_2) react with hydrogen gas (H_2).

1. Analyze the Problem

Known: _____

Unknown: _____

You are given the mass of the reactant, N_2, and must determine the mass of the product NH_3. Do a mass-to-mass conversion.

2. Solve for the Unknown

Write the balanced chemical equation for the reaction.

$$\boxed{}\ N_2(g) + \boxed{}\ H_2(g) = \boxed{}\ NH_3(g)$$

Convert grams of $N_2(g)$ to moles of $N_2(g)$ using the inverse of molar mass as the conversion factor.

$$\boxed{}\ g\ N_2\ (g) \times \frac{1\ mol\ N_2}{\boxed{}\ g\ N_2} = \boxed{}\ mol\ N_2$$

List the mole ratios for this equation.

Multiply moles of N_2 by the mole ratio that converts N_2 to NH_3.

$$\boxed{}\ mol\ N_2 \times \frac{\boxed{}\ mol\ NH_3}{\boxed{}\ mol\ N_2} = \boxed{}\ mol\ NH_3$$

Multiply moles of NH_3 by the molar mass.

$$\boxed{}\ mol\ NH_3 \times \frac{\boxed{}\ g\ NH_3}{1\ mol\ NH_3} = \boxed{}\ g\ NH_3$$

3. Evaluate the Answer

The given mass has $\boxed{}$ significant figures, so the mass of NH_3 must have $\boxed{}$ significant figures.

2 Stoichiometric Calculations (continued)

REVIEW IT!

17. **Explain** why a balanced chemical equation is needed to solve a stoichiometric problem.

_____

_____

18. **List** the four steps used in solving stoichiometric problems.

_____

_____

_____

19. **Describe** how a mole ratio is correctly expressed when it is used to solve a stoichiometric problem.

_____

20. **Apply** How can you determine the mass of liquid bromine (Br_2) needed to react completely with a given mass of magnesium?

_____

_____

_____

21. **Calculate** Hydrogen reacts with excess nitrogen as follows:

$$N_2(g) + 3H_2(g) \rightarrow 2NH_3(g)$$

If 2.70 g of H_2 reacts, how many grams of NH_3 is formed?

_____

22. **Design** a concept map for the following reaction.

$$CaCO_3(s) + 2HCl(aq) \rightarrow CaCl_2(aq) + H_2O(l) + CO_2(g)$$

The concept map should explain how to determine the mass of $CaCl_2$ produced from a given mass of HCl.

Copyright © McGraw-Hill Education

10 Stoichiometry

3 Limiting Reactants

2 Stoichiometric Calculations (continued)

BUILD TO THE ESSENTIAL QUESTION

Read the items under Build to the Essential Question at the beginning of the lesson. Restate each in your own words.

_____

_____

_____

REVIEW VOCABULARY

molar mass

Recall the definition of the Review Vocabulary term.

molar mass _____

_____

NEW VOCABULARY

limiting reactant

excess reactant

Define each New Vocabulary term.

limiting reactant _____

_____

excess reactant _____

_____

GET IT? **Extend** How many more hydrogen molecules would be needed to completely react with the excess nitrogen molecules shown in **Figure 5?**

_____

Organize information about limiting reactants.

I. _____

   A. Limiting reactant

      1. _____

      2. _____

   B. _____

II. Calculating the product when a reactant is limited

   A. _____

      1. Convert the masses to moles.

      2. Multiply each mass by the inverse of the molar mass.

   B. _____

   C. _____

      _____

   D. Determine the amount of product that can be made with the moles of the limiting reactant.

Solve Read Example Problem 5 in your text.

YOU TRY IT

Problem

If 100.0 g of sulfur reacts with 50.0 g of chlorine, what mass of disulfur dichloride is produced?

1. Analyze the Problem

Known: _____

Unknown: _____

2. Solve for the Unknown

Write the balanced chemical equation.

List the mole ratios for this equation.

Multiply each mass by the inverse of molar mass.

Calculate the actual ratio of available moles.

Determine the limiting reactant.

_____

_____

Multiply the number of moles of the limiting reactant by the mole ratio of the product to the limiting reactant.

Multiply moles of the product by the molar mass.

Multiply moles of the excess reactant by the molar mass.

Subtract the mass of the excess reactant needed from the mass available.

3. Evaluate the Answer

The given mass has ⬜ significant figures, so the mass of the

unknown must have ⬜ significant figures.

3 Limiting Reactants (continued)

REVIEW IT!

25. Describe the reason why a reaction between two substances comes to an end.

_____

_____

_____

26. Identify the limiting and the excess reactant in each reaction.

a. Wood burns in a campfire.

b. Airborne sulfur reacts with the silver plating on a teapot to produce tarnish (silver sulfide).

c. Baking powder in batter decomposes to produce carbon dioxide.

_____

_____

_____

_____

27. Analyze Tetraphosphorus trisulphide (P_4S_3) is used in the match heads of some matches. It is produced in the reaction $8P_4 + 3S_8 \rightarrow 8P_4S_3$. Determine which of the following statements are incorrect, and rewrite the incorrect statements to make them correct.

a. 4 mol P_4 reacts with 1.5 mol S_8 to form 4 mol P_4S_3.

b. Sulfur is the limiting reactant when 4 mol P_4 and 4 mol S_8 react.

c. 6 mol P_4 reacts with 6 mol S_8, forming 1320 g P_4S_3.

_____

_____

_____

_____

10 Stoichiometry

4 Percent Yield

BUILD TO THE ESSENTIAL QUESTION

Read the items under Build to the Essential Question at the beginning of the lesson. Restate each in your own words.

_____

_____

REVIEW VOCABULARY

process

Recall the definition of the Review Vocabulary term.

process _____

_____

NEW VOCABULARY

theoretical yield

actual yield

percent yield

Define each New Vocabulary term.

theoretical yield _____

_____

actual yield _____

_____

percent yield _____

_____

Write the formula for percent yield.

$$\frac{\underline{\hspace{3cm}} \text{ (from an experiment)}}{\underline{\hspace{3cm}} \text{ (from stoichiometric calculations)}} \times \underline{\hspace{1cm}} = \text{percent yield}$$

4 Percent Yield (continued)

Solve Read Example Problem 6 in your text.

YOU TRY IT

Problem

When 100.0 kg sand (SiO_2) are processed with carbon (C) and 51.4 kg SiC are recovered, what is the percent yield of SiC?

1. Analyze the Problem

Known: _____

Unknown: _____

2. Solve for the Unknown

Write the balanced chemical equation.

_____

Determine the mole ratio that converts _____ to _____.

Convert kg to g.

100 kg SiO_2 = _____ g, 51.4 kg SiC = _____ g

Convert mass to moles using the inverse of molar mass.

Use the appropriate mole ratio to convert mol SiO_2 to mol SiC.

Calculate the theoretical yield. Multiply mol SiC by the molar mass.

Divide the actual yield by the theoretical yield and multiply by 100.

3. Evaluate the Answer

The quantities have ☐ significant figures, so the percent yield must have ☐ significant figures.

4 Percent Yield (continued)

REVIEW IT!

31. **Identify** which type of yield—theoretical yield, actual yield, or percent yield—is a measure of the efficiency of a chemical reaction.

_____

32. **List** several reasons why the actual yield from a chemical reaction is not usually equal to the theoretical yield.

_____

_____

_____

33. **Explain** how percent yield is calculated.

_____

_____

34. **Apply** In an experiment, you combine 83.77 g of iron with an excess of sulfur and then heat the mixture to obtain iron(III) sulfide.

$$2Fe(s) + 3S(s) \rightarrow Fe_2S_3(s)$$

What is the theoretical yield, in grams, of iron(III) sulfide?

_____

35. **Calculate** the percent yield of the reaction of magnesium with excess oxygen.

$$2Mg(s) + O_2(g) \rightarrow 2MgO(s)$$

Reaction Data	
Mass of empty crucible	35.67 g
Mass of crucible and Mg	38.06 g
Mass of crucible and MgO (after heating)	39.15 g

_____

_____

11 States of Matter

ESSENTIAL QUESTION

Write the Essential Question for this chapter.

_____

_____

_____

Use the "What I Know" column to list the things you know about the Essential Question. Then list the questions you have about the Essential Question in the "What I Want to Find Out" column. As you read the chapter, fill in the "What I Learned" column.

K _What I Know_	W _What I Want to Find Out_	L _What I Learned_

11 States of Matter

1 Gases

BUILD TO THE ESSENTIAL QUESTION

Read the items under Build to the Essential Question at the beginning of the lesson. Restate each in your own words.

_____

_____

_____

REVIEW VOCABULARY

kinetic energy

Recall the definition of the Review Vocabulary term.

kinetic energy

_____

NEW VOCABULARY

kinetic-molecular theory

elastic collision

temperature

diffusion

Graham's law of effusion

pressure

barometer

pascal

atmosphere

Dalton's law of partial pressures

Define each New Vocabulary term.

kinetic-molecular theory

_____

elastic collision

_____

temperature

_____

_____

diffusion

_____

_____

Graham's law of effusion

_____

_____

pressure

_____

barometer

_____

pascal

_____

_____

atmosphere

_____

Dalton's law of partial pressures

_____

_____

1 Gases (continued)

Distinguish between the three main physical properties of gas particles by completing the passages below.

1. Size is very _____. It is assumed that there are _____ significant _____ or _____ forces among gas particles.
2. Motion is _____ moving in a _____ pattern. It is assumed that gas particles move in a _____ path until they _____.
3. The Energy is _____. The _____ and _____ of a _____ determine the kinetic _____.

Describe kinetic energy in equation form by completing the table below.

KE = 1/2mv²	Variable	Definition
KE		
m		
v		

Describe the following concepts as they relate to the behaviors of gases by completing the passages below.

low density—Gases have low density (_____ per _____) in comparison to _____. The difference in density is partly due to the mass of the _____ and also because there is a great deal of _____ between gas particles.

compression and expansion—The large amount of _____ between gas particles allows them to be _____, or pushed, into a _____ volume. Once the pressure is _____, the particles _____ to the original _____.

diffusion and effusion—Because there are no _____ forces of _____ between gas particles, gases _____ past one another. This _____ motion allows gases to mix until they are _____. The movement of _____ past one another is called _____. The process of allowing a gas to escape through a tiny opening is called _____.

Write the proportional statement based on Graham's law of effusion that allows you to compare the diffusion rate of two different gases.

GET IT? **Explain** why the rate of diffusion depends on the mass of the particles.

_____

_____

Describe pressure as it relates to the behaviors of gases.

_____

_____

Distinguish between a barometer and a manometer.

_____

_____

Explore the relationship between different units of pressure by filling in the table below.

Unit Name (unit symbol)	Conversion Ratio: 1 atm = _____	Conversion Ratio: 1 kPa = _____
kilopascal ( )		
millimeters of mercury ( )		
torr		
pounds per square inch (or)		
atmosphere ( )		

1 Gases (continued)

8. Explain Use the kinetic theory to explain the behavior of gases.

_____

_____

9. Describe how the mass of a gas particle affects its rate of effusion and diffusion.

_____

_____

10. Explain how gas pressure is measured.

_____

_____

_____

11. Explain why the container of water must be inverted when a gas is collected by displacement of water.

_____

_____

_____

12. Describe Dalton's Law of partial pressures, then calculate the pressure of gas B as follows. Suppose two gases in a container have a total pressure of 1.20 atm. What is the pressure of Gas B if the partial pressure of Gas A is 0.75 atm?

_____

_____

_____

13. Infer whether or not temperature has any effect on the diffusion rate of a gas. Explain your answer.

_____

_____

_____

11 States of Matter

2 Forces of Attraction

BUILD TO THE ESSENTIAL QUESTION

Read the items under Build to the Essential Question at the beginning of the lesson. Restate each in your own words.

_____

_____

_____

REVIEW VOCABULARY

polar covalent

Recall the definition of the Review Vocabulary term.

polar covalent

_____

_____

NEW VOCABULARY

dispersion forces

dipole-dipole force

hydrogen bond

Define each New Vocabulary term.

dispersion forces

_____

_____

dipole-dipole force

_____

_____

hydrogen bond

_____

_____

Compare and contrast intramolecular forces by completing the table below.

Force	Basis of Attraction	Example
Ionic		
Covalent		
Metallic		

Compare intermolecular forces by completing the table below.

Force	Basis of Attraction	Example
Dispersion		
Dipole-dipole		
Hydrogen bond		

GET IT? **Explain** why dispersion forces form.

_____

_____

_____

GET IT? **Infer** the physical state of the element astatine at room temperature and explain your reasoning.

_____

_____

_____

GET IT? **Compare** dipole-dipole forces and dispersion forces.

_____

_____

_____

GET IT? **Distinguish** between the forces that hold atoms together in a water molecule and the attractive forces that act between water molecules.

_____

_____

_____

2 Forces of Attraction (continued)

ACADEMIC VOCABULARY	Define the following term.
orient	orient _____
approach	approach _____

REVIEW IT!

14. Explain what determines a substance's state at a given temperature.

_____

_____

_____

15. Compare and contrast intermolecular forces and intramolecular forces.

_____

_____

_____

16. Evaluate Which of the molecules listed below can form hydrogen bonds? For which of the molecules would dispersion forces be the only intermolecular force? Give reasons for your answers.

   a. H_2 **b.** H_2S **c.** HCl **d.** HF

_____

_____

17. Intepret Data In a methane molecule (CH_4), there are four single covalent bonds. In an octane molecule (C_8H_{18}), there are 25 single covalent bonds. How does the number of bonds affect the dispersion forces in samples of methane and octane? Which compound is a gas at room temperature? Which compound is a liquid?

_____

_____

11 States of Matter

3 Liquids and Solids

3 Liquids and Solids (continued)

BUILD TO THE ESSENTIAL QUESTION

Read the items under Build to the Essential Question at the beginning of the lesson. Restate each in your own words.

_____

_____

_____

REVIEW VOCABULARY

meniscus

Recall the definition of the Review Vocabulary term.

meniscus

_____

_____

NEW VOCABULARY

viscosity

surface tension

surfactant

crystalline solid

unit cell

allotrope

amorphous solid

Define each New Vocabulary term.

viscosity

_____

_____

surface tension

_____

_____

surfactant

_____

_____

crystalline solid

_____

_____

unit cell

_____

_____

allotrope

_____

_____

amorphous solid

_____

_____

3 Liquids and Solids (continued)

Compare and contrast the following paired concepts as they relate to the properties of liquids by completing the following statements.

Density and compression: A liquid can take the _____, but its volume is _____. The density of a liquid is _____ than the density of the same substance as a _____. Liquids cannot usually be _____ except under _____ pressure.

Fluidity and viscosity: Fluidity is the ability to _____. Liquids flow through each other but at a _____ than _____ do. Viscosity is the measure of the _____ of a liquid to _____. The stronger _____ slow down the ability to flow, which _____ resistance (viscosity).

Viscosity and temperature: Temperature affects the _____ of a _____. Viscosity _____ with temperature.

Analyze the relationship between viscosity, temperature, and change in kinetic energy by completing the table.

Temperature	Δ KE	Viscosity	Effect in Liquid
increases			flows faster
decreases		increases	
stays the same	no change		

GET IT? **Infer** why it is important for motor oil to remain viscous.

_____

_____

3 Liquids and Solids (continued)

Explain surface tension by completing the web diagram below.

The energy required to increase the

A measure of the by interior particles

Atomic

The stronger the between particles, the the surface tension

The surface tension of water is because its molecules form hydrogen bonds

Describe the following concepts as they relate to the properties of liquids by completing the following passages.

Capillary action is _____

_____

Cohesion is _____

Adhesion is _____

3 Liquids and Solids (continued)

GET IT? **Describe** in your own words why ice floats in water.

_____

_____

Compare the different types of crystalline solids by completing the following table.

Type	Unit Particles	Characteristics	Examples
Atomic			
Molecular			
Covalent network			
Ionic			
Metallic			

GET IT? **Describe** the properties of metals that make them useful for making jewelry.

_____

_____

3 Liquids and Solids (continued)

REVIEW IT!

18. Differentiate between solids and liquids in terms of the arrangement and motion of particles.

_____

_____

19. Describe the factors that affect viscosity.

_____

_____

20. Explain why soap and water are used to clean clothing instead of water alone.

_____

_____

21. Compare a unit cell and a crystal lattice.

_____

22. Describe the difference between a molecular solid and a covalent network solid.

_____

_____

_____

23. Explain why water forms a meniscus when it is in a graduated cylinder.

_____

_____

_____

24. Infer why the surface of mercury in a thermometer is convex; that is, the surface is higher at the center.

_____

_____

_____

3 Liquids and Solids (continued)

25. **Predict** which solid is more likely to be amorphous—one formed by allowing a molten material to cool slowly to room temperature or one formed by quickly cooling the same material in an ice bath.

_____

_____

_____

_____

_____

26. **Design** an experiment to compare the relative abilities of water and isopropyl alcohol to support skipping stones. Include a prediction about which liquid will be better, along with a brief explanation of your prediction.

_____

_____

_____

_____

_____

11 States of Matter

4 Phase Changes

BUILD TO THE ESSENTIAL QUESTION

Read the items under Build to the Essential Question at the beginning of the lesson. Restate each in your own words.

_____

_____

REVIEW VOCABULARY

phase change

Recall the definition of the Review Vocabulary term.

phase change

_____

NEW VOCABULARY

melting point

vaporization

evaporation

vapor pressure

boiling point

freezing point

condensation

deposition

phase diagram

triple point

Define each New Vocabulary term.

melting point

_____

_____

vaporization

_____

evaporation

_____

vapor pressure

boiling point

_____

freezing point

_____

condensation

deposition

_____

phase diagram

_____

_____

triple point

_____

Classify the types of phase changes by completing the table below. Use Figure 22 in your text for reference.

Phase Transition	Type of Transition
gas to solid	
solid to liquid	
liquid to gas	
liquid to solid	
	condensation
solid to gas	

Describe the phase changes that require energy by completing the following outline.

   I. Melting

      A. Heat energy disrupts _____ in ice.

      B. The amount of energy required depends on _____.

      C. The melting point is the temperature at which _____.

      D. The melting point of _____ may be unspecified.

  II. Vaporization

      A. In liquid water, some particles have more _____.

      B. Particles that escape from liquid enter the _____.

      C. When vaporization occurs only at a surface it is called _____.

      D. The pressure exerted by a vapor over a liquid is called _____.

      E. The temperature at which vapor pressure equals atmospheric pressure is called the _____.

 III. Sublimation

      A. Many solids can become gases without _____.

      B. Some solids sublime at _____.

      C. The process of _____ is an example of sublimation.

GET IT? **Explain** when the term vapor should be used to describe the gas phase.

_____

_____

Organize the phase changes that release energy. Identify the phase, describe the process, and identify the reverse process by completing the table below.

Phase Change	Process Description	Reverse Process
condensation		vaporization
	process in which a liquid becomes a solid	
deposition		sublimation

GET IT? **Describe** the condensation of water vapor in the atmosphere.

_____

Explain how the critical point affects water.

_____

_____

_____

Identify normal freezing point, normal boiling point, critical point, and triple point in the phase diagram for H_2O below. Use Figure 28 in your text for reference.

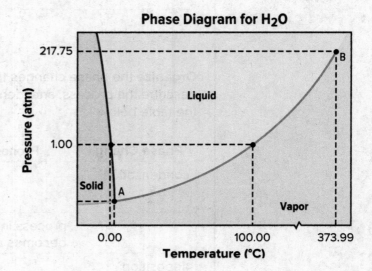

Phase Diagram for H_2O

Determine the phase of water at 2.00 atm and 100.00°C.

_____

GET IT? **Contrast** the slope of the red line in water's phase diagram with that of the red line in carbon dioxide's phase diagram. How do water and carbon dioxide differ in their reaction to increased pressure at the solid/liquid boundary?

_____

_____

4 Phase Changes (continued)

REVIEW IT!

27. Distinguish between how endothermic and exothermic processes can result in phase changes.

_____

_____

_____

28. Explain the difference between the processes of melting and freezing.

_____

_____

29. Differentiate the phase changes between a solid and a gas.

_____

_____

_____

30. Differentiate solids, liquids, and gases based on the phase changes of sublimation and evaporation.

_____

_____

_____

31. Describe the information that a phase diagram supplies.

_____

_____

32. Explain what the triple point and the critical point on a phase diagram represent.

_____

_____

33. Determine the phase of water at 75.00°C and 3.00 atm using **Figure 28.**

12 Gases

ESSENTIAL QUESTION

Write the Essential Question for this chapter.

_____

_____

_____

Use the "What I Know" column to list the things you know about the Essential Question. Then list the questions you have about the Essential Question in the "What I Want to Find Out" column. As you read the chapter, fill in the "What I Learned" column.

K *What I Know*	W *What I Want to Find Out*	L *What I Learned*

Copyright © McGraw-Hill Education

12 Gases

1 The Gas Laws

BUILD TO THE ESSENTIAL QUESTION

Read the items under Build to the Essential Question at the beginning of the lesson. Restate each in your own words.

_____

_____

REVIEW VOCABULARY

scientific law

Recall the definition of the Review Vocabulary term.

scientific law

_____

_____

NEW VOCABULARY

Boyle's law

absolute zero

Charles's law

Gay-Lussac's law

combined gas law

Define each New Vocabulary term.

Boyle's law

_____

_____

absolute zero

_____

Charles's law

_____

_____

Gay-Lussac's law

_____

_____

combined gas law

_____

_____

1 The Gas Laws (continued)

YOU TRY IT

Problem

Helium gas in a balloon is compressed from 4.0 L to 2.5 L at constant temperature. The gas's pressure at 4.0 L is 210 kPa. Determine the pressure at 2.5 L.

1. Analyze the Problem

Known	Unknown
$V_1 =$ _____	P_2 _____
$V_2 =$ _____	
$P_1 =$ _____	

Use the equation for Boyle's law to solve for P_2.

2. Solve for the Unknown

Write the equation for Boyle's law: _____

To solve for P_2, divide both sides by V_2. $P_2 =$

Substitute the known values. $P_2 =$

Solve for P_2. $P_2 =$ _____

3. Evaluate the Answer

When the volume is _____, the pressure is _____. The answer is in _____, a unit of pressure.

GET IT? Explain why the second graph in Figure 2 shows a direct proportion, but the first graph does not.

_____

_____

_____

_____

Summarize Fill in the blanks to help you take notes while you read Example Problem 2.

Problem

A gas sample at 40.0°C occupies a volume of 2.32 L. Assuming the pressure is constant, if the temperature is raised to 75.0°C, what will the volume be?

1. Analyze the Problem

Known	Unknown
$T_1 = $ _____	
$V_1 = $ _____	$V_2 = $ _____
$T_2 = $ _____	

Use Charles's law and the known values for T_1, V_1, and T_2 to solve for V_2.

2. Solve for the Unknown

Convert the T_1 and T_2 Celsius temperatures to kelvin:

$T_1 = 273 + 40.0°C = $ _____ K $T_2 = 273 + 75.0°C = $ _____ K

Write the equation for Charles's law:

To solve for V_2, multiply both sides by T_2:

$$V_2 = $$

Substitute known values:

$$V_2 = $$

Solve for V_2.

$$V_2 = \text{_____}$$

3. Evaluate the Answer

When temperature in kelvin increases by a small amount, the volume _____ by a small amount. The answer is in _____, a unit for volume.

1 The Gas Laws (continued)

GET IT? **Compare and contrast** the graphs in Figures 2 and 3.

_____

_____

_____

Solve Read Example Problem 3 in your text.

YOU TRY IT

Problem

The pressure of a gas stored in a refrigerated container is 4.0 atm at 22.0°C. Determine the pressure in the tank if the temperature is lowered to 0.0°C.

1. **Analyze the Problem**

   Known   **Unknown**

   P_1 = 4.0 atm T_2 = _____ P_2 = ? _____

   T_1 = _____

   Use Gay-Lussac's law and the known values to solve for P_2.

2. **Solve for the Unknown**

   Convert the T_1 and T_2 Celsius figures to kelvin.

   T_1 = _____ + 22.0°C = _____ K

   T_2 = 273 + _____ °C = _____ K

   Write the equation for Gay-Lussac's law.

   To solve for P_2, multiply both sides by T_2.

   P_2 =

   Substitute known values.

   P_2 =

   P_2 = 3.7 atm

3. **Evaluate the Answer**

   The temperature _____ and the pressure _____.

1 The Gas Laws (continued)

Describe the combined gas law.

_____

_____

Write the combined gas law equation.

Pressure is inversely proportional to _____ and directly proportional
to _____. Volume also is _____ to temperature.

GET IT? **Derive** Charles's and Gay-Lussac's laws from the combined
gas law.

_____

_____

_____

_____

Solve Read Example Problem 4 in your text.

YOU TRY IT
Problem

A gas at 100.0 kPa and 30.0°C has an initial volume of 1.00 L.
Determine the temperature that could support the gas at 200.0 kPa
and a volume of 0.50 L.

1. Analyze the Problem

Known:

$P_1 =$ _____ $V_1 =$ _____   Unknown:

$P_2 =$ _____ $V_2 =$ _____ $T_2 = ?$ °C

$T_1 =$ _____

Remember that volume increases as temperature increases, and
volume is inversely proportional to pressure.

1 The Gas Laws (continued)

2. Solve for the Unknown

Convert the T_1 Celsius temperature to kelvin.

$T_1 = \underline{\hspace{1cm}} + 30.0°C = \underline{\hspace{1cm}} K$

Write the combined gas law equation.

To solve for T_2, multiply both sides of the equation by T_2.

Multiply both sides of the equation by T_1.

$$T_2 \, P_1 \, V_1 = \underline{\hspace{2cm}}$$

Divide both sides of the equation by $P_1 \, V_1$.

$$T_2 = $$

Substitute known values.

Solve for T_2.

$$T_2 = 303 \text{ K} - 273 \text{ K} = 30.0°C$$

3. Evaluate the Answer

As pressure \underline{\hspace{2cm}} and volume \underline{\hspace{2.5cm}} in proportional amounts, the temperature remained constant.

1 The Gas Laws (continued)

REVIEW IT!

14. State the relationships between pressure, temperature, and volume of a fixed amount of gas.

_____

_____

15. Explain Which of the three variables that apply to equal amounts of gases are directly proportional? Which are inversely proportional?

_____

16. Analyze A weather balloon is released into the atmosphere. You know the initial volume, temperature, and air pressure. What information will you need to predict its volume when it reaches its final altitude? Which law would you use to calculate this volume?

_____

_____

17. Infer why gases such as the oxygen used at hospitals are compressed. Why must compressed gases be shielded from high temperatures? What must happen to compressed oxygen before it can be inhaled?

_____

_____

18. Calculate A rigid plastic container holds 1.00 L of methane gas at 660 torr pressure when the temperature is 22.0°C. How much pressure will the gas exert if the temperature is raised to 44.6°C?

_____

19. Design a concept map that shows the relationships between pressure, volume, and temperature in Boyle's, Charles's, and Gay-Lussac's laws.

Copyright © McGraw-Hill Education

12 Gases

2 The Ideal Gas Law

2 The Ideal Gas Law (continued)

BUILD TO THE ESSENTIAL QUESTION

Read the items under Build to the Essential Question at the beginning of the lesson. Restate each in your own words.

_____

_____

REVIEW VOCABULARY

mole

Recall the definition of the Review Vocabulary term.

mole
_____

_____

_____

NEW VOCABULARY

Avogadro's principle

molar volume

standard temperature and pressure (STP)

ideal gas constant (R)

ideal gas law

Define each New Vocabulary term.

Avogadro's principle
_____

_____

molar volume
_____

_____

standard temperature and pressure (STP)
_____

_____

ideal gas constant (R)
_____

_____

ideal gas law
_____

_____

2 The Ideal Gas Law (continued)

Explain Avogadro's principle by completing the paragraph below.

Avogadro's principle states that _____

_____. The

_____ volume for a gas is the volume that one mole occupies at

_____ of pressure and a temperature of _____.

Convert the following volumes of a gas at STP to moles by using 22.4 L/mol as the conversion factor.

$$2.50 \text{ L} \times \frac{1 \text{ mol}}{22.4 \text{ L}} = \underline{\hspace{2cm}}$$

$$7.34 \text{ L} \times \frac{1 \text{ mol}}{22.4 \text{ L}} = \underline{\hspace{2cm}}$$

$$4.7 \text{ L} \times \frac{1 \text{ mol}}{22.4 \text{ L}} = \underline{\hspace{2cm}}$$

2 The Ideal Gas Law (continued)

Analyze the ideal gas law.

The equation is written _____ = _____.

P represents _____.

V represents _____.

n represents the number of _____ of gas present.

R represents the _____.

_____ represents temperature.

The ideal gas law states that _____

_____

_____. The value of R depends on the units used

for _____.

GET IT? **Explain** why the number of moles, n, was added to the denominator of the equation $\frac{PV}{nT}$ = constant.

_____

_____

Describe the properties of an ideal gas.

_____

_____

Describe the properties of a real gas.

_____

_____

GET IT? **Explain** the relationship between the kinetic-molecular theory and an ideal gas.

_____

_____

2 The Ideal Gas Law (continued)

Summarize Fill in the blanks to help you take notes while you read Example Problem 6.

Problem

Calculate the number of moles of a gas contained in a 3.0-L vessel at 3.00×10^2 K with a pressure of 1.50 atm.

1. **Analyze the Problem**

   Known: **Unknown:**

   $V =$ _____ $n = ?$ mol

   $T =$ _____

   $P =$ _____

   $R =$

   Use the known values to find the value of n.

2. **Solve for the Unknown**

   Write the ideal gas law equation.

   _____

   To solve for n, divide both sides by RT.

   $n =$

   Substitute known values into the equation.

   $n =$

   Solve for n.

   $n =$

   $n =$ _____

3. **Evaluate the Answer**

   The answer agrees with the prediction that the number of moles will be _____ one mole. The unit in the answer is the _____.

2 The Ideal Gas Law (continued)

REVIEW IT!

31. **Explain** why Avogadro's principle holds true for ideal gases that have small particles and for ideal gases that have large particles.

_____

_____

32. **State** the equation for the ideal gas law.

_____

33. **Analyze** how the ideal gas law applies to real gases using the kinetic molecular theory.

_____

_____

34. **Predict** the conditions under which a real gas might deviate from ideal behavior.

_____

_____

35. **List** common units for each variable in the ideal gas law.

_____

36. **Calculate** A 2.00-L flask is filled with propane gas (C_3H_8) at a pressure of 1.00 atm and a temperature of −15.0°C. What is the mass of the propane in the flask?

_____

37. **Make and Use Graphs** For every 6°C drop in temperature, the air pressure in a car's tires goes down by about 1 psi (14.7 psi = 1.00 atm). Make a graph illustrating the change in tire pressure from 20°C to −20°C (assume 30.0 psi at 20°C).

12 Gases

3 Gas Stoichiometry

BUILD TO THE ESSENTIAL QUESTION

Read the items under Build to the Essential Question at the beginning of the lesson. Restate each in your own words.

_____

_____

REVIEW VOCABULARY

coefficient

Recall the definition of the Review Vocabulary term.

coefficient

_____

_____

ACADEMIC VOCABULARY

ratio

Define the following terms.

ratio

_____

_____

Science Notebook • Gases

218

Copyright © McGraw-Hill Education

3 Gas Stoichiometry (continued)

Indicate the moles and volume for the reaction below. Use Figure 10 as a reference.

$$2C_4H_{10}(g) \quad + \quad 13O_2(g) \quad \longrightarrow \quad 8CO_2(g) \quad + \quad 10H_2O(g)$$

_____ moles   _____ moles   _____ moles   _____ moles

_____ volumes   _____ volumes   _____ volumes   _____ volumes

The coefficients in the balanced equation represent _____ amounts

and relative _____.

Summarize Fill in the blanks to help you take notes while you read Example Problem 7.

Problem

Determine the volume of oxygen gas needed for the complete combustion of 4.00 L of propane gas (C_3H_8).

1. Analyze the Problem

Known:	Unknown:

V of $C_3H_8 = $ _____ V of $O_2 = ?$ L

Use the known volume of 4.00 L to find the volume needed for the combustion.

2. Solve for the Unknown

Write the balanced equation for the combustion of C_3H_8.

_____

Write the volume ratio.

Multiply the known volume of propane by the volume ratio to find the volume of O_2.

3. Evaluate the Answer

The coefficients of the reactants show that the quantity of _____ consumed is greater than the amount of propane. The unit of the answer is the _____, a unit of volume.

3 Gas Stoichiometry (continued)

REVIEW IT!

46. Explain When fluorine gas combines with water vapor, the following reaction occurs.

$$2F_2(g) + 2H_2O(g) \rightarrow O_2(g) + 4HF(g)$$

If the reaction starts with 2 L of fluorine gas, how many liters of water vapor react with the fluorine, and how many liters of oxygen and hydrogen fluoride are produced?

_____

_____

47. Analyze Is the volume of a gas directly or inversely proportional to the number of moles of a gas at constant temperature and pressure? Explain.

_____

_____

48. Calculate One mole of a gas occupies a volume of 22.4 L at STP. Calculate the temperature and pressure conditions needed to fit 2 mol of a gas into a volume of 22.4 L.

_____

_____

_____

49. Interpret Data Ethene gas (C_2H_4) reacts with oxygen to form carbon dioxide and water. Write a balanced equation for this reaction, then find the mole ratios of substances on each side of the equation.

_____

_____

_____

13 Mixtures and Solutions

ESSENTIAL QUESTION

Write the Essential Question for this chapter.

_____

_____

_____

Use the "What I Know" column to list the things you know about the Essential Question. Then list the questions you have about the Essential Question in the "What I Want to Find Out" column. As you read the chapter, fill in the "What I Learned" column.

K *What I Know*	W *What I Want to Find Out*	L *What I Learned*

13 Mixtures and Solutions

1 Types of Mixtures

BUILD TO THE ESSENTIAL QUESTION
Read the items under Build to the Essential Question at the beginning of the lesson. Restate each in your own words.

_____

_____

REVIEW VOCABULARY

solute

Recall the definition of the Review Vocabulary term.

solute _____

_____

NEW VOCABULARY

suspension

colloid

Brownian motion

Tyndall effect

soluble

miscible

insoluble

immiscible

Define each New Vocabulary term.

suspension _____

_____

colloid _____

_____

Brownian motion _____

_____

Tyndall effect _____

_____

miscible _____

_____

immiscible _____

_____

Compare and contrast soluble and insoluble substances.

_____

_____

1 Types of Mixtures (continued)

Compare and contrast miscible and immiscible liquids.

_____

_____

List three properties of a suspension.

1. _____

2. _____

3. _____

State three examples of suspensions.

1. _____

2. _____

3. _____

Identify four properties of a colloid.

1. _____

2. _____

3. _____

4. _____

GET IT? **Describe** two reasons why particles in a colloid do not settle out.

_____

_____

_____

_____

Copyright © McGraw-Hill Education

1 Types of Mixtures (continued)

Explain why particles in Brownian motion do not settle out.

_____

_____

_____

_____

_____

_____

Identify each of the following mixtures as a suspension, dilute colloid, or concentrated colloid. Base your answers on the property described.

Property	Type of Solution
cloudy mixture with particles that move erratically	
large particles with thixotropic behavior	
clear mixture with particles that scatter light	

REVIEW IT!

1. **Explain** Use the properties of seawater to describe the characteristics of mixtures.

_____

_____

2. **Distinguish** between suspensions and colloids.

_____

_____

1 Types of Mixtures (continued)

3. **Identify** the various types of solutions. Describe the characteristics of each type of solution.

_____

_____

4. **Explain** Use the Tyndall effect to explain why it is more difficult to drive through fog using high beams than using low beams.

_____

_____

_____

5. **Describe** different types of colloids.

_____

_____

6. **Explain** Why do dispersed colloid particles stay dispersed?

_____

_____

7. **Summarize** What causes Brownian motion?

_____

_____

8. **Compare and Contrast** Make a table that compares the properties of suspensions, colloids, and solutions.

13 Mixtures and Solutions

2 Solution Concentration

BUILD TO THE ESSENTIAL QUESTION

Read the items under Build to the Essential Question at the beginning of the lesson. Restate each in your own words.

_____

_____

REVIEW VOCABULARY

solvent

Recall the definition of the Review Vocabulary term.

solvent _____

_____

NEW VOCABULARY

concentration

molarity

molality

mole fraction

Define each New Vocabulary term.

concentration _____

_____

_____

molarity _____

_____

molality _____

_____

mole fraction _____

_____

2 Solution Concentration (continued)

Analyze the similarities in the concentration ratios shown in Table 3 in your text.

_____

_____

_____

Write the equation for determining percent by mass.

Percent by mass =

Summarize Fill in the blanks to help you take notes as you read Example Problem 1.

Problem

Determine the percent by mass of 3.6 g NaCl in 100.0 g H_2O.

1. Analyze the Problem

List the knowns and unknowns.

Known:	Unknown:
mass of solute = _____	percent by mass = ?
mass of solvent = _____	

2. Solve for the Unknown

Find the mass of the solution.

mass of solution = grams of solute + grams of solvent

mass of solution = 3.6 g + _____ = _____

Substitute the known values into the percent by mass equation.

percent by mass =

3. Evaluate the Answer

The answer should be a small percent, to match the small quantity of _____. The mass of sodium chloride was given in two significant figures, therefore, the answer should have _____ significant figures.

2 Solution Concentration (continued)

Describe how to calculate the molarity of a solution by completing the following statements.

To calculate the _____ of a solution, you must know the amount of dissolved _____ and the volume of _____.

The following equation is used: molarity (M) = _____ of solute per liters of _____.

Explain why you may need less than one liter of water to prepare a molar solution of one liter.

_____

GET IT? **Determine** What is the molar concentration of a liter solution with 0.5 mol of solute?

_____

Write the expression that describes the relationship between a stock solution and a dilute solution.

_____

M_1 = _____

V_1 = _____

M_2 = _____

V_2 = _____

ACADEMIC VOCABULARY

concentrated

Define the following term.

concentrated

_____

_____

2 Solution Concentration (continued)

Explain how the volume and mass of a solution change with temperature.

The volume may _____ when heated or _____ when cooled. The mass of the solution _____ change.

Write the mole fraction equations for a solvent (X_A) and a solute (X_B) below.

$X_A =$ $X_B =$

Evaluate the mole fraction for the values given in problem 4 on page 487 of your text. The number of moles for 100 g H_2O is given.

$n_A = 5.55$ mol H_2O $n_B =$ _____ mol NaCl

$X_{H_2O} =$ $=$ _____

$X_{NaCl} =$ $=$ _____

$X_{H_2O} + X_{NaCl} = 1.000$

_____ + _____ = 1.000

REAL-WORLD CONNECTION

Describe how the mole fractions for a solution are similar to the pieces of a pie.

_____

_____

_____

2 Solution Concentration (continued)

REVIEW IT!

31. **Compare and contrast** five quantitative ways to describe the composition of solutions.

_____

_____

_____

32. **Explain** the similarities and differences between a 1M solution of NaOH and a 1m solution of NaOH.

_____

_____

_____

33. **Calculate** A can of chicken broth contains 450 mg of sodium chloride in 240.0 g of broth. What is the percent by mass of sodium chloride in the broth?

_____

_____

_____

34. **Solve** How much ammonium chloride (NH_4Cl), in grams, is needed to produce 2.5 L of a 0.5M aqueous solution?

_____

_____

_____

35. **Outline** the laboratory procedure for preparing a specific volume of a dilute solution from a concentrated stock solution.

_____

_____

_____

13 Mixtures and Solutions

3 Factors Affecting Solvation

BUILD TO THE ESSENTIAL QUESTION

Read the items under Build to the Essential Question at the beginning of the lesson. Restate each in your own words.

_____

_____

REVIEW VOCABULARY

exothermic

Recall the definition of the Review Vocabulary term.

exothermic

_____

_____

NEW VOCABULARY

solvation

heat of solution

unsaturated solution

saturated solution

supersaturated solution

Henry's law

Define each New Vocabulary term.

solvation

_____

_____

heat of solution

_____

_____

unsaturated solution

_____

_____

supersaturated solution

_____

_____

Henry's law

_____

_____

Compare and contrast _saturated solutions and unsaturated solutions._

_____

_____

_____

_____

Describe solutions by completing the following statements.

A solution may exist in gas, solid, or liquid form, depending on the state of its _____. Some combinations of substances easily form _____ and others do not. A substance that does not _____ in a solvent is _____ in that solvent.

Write the general rule to determine if solvation will occur.

_____

_____

List three factors that must be known about component substances to determine if solvation will occur.

1. _____

2. _____

3. _____

Sequence the steps required for a sodium chloride crystal to dissolve in water.

_____ The charged ends of water molecules attract the positive Na ions and the negative Cl ions.

_____ The ions from the crystal break away from the surface.

_____ Water molecules collide with the surface of the crystal.

_____ NaCl crystals are placed in water.

_____ Solvation continues until the entire crystal has dissolved.

_____ The attraction between the dipoles and the ions are stronger than the attractions among the ions in the crystal.

GET IT? **Describe** what happens when a solid ionic compound dissolves in water.

_____

_____

_____

3 Factors Affecting Solvation (continued)

GET IT? **Explain** why stirring makes a solid solute such as sugar dissolve faster in a solvent such as water.

_____

_____

_____

Organize the following table on factors that can increase the rate of solvation by increasing the number of collisions.

Factor	Increase Collisions By
agitating the mixture	
breaking particles into smaller pieces	
increasing temperature of the solvent	

Explain how solubility is expressed in units of measurement.

_____

Review Table 4 in your text to determine the solubility of the following compounds in water.

Ca(OH)$_2$ at 20°C _____

KCl at 60°C _____

Describe each of these solubility states.

State	Description
continuing solvation	
dynamic equilibrium	
saturated solution	
unsaturated solution	

3 Factors Affecting Solvation (continued)

Describe how solubility changes with temperature for most substances.

_____

Explain why gases are less soluble as temperature increases.

_____

_____

Describe the relationship between solubility and pressure.

_____

Write the equation for Henry's law.

Summarize Fill in the blanks to help you take notes while you read Example Problem 5.

Problem

Find how much of a gas will dissolve in 1.0 L of water at 1.0 atm, if 0.85 g of that gas will dissolve in 1.0 L of water at 4.0 atm and temperature does not change.

1. Analyze the Problem

List the knowns and unknowns.

Known: **Unknown:**

$S_1 =$ _____

$P_1 =$ _____ $S_2 =$ _____

$P_2 =$ _____

2. Solve for the Unknown

Rearrange Henry's Law to solve for S_2.

$S_2 =$ _____

Substitute known values and solve.

$S_2 =$ _____ $\dfrac{(1.0\ atm)}{\text{_____}} =$ _____

3. Evaluate the Answer

The solubility _____ as expected due to the _____ in pressure.

3 Factors Affecting Solvation (continued)

REVIEW IT!

39. Describe factors that affect the formation of solutions.

_____

40. Define *solubility*.

_____

_____

41. Describe how intermolecular forces affect solvation.

_____

_____

42. Explain on a particle basis why the vapor pressure of a solution is lower than that of the pure solvent.

_____

_____

43. Summarize If a seed crystal is added to a supersaturated solution, how would you characterize the resulting solution?

_____

_____

44. Make and Use Graphs Use the information in **Table 4** to graph the solubilities of aluminum sulfate, lithium sulfate, and potassium chloride at 0°C, 20°C, 60°C, and 100°C. Which substance's solubility is most affected by increasing temperature?

13 Mixtures and Solutions

4 Colligative Properties of Solutions

BUILD TO THE ESSENTIAL QUESTION

Read the items under Build to the Essential Question at the beginning of the lesson. Restate each in your own words.

_____

_____

REVIEW VOCABULARY

ion

Recall the definition of the Review Vocabulary term.

ion _____

_____

NEW VOCABULARY

colligative property

vapor pressure lowering

boiling point elevation

freezing point depression

osmosis

osmotic pressure

Define each New Vocabulary term.

colligative property _____

_____

vapor pressure lowering _____

_____

boiling point elevation _____

_____

freezing point depression _____

_____

osmosis _____

_____

osmotic pressure _____

_____

_____

4 Colligative Properties of Solutions (continued)

Compare and contrast electrolytes and nonelectrolytes.

Substances like sodium chloride that _____ in water and conduct

an _____ are called _____. Substances like sucrose

that dissolve in water but do not _____ and do not conduct an

electric current are called _____.

GET IT? **Infer** Which compound would have the greater effect on colligative properties, sodium chloride or sucrose?

_____

_____

Summarize why vapor pressure lowering is a colligative property. Include an explanation of vapor pressure.

_____

_____

_____

_____

_____

_____

Explain boiling point elevation by completing the following statements.

A liquid boils when its _____ equals _____.

Adding a nonvolatile solute lowers the solvent's _____ pressure.

More _____ energy must be added to reach the solvent's

_____. The greater the number of _____ particles in the

solution is, the greater the _____ elevation will be.

Describe how the difference between the solid lines and dashed line corresponds to vapor pressure lowering, boiling point elevation, and freezing point depression. Use specific data from the graph to support your answer.

_____

_____

_____

_____

Describe why the freezing point changes when a solute is added to a solution.

_____

_____

_____

_____

Evaluate the diagram of a semipermeable membrane separating a sucrose-water solution on one side and water on the other side. Draw an arrow to show in which direction more water will flow and circle the side which has the greater osmotic pressure.

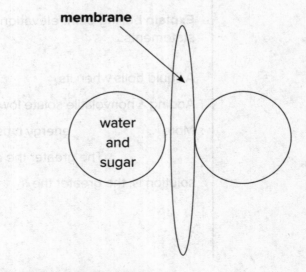

membrane

water
and
sugar

4 Colligative Properties of Solutions (continued)

REVIEW IT!

48. Explain the nature of colligative properties.

_____

_____

_____

49. Describe four colligative properties of solutions.

_____

_____

_____

_____

_____

50. Explain why a solution has a higher boiling point than that of the pure solvent.

_____

_____

_____

51. Solve An aqueous solution of calcium chloride ($CaCl_2$) boils at 101.3°C. How many kilograms of calcium chloride were dissolved in 1000.0 g of the solvent?

_____

_____

_____

_____

52. Calculate the boiling point elevation of a solution containing 50.0 g of glucose ($C_6H_{12}O_6$) dissolved in 500.0 g of water. Calculate the freezing point depression for the same solution.

_____

_____

_____

_____

_____

53. Investigate A lab technician determines the boiling point elevation of an aqueous solution of a nonvolatile, nonelectrolyte to be 1.12°C. What is the solution's molality?

_____

_____

_____

_____

_____

14 Energy and Chemical Change

ESSENTIAL QUESTION

Write the Essential Question for this chapter.

_____

_____

_____

Use the "What I Know" column to list the things you know about the Essential Question. Then list the questions you have about the Essential Question in the "What I Want to Find Out" column. As you read the chapter, fill in the "What I Learned" column.

K _What I Know_	W _What I Want to Find Out_	L _What I Learned_

14 Energy and Chemical Change

1 Energy

14 Energy and

BUILD TO THE ESSENTIAL QUESTION

Read the items under Build to the Essential Question at the beginning of the lesson. Restate each in your own words.

_____

_____

REVIEW VOCABULARY

temperature

Recall the definition of the Review Vocabulary term.

temperature _____

_____

NEW VOCABULARY

energy

law of conservation of energy

chemical potential energy

heat

calorie

joule

specific heat

Define each New Vocabulary term.

energy _____

_____

law of conservation of energy _____

_____

_____

chemical potential energy _____

_____

heat _____

_____

calorie _____

_____

joule _____

_____

specific heat _____

_____

1 Energy (continued)

Compare and contrast kinetic energy with potential energy.

_____

_____

On the curve below that represents a skier on a ski slope, label the place of greatest kinetic energy A, least kinetic energy B, greatest potential energy C, and least potential energy D.

Describe the skier above as a function of the law of conservation of energy.

_____

_____

_____

Explain chemical potential energy.

Chemical _____ energy of a substance is a result of the

arrangement of its _____ and the strength of the _____

joining the atoms. During some _____ reactions, such as

burning_____, much of the potential energy may be released

as _____. Some of the energy may be converted to work,

which is a form of _____ energy.

GET IT? **State** the law of conservation of energy in your own words.

_____

_____

1 Energy (continued)

Identify each symbol in the equation for specific heat.

$$q = c \times m \times \Delta T$$

_____ represents heat absorbed or released.

_____ represents the specific heat of the substance.

_____ represents mass of a sample in grams.

_____ represents a change in temperature.

Summarize. Fill in the blanks to help you take notes while you read Example Problem 2.

Problem

The temperature of a sample of iron with a mass of 10.0 g changed from 50.4°C to 25.0°C with the release of 114 J heat. Determine the specific heat of iron.

1. Analyze the Problem

Known:	Unknown:

energy released = _____   specific heat of iron = ?

$\Delta T =$ _____

mass of iron = _____

2. Solve for the Unknown

Write the equation for heat absorption.

_____

Solve for *c*.

_____

3. Evaluate the Answer

If the values used in the calculations have _____ significant figures, then the answer must also have _____ significant figures. The calculated value matches the value for iron in Table 2.

REVIEW IT!

7. **Explain** how energy changes from one form to another in an exothermic reaction. In an endothermic reaction.

_____

_____

_____

8. **Differentiate** between kinetic and potential energy in the following examples: two separated magnets; an avalanche of snow; books on library shelves; a mountain stream; a stock-car race; separation of charge in a battery.

_____

_____

_____

_____

9. **Explain** how the light and heat of a burning candle are related to chemical potential energy.

_____

_____

_____

10. **Calculate** the amount of heat absorbed when 5.50 g of aluminum is heated from 25.0°C to 95.0°C. The specific heat of aluminum is 0.897 J/(g·°C).

_____

_____

11. **Interpret Data** Equal masses of aluminum, gold, iron, and silver were left to sit in the Sun at the same time and for the same length of time. Use **Table 2** to arrange the four metals according to the increase in their temperatures from largest increase to smallest.

_____

_____

14 Energy and Chemical Change

2 Heat

BUILD TO THE ESSENTIAL QUESTION

Read the items under Build to the Essential Question at the beginning of the lesson. Restate each in your own words.

_____

_____

REVIEW VOCABULARY

pressure

Recall the definition of the Review Vocabulary term.

pressure

_____

NEW VOCABULARY

calorimeter

thermochemistry

system

surroundings

universe

enthalpy

enthalpy (heat)
  of reaction

Define each New Vocabulary term.

calorimeter

_____

_____

thermochemistry

_____

_____

system

_____

_____

surroundings

_____

_____

universe

_____

_____

enthalpy

_____

_____

enthalpy (heat) of reaction

_____

_____

Describe how a calorimeter measures heat.

_____

_____

_____

$$q = m \times c \times \Delta T$$

GET IT? **Define** the four variables in the equation above.

_____

_____

Summarize Fill in the blanks to help you take notes while you read Example Problem 3.

Problem

Determine the specific heat of a piece of metal with a mass of 4.68 g

that _____ 256 J of heat when its temperature increases

by 182°C, and explain if the metal could be an _____.

1. Analyze the problem

Known: mass of metal = _____

quantity of heat absorbed = _____

_____ = 182°C

Unknown: specific heat, c = ? J/(g · °C)

2. Solve for the Unknown

Write the equation for absorption of heat.

$q =$ _____

Solve for c by dividing both sides of the equation by $m \times \Delta T$.

$c =$ _____

2 Heat (continued)

Substitute the known values into the equation.

$c =$ _____ = _____

Table 2 indicates the metal could be _____.

3. Evaluate the Answer

The quantities used in the calculation have _____ significant figures, and the answer is correctly stated with _____ significant figures. The calculation yielded the _____ unit, and the calculated _____ is the same as that for _____.

Compare and contrast exothermic and endothermic reactions.

_____

_____

Write the symbol for enthalpy (heat) of reaction.

_____

Explain why chemists prefer to measure change in heat energy, rather than the total amount of heat energy present.

_____

_____

_____

_____

REVIEW IT!

16. **Describe** how you would calculate the amount of heat absorbed or released by a substance when its temperature changes.

_____

_____

17. **Explain** why ΔH for an exothermic reaction always has a negative value.

_____

18. **Explain** why a measured volume of water is an essential part of a calorimeter.

_____

19. **Explain** why you need to know the specific heat of a substance in order to calculate how much heat is gained or lost by the substance as a result of a temperature change.

_____

_____

20. **Describe** what the system means in thermodynamics, and explain how the system is related to the surroundings and the universe.

_____

_____

21. **Calculate** the specific heat in J/(g·°C) of an unknown substance if a 2.50-g sample releases 12.0 cal as its temperature changes from 25.0°C to 20.0°C.

_____

22. **Design an Experiment** Describe a procedure you could follow to determine the specific heat of a 45-g piece of metal.

14 Energy and Chemical Change

3 Thermochemical Equations

BUILD TO THE ESSENTIAL QUESTION

Read the items under Build to the Essential Question at the beginning of the lesson. Restate each in your own words.

_____

_____

_____

REVIEW VOCABULARY

combustion reaction

Recall the definition of the Review Vocabulary term.

combustion reaction

_____

_____

NEW VOCABULARY

thermochemical equation

enthalpy (heat) of combustion

molar enthalpy (heat) of vaporization

molar enthalpy (heat) of fusion

Define each New Vocabulary term.

thermochemical equation

_____

_____

_____

enthalpy (heat) of combustion

_____

_____

molar enthalpy (heat) of vaporization

_____

_____

molar enthalpy (heat) of fusion

_____

_____

3 Thermochemical Equations (continued)

Identify which of the reactions below is endothermic, and explain how you know.

1. $4Fe(s) + 3O_2(g) \rightarrow 2Fe_2O_3(s)$ $\Delta H = -1625$ kJ
2. $NH_4NO_3(s) \rightarrow NH_4^+ (aq) + NO_3^- (aq)$ $\Delta H = 27$ kJ

_____

_____

_____

Identify which of the reactions below is exothermic, and explain how you know.

1. $4Fe(s) + 3O_2(g) \rightarrow 2Fe_2O_3(s)$ $\Delta H = -1625$ kJ
2. $NH_4NO_3(s) \rightarrow NH_4^+ (aq) + NO_3^- (aq)$ $\Delta H = 27$ kJ

_____

_____

_____

Name the common states of matter.

_____

3 Thermochemical Equations (continued)

Explain changes in physical states by completing the sentences below.

During vaporization, a _____ becomes a _____.

Energy must be _____ by the liquid.

During condensation, a _____ becomes a _____.

Energy is _____ by the gas.

During fusion of ice, a _____ becomes a _____.

Energy is _____ by the solid.

Identify what the following equations represent.

$\Delta H_{vap} = -\Delta H_{cond}$

_____

_____

$\Delta H_{fus} = -\Delta H_{solid}$

_____

_____

GET IT? **Categorize** condensation, solidification, vaporization, and fusion as exothermic or endothermic processes.

_____

_____

_____

REAL-WORLD CONNECTION

Explain why a farmer would spray his orange trees with water when he knows the overnight temperature will be below 30°C.

_____

_____

3 Thermochemical Equations (continued)

REVIEW IT!

26. **Write** a thermochemical equation for the combustion of ethanol (C_2H_5OH).
$\Delta H_{comb} = -1367$ kJ/mol

_____

_____

27. **Distinguish** Which of the following processes are exothermic? Endothermic?

a. $C_2H_5OH(l) \longrightarrow C_2H_5OH(g)$ **d.** $NH_3(g) \longrightarrow NH_3(l)$

b. $Br_2(l) \longrightarrow Br_2(s)$ **e.** $NaCl(s) \longrightarrow NaCl(l)$

c. $C_5H_{12}(g) + 8O_2(g) \longrightarrow 5CO_2(g) + 6H_2O(l)$

_____

_____

28. **Explain** how you could calculate the heat released in freezing 0.250 mol water.

_____

_____

29. **Calculate** How much heat is released by the combustion of 206 g of hydrogen gas?

$\Delta H_{comb} = -286$kJ/mol

_____

_____

30. **Apply** The molar heat of vaporization of ammonia is 23.3 kJ/mol. What is the molar heat of condensation of ammonia?

_____

31. **Interpret Scientific Illustrations** The reaction A $\longrightarrow$ C is shown in the enthalpy diagram at right. Is the reaction exothermic or endothermic? Explain your answer.

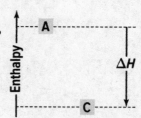

_____

_____

_____

14 Energy and Chemical Change

4 Calculating Enthalpy Change

BUILD TO THE ESSENTIAL QUESTION

Read the items under Build to the Essential Question at the beginning of the lesson. Restate each in your own words.

_____

_____

REVIEW VOCABULARY

allotrope

Recall the definition of the Review Vocabulary term.

allotrope _____

_____

NEW VOCABULARY

Hess's law

standard enthalpy (heat) of
formation

Define each New Vocabulary term.

Hess's law _____

_____

_____

standard enthalpy (heat) of formation _____

_____

_____

_____

4 Calculating Enthalpy Change (continued)

Describe Hess's law by completing the following statement.

_____ is used to determine the _____ of a system by imagining that each reaction is part of a _____ , each of which has a known ΔH.

Examine Figure 13. Read the caption and follow the arrows. Then apply Hess's law to fill in the blanks below.

ΔH for equation **c** _____

ΔH for equation **d** _____

sum of ΔH for equations **c** and **d** _____

In other words, the _____ for the conversion of S and O_2 to SO_3 is _____

GET IT? **Compare** the equation above with the thermochemical equation developed on the previous page. How are they different?

_____

_____

_____

_____

Explain standard enthalpy of formation of elements and compounds by completing the following statements.

An element's _____ is the normal _____ state at one _____ pressure and _____. For example, the standard state for iron is _____, for mercury is _____, and for oxygen is _____. Free elements such as these are assigned a ΔH_f^0 or _____ of exactly _____. The ΔH_f^0 of many _____ has been measured _____. For example, the standard enthalpies of formation for the following compounds are:

NO_2(g) _____ SO_3(g) _____ SF_6(g) _____

4 Calculating Enthalpy Change (continued)

Write the formula that sums up the procedure for combining standard heats of formation equations to produce the desired equation and its ΔH_{rxn}^0.

This equation says to _____ the _____ of heats of

_____ of the _____ from the sum of the _____

of formation of the _____.

Summarize Fill in the blanks to help you take notes as you work through Example Problem 6.

Problem

Calculate ΔH_{rxn}^0 for the combustion of methane.

$$CH_4(g) + 2O_2(g) \longrightarrow CO_2(g) + 2H_2O(l)$$

1. Analyze the Problem

Use the formula $\Delta H_{rxn}^0 = \sum \Delta H_f^0 \text{ (products)} - \sum \Delta H_f^0$ (reactants) with data from Table R-11.

Known:

$\Delta H_f^0 (CO_2) = $ _____

$\Delta H_f^0 (H_2O) = $ _____

$\Delta H_f^0 (CH_4) = $ _____

$\Delta H_f^0 (O_2) = $ _____

Unknown:

$\Delta H_{rxn}^0 = ? \text{ kJ}$

4 Calculating Enthalpy Change (continued)

2. Solve for the Unknown

Use the formula $\Delta H^0_{rxn} = \sum \Delta H^0_f \text{ (products)} - \sum \Delta H^0_f \text{ (reactants)}$

Substitute values in the formula

$\Delta H^0_{rxn} =$ _____

$\Delta H^0_{rxn} =$ _____ = _____

3. Evaluate the Answer

All values are _____ to the stated place. The calculated value matches that in Table R-11.

REAL-WORLD CONNECTION

Your family needs to choose a system to heat the new home you are building. From what you have learned so far, write down four questions you will use to evaluate the systems available.

1. _____

2. _____

3. _____

4. _____

REVIEW IT!

38. Explain what is meant by Hess's law and how it is used to determine ΔH^0_{rxn}.

_____

_____

_____

39. Explain in words the formula that can be used to determine ΔH^0_{rxn} when using Hess's law.

_____

_____

_____

_____

4 Calculating Enthalpy Change (continued)

40. Describe how the elements in their standard states are defined on the scale of standard enthalpies of formation.

_____

_____

41. Examine the data in **Table 5**. What conclusion can you draw about the stabilities of the compounds listed relative to the elements in their standard states? Recall that low energy is associated with stability.

_____

_____

_____

42. Calculate Use Hess's law to determine ΔH for the reaction $NO(g) + O(g) \longrightarrow NO_2(g)$ $\Delta H = ?$ given the following reactions. Show your work.

$O_2(g) \longrightarrow 2O(g)$ $\Delta H = +495$ kJ

$2O_3(g) \longrightarrow 3O_2(g)$ $\Delta H = -427$ kJ

$NO(g) + O_3(g) \longrightarrow NO_2(g) + O_2(g)$ $\Delta H = -199$ kJ

_____

_____

43. Interpret Scientific Illustrations Use the data below to draw a diagram of standard heats of formation similar to Figure 15 and use your diagram to determine the heat of vaporization of water at 298 K.

Liquid water: $\Delta H_f^0 = -285.8$ kJ/mol

Gaseous water: $\Delta H_f^0 = -241.8$ kJ/mol

14 Energy and Chemical Change

5 Reaction Spontaneity

BUILD TO THE ESSENTIAL QUESTION

Read the items under Build to the Essential Question at the beginning of the lesson. Restate each in your own words.

_____

_____

REVIEW VOCABULARY

vaporization

Recall the definition of the Review Vocabulary term.

vaporization

_____

NEW VOCABULARY

spontaneous process

entropy

second law of thermodynamics

free energy

Define each New Vocabulary term.

spontaneous process

_____

entropy

_____

second law of thermodynamics

_____

_____

_____

free energy

_____

5 Reaction Spontaneity (continued)

Compare and contrast spontaneous processes and non-spontaneous processes.

_____

_____

_____

_____

_____

Identify the parts of the entropy equation.

$$\Delta S_{system} = S_{products} - S_{reactants}$$

ΔS represents _____

S represents _____

List five reactions or processes in which it is possible to predict the change in entropy. For each process, indicate whether entropy will increase or decrease.

1. _____

2. _____

3. _____

_____

4. _____

5. _____

Write the equation for the standard free energy change under standard conditions.

_____

Predict whether entropy increases or decreases for the reaction below and explain your reasoning.

$N_2(g) + 3H_2(g) \rightarrow 2NH_3(g)$

_____

_____

Describe free energy changes by writing the word positive or negative in the appropriate blank.

If the sign of the free energy change is _____ , the reaction is spontaneous.

If the sign of the free energy change is _____ , the reaction is non-spontaneous.

Explain how ΔH^0_{system} and ΔS^0_{system} affect reaction spontaneity by completing the following table.

How ΔH^0_{system} and ΔS^0_{system} Affect Reaction Spontaneity		
	$-\Delta H^0_{system}$	$+\Delta H^0_{system}$
$+\Delta S^0_{system}$		
$-\Delta S^0_{system}$		

ACADEMIC VOCABULARY

demonstrate

Define the following term.

demonstrate _____

5 Reaction Spontaneity (continued)

REVIEW IT!

48. Compare and contrast spontaneous and nonspontaneous reactions.

_____

_____

_____

49. Describe how a system's entropy changes if the system becomes more disordered during a process.

_____

_____

50. Decide Does the entropy of a system increase or decrease when you dissolve a cube of sugar in a cup of tea? Define the system, and explain your answer.

_____

_____

_____

51. Determine whether the system $\Delta H_{system} = -20.5$ kJ, T = 298 K, and $\Delta S_{system} = -35.0$ J/K is spontaneous or nonspontaneous.

_____

_____

52. Outline Use the headings to outline the section. Under each heading, summarize the important ideas discussed.

_____

_____

_____

_____

15 Reaction Rates

ESSENTIAL QUESTION

Write the Essential Question for this chapter.

_____

_____

_____

Use the "What I Know" column to list the things you know about the Essential Question. Then list the questions you have about the Essential Question in the "What I Want to Find Out" column. As you read the chapter, fill in the "What I Learned" column.

K _What I Know_	W _What I Want to Find Out_	L _What I Learned_

15 Reaction Rates

1 A Model for Reaction Rates

BUILD TO THE ESSENTIAL QUESTION

Read the items under Build to the Essential Question at the beginning of the lesson. Restate each in your own words.

_____

_____

_____

REVIEW VOCABULARY

energy

Recall the definition of the Review Vocabulary term.

energy

_____

_____

NEW VOCABULARY

reaction rate

collision theory

activated complex

activation energy

Define each New Vocabulary term.

reaction rate

_____

_____

collision theory

_____

_____

activated complex

_____

_____

activation energy

_____

_____

1 A Model for Reaction Rates (continued)

Identify what each phrase or symbol represents in this equation.

$$\text{Average rate} = \frac{\Delta \text{quantity}}{\Delta t}$$

Average rate = the average is used because the rate changes over time

$\Delta = $ _____

$t = $ _____

Summarize Fill in the blanks to help you take notes while you read Example Problem 1.

Problem

Calculate the average reaction rate of the chemical reaction using the _____ of butyl chloride in _____.

1. **Analyze the Problem**

   Known: Unknown:

   _____   _____

   _____

   $[C_4H_9Cl]$ at $t_1 = 0.220M$

   _____

2. **Solve for the Unknown**

   Write the equation.

   Average reaction rate =

   Insert known quantities.

   Solve for the average rate $= -\dfrac{}{4.00 \text{ s} - 0.00 \text{ s}}$

   $= \boxed{}$

   Average reaction rate $= \boxed{}$

3. **Evaluate the Answer**

   The answer is correctly expressed in _____ significant figures.

1 A Model for Reaction Rates (continued)

Describe how each of the items below affects a reaction.

collision theory

_____

orientation and the activated complex

_____

_____

activation energy and reaction

_____

_____

_____

GET IT? **Predict** why a collision between two particles is necessary for a reaction to occur.

_____

_____

Explain activation energy by completing the following paragraph.

Some reactions have enough _____ to overcome the _____ _____ of the reaction in order to form products. These are called _____. After the _____ is formed, _____ is released. In other reactions the reactants must absorb energy to overcome the _____ of the reaction. These reactions are called _____.

GET IT? **Explain** how you can tell from the graph that the reaction described is an exothermic reaction.

_____

_____

GET IT? **Compare** Figures 5 and 6 to determine whether the activation energy for the forward reaction is larger or smaller than the activation energy for the reverse reaction.

_____

_____

1 A Model for Reaction Rates (continued)

ACADEMIC VOCABULARY	Define the following term.
investigate	investigate _____
	_____

REVIEW IT!

4. Relate collision theory to reaction rate.

_____

_____

5. Explain what the reaction rate indicates about a particular chemical reaction.

_____

_____

6. Compare the concentrations of the reactants and products during the course of a chemical reaction (assuming no additional reactants are added).

_____

_____

7. Compare the average reaction rate measured over an initial, short time interval to one measured over a long time interval.

_____

_____

8. Describe the relationship between activation energy and the rate of a reaction.

_____

9. Summarize what happens during the brief existence of an activated complex.

_____

_____

1 A Model for Reaction Rates (continued)

1 A Model for Reaction Rates (continued)

10. Apply collision theory to explain why collisions between two reacting particles do not always result in the formation of a product.

_____

_____

_____

_____

11. Interpret how the speed of a chemical reaction is related to the spontaneity of the reaction.

_____

_____

12. Calculate the average rate of a reaction between hypothetical molecules A and B if the concentration of A changes from 1.00*M* to 0.50*M* in 2.00 s.

_____

_____

_____

_____

_____

15 Reaction Rates

2 Factors Affecting Reaction Rates

BUILD TO THE ESSENTIAL QUESTION

Read the items under Build to the Essential Question at the beginning of the lesson. Restate each in your own words.

_____

_____

REVIEW VOCABULARY

concentration

Recall the definition of the Review Vocabulary term.

concentration

_____

_____

NEW VOCABULARY

catalyst

inhibitor

heterogeneous catalyst

homogeneous catalyst

Define each New Vocabulary term.

catalyst

_____

_____

inhibitor

_____

_____

heterogeneous catalyst

_____

_____

homogeneous catalyst

_____

_____

Explain how reactants influence the rate at which a chemical reaction occurs by completing the following statement.

As the reactant increases, the _____ increases.

2 Factors Affecting Reaction Rates (continued)

Explain the effect each of the following has on the rate of a reaction.

reactivity of reactants

_____

concentration

_____

surface area

_____

temperature

_____

catalyst

_____

inhibitors

_____

GET IT? **Predict** what would happen to the rate of the reaction if the concentration of A was increased.

_____

_____

_____

GET IT? **Determine** the relative reaction rate at 325 K.

_____

_____

GET IT? **Determine** from the graph how the use of a catalyst affects the energy released in the reaction.

_____

_____

_____

2 Factors Affecting Reaction Rates (continued)

REVIEW IT!

13. **Explain** why magnesium metal reacts with hydrochloric acid (HCl) at a faster rate than iron does.

_____

_____

14. **Explain** how collision theory accounts for the effect of concentration on reaction rate.

_____

_____

15. **Explain** the difference between a catalyst and an inhibitor.

_____

_____

16. **Describe** the effect on the rate of a reaction if one of the reactants is ground to a powder rather than used as a single chunk.

_____

_____

17. **Infer** If increasing the temperature of a reaction by 10 K approximately doubles the reaction rate, what would be the effect of increasing the temperature by 20 K?

_____

_____

18. **Research** how catalysts are used in industry, in agriculture, or in the treatment of contaminated soil, waste, or water. Write a short report summarizing your findings about the role of a catalyst in one of these applications.

_____

_____

_____

_____

_____

15 Reaction Rates

3 Reaction Rate Laws

BUILD TO THE ESSENTIAL QUESTION

Read the items under Build to the Essential Question at the beginning of the lesson. Restate each in your own words.

_____

_____

_____

REVIEW VOCABULARY

reactant

Recall the definition of the Review Vocabulary term.

reactant

_____

_____

NEW VOCABULARY

rate law

specific rate constant

reaction order

method of initial rates

Define each New Vocabulary term.

rate law

_____

_____

specific rate constant

_____

_____

reaction order

_____

_____

method of initial rates

_____

_____

_____

3 Reaction Rate Laws (continued)

Explain what each symbol represents in the following equation.

Rate = $k[A]$

k = _____

_____

$[A]$ = _____

GET IT? **Apply** Using the graph, determine the initial reaction rate when $[H_2O_2]$ is 1.50 mol/L.

_____

Analyze the rate law reaction for the decomposition of hydrogen peroxide.

$2H_2O_2 \longrightarrow 2H_2O + O_2$

rate law equation: rate = $k[A]$, where $[A]$ = _____

insert the reactant: rate = _____

Express the rate law reaction for this chemical reaction.

chemical equation: $2NO(g) + 2H_2(g) \longrightarrow N_2(g) + 2H_2O(g)$

rate law equation: rate = _____, where $[A]$ represents

the reactant _____ and $[B]$ represents the

reactant _____

insert the reactants: rate = _____

GET IT? **Infer** If the reaction order for a reactant is first order, how will the rate of the reaction change if the concentration of the reactant is tripled?

_____

_____

GET IT? **Explain** how you can determine the overall order of the reaction from the rate equation.

_____

3 Reaction Rate Laws (continued)

Relate how the reaction rate varies with:

concentration

_____

_____

the overall reaction order

_____

_____

Explain reaction order by completing the following sentences.

One of the means of determining reaction order is by comparing

_____ of a reaction with varying

_____. This is known as the method of

_____. This method requires experimentation with

differing _____ of the reactants and comparing the

_____ of the reaction at each quantity. While the rate

law for a reaction can tell you the reaction rate, the rate constant k,

and the _____, actual _____ and

_____ of a complex reaction can be determined only through

experimentation.

REAL-WORLD CONNECTION

Consider whether an average of a student's grades on all chemistry tests is or is not a better way of determining a final grade as compared to using just one test score. Explain which is better and why.

_____

_____

_____

_____

3 Reaction Rate Laws (continued)

REVIEW IT!

23. **Explain** what the rate law for a chemical reaction tells you about the reaction.

_____

_____

24. **Apply** the rate-law equations to show the difference between a first-order reaction with a single reactant and a second-order reaction with a single reactant.

_____

_____

25. **Explain** the function of the specific rate constant in a rate-law equation.

_____

26. **Explain** Under what circumstance is the specific rate constant (k) not a constant? What does the size of k indicate about the rate of a reaction?

_____

_____

27. **Suggest** a reason why, when given the rate of a chemical reaction, it is important to know that the reaction rate is an average reaction rate.

_____

_____

_____

28. **Explain** how the exponents in the rate equation for a chemical reaction relate to the coefficients in the chemical equation.

_____

_____

_____

3 Reaction Rate Laws (continued)

29. Determine the overall reaction order for a reaction between A and B for which the rate law is rate = k[A]^2[B]^2.

_____

_____

30. Design an Experiment Explain how you would design an experiment to determine the rate law for the general reaction aA + bB → products using the method of initial rates.

_____

_____

_____

_____

_____

_____

_____

15 Reaction Rates

4 Instantaneous Reaction Rates and Reaction Mechanisms

BUILD TO THE ESSENTIAL QUESTION

Read the items under Build to the Essential Question at the beginning of the lesson. Restate each in your own words.

_____

_____

REVIEW VOCABULARY

decomposition reaction

Recall the definition of the Review Vocabulary term.

decomposition reaction

_____

_____

NEW VOCABULARY

instantaneous rate

complex reaction

reaction mechanism

intermediate

rate-determining step

Define each New Vocabulary term.

instantaneous rate

_____

_____

complex reaction

_____

_____

reaction mechanism

_____

_____

intermediate

_____

_____

rate-determining step

_____

_____

4 Instantaneous Reaction Rates and Reaction Mechanisms (continued)

GET IT? **Identify** the variables that are plotted on the y-axis and on the x-axis.

_____

_____

Summarize Fill in the blanks to help you take notes while you read Example Problem 2.

Problem

Calculate the instantaneous rate for this reaction, given the quantities for NO and H_2.

$$2NO(g) + H_2(g) \longrightarrow N_2O(g) + H_2O(g)$$

1. **Analyze the Problem**

   Known: Unknown:

   quantity of [NO] = 0.00200M rate = ? mol/(L·s)

   quantity of [H_2] = _____

   k = _____

2. **Solve for the Unknown**

   Insert the known quantities into the rate law equation.

   rate = _____

   rate = _____

   rate = _____

3. **Evaluate the Answer**

   Are your units correct? Is your magnitude reasonable?

4 Instantaneous Reaction Rates and Reaction Mechanisms (continued)

Compare the reaction mechanism using the terms complex, intermediate, and rate-determining step to the process of building a car. Show that you understand the vocabulary.

_____

_____

_____

_____

_____

GET IT? **Explain** the importance of the methods of femtochemistry to the study of reaction mechanisms.

_____

_____

GET IT? **Determine** from the graph whether the overall reaction is exothermic or endothermic.

_____

_____

REAL-WORLD CONNECTION

Suppose you obtain a part-time job working for a lawn care business. Your new boss wants you to help her choose the right fertilizer for most of the lawns you will see. Use the terms from this chapter to explain to your boss what she should look for in a fertilizer.

_____

_____

_____

4 Instantaneous Reaction Rates and Reaction Mechanisms (continued)

REVIEW IT!

34. Compare and contrast an elementary chemical reaction with a complex chemical reaction.

_____

_____

35. Explain how the rate law for a chemical reaction is used to determine the instantaneous rate of the reaction.

_____

_____

36. Define a reaction mechanism and an intermediate.

_____

_____

_____

37. Distinguish between an intermediate and an activated complex.

_____

_____

_____

38. Relate the size of the activation energy of an elementary step in a complex reaction to the rate of that step.

_____

39. Calculate A reaction between A and B to form AB is first order in A and first order in B. The rate constant, k, equals 0.500 mol/(L•s). What is the rate of the reaction when $[A] = 2.00 \times 10^{-2}$ M and $[B] = 1.50 \times 10^{-2}$ M?

_____

_____

_____

16 Chemical Equilibrium

ESSENTIAL QUESTION

Write the Essential Question for this chapter.

_____

_____

_____

Use the "What I Know" column to list the things you know about the Essential Question. Then list the questions you have about the Essential Question in the "What I Want to Find Out" column. As you read the chapter, fill in the "What I Learned" column.

K _What I Know_	W _What I Want to Find Out_	L _What I Learned_

16 Chemical Equilibrium

1 A State of Dynamic Balance

BUILD TO THE ESSENTIAL QUESTION

Read the items under Build to the Essential Question at the beginning of the lesson. Restate each in your own words.

_____

_____

_____

REVIEW VOCABULARY

free energy

Recall the definition of the Review Vocabulary term.

free energy _____

_____

_____

NEW VOCABULARY

reversible reaction

chemical equilibrium

law of chemical equilibrium

equilibrium constant

homogeneous equilibrium

heterogeneous equilibrium

Define each New Vocabulary term.

reversible reaction _____

_____

chemical equilibrium _____

_____

law of chemical equilibrium _____

_____

equilibrium constant _____

_____

homogeneous equilibrium _____

_____

heterogeneous equilibrium _____

_____

Explain reversible reactions by inserting the words left and right in the following statements.

The reactants for the forward reaction are on the _____. The products are on the _____. The reactants for the reverse reaction are on the _____. The products are on the _____.

List the reactants and products of the following reversible reaction.

$N_2(g) + 3H_2(g) \rightleftharpoons 2NH_3(g)$

	Reactants	**Products**
Forward reaction		
Reverse reaction		

Complete the following statement.

The state in which forward and reverse reactions balance each other because they take place at equal rates is called _____.

Although a chemical reaction may be in equilibrium, the _____ and _____ may continually be _____ because chemical equilibrium is a dynamic process.

GET IT? **Describe** the slopes of the curves in Figure 2 for the reactants and for the product on the left of the vertical dotted line. How do the slopes differ on the right of the dotted line?

_____

_____

_____

_____

1 A State of Dynamic Balance (continued)

Identify the parts of the equilibrium constant expression.

$$K_{eq} = \frac{[C]^c\,[D]^d}{[A]^a\,[B]^b}$$

K_{eq} = _____

[C][D] = _____

[A][B] = _____

a, b, c, and d = _____

GET IT? **Explain** the meaning of a double arrow in chemical equations.

_____

_____

Write the equilibrium constant expression for the following balanced chemical equation.

$N_2(g) + 3H_2(g) \rightleftharpoons 2NH_3(g)$

K_{eq} = _____

Compare and contrast homogeneous equilibrium and heterogeneous equilibrium by completing the following sentences.

Homogeneous equilibrium occurs when _____ and

_____ of a reaction are in the _____ physical state.

Heterogeneous equilibrium occurs when _____ and

_____ of a reaction are in more than _____ physical

state. Equilibrium depends on the _____ in the

system.

Write the equilibrium expression for this reaction.

$I_2(s) \rightleftharpoons I_2(g)$

_____

GET IT? **Explain** why it is important that all reactants and products be present at equilibrium.

_____

_____

_____

Summarize Fill in the blanks to help you take notes while you read Example Problem 3.

Problem

Calculate the value of K_{eq} for the equilibrium constant expression.

$$K_{eq} = \frac{[NH_3]^2}{[N_2][H_2]^3}$$

1. Analyze the Problem

List the knowns and unknowns.

Known: the equilibrium constant expression:

_____

Known: the concentration of each reactant and product:

$[NH_3]$ _____

$[N_2]$ _____

$[H_2]$ _____

Unknown: the value of the equilibrium constant

2. Solve for the Unknown

Substitute the _____ into the equilibrium

_____ and calculate its value.

$$K_{eq} = \frac{\rule{2cm}{0.4pt}}{[0.533]} = \rule{1.5cm}{0.4pt}$$

3. Evaluate the Answer

The given concentrations have _____ significant figures, therefore the answer must have _____ significant figures.

1 A State of Dynamic Balance (continued)

REVIEW IT!

8. **Explain** how the size of the equilibrium constant relates to the amount of product formed at equilibrium.

_____

_____

9. **Compare** homogeneous and heterogeneous equilibria.

_____

_____

10. **List** three characteristics a reaction mixture must have if it is to attain a state of chemical equilibrium.

_____

_____

_____

11. **Calculate** Determine the value of K_{eq} at 400 K for this equation: $PCl_5(g) \rightleftharpoons PCl_3(g) + Cl_2(g)$ if $[PCl_5] = 0.135$ mol/L, $[PCl_3] = 0.550$ mol/L, and $[Cl_2] = 0.550$ mol/L.

_____

_____

12. **Interpret Data** The table below shows the value of the equilibrium constant for a reaction at three different temperatures. At which temperature is the concentration of the products the greatest? Explain your answer.

K_{eq} and Temperature		
263 K	273 K	373 K
0.0250	0.500	4.500

_____

_____

_____

16 Chemical Equilibrium

2 Factors Affecting Chemical Equilibrium

BUILD TO THE ESSENTIAL QUESTION

Read the items under Build to the Essential Question at the beginning of the lesson. Restate each in your own words.

_____

_____

REVIEW VOCABULARY

reaction rate

Recall the definition of the Review Vocabulary term.

reaction rate _____

_____

_____

NEW VOCABULARY

Le Châtelier's principle

Define the following New Vocabulary term.

Le Châtelier's principle _____

_____

_____

2 Factors Affecting Chemical Equilibrium (continued)

Determine how each of the following changes affects a system in equilibrium. Write a sentence that includes the term(s) in parentheses.

changes in concentration (collisions)

_____

_____

_____

changes in volume (pressure, products)

_____

_____

_____

changes in temperature (endothermic, exothermic)

_____

_____

_____

_____

REAL-WORLD CONNECTION
Describe how your body would relieve the stress placed on it by climbing to a high altitude.

_____

_____

2 Factors Affecting Chemical Equilibrium (continued)

REVIEW IT!

13. **Explain** how a system at equilibrium responds to a stress and list factors that can be stresses on an equilibrium system.

_____

_____

14. **Explain** how decreasing the volume of the reaction vessel affects each equilibrium.

   a. $2SO_2(g) + O_2(g) \rightleftharpoons 2SO_3(g)$

   b. $H_2(g) + Cl_2(g) \rightleftharpoons 2HCl(g)$

_____

_____

15. **Decide** whether higher or lower temperatures will produce more CH_3CHO in the following equilibrium. $C_2H_2(g) + H_2O(g) \rightleftharpoons CH_3CHO(g)$ $\Delta H° = -151\ kJ$

_____

16. **Demonstrate** The table below shows the concentrations of Substances A and B in two reaction mixtures. A and B react according to the equation $2A \rightleftharpoons B$; $K_{eq} = 200$. Are the two mixtures at different equilibrium positions?

Concentration Data in mol/L		
Reaction	[A]	[B]
1	0.100	0.200
2	0.0500	0.500

_____

17. **Design** a concept map that shows ways in which Le Châtelier's principle can be applied to increase the products in a system at equilibrium and to increase the reactants in such a system.

16 Chemical Equilibrium

3 Using Equilibrium Constants

BUILD TO THE ESSENTIAL QUESTION

Read the items under Build to the Essential Question at the beginning of the lesson. Restate each in your own words.

_____

_____

REVIEW VOCABULARY

solubility

Recall the definition of the Review Vocabulary term.

solubility _____

_____

_____

NEW VOCABULARY

solubility product
  constant

common ion

common ion effect

Define each New Vocabulary term.

solubility product constant _____

_____

_____

common ion _____

_____

common ion effect _____

_____

_____

3 Using Equilibrium Constants (continued)

Summarize Fill in the blanks to help you take notes while you read Example Problem 4.

Problem

At 1405 K, hydrogen sulfide _____ to form

_____ and a diatomic _____ molecule, S_2. The

_____ for the reaction is 2.27×10^{-3}.

$$2H_2S(g) \rightleftharpoons 2H_2(g) + S_2(g)$$

What is the concentration of $H_2(g)$ if

$[S_2] = 0.0540$ mol/L and $[H_2S] = 0.184$ mol/L?

1. Analyze the Problem

List the knowns and unknowns.

Known:	Unknown:
$K_{eq} = $ _____	$[H_2] = $ _____
$[S_2] = $ _____	
$[H_2S] = $ _____	

2. Solve for the Unknown

Write the equilibrium constant expression.

$K_{eq} = $

_____

Substitute known quantities.

_____

Solve for the unknown.

_____

_____

_____

3. Evaluate the Answer

The number of significant figures in the data is _____

Therefore, the number of significant figures in the answer must be _____.

3 Using Equilibrium Constants (continued)

Describe solubility equilibrium.

_____

_____

Identify the part of the equation that shows equilibrium and circle it.

$$BaSO_4(s) \rightleftharpoons Ba^{2+}(aq) + SO_4^{2-}(aq)$$

Explain solubility by completing the following statements.

_____ is the amount of a substance that will _____ in a

given volume of _____.

K_{sp} represents the _____.

K_{sp} is the _____ of the concentration _____ each

raised to the power equal to the _____ of the ion in the

_____.

K_{sp} depends only on the _____ of the _____ in a

saturated _____.

GET IT? **Explain** the conditions under which you would predict that a precipitate would form.

_____

_____

Summarize Fill in the blanks to help you take notes while you read Example Problem 5.

Problem

Calculate the solubility in mol/L of copper(II) carbonate ($CuCO_3$) at 298 K.

1. Analyze the Problem

List the knowns and unknowns.

Known: **Unknown:**

K_{sp} ($CuCO_3$) = _____ solubility ($CuCO_3$) = _____

3 Using Equilibrium Constants (continued)

2. Solve for the Unknown

Write the balanced chemical equation.

_____

Write the solubility constant expression (remember only the ions are used).

_____

$s = [Cu^{2+}] = $ _____

Substitute s for $[Cu^{2+}]$ and _____

_____

_____

3. Evaluate the Answer

K_{sp} has _____ significant figures, so the answer must be expressed with _____ significant figures.

Discuss the common ion effect by completing the following paragraph.

An ion that is common to two or more ionic compounds is known as a _____. The lowering of the solubility of a substance by the presence of a common ion is called the _____.

3 Using Equilibrium Constants (continued)

REVIEW IT!

27. List the information you would need in order to calculate the concentration of a product in a reaction mixture at equilibrium.

_____

28. Explain how to use the solubility product constant to calculate the solubility of a sparingly soluble ionic compound.

_____

_____

_____

29. Describe how the presence of a common ion reduces the solubility of an ionic compound.

_____

_____

30. Explain the difference between K_{sp} and Q_{sp}. Is Q_{sp} an equilibrium constant?

_____

_____

_____

31. Calculate The K_{sp} of magnesium carbonate ($MgCO_3$) is 2.6×10^{-9}. What is the solubility of $MgCO_3$ in pure water?

_____

32. Design an experiment based on solubilities to demonstrate which of two ions, Mg^{2+} or Pb^{2+}, is contained in an aqueous solution. Solubility information about ionic compounds is given in **Tables R-3** and **R-8** in the Student Resources appendix.

_____

_____

_____

_____

17 Acids and Bases

ESSENTIAL QUESTION

Write the Essential Question for this chapter.

_____

_____

_____

Use the "What I Know" column to list the things you know about the Essential Question. Then list the questions you have about the Essential Question in the "What I Want to Find Out" column. As you read the chapter, fill in the "What I Learned" column.

K _What I Know_	W _What I Want to Find Out_	L _What I Learned_

17 Acids and Bases

1 Introduction to Acids and Bases

BUILD TO THE ESSENTIAL QUESTION

Read the items under Build to the Essential Question at the beginning of the lesson. Restate each in your own words.

_____

REVIEW VOCABULARY

Lewis structure

Recall the definition of the Review Vocabulary term.

Lewis structure

_____

NEW VOCABULARY

acidic solution

basic solution

Arrhenius model

Brønsted-Lowry model

conjugate acid

conjugate base

conjugate acid-base pair

amphoteric

Lewis model

Define each New Vocabulary term.

acidic solution

_____

basic solution

_____

Arrhenius model

_____

_____

Bronsted-Lowry model

_____

conjugate acid

_____

conjugate base

_____

conjugate acid-base pair

_____

amphoteric

Lewis model

_____

Compare and contrast the properties of an acid and a base by placing an X in the Acid column if the property applies to an acid and in the Base column if the property applies to a base.

Acid	Properties	Base
	tastes sour	
	tastes bitter	
	feels slippery	
	affects color	
	reacts with metal	
	conducts electricity	
	has more hydrogen ions than hydroxide ions	
	has more hydroxide ions than hydrogen ions	

Write the chemical equation for the self-ionization of water.

Analyze why the Arrhenius model of acids and bases does NOT include ammonia (NH_3) in solution as a base.

_____

_____

_____

Identify which of the following statements describes the Arrhenius model and which describes the Brønsted-Lowry model by filling in the blanks.

The _____ model is based on the dissociation of compounds,

while the _____ model is based on the donation and

acceptance of hydrogen ions. Conjugate acid-base pairs are a

component of the _____ model and are NOT a

component of the _____ model.

1 Introduction to Acids and Bases (continued)

GET IT? **Explain** how the ion HCO_3^- can be both an acid and a base.

_____

_____

_____

Describe what happens in the forward and reverse reactions when ammonia is dissolved in water. Identify the conjugate acid, the conjugate base, and the two conjugate acid-base pairs.

_____

_____

_____

_____

_____

_____

_____

_____

Explain what a polyprotic acid is.

_____

_____

Sequence _the following equations in the steps of the ionization of phosphoric acid in the correct order._

_____ $HPO_4^{2-}(aq) + H_2O(l) \rightleftharpoons H_3O^+(aq) + PO_4^{3-}(aq)$

_____ $H_3PO_4(aq) + H_2O(l) \rightleftharpoons H_3O^+(aq) + H_2PO_4^{2-}(aq)$

_____ $H_2PO_4^-(aq) + H_2O(l) \rightleftharpoons H_3O^+(aq) + HPO_4^-(aq)$

ACADEMIC VOCABULARY

Conform

Define the following term.

Conform _____

_____

1 Introduction to Acids and Bases (continued)

REVIEW IT!

5. Explain why many Lewis acids and bases are not classified as Arrhenius or Brønsted-Lowry acids and bases.

_____

_____

_____

_____

_____

6. Compare the physical and chemical properties of acids and bases.

_____

_____

_____

_____

7. Explain how the concentrations of hydrogen ions and hydroxide ions determine whether a solution is acidic, basic, or neutral.

_____

_____

8. Explain why many compounds that contain one or more hydrogen atoms are not classified as Arrhenius acids.

_____

_____

9. Identify the conjugate acid-base pairs in the following equation.
$$HNO_2 + H_2O \rightleftharpoons NO_2^- + H_3O^+$$

_____

_____

10. **Write** the Lewis structure for phosphorus trichloride (PCl_3). Is PCl_3 a Lewis acid, a Lewis base, or neither?

_____

_____

_____

17 Acids and Bases

2 Strengths of Acids and Bases

BUILD TO THE ESSENTIAL QUESTION

Read the items under Build to the Essential Question at the beginning of the lesson. Restate each in your own words.

_____

_____

REVIEW VOCABULARY

electrolyte

Recall the definition of the Review Vocabulary term.

electrolyte _____

_____

NEW VOCABULARY

strong acid

weak acid

acid ionization constant

strong base

weak base

base ionization constant

Define each New Vocabulary term.

strong acid _____

_____

weak acid _____

_____

acid ionization constant _____

_____

strong base _____

_____

weak base _____

_____

base ionization constant _____

_____

Explain why all acids are not equal in strength.

_____

_____

Identify the acids in the following table as strong or weak.

Acid	Strong or Weak	Acid	Strong or Weak
acetic		hydroiodic	
carbonic		hydrosulfuric	
		hypochlorous	
hydrochloric		nitric	
hydrofluoric		sulfuric	

Describe the difference in conductivity between strong and weak acids.

_____

_____

_____

Analyze equilibrium constant expressions by completing the following statements.

The concentration of liquid water in the denominator of an equilibrium

constant expression is considered to be _____ in dilute aqueous

solutions. Therefore, liquid water can be _____ K_{eq} to give

a new equilibrium constant, K_a. For weak acids, the equilibrium

_____ of the _____ in the numerator tends to be small

compared to the equilibrium _____ of the _____ in the

denominator. The weakest acids have the _____ K_a values because

their solutions have the highest concentrations of _____ acid

molecules.

GET IT? **Summarize** the important difference between strong acids and weak acids in terms of the battle of the bases.

_____

_____

_____

_____

Compare and contrast the strengths of acids and bases by completing this concept map using the terms ionize, ionization constant, strong, stronger, weak, and weaker.

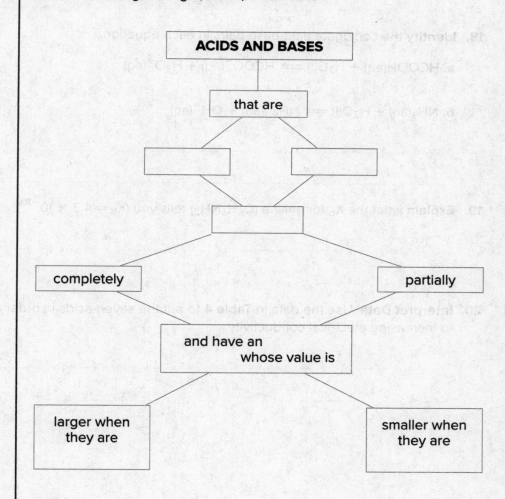

ACIDS AND BASES

that are

completely

partially

and have an
whose value is

larger when
they are

smaller when
they are

2 Strengths of Acids and Bases (continued)

REVIEW IT!

16. **Describe** the contents of dilute aqueous solutions of the strong acid HI and the weak acid HCOOH.

_____

_____

_____

17. **Relate** the strength of a weak acid to the strength of its conjugate base.

_____

_____

18. **Identify** the conjugate acid-base pairs in each equation.

a. $HCOOH(aq) + H_2O(l) \rightleftharpoons HCOO^-(aq) + H_3O^+(aq)$

b. $NH_3(aq) + H_2O(l) \rightleftharpoons NH_4^+(aq) + OH^-(aq)$

_____

_____

19. **Explain** what the K_b for aniline ($C_6H_5NH_2$) tells you ($K_b = 4.3 \times 10^{-10}$).

_____

_____

20. **Interpret Data** Use the data in **Table 4** to put the seven acids in order according to increasing electrical conductivity.

_____

_____

17 Acids and Bases

3 Hydrogen Ions and pH

BUILD TO THE ESSENTIAL QUESTION

Read the items under Build to the Essential Question at the beginning of the lesson. Restate each in your own words.

_____

_____

_____

REVIEW VOCABULARY

Le Châtelier's principle

Recall the definition of the Review Vocabulary term.

Le Châtelier's principle

_____

_____

NEW VOCABULARY

ion product constant
 for water

pH

pOH

Define each New Vocabualry term.

ion product constant for water

_____

_____

pH

_____

_____

pOH

_____

_____

Describe how the ion product constant for water is derived from the self-ionization equation.

$$H_2O(l) \rightleftharpoons \underline{\hspace{3cm}}$$

$$K_{eq} = \underline{\hspace{2.5cm}}$$

$$K_{eq}[H_2O] = \underline{\hspace{2.5cm}}$$

$$K_w = [H^+][OH^-] = \underline{\hspace{4cm}}$$

3 Hydrogen Ions and pH (continued)

Summarize Fill in the blanks to help you take notes while you read Example Problem 1.

Problem

Calculate [OH⁻] using _____ and the concentration of _____, and determine if the solution is acidic, basic, or neutral.

Step 1: Analyze the Problem

Known: **Unknown:**

$[H^+] =$ _____ $[OH^-] = ?$ mol/L

$K_w =$ _____

Write what you can predict about [OH⁻]:

_____

Step 2: Solve for the Unknown

Write the ion product constant expression.

$K_w =$ _____

Solve for [OH⁻] by _____.

$[OH^-] =$ _____

$[OH^-] =$ _____

Since $[H^+] > [OH^-]$, _____.

Step 3: Evaluate the Answer

The answer is correctly stated with _____ significant figures because [H⁺] and [OH⁻] each have two. The hydroxide ion concentration _____ the prediction.

3 Hydrogen Ions and pH (continued)

Compare and contrast pH and pOH by completing the following table.

Solution Type	Scale Measure	Relationship (Equation)
acid	pH	
base		
acid and base		

Analyze the process of calculating pH and pOH from the hydroxide concentration.

_____

_____

Describe the process of calculating the hydrogen ion and hydroxide ion concentrations from pH.

_____

_____

_____

Describe the process of calculating K_a from pH for a 0.100M weak acid.

_____

_____

_____

_____

_____

3 Hydrogen Ions and pH (continued)

REVIEW IT!

33. Relate acidity and basicity to hydronium and hydroxyl ion concentration and pH.

_____

_____

_____

34. Describe how you can determine the pH of a solution if you know its pOH.

_____

35. Explain the significance of K_w in aqueous solutions.

_____

_____

36. Explain, using Le Châtelier's principle, what happens to the $[H^+]$ of a $0.10M$ solution of acetic acid when a drop of NaOH solution is added.

_____

_____

_____

37. List the information needed to calculate the K_a of a weak acid.

_____

38. Calculate The pH of a tomato is approximately 4.50. What are $[H^+]$ and $[OH^-]$ in a tomato?

_____

_____

_____

39. Determine the pH of a solution that contains 1.0×10^{-9} mol of OH^- ions per liter.

_____

_____

3 Hydrogen Ions and pH (continued)

40. **Calculate** the pH of the following solutions.

    a. 1.0M HI

    b. 0.050M HNO_3

    c. 1.0M KOH

    d. $2.4 \times 10^{-5}M$ $Mg(OH)_2$

_____

_____

_____

41. **Interpret Diagrams** Refer to **Figure 15** to answer these questions:

What happens to the $[H^+]$, $[OH^-]$, pH, and pOH as a neutral solution becomes more acidic? As a neutral solution become more basic?

_____

_____

_____

_____

_____

17 Acids and Bases

4 Neutralization

Read the items under Build to the Essential Question at the beginning of the lesson. Restate each in your own words.

_____

REVIEW VOCABULARY

stoichiometry

Recall the definition of the Review Vocabulary term.

stoichiometry _____

_____

_____

NEW VOCABULARY

neutralization reaction

salt

titration

titrant

equivalence point

acid-base indicator

end point

salt hydrolysis

buffer

buffer capacity

Define each New Vocabulary term.

neutralization reaction _____

_____

salt _____

titration _____

_____

titrant _____

equivalence point _____

_____

acid-base indicator _____

_____

end point _____

_____

salt hydrolysis _____

_____

buffer _____

_____

buffer capacity _____

_____

4 Neutralization (continued)

Write the full equation of the neutralization reaction for magnesium hydroxide and hydrochloric acid.

_____

Draw the titration curve for 50.0 mL 0.100M HCl titrated with 0.100M NaOH. Label the pH and volume axes, as well as the equivalence point.

Describe the indicator that matches each of the following pH levels. Use Figure 24 as a guide.

pH	Indicator
7.2	
4.2	
1.8	
1–12	

GET IT? **Write** the complete ionic equation and the net ionic equation for the neutralization of HNO_3 by KOH.

_____

_____

_____

Identify two ways in which the graphs in Figure 20 are different.

_____

_____

_____

_____

_____

4 Neutralization (continued)

Explain the process for calculating the molarity of an unknown HCOOH solution by completing the equations below.

Balanced equation:

$HCOOH(aq) + NaOH(aq) \rightarrow HCOONa(aq) + H_2O(l)$

18.28 mL NaOH × _____ = _____ L NaOH

0.01828 L NaOH × _____

= _____ mol NaOH

1.828×10^{-3} mol NaOH × _____

= _____ mol HCOOH

1.828×10^{-3} mol HCOOH / _____

= _____ *M* HCOOH

Describe salt hydrolysis by completing the following statements.

Some aqueous salt solutions are neutral, some are basic, and some are

_____. The reason for this is a process known as _____. In

this process, the anions of the dissociated salt donate _____

to water. Salts that will hydrolyze have a weak acid and a _____

or a strong acid and a _____. A salt formed from a strong acid

and a weak base will form an _____. A salt formed from a

strong base and a weak acid will form a _____. Salts formed

from weak acids and bases or from strong acids and bases will not

hydrolyze and form _____.

4 Neutralization (continued)

Explain how a buffer works by completing the table below.

The equation at equilibrium	$HF(aq) \rightleftharpoons H^+(aq) + F^-(aq)$	
Δ Condition	Equilibrium Shift	The Process
add acid	left	The H^+ ions react with F^- ions to form .
add base	right	The OH^- ions react with H^+ ions to form water. This decreases the concentration of the H^+ ions so that
A greater solution leads to a	of the buffering molecules and ions in the of the solution.	
A buffer has a base with its	of an acid and its or .	

REAL-WORLD CONNECTION

Suppose you are on the bench for your school's soccer team when one of the players comes out of the game with a cramp. A teammate suggests that she start breathing into a paper bag to recover sooner. Explain whether or not this is good advice.

_____

_____

_____

4 Neutralization (continued)

REVIEW IT!

46. Explain why the net ionic equation for the neutralization reaction of any strong acid with any strong base is always the same.

_____

_____

47. Explain the difference between the equivalence point and the end point of a titration.

_____

_____

_____

48. Compare the results of two experiments: First, a small amount of base is added to an unbuffered solution with a pH of 7. Second, the same amount of base is added to a buffered solution with a pH of 7.

_____

49. Calculate the molarity of a solution of hydrobromic acid (HBr) if 30.35 mL of 0.1000M NaOH is required to titrate 25.00 mL of the acid to the equivalence point.

_____

_____

50. Interpret What substances could be used to make a buffer solution with a pH of 9.4. How should the amounts of the substances be related? Use **Table 7**.

_____

_____

51. Design an Experiment Describe how you would design and perform a titration in which you use 0.250M HNO$_3$ to determine the molarity of a cesium hydroxide solution. Include the formula and net ionic equations.

_____

_____

_____

_____

_____

18 Redox Reactions

ESSENTIAL QUESTION

Write the Essential Question for this chapter.

_____

_____

_____

Use the "What I Know" column to list the things you know about the Essential Question. Then list the questions you have about the Essential Question in the "What I Want to Find Out" column. As you read the chapter, fill in the "What I Learned" column.

| K
What I Know | W
What I Want to Find Out | L
What I Learned |
|---|---|---|
| | | |

18 Redox Reactions

1 Oxidation and Reduction

BUILD TO THE ESSENTIAL QUESTION

Read the items under Build to the Essential Question at the beginning of the lesson. Restate each in your own words.

_____

_____

REVIEW VOCABULARY

spectator ion

Recall the definition of the Review Vocabulary term.

spectator ion _____

_____

NEW VOCABULARY

oxidation-reduction reaction

redox reaction

oxidation

reduction

oxidation number

oxidizing agent

reducing agent

Define each New Vocabulary term.

oxidation-reduction reaction _____

_____

redox reaction _____

oxidation _____

reduction _____

oxidation number _____

_____

oxidizing agent _____

_____

reducing agent _____

_____

Describe redox reactions by completing the statement below. Use Figure 1 in your text as reference.

A redox reaction consists of two complimentary processes. Oxidation

results in a _____ and an increased _____

Reduction results in a _____ and a _____

oxidation number.

1 Oxidation and Reduction (continued)

GET IT? **Determine** Which element is more likely to gain electrons, potassium or chlorine?

_____

Compare and contrast an oxidizing agent and a reducing agent.

_____

_____

_____

Summarize Fill in the blanks to help you take notes while you read. Example Problem 1

Problem

Write the equation for the redox reaction:

$$2Al + 2Fe^{3+} \, 3O^{2-} \longrightarrow 2Al^{3+} + 2Fe + 3O^{2-}$$

Identify what is _____ and what is _____ in the

reaction. Identify the _____ and the _____.

1. Analyze the Problem

Known: _____

Unknown: _____

2. Solve for the Unknown

Al becomes Al^{3+} and _____ electrons.

Fe^{3+} becomes Fe and gains _____ electrons.

3. Evaluate the Answer

Aluminum _____ electrons and is _____. It is the

_____ agent. Iron _____ electrons and is _____.

It is the _____ agent.

1 Oxidation and Reduction (continued)

Describe the rules for determining oxidation numbers by completing these statements.

1. The oxidation number of an uncombined atom is _____.

2. The oxidation number of a monatomic ion is equal to
   _____

3. The oxidation number of the more electronegative atom in a molecule or a complex ion is the same as _____

4. The oxidation number of fluorine, the most electronegative element, when it is bonded to another element is _____

5. The oxidation number of oxygen in compounds is _____, except in peroxides where it is _____. The oxidation number of oxygen when it bonds to fluorine is _____.

6. The oxidation number of hydrogen in most of its compounds is _____.

7. The oxidation numbers of the metal atom in the compounds formed by the metals of groups 1 and 2 and aluminum in group 13 are _____, respectively. These oxidation numbers are equal to _____.

8. The sum of the oxidation numbers in a neutral compound is _____.

9. The sum of the oxidation numbers of the atoms in a polyatomic ion is equal to _____.

Describe the redox reaction for the equation listed below. Use the example on page 688 of your text to complete the table, then label the oxidation numbers of the elements in the equation and indicate the change in each.

$$2Al + Fe_2O_3 \longrightarrow 2Fe + Al_2O_3$$

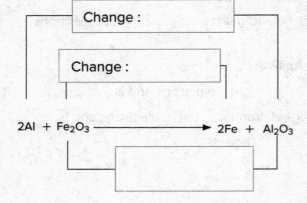

Element	Oxidation Number	Rule
Al		
Fe in Fe_2O_3		
O in Fe_2O_3		
Fe		
Al in Al_2O_3		
O in Al_2O_3		

1 Oxidation and Reduction (continued)

REVIEW IT!

9. **Explain** why oxidation and reduction must always occur together.

_____

_____

10. **Describe** the roles of oxidizing agents and reducing agents in a redox reaction. How is each changed in the reaction?

_____

_____

_____

11. **Write** the equation for the reaction of iron metal with hydrobromic acid to form aqueous iron(III) bromide and hydrogen gas. Determine the change in oxidation number for the element that is reduced and the element that is oxidized.

_____

12. **Determine** the oxidation number of the boldface element in these compounds.

   a. **H**NO_3 c. **Sb**$_2O_5$

   b. Ca$_3$**N**$_2$ d. Cu**W**O_4

_____

_____

13. **Determine** the oxidation number of the boldface element in these ions.

   a. **I**O_4^- c. **B**$_4O_7^{2-}$

   b. **Mn**O_4^- d. **N**H_2^-

_____

14. **Make and Use Graphs** Alkali metals are strong reducing agents. Make a graph showing how the reducing abilities of the alkali metals increase or decrease as you move down the family from sodium to francium.

_____

_____

_____

18 Redox Reactions

2 Balancing Redox Equations

BUILD TO THE ESSENTIAL QUESTION

Read the items under Build to the Essential Question at the beginning of the lesson. Restate each in your own words.

_____

_____

_____

REVIEW VOCABULARY

net ionic equation

Recall the definition of the Review Vocabulary term.

net ionic equation _____

_____

NEW VOCABULARY

oxidation-number method

species

half-reaction

Define each New Vocabulary term.

oxidation-number method _____

_____

_____

species _____

half-reaction _____

_____

Sequence the steps for balancing redox reactions by the oxidation—number method.

_____ Identify the atoms that are oxidized and the atoms that are reduced.

_____ Assign oxidation numbers to all atoms in the equation.

_____ Make the change in oxidation numbers equal in magnitude by adjusting coefficients in the equation.

_____ If necessary, use the conventional method to balance the remainder of the equation.

_____ Determine the change in oxidation number for the atoms that are oxidized and for the atoms that are reduced.

2 Balancing Redox Equations (continued)

Summarize Fill in the blanks to help you take notes while you read Example Problem 3.

Problem

Balance the _____ equation for the _____ that produces

_____.

$Cu + HNO_3 \longrightarrow Cu(NO_3)_2 + NO_2 + H_2O$

1. Analyze the Problem

Known:

The formulas for the reactants and _____, the rules for

determining _____, and the fact that the increase

in the oxidation number of the _____ must equal the

_____ of the reduced atoms.

Unknown: _____

2. Solve for the Unknown

Step 1 Assign oxidation numbers to all the atoms in the equation.

_____

$Cu + H\,N\,O_3 \longrightarrow Cu(N\,O_3)_2 + N\,O_2 + H_2\,O$

Step 2 Identify which atoms are oxidized (using thin arrows) and which are reduced (using thick arrows).

_____

$Cu + H\,N\,O_3 \longrightarrow Cu(NO_3)_2 + N\,O_2 + H_2O$

Step 3 Determine the change in oxidation number for the atoms that are oxidized and for the atoms that are reduced. Complete the following tables.

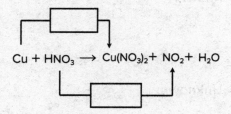

$Cu + HNO_3 \longrightarrow Cu(NO_3)_2 + NO_2 + H_2O$

Step 4 To make the net changes in oxidation number have the same magnitude, HNO_3 on the left and NO_2 on the right must be multiplied by _____.

2 Balancing Redox Equations (continued)

Step 5 Increase the coefficient of HNO_3 from 2 to _____ to balance the nitrogen atoms in the products. Add a coefficient of _____ to H_2O to balance the number of hydrogen atoms on the left.

3. Evaluate the Answer

The number of atoms of each element is _____ on both sides of the equation. No subscripts have been _____.

Describe the difference in the way each of the equations for the oxidation of copper by nitric acid are written.

$Cu(s) + 4HNO_3(aq) \longrightarrow Cu(NO_3)_2(aq) + 2NO_2(g) + 2H_2O(l)$

$Cu(s) + 4H^+(aq) + 4NO_3^-(aq) \longrightarrow Cu^{2+}(aq) + 2NO_3^-(aq) + 2NO_2(g) + 2H_2O(l)$

_____

_____

_____

Solve Read Example Problem 4 in your text.

YOU TRY IT

Problem

Balance the net ionic redox equation for the reaction between the perchlorate ion and the iodide ion in acid solution.

$ClO_3^-(aq) + I^-(aq) \longrightarrow Cl^-(aq) + I_2(s)$ (in acid solution)

1. Analyze the Problem

Known: _____

_____

Unknown: _____

2 Balancing Redox Equations (continued)

2. Solve for the Unknown

Step 1 Assign oxidation numbers to all the atoms in the equation.

$Cl\,O_3^-\,(aq) + I^-(aq) \longrightarrow Cl^-(aq) + I_2(s)$ (in acid solution)

Step 2 Identify which atoms are oxidized (using thin arrows) and which are reduced (using thick arrows).

$Cl\,O_3^-\,(aq) + I^-(aq) \longrightarrow Cl^-(aq) + I_2(s)$ (in acid solution)

Step 3 Determine the change in oxidation number for the atoms that are oxidized and for the atoms that are reduced. Complete the following tables.

$ClO_3^-(aq) + I^-(aq) \longrightarrow Cl^-(aq) + I_2(s)$ (in acid solution)

Step 4 To make the net changes in oxidation number have the same magnitude, place the appropriate coefficients in front of the formulas in the equation.

$ClO_3^-(aq) + 6I^-(aq) \longrightarrow Cl^-(aq) + 3I_2(s)$ (in acid solution)

Step 5 Write an equation that adds enough hydrogen ions and water molecules to balance the oxygen atoms on both sides.

3. Evaluate the Answer

The number of atoms of each element is _____ on both sides of the equation. The net charge on the right _____ the net charge on the left. No subscripts have been _____ .

2 Balancing Redox Equations (continued)

Identify the number of species in each reaction. Then, show the oxidation half—reaction and the reduction half—reaction for each equation.

Reaction	No. of Species	Half-Reaction	
		Oxidation	Reduction
$4Fe + 3O_2 \rightarrow 2Fe_2O_3$			
$4Fe + 3Cl_2 \rightarrow 2Fe_2Cl_3$			

Sequence the steps for balancing by half-reactions.

_____ Adjust the coefficients so that the number of electrons lost in oxidation equals the number of electrons gained in reduction.

_____ Write the net ionic equation for the reaction, omitting spectator ions.

_____ Add the balance half-reactions and return spectator ions.

_____ Write the oxidation and reduction half-reactions for the net ionic equation.

_____ Balance the atoms and charges in each half-reaction.

2 Balancing Redox Equations (continued)

Summarize Fill in the blanks to help you take notes while you read Example Problem 5.

Problem

Balance the redox equation for the _____ of permanganate and sulfur dioxide when sulfur dioxide _____ is bubbled into an _____ solution of _____.

$$KMnO_4(aq) + SO_2(g) \rightarrow MnSO_4(aq) + K_2SO_4(aq)$$

1. Analyze the problem

Known: _____

_____

Unknown: _____

_____

2. Solve for the Unknown

Step 1: Write the net ionic equation for the reaction:

_____

Step 2: Using rule number 5, the oxidation number for Mn in MnO_4^- is _____. Using rule number 2, the oxidation number for Mn^{2+} is _____. The reduction half-reaction is

_____.

Step 3(a): Balance the atoms and charges in the half-reaction.

_____.

2 Balancing Redox Equations (continued)

Step 3(b): The _____ ions are readily available and can be used to balance the charge in half-reactions in acid solutions. The number of H^+ ions added to the right side of the oxidation half-reaction is _____. The number of H^+ ions added to the left side of the reduction half-reaction is _____.

Write the oxidation half-reaction: _____.

Write the reduction half-reaction: _____

_____.

Step 4: The number of electrons lost in oxidation is _____. The number of electrons gained in reduction is _____. The least common multiple of these numbers is _____. To balance the half-reactions, the atoms in the oxidation half-reaction must be multiplied by _____ and the atoms in the reduction half-reaction must be multiplied by _____.

The oxidation half-reaction is now

_____

The reduction half-reaction is now

_____

Step 5 After adding the balanced half-reactions, write the redox reaction equation:

_____

_____

Cancel or reduce like terms on both sides of the equation, then write the simplified equation:

_____

Return spectator ions _____ and restore the state descriptions.

_____

_____

3. Evaluate the Answer

The number of _____ for each element is _____ on both sides of the equation and none of the subscripts have been changed.

Science Notebook • Redox Reactions
326

Copyright © McGraw-Hill Education

2 Balancing Redox Equations (continued)

REVIEW IT!

26. Explain how changes in oxidation number are related to the electrons transferred in a redox reaction. How are the changes related to the processes of oxidation and reduction?

_____

_____

_____

_____

27. Describe why it is important to know the conditions under which an aqueous oxidation-reduction reaction takes place in order to balance the ionic equation for the reaction.

_____

_____

_____

28. Explain the steps of the oxidation-number method of balancing equations.

_____

29. State what an oxidation half-reaction shows. What does a reduction half-reaction show?

_____

_____

_____

30. Write the oxidation and reduction half-reactions for the redox equation.
$Pb(s) + Pd(NO_3)_2(aq) \rightarrow Pb(NO_3)_2(aq) + Pd(s)$

_____

31. Determine The oxidation half-reaction of a redox reaction is $Sn^{2+} \rightarrow Sn^{4+} + 2e^-$, and the reduction half-reaction is $Au^{3+} + 3e^- \rightarrow Au$. What minimum numbers of tin(II) ions and gold(III) ions would have to react in order to have zero electrons left over?

_____

2 Balancing Redox Equations (continued)

32. Apply Balance the following equations.

    a. $HClO_3(aq) \rightarrow ClO_2(g) + HClO_4(aq) + H_2O(l)$

    b. $H_2SeO_3(aq) + HClO_3(aq) \rightarrow H_2SeO_4(aq) + Cl_2(g) + H_2O(l)$

    c. $Cr_2O_7{}^{2-}(aq) + Fe^{2+}(aq) \rightarrow Cr^{3+}(aq) + Fe^{3+}(aq)$ (in acidic solution)

_____

_____

_____

19 Electrochemistry

ESSENTIAL QUESTION

Write the Essential Question for this chapter.

_____

_____

_____

Use the "What I Know" column to list the things you know about the Essential Question. Then list the questions you have about the Essential Question in the "What I Want to Find Out" column. As you read the chapter, fill in the "What I Learned" column.

K _What I Know_	W _What I Want to Find Out_	L _What I Learned_

19 Electrochemistry

1 Voltaic Cells

BUILD TO THE ESSENTIAL QUESTION

Read the items under Build to the Essential Question at the beginning of the lesson. Restate each in your own words.

_____

_____

REVIEW VOCABULARY

oxidation

reduction

Recall the definition of each Review Vocabulary term.

oxidation _____

_____

reduction _____

_____

NEW VOCABULARY

salt bridge

electrochemical cell

voltaic cell

half-cell

anode

cathode

reduction potential

standard hydrogen
  electrode

Define each New Vocabulary term.

salt bridge _____

_____

electrochemical cell _____

_____

voltaic cell _____

_____

half-cell _____

_____

anode _____

cathode _____

reduction potential _____

standard hydrogen electrode _____

ACADEMIC VOCABULARY

correspond

Define the following Academic Vocabulary term.

correspond _____

1 Voltaic Cells (continued)

Explain the branch of chemistry called electrochemistry.

_____

_____

Write the half-reactions of copper and zinc as indicated in Figure 2.

_____ (reduction half-reaction: electrons _____)

_____ (oxidation half-reaction: electrons _____)

Explain how an electrochemical cell uses a redox reaction.

_____

_____

Complete each of the following statements.

1. The electrode where oxidation takes place is called the _____

2. The electrode where reduction takes place is called the _____

3. An object's potential energy is _____

4. In electrochemistry, _____ is a
   measure of the amount of _____ that can be generated
   from a _____ to do work.

1 Voltaic Cells (continued)

Sequence the steps of the electrochemical process that occur in a zinc-copper voltaic cell. The first one has been done for you.

_____ To complete the circuit, both positive and negative ions move through the salt bridge. The two half-reactions can be summed to show the overall cell reaction.

_____ The electrons flow from the zinc strip and pass through the external circuit to the copper strip.

___1___ Electrons are produced in the oxidation half-cell according to this half-reaction: $Zn(s) \rightarrow Zn^{2+}(aq) + 2e^-$.

_____ Electrons enter the reduction half-cell where the following half-reaction occurs: $Cu^{2+}(aq) + 2e^- \rightarrow Cu(s)$.

Describe reduction potential in relation to an electrode.

_____

_____

_____

Analyze Table 1. Some of the standard reduction potentials (E^0 (V)) are positive, some are negative. Explain the difference.

_____

_____

_____

Write the abbreviated E^0 and half-reaction for each of the following:

Element	Half-Reaction	E^0 (V)
Li		
Au		
$PbSO_4$		
Na		

1 Voltaic Cells (continued)

Summarize Fill the blanks to help you take notes while you read Example Problem 1.

Problem

Determine the overall cell reaction and the standard potential for the half-cells of a voltaic cell.

$$I_2(s) + 2e^- \rightarrow 2I^-(aq)$$

$$Fe^{2+}(aq) + 2e^- \rightarrow Fe(s)$$

1. Analyze the Problem

List the known and the unknown.

Known: Standard reduction potentials for the half-cells

_____

Unknown: _____

2. Solve for the Unknown

Find the standard reduction potentials for half-reactions.

$$E^0_{I_2|I^-} = \underline{\hspace{6cm}}$$

$$E^0_{Fe^{2+}|Fe} = \underline{\hspace{6cm}}$$

Rewrite the half–reactions in the correct direction.

reduction half–cell reaction: _____

oxidation half–cell reaction: _____

overall cell reaction: _____

Balance the reaction if necessary.

_____

Calculate the cell's standard potential.

$$E^0_{cell} = E^0_{reduction} - E^0_{oxidation}$$

$$E^0_{cell} = +0.536\ V - \underline{\hspace{5cm}}$$

$$E^0_{cell} = + \underline{\hspace{5cm}}$$

Write the reaction using cell notation.

_____

1 Voltaic Cells (continued)

3. Evaluate the Answer

The answer seems reasonable given the _____

of the _____ that comprise it.

Write the steps for the process of predicting whether any proposed redox reaction will occur spontaneously.

1. _____

2. _____

3. _____

   _____

4. _____

5. _____

GET IT? **Identify** the sign of the potential of a redox reaction that occurs spontaneously.

_____

REVIEW IT!

10. **Describe** the conditions under which a redox reaction causes an electric current to flow through a wire.

_____

_____

_____

11. **Identify** the components of a voltaic cell. Explain the role of each component in the operation of the cell.

_____

_____

_____

_____

Copyright © McGraw-Hill Education

1 Voltaic Cells (continued)

12. **Write** the balanced equation for the spontaneous cell reaction that occurs in a cell with these reduction half-reactions.

   a. $Ag^+(aq) + e^- \rightarrow Ag(s)$ and $Ni^{2+}(aq) + 2e^- \rightarrow Ni(s)$

   b. $Mg^{2+}(aq) + 2e^- \rightarrow Mg(s)$ and $2H^+(aq) + 2e^- \rightarrow H_2(g)$

   c. $Sn^{2+}(aq) + 2e^- \rightarrow Sn(s)$ and $Fe^{3+}(aq) + 3e^- \rightarrow Fe(s)$

   d. $PbI_2(s) + 2e^- \rightarrow Pb(s) + 2I^-(aq)$ and $Pt^{2+}(aq) + 2e^- \rightarrow Pt(s)$

   _____

   _____

   _____

13. **Determine** the standard potential for electrochemical cells in which each equation represents the overall cell reaction. Identify the reactions as spontaneous or nonspontaneous as written.

   a. $2Al^{3+}(aq) + 3Cu(s) \rightarrow 3Cu^{2+}(aq) + 2Al(s)$

   b. $Hg^{2+}(aq) + 2Cu^+(aq) \rightarrow 2Cu^{2+}(aq) + Hg(l)$

   c. $Cd(s) + 2NO_3^-(aq) + 4H^+(aq) \rightarrow Cd^{2+}(aq) + 2NO_2(g) + 2H_2O(l)$

   _____

   _____

14. **Design** a concept map for Section 1, starting with the term electrochemical cell. Incorporate all the new vocabulary terms in your map.

19 Electrochemistry

2 Batteries

Read the items under Build to the Essential Question at the beginning of the lesson. Restate each in your own words.

_____

_____

REVIEW VOCABULARY

reversible reaction

Recall the definition of the Review Vocabulary term.

reversible reaction

_____

_____

NEW VOCABULARY

battery

dry cell

primary battery

secondary battery

fuel cell

corrosion

galvanization

Define each New Vocabulary term.

battery

_____

dry cell

primary battery

_____

secondary battery

_____

fuel cell

_____

corrosion

_____

galvanization

_____

_____

Copyright © McGraw-Hill Education

2 Batteries (continued)

Write the oxidation half-reaction for the dry cell of the most commonly used voltaic cell.

_____

List the paste and cathode type for each of the following batteries. So-called dry-cell batteries contain different moist pastes in which the cathode half-reaction takes place.

Zinc-carbon battery

Paste _____

Cathode type _____

Alkaline battery

Paste _____

Cathode type _____

GET IT? **Identity** the half-reaction that occurs in both alkaline and silver batteries.

_____

GET IT? **Compare** the redox reactions that take place in primary batteries and secondary batteries.

_____

_____

Compare and contrast primary and secondary batteries.

_____

_____

_____

_____

2 Batteries (continued)

Explain how the following overall reaction of lead-acid batteries is different from traditional redox reactions.

$$Pb(s) + PbO_2(s) + 4H^+ (aq) + 2SO_4^{2-} (aq) \rightarrow 2PbSO_4(s) + 2H_2O(l)$$

_____

_____

_____

_____

List two reasons that scientists and engineers have focused a lot of attention on the element lithium to make batteries.

1. _____

2. _____

_____

Describe two applications of lightweight lithium batteries.

_____

_____

GET IT? **List** three advantages of lithium batteries.

_____

_____

2 Batteries (continued)

Explain the makeup of a fuel cell by completing the following paragraph and accompanying reactions.

In a fuel cell, each electrode _____

that allows contact between the _____

_____. The walls of the chamber also contain _____

such as powdered platinum or palladium, which _____.

oxidation half-reaction: _____

reduction half-reaction: _____

overall cell reaction: _____

The overall cell reaction is the same as the equation for the

_____.

List three reasons why PEMs are used instead of a liquid electrode.

_____

_____

_____

GET IT? **Compare** fuel cells with other voltaic cells to find an important way in which they are different.

_____

_____

Draw and label the parts of the corrosion reaction in Figure 15. Be sure to identify the anode and cathode.

2 Batteries (continued)

Explain why rusting is a slow process. List a way that it might be sped up in certain areas.

_____

_____

_____

_____

Explain the two ways galvanizing helps prevent corrosion.

1. _____

_____

_____

2. _____

_____

_____

_____

REVIEW IT!

15. **Identify** what is reduced and what is oxidized in the zinc-carbon dry-cell battery. What features make the alkaline dry cell an improvement over the earlier type of dry-cell battery?

_____

_____

_____

_____

2 Batteries (continued)

16. Explain what happens when a battery is recharged.

_____

_____

17. Describe the half-reactions that occur in a hydrogen fuel cell, and write the equation for the overall reaction.

_____

_____

_____

_____

18. Describe the function of a sacrificial anode. How is the function of a sacrificial anode similar to galvanization?

_____

_____

_____

_____

19. Explain why lithium is a good choice for the anode of a battery.

_____

_____

_____

20. Calculate Use data from **Table 1** to calculate the cell potential of the hydrogen-oxygen fuel cell.

_____

_____

21. Design an Experiment Use your knowledge of acids to devise a method for determining whether a lead-acid battery can deliver full charge or is beginning to run down.

_____

_____

_____

_____

19 Electrochemistry

3 Electrolysis

Read the items under Build to the Essential Question at the beginning of the lesson. Restate each in your own words.

_____

_____

REVIEW VOCABULARY

redox reaction

Recall the definition of the Review Vocabulary term.

redox reaction

_____

_____

NEW VOCABULARY

electrolysis

electrolytic cell

Define each New Vocabulary term.

electrolysis

_____

electrolytic cell

_____

Describe how it is possible to reverse a spontaneous redox reaction in an electrochemical cell.

_____

_____

_____

SCIENCE USAGE v. COMMON USAGE

Reduce

Science usage: to decrease an atom's oxidation number by the addition of electrons.

Zinc reduces copper(II) ions to copper atoms by releasing two electrons.

Common usage: to diminish in size, amount, extent, or number

The number of dancers had to be reduced because the stage was too small.

3 Electrolysis (continued)

Compare the reactions involved in sodium chloride to those in the electrolysis of brine.

_____

_____

_____

GET IT? **Explain** why the sodium chloride must be molten in the Down's cell.

_____

GET IT? **Name** the species that is oxidized and the species that is reduced in the electrolysis of brine.

_____

Explain the importance of electrolysis in the purification of metals.

_____

_____

_____

_____

_____

_____

REVIEW IT!

22. Define electrolysis and relate the definition to the spontaneity of redox reactions.

_____

_____

3 Electrolysis (continued)

23. **Explain** why the products of the electrolysis of brine and the electrolysis of molten sodium chloride are different.

_____

24. **Describe** how impure copper obtained from the smelting of ore is purified by electrolysis.

_____

_____

25. **Explain,** by referring to the Hall-Héroult process, why recycling aluminum is very important.

_____

_____

26. **Describe** the anode and cathode of an electrolytic cell in which gold is to be plated on an object.

_____

27. **Explain** why producing a kilogram of silver from its ions by electrolysis requires much less electric energy than producing a kilogram of aluminum from its ions.

_____

_____

_____

28. **Calculate** Use **Table 1** to calculate the voltage of the Down's cell. Should the potential be positive or negative?

_____

_____

29. **Summarize** Write a short paragraph answering each of the three questions under Build to the Essential Question for Lesson 3 in your own words.

_____

_____

_____

20 Hydrocarbons

ESSENTIAL QUESTION

Write the Essential Question for this chapter.

_____

_____

_____

Use the "What I Know" column to list the things you know about the Essential Question. Then list the questions you have about the Essential Question in the "What I Want to Find Out" column. As you read the chapter, fill in the "What I Learned" column.

K _What I Know_	W _What I Want to Find Out_	L _What I Learned_

20 Hydrocarbons

1 Introduction to Hydrocarbons

BUILD TO THE ESSENTIAL QUESTION

Read the items under Build to the Essential Question at the beginning of the lesson. Restate each in your own words.

_____

_____

_____

REVIEW VOCABULARY

microorganism

Recall the definition of the Review Vocabulary term.

microorganism

_____

NEW VOCABULARY

organic compound

hydrocarbon

saturated hydrocarbon

unsaturated hydrocarbon

fractional distillation

cracking

Define each New Vocabulary term.

organic compound

_____

hydrocarbon

_____

saturated hydrocarbon

_____

unsaturated hydrocarbon

_____

fractional distillation

_____

cracking

_____

1 Introduction to Hydrocarbons (continued)

Explain the evolution of the contemporary understanding of the term *organic compound*.

> In the early nineteenth century, chemists referred to the variety of carbon compounds produced by living things as **organic compounds**.

> Today the term **organic compound** is applied to all carbon-containing compounds with the primary exceptions of carbon oxides, carbides, and carbonates, which are considered inorganic.

GET IT? **Explain** why carbon forms many compounds.

Label the web below with the correct name for each model of methane.

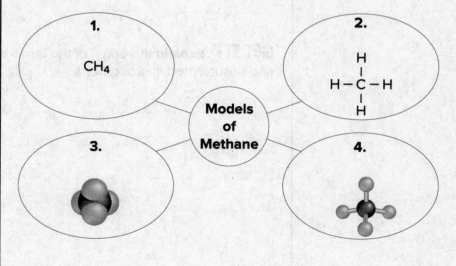

1. CH₄

2.
H
|
H — C — H
|
H

3.

Models of Methane

4.

1 **Introduction to Hydrocarbons** (continued)

GET IT? **Name** two uses of methane or natural gas in your home or community.

_____

Organize the outline below.

I. Ways that carbon atoms bond to each other

    A. _____

        1. share _____

        2. also called _____

    B. _____

        1. share _____

        2. also called _____

    C. _____

        1. share _____

        2. also called _____

Draw models of each carbon-carbon bond and label them appropriately.

Single Covalent Bond	Double Covalent Bond	Triple Covalent Bond
C C	C C	C C

GET IT? **Explain** the origin of the terms _saturated hydrocarbons_ and _unsaturated hydrocarbons_.

_____

_____

_____

_____

Identify natural sources of hydrocarbons by completing the following statements.

The main natural source of hydrocarbons is _____, a complex mixture containing more than a thousand _____.

Petroleum is more useful to humans when _____

_____, called _____ Separation is carried out by

_____

_____, a process called fractional distillation.

Sequence the process of fractional distillation.

_____ Vapors travel up through the column.

_____ Temperature is controlled to remain near 400° at the bottom of the fractionating tower.

_____ Hydrocarbons with fewer carbon atoms remain in the vapor phase until they reach regions of cooler temperatures farther up the column.

_____ Hydrocarbons with more carbon atoms condense closer to the bottom of the tower and are drawn off.

_____ Petroleum boils and gradually moves toward the top.

Match the names of these two processes with their definitions.

1. fractional distillation   **2.** cracking

_____ is done to break the larger molecules of petroleum components into smaller molecules.

_____ separates petroleum into simpler components.

GET IT? **Describe** the process in which large-chain hydrocarbons are broken into more-desirable smaller-chain hydrocarbons.

_____

_____

_____

1 Introduction to Hydrocarbons (continued)

REVIEW IT!

1. **Identify** three applications of hydrocarbons as a source of energy and raw materials.

_____

_____

2. **Name** an organic compound and explain what an organic chemist studies.

_____

_____

3. **Identify** what each of the four molecular models highlights about a molecule.

_____

_____

4. **Compare and contrast** saturated and unsaturated hydrocarbons.

_____

_____

_____

5. **Describe** the process of fractional distillation.

_____

_____

6. **Infer** Some shortening products are described as "hydrogenated vegetable oil," which are oils that reacted with hydrogen in the presence of a catalyst. Form a hypothesis to explain why hydrogen reacted with the oils.

_____

_____

7. **Interpret Data** Refer to **Figure 6**. What property of hydrocarbon molecules correlates to the viscosity of a particular fraction when it is cooled to room temperature?

20 Hydrocarbons

2 Alkanes

Read the items under Build to the Essential Question at the beginning of the lesson. Restate each in your own words.

_____

_____

REVIEW VOCABULARY

IUPAC (International Union of Pure and Applied Chemistry)

Recall the definition of the Review Vocabulary term.

IUPAC (International Union of Pure and Applied Chemistry)

_____

_____

_____

NEW VOCABULARY

alkane

homologous series

parent chain

substituent group

cyclic hydrocarbon

cycloalkane

Define each New Vocabulary term.

alkane

_____

homologous series

_____

parent chain

_____

substituent group

_____

cyclic hydrocarbon

_____

cycloalkane

_____

ACADEMIC VOCABULARY

substitute

Define the following term.

substitute

_____

2 Alkanes (continued)

Compare and contrast the models in the table below.

Type of Model	Description of Model
1. Molecular formula	
2. Structural formula	
3. Space-filling model	
4. Ball-and-stick model	

Describe straight-chain alkanes by completing the following sentences.

The first four compounds in the straight-chain series of alkanes are

_____. The names of all alkanes

end in _____. Because the first four alkanes were named before

there was a complete understanding of alkane structures, their names

do not have _____ as do the alkanes with

_____ in a chain. Chemists use _____

_____ to save space.

Explain the structural formula of the following hydrocarbons. The first
has been done for you.

1. Methane is formed from one atom of carbon and four
atoms of hydrogen.

2. Butane is formed _____

3. Octane is formed _____

_____

4. Decane is formed _____

_____

GET IT? **Write** the molecular formula for an alkane that has 13
carbon atoms in its molecular structure.

_____

2 Alkanes (continued)

GET IT? **Describe** the difference in the molecular structures of butane and isobutane.

_____

_____

Describe naming branched-chain alkanes.

> A straight-chain and a branched- chain alkane can have the same molecular formula.

> **PRINCIPLE**
> Therefore, the name of an organic compound also must describe

> **NAMING PROCESS**
> Branched-chain alkanes are viewed as consisting of a

> **NAMING, PART 1**
> The longest continuous chain of carbon atom is called the

> **NAMING, PART 2**
> All side branches are called   because they appear to substitute for a hydrogen atom in the straight chain.

> **NAMING, PART 3**
> Each alkane-based substituent group branching from the parent chain is named

2 Alkanes (continued)

Organize the concept web below.

organic compounds that contain
_____

cyclic hydrocarbon

cycloalkanes

The prefix *cyclo–* indicates a hydrocarbon with a _____ ; the

suffix *-ane* indicates compound has only _____ .

GET IT? **Evaluate** If the prefix *cyclo-* is present in the name of an
alkane, what do you know about the alkane?

_____

Classify the properties of alkanes into categories.

General Properties (3)	Physical Properties (4)	Chemical Properties (2)

2 Alkanes (continued)

REVIEW IT!

12. Describe the main structural characteristics of alkane molecules.

_____

_____

13. Name the following structures using IUPAC rules.

a.

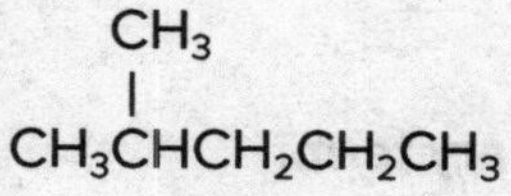

$$CH_3$$
$$|$$
$$CH_3CHCH_2CH_2CH_3$$

b.

$$CH_3$$
$$|$$
$$CH_3CCH_3$$
$$|$$
$$CH_3$$

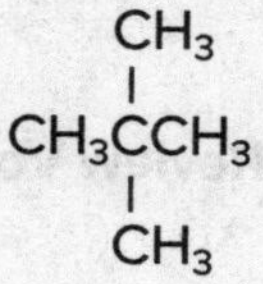

c.

_____

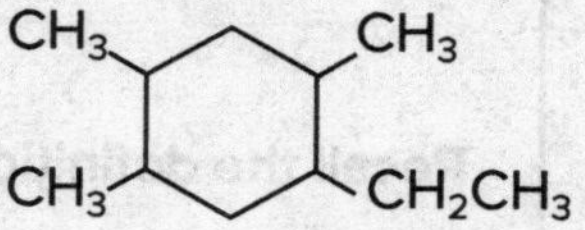

14. Describe the general properties of alkanes.

_____

_____

_____

15. Draw the molecular structure for each of the following.

a. 3,4-diethylheptane

b. 4-isopropyl-3-methyldecane

c. 1-ethyl-4-methylcyclohexane

d. 1,2-dimethylcyclopropane

16. Interpret Chemical Structures Why is the name 3-butylpentane incorrect? Based on this name, write the structural formula for the compound. What is the correct IUPAC name for 3-butylpentane?

_____

_____

20 Hydrocarbons

3 Alkenes and Alkynes

BUILD TO THE ESSENTIAL QUESTION

Read the items under Build to the Essential Question at the beginning of the lesson. Restate each in your own words.

_____

_____

_____

REVIEW VOCABULARY

hormone

Recall the definition of the Review Vocabulary term.

hormone

_____

_____

NEW VOCABULARY

alkene

alkyne

Define each New Vocabulary term.

alkene

_____

_____

alkyne

_____

Identify five facts about alkenes as discussed in your text.

1. _____

_____

2. _____

_____

3. _____

_____

4. _____

_____

5. _____

_____

3 Alkenes and Alkynes (continued)

Sequence the factors involved in naming an alkene with four or more carbons in the chain using the web below.

1. change the –ane ending of the corresponding alkane to

2. Specify the location of the

Naming Alkenes

3. Number of the carbons in the parent chain starting at the end of the chain that will give the first carbon in the double bond the

4. Use only that number in the

GET IT? **Infer** why it is necessary to identify where the double bond is located in the name of an alkene.

_____

_____

Summarize Use the following to help you take notes as you read Example Problem 3 in your text.

Problem

Name the following alkene.

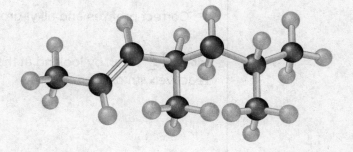

3 Alkenes and Alkynes (continued)

1. Analyze the Problem

You are given a branch-chained alkene that contains one double bond and two alkyl groups. Follow the IUPAC rules to name the organic compound.

2. Solve for the Unknown

a. The longest continuous carbon chain that includes the double bond contains _____ carbons. The _____ alkane is heptane, but the name is changed to _____ because a double bond is present. *Write the 2-heptene parent chain.*

b. and c. Number the chain to give the lowest number to the double bond and name each substituent.

d. Determine how many of each substituent is present, and assign the correct prefix to represent that number. Then, include the position numbers to get the complete prefix.

e. The names of substituents _____
_____.

f. Apply the complete prefix to the name of the parent alkene chain. Use commas to separate numbers and hyphens between numbers and words. Write the name _____.

3. Evaluate the Answer

The longest carbon chain includes the _____, and the position of the double bond has the _____. Correct prefixes and alkyl-group names _____.

GET IT? **Infer**, by looking at the bonds in ethyne, why it is highly reactive with oxygen.

_____
_____
_____

REVIEW IT!

19. **Describe** how the molecular structures of alkenes and alkynes differ from the structure of alkanes.

_____

_____

_____

20. **Identify** how the chemical properties of alkenes and alkynes differ from those of alkanes.

_____

_____

_____

21. **Explain** Name the structures shown using IUPAC rules.

a.

$$CH \equiv CCH_2$$

with CH_3 above the second carbon

b.

$$CH_3CH_2CHCH = CHCH_2CH_3$$

with CH_3 above

_____

22. **Draw** the molecular structures of 4-methyl-1,3-pentadiene and 2,3-dimethyl-2-butene.

```




```

23. **Infer** how the boiling and freezing points of alkynes compare with those of alkanes with the same number of carbon atoms. Explain your reasoning, then research data to see if it supports your idea.

_____

_____

24. **Predict** What geometric arrangement would you expect from the bonds surrounding the carbon atom in alkanes, alkenes, and alkynes? _(Hint: VSEPR theory can be used to predict the shape.)_

_____

_____

_____

20 Hydrocarbons

4 Hydrocarbon Isomers

Read the items under Build to the Essential Question at the beginning of the lesson. Restate each in your own words.

_____

_____

_____

REVIEW VOCABULARY

electromagnetic radiation

Recall the definition of the Review Vocabulary term.

electromagnetic radiation _____

_____

_____

NEW VOCABULARY

isomer

structural isomer

stereoisomer

geometric isomer

chirality

asymmetric carbon

optical isomer

optical rotation

Define each New Vocabulary term.

isomer _____

_____

structural isomer _____

_____

stereoisomer _____

_____

geometric isomer _____

_____

chirality _____

asymmetric carbon _____

_____

optical isomer _____

_____

optical rotation _____

_____

_____

4 Hydrocarbon Isomers (continued)

Organize the outline below.

I. _____: Two or more compounds that have the same molecular formula but different molecular structures.

  A. Two types of isomers

    1. Structural isomers

      a. _____

      b. _____

      _____

        i. Examples include _____

        _____ .

    2. Stereoisomers

      a. _____

      _____

        i. _____

        ii. _____

      _____

      b. _____

        i. Result from different arrangements of groups around a double bond

        ii. Possible _____ with *trans*-fatty acids

        iii. The _____ seem not to be as harmful.

GET IT? **Explain** how structural and geometric isomers differ.

_____

_____

_____

_____

4 Hydrocarbon Isomers (continued)

Describe chirality by completing the flow chart below.

chirality occurs whenever	a compound contains an	which has _____ or _____ attached to it

These isomers are called	The molecules are _____ very much	The four groups can be

Identify the types of isomers shown below. Which pair are optical isomers?

d-glyceraldehyde   l-glyceraldehyde

```
      CHO                        CHO
       |                          |
  H —  C  — OH             HO —   C  — H
       |                          |
      CH₂OH                      CH₂OH
```

ethanol   methoxymethane

```
      H   H                   H       H
      |   |  ⟍ H              |       |
  H — C = C — O          H —  C — O —  C — H
      |   |                   |       |
      H   H                   H       H
```

trans-1, 2-dichloroethene   cis-1, 2-dichloroethene

```
  H ⟍       ⟋ Cl           H ⟍       ⟋ H
      C  =  C                   C  =  C
  Cl ⟋       ⟍ H           Cl ⟋       ⟍ Cl
```

4 Hydrocarbon Isomers (continued)

REVIEW IT!

25. Draw on a separate sheet of paper all of the structural isomers possible for the alkane with the molecular formula C_6H_{14}. Show only the carbon chains.

_____

_____

26. Explain the difference between structural isomers and stereoisomers.

_____

_____

_____

27. Draw the structures of *cis*-3-hexene and *trans*-3-hexene.

28. Infer why living organisms can make use of only one chiral form of a substance.

_____

_____

29. Evaluate A certain reaction yields 80% *trans*-2-pentene and 20% *cis*-2-pentene. Draw the structures of these two geometric isomers, and develop a hypothesis to explain why the isomers form in the proportions cited.

30. Formulate Models Starting with a single carbon atom, draw two different optical isomers by attaching the following atoms or groups to the carbon: $-H$, $-CH_3$, $-CH_2CH_3$, and $-CH_2CH_2CH_3$.

20 Hydrocarbons

5 Aromatic Hydrocarbons

BUILD TO THE ESSENTIAL QUESTION
Read the items under Build to the Essential Question at the beginning of the lesson. Restate each in your own words.

_____

_____

REVIEW VOCABULARY

hybrid orbitals

Recall the definition of the Review Vocabulary term.

hybrid orbitals _____

_____

NEW VOCABULARY

aromatic compound

aliphatic compound

Define each New Vocabulary term.

aromatic compound _____

_____

aliphatic compound _____

_____

GET IT? **Explain** What do many natural dyes and essential oils for perfumes have in common?

GET IT? **Infer** why the terms aromatic compound and aliphatic compound continue to be used by chemists today.

_____

_____

5 Aromatic Hydrocarbons (continued)

Classify the properties of aromatic and aliphatic compounds.

	Structural Characteristics	Reactivity
Aromatic Compounds		
Aliphatic Compounds		

Model Draw a model of a fused ring system.

Explain how substituted benzene rings are numbered.

_____

_____

Number the substituted benzene ring in the structure below, then name the structure.

GET IT? **Explain** what the circle means inside the six-membered ring structure in **Figure 27**.

_____

5 Aromatic Hydrocarbons (continued)

REVIEW IT!

33. Explain benzene's structure and how it makes the molecule unusually stable.

_____

_____

_____

34. Explain how aromatic hydrocarbons differ from aliphatic hydrocarbons.

_____

_____

_____

35. Describe the properties of benzene that made chemists think it was not an alkene with several double bonds.

_____

_____

_____

36. Name the following structures.

a.
$$CH \equiv C\underset{\underset{CH_3}{|}}{C}H_2$$

b.
$$CH_3CH_2\underset{\underset{CH_3}{|}}{C}HCH = CHCH_2CH_3$$

_____

37. Explain why the connection between benzopyrene and cancer was significant.

_____

_____

_____

_____

21 Substituted Hydrocarbons and Their Reactions

ESSENTIAL QUESTION

Write the Essential Question for this chapter.

_____

_____

_____

Use the "What I Know" column to list the things you know about the Essential Question. Then list the questions you have about the Essential Question in the "What I Want to Find Out" column. As you read the chapter, fill in the "What I Learned" column.

K What I Know	W What I Want to Find Out	L What I Learned

21 Substituted Hydrocarbons and Their Reactions

1 Alkyl Halides and Aryl Halides

BUILD TO THE ESSENTIAL QUESTION

Read the items under Build to the Essential Question at the beginning of the lesson. Restate each in your own words.

_____

_____

REVIEW VOCABULARY

aliphatic compound

Recall the definition of the Review Vocabulary term.

aliphatic compound

_____

NEW VOCABULARY

functional group

halocarbon

alkyl halide

aryl halide

plastic

Use your text to define each term.

functional group

_____

halocarbon

_____

alkyl halide

_____

aryl halide

_____

plastic

_____

1 Alkyl Halides and Aryl Halides (continued)

Describe how a functional group can be helpful in determining how a molecule reacts.

_____

_____

_____

_____

Identify the meaning of each of the following symbols for functional groups.

* represents _____

R and R' represent _____

_____

Organize information about organic compounds and their functional groups by completing the table below.

Compound Type	General Formula	Functional Group
Halocarbon		Halogen
	R-OH	
		Ether
	$R-NH_2$	
Aldehyde		
		Carbonyl
		Carboxyl
		Ester
		Amide

1 Alkyl Halides and Aryl Halides (continued)

Compare and contrast alkyl halides and aryl halides.

_____

_____

_____

Describe how to name halocarbons by completing the following paragraph.

Organic molecules containing functional groups are given IUPAC names based on their _____. For the alkyl halides, a prefix indicates which _____ is present. The prefixes are formed by

_____

GET IT? **Infer** why the lowest possible position number is used to name an aryl halide instead of using a randomly chosen position number.

_____

_____

Examine Table 2. Write three observations you make regarding the compounds listed in the table.

1. _____

_____

2. _____

_____

3. _____

GET IT? **Explain** the relationship between the number of electrons in the halogen and the boiling point.

_____

_____

1 Alkyl Halides and Aryl Halides (continued)

GET IT? **Explain** why alkyl halides are often used in the chemical industry as starting materials instead of alkanes.

_____

_____

REVIEW IT!

4. **Compare and contrast** alkyl halides and aryl halides.

_____

_____

_____

_____

5. **Draw** structures for the following molecules.

   a. 2-chlorobutane   **c.** 1,1,1-trichloroethane

   b. 1,3-difluorohexane   **d.** 1-bromo-4-chlorobenzene

6. **Define** _functional group_ and name the group present in each of the following structures. Name the type of organic compound each substance represents.

   a. $CH_3CH_2CH_2OH$ **c.** $CH_3CH_2NH_2$

   b. CH_3CH_2F **d.**
$$CH_3C\overset{\overset{\textstyle O}{\|}}{-}OH$$

_____

_____

_____

1 Alkyl Halides and Aryl Halides (continued)

7. **Evaluate** How would you expect the boiling points of propane and 1-chloropropane to compare? Explain your answer.

_____

_____

_____

8. **Interpret** Scientific Illustrations Examine the pair of substituted hydrocarbons shown, and decide whether it represents a pair of optical isomers. Explain your answer.

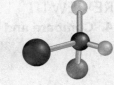

_____

_____

21 Substituted Hydrocarbons and Their Reactions

2 Alcohols, Ethers, and Amines

BUILD TO THE ESSENTIAL QUESTION

Read the items under Build to the Essential Question at the beginning of the lesson. Restate each in your own words.

_____

_____

_____

_____

REVIEW VOCABULARY

miscible

Recall the definition of the Review Vocabulary term.

miscible

_____

_____

NEW VOCABULARY

hydroxyl group

alcohol

denatured alcohol

ether

amine

substitution reaction

halogenation

Define each New Vocabulary term.

hydroxyl group

_____

alcohol

_____

denatured alcohol

_____

ether

_____

amine

_____

substitution reaction

_____

halogenation

_____

ACADEMIC VOCABULARY

bond

Define the following term.

bond

_____

Describe alcohols by completing the following sentence.

Because they readily form hydrogen bonds, alcohols have _____ boiling points and _____ water solubility than other organic compounds.

Write the general formula for an alcohol:

_____

Draw structures for the following molecules.

1-butanol

2-butanol

GET IT? **Explain** why *4-butanol and 3-butanol* are not the correct names for the compounds in **Figure 7a** and **7b**.

_____

_____

GET IT? **Explain** why numbers are not used to name the compound shown in **Figure 8a**.

_____

_____

Describe ethers by completing the following sentence.

Ethers are similar to _____ as they are compounds in which oxygen is bonded to _____. Ethers are different from alcohols because the oxygen atom bonds with _____ carbon atoms. Ethers are much less _____ in water than alcohols because they have no _____ to donate to a hydrogen bond.

2 Alcohols, Ethers, and Amines (continued)

Write the general formula for ethers:

_____

Draw a structure for the following molecule.

ethyl ether

GET IT? **Infer** why ethyl ether is undesirable as an anesthetic.

_____

Complete the following sentence.

Amines contain _____ atoms bonded to carbon atoms in

_____ chains or _____ rings. Amines are responsible for

many of the _____ associated with decay.

Write the general formula for amines:

_____

Draw a structure for the following molecule.

ethylamine

Sequence the steps needed to add Cl_2 to ethane to create
chloroethane. Use the reaction from Table 3 as a reference.

1. _____

2. _____

3. _____

4. _____

2 Alcohols, Ethers, and Amines (continued)

Create another substitution reaction using Br_2 and methane. Label molecules in each part of the reaction.

_____

_____

GET IT? **Draw** the molecular structure of halothane.

REVIEW IT!

9. Identify two elements that are commonly found in functional groups.

_____

_____

_____

10. Identify the functional group present in each of the following structures. Name the substance represented by each structure.

a.
$$NH_2$$
$$|$$
$$CH_3CHCH_3$$

b. 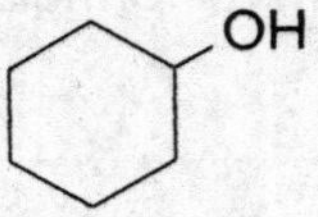
OH (on cyclohexane ring)

c. $CH_3 — O — CH_2CH_2CH_3$

_____

_____

_____

_____

2 Alcohols, Ethers, and Amines (continued)

11. **Draw** the structure for each molecule.

    a. 1-propanol

    c. propyl ether

    b. 1,3-cyclopentanediol

    d. 1,2-propanediamine

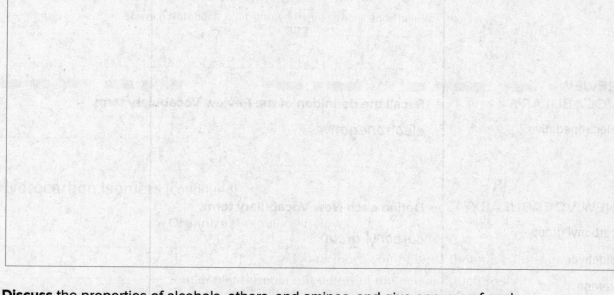

12. **Discuss** the properties of alcohols, ethers, and amines, and give one use of each.

_____

_____

_____

_____

_____

13. **Analyze** Based on the molecular structures below, which compound is likely more water-soluble? Explain your reasoning.

$$CH_3 - O - CH_3 \qquad \begin{matrix} OH \\ | \\ CH_3CH_2 \end{matrix}$$

_____

_____

_____

_____

21 Substituted Hydrocarbons and Their Reactions

3 Carbonyl Compounds

BUILD TO THE ESSENTIAL QUESTION

Read the items under Build to the Essential Question at the beginning of the lesson. Restate each in your own words.

_____

_____

_____

REVIEW VOCABULARY

electronegative

Recall the definition of the Review Vocabulary term.

electronegative

_____

_____

NEW VOCABULARY

carbonyl group

aldehyde

ketone

carboxylic acid

carboxyl group

ester

amide

condensation reaction

Define each New Vocabulary term.

carbonyl group

_____

aldehyde

_____

_____

_____

ketone

_____

_____

carboxylic acid

_____

carboxyl group

_____

ester

_____

_____

amide

_____

_____

condensation reaction

_____

_____

3 Carbonyl Compounds (continued)

Identify five important classes of organic compounds containing or made from carbonyl compounds:

a. _____

b. _____

c. _____

d. _____

e. _____

GET IT? **Identify** two uses for aldehydes.

_____

_____

Describe the common structure of aldehydes and ketones.

_____

_____

GET IT? **Explain** why the name of a ketone will not use the prefix 1- to indicate the location of the carbonyl group.

_____

_____

Draw a molecule of a carboxylic acid.

3 Carbonyl Compounds (continued)

GET IT? **Explain** how the name *ethanoic* acid is derived.

_____

_____

_____

GET IT? **Evaluate** Using the information presented, explain why carboxylic acids are classified as acids.

_____

_____

Describe organic compounds that are derived from carboxylic acids by completing the following paragraph.

Several classes of organic compound have structures in which the

_____ of a carboxylic acid is replaced by

_____ or _____. The two most common

types are _____.

GET IT? **Describe** how an amide differs from a carboxylic acid.

_____

_____

GET IT? **Identify** Examine the structural formulas of ethanamide and acetaminophen in **Table 11.** What components do the molecules share that allow each compound to be classified as an amide?

_____

_____

3 Carbonyl Compounds (continued)

GET IT? **Identify** an amide that is found in the human body.

_____

Sequence the steps for a condensation reaction.

_____ A small molecule, such as water, is lost.

_____ Two organic molecules combine.

_____ A more complex molecule is formed.

Complete the following condensation reaction.

R–COOH + R'–OH $\longrightarrow$ _____

Identify the functional group that corresponds to each of the following:

a. _–ine_ at the end of each halogen name to _–o_ _____

b. adding _–amine_ as the suffix _____

c. _–ane_ of the parent alkane to _–ol_ _____

d. replacing _–e_ ending with _–amide_ _____

e. _–e_ at the end of the name to _–al_ _____

f. _–ane_ of the parent alkane to _–anoic_ acid _____

g. _–ic_ acid ending replaced by _–ate_ _____

h. _–e_ at the end of the alkane replaced by _–one_ _____

3 Carbonyl Compounds (continued)

REVIEW IT!

14. **Classify** each of the carbonyl compounds as one of the types of organic substances you have studied in this section.

a. $CH_3CH_2 - O - \overset{\overset{\displaystyle O}{\|}}{C} - CH_3$

b. $CH_3CH_2CH_2\overset{\overset{\displaystyle O}{\|}}{C} - NH_2$

c.

d. $CH_3CH_2CH_2\overset{\overset{\displaystyle O}{\|}}{CH}$

_____

_____

15. **Describe** the products of a condensation reaction between a carboxylic acid and an alcohol.

_____

_____

16. **Determine** The general formula for alkanes is C_nH_{2n+2}. Derive a general formula to represent an aldehyde, a ketone, and a carboxylic acid.

_____

_____

17. **Infer** why water-soluble organic compounds with carboxyl groups exhibit acidic properties in solutions, whereas similar compounds with aldehyde structures do not exhibit these properties.

_____

_____

21 Substituted Hydrocarbons and Their Reactions

4 Other Reactions of Organic Compounds

BUILD TO THE ESSENTIAL QUESTION

Read the items under Build to the Essential Question at the beginning of the lesson. Restate each in your own words.

_____

_____

REVIEW VOCABULARY

catalyst

Recall the definition of the Review Vocabulary term.

catalyst _____

_____

NEW VOCABULARY

elimination reaction

dehydrogenation reaction

dehydration reaction

addition reaction

hydration reaction

hydrogenation reaction

Define each New Vocabulary term.

elimination reaction _____

_____

_____

dehydrogenation reaction _____

_____

dehydration reaction _____

_____

addition reaction _____

_____

hydration reaction _____

_____

hydrogenation reaction _____

_____

4 Other Reactions of Organic Compounds (continued)

List what needs to happen for chemical reactions of organic substances to occur. Include when and why a catalyst might be needed.

1. _____

2. _____

3. _____

_____

GET IT? **Define** *elimination reaction* in your own words.

_____

_____

_____

Review the section and give an example formula for each of the following reaction types.

addition reaction

_____

hydration reaction

_____

dehydrogenation reaction

_____

dehydration reaction

_____

hydrogenation reaction

_____

_____

elimination reaction

_____

_____

GET IT? **Identify** the reaction that is the reverse of a hydrogenation reaction.

_____

GET IT? **Identify** Use **Table 13** to identify two possible products that are produced when the aldehyde is further oxidized.

_____

GET IT? **Write** the equation using molecular structures like those in **Table 13** for the formation of propanoic acid.

Write the generic equation representing an addition reaction between an alkene and an alkyl halide.

_____

Draw the formula for the the reaction between cyclopentene and hydrogen bromide.

_____

4 Other Reactions of Organic Compounds (continued)

REVIEW IT!

18. **Classify** each reaction as substitution, elimination, addition, or condensation.

    a. $CH_3CH = CHCH_2CH_3 + H_2 \rightarrow CH_3CH_2 — CH_2CH_2CH_3$

    b. $\begin{array}{c} CH_3CH_2CH_2CHCH_3 \\ | \\ OH \end{array} \rightarrow CH_3CH_2CH = CHCH_3 + H_2O$

    _____

    _____

19. **Identify** the type of organic reaction that would best accomplish each conversion.

    a. alkyl halide → alkene   c. alcohol + carboxylic acid → ester

    b. alkene → alcohol   d. alkene → alkyl dihalide

    _____

    _____

20. **Complete** each equation by writing the condensed structural formula for the product that is most likely to form.

    a. $CH_3CH = CHCH_2CH_3 + H_2 \rightarrow$

    b. $\begin{array}{c} CH_3CH_2CHCH_2CH_3 + OH^- \\ | \\ Cl \end{array} \rightarrow$

    _____

    _____

21. **Predicting Products** Explain why the hydration reaction involving 1-butene might yield two products, but the hydration reaction of 2-butene yields only one.

    _____

    _____

    _____

Copyright © McGraw-Hill Education

21 Substituted Hydrocarbons and Their Reactions

5 Polymers

REVIEW
VOCABULARY

molecular mass

NEW VOCABULARY

polymer

monomer

polymerization reaction

addition polymerization

condensation
  polymerization

thermoplastic

thermosetting

BUILD TO THE ESSENTIAL QUESTION

Read the items under Build to the Essential Question at the beginning of the lesson. Restate each in your own words.

_____

_____

Recall the definition of the Review Vocabulary term.

molecular mass

_____

_____

Define each New Vocabulary term.

polymer

_____

monomer

_____

polymerization reaction

_____

addition polymerization

_____

condensation polymerization

_____

_____

thermoplastic

_____

thermosetting

_____

_____

5 Polymers (continued)

Identify the monomers or polymers.

Monomer (s)	Polymer (s)
Ethylene	
	Nylon 6,6
Urethane	

GET IT? **Compare and contrast** a monomer and a structural unit of a polymer.

_____

_____

_____

Compare and contrast condensation polymerization with addition polymerization by placing the terms below into the Venn diagram.

- all atoms present in final product

- small by-product, usually water

- involves the bonding of monomers

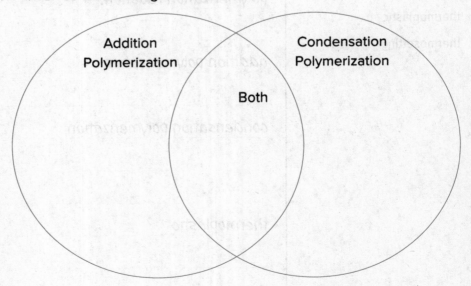

Identify the common polymer. Use **Table 14** in your text as a reference.

Use	Polymers
Foam furniture cushions	
A planter	
Nonstick cookware	
Food wrap	
Windows	
Clothing	
Carpet	
Water pipes	
Beverage containers	

Identify four reasons that many different polymers are widely used in manufacturing.

1. _____

2. _____

3. _____

4. _____

Describe the melting characteristics of thermoplastic polymers and thermosetting polymers.

Thermoplastic polymers _____

_____

Thermosetting polymers _____

_____

5 Polymers (continued)

GET IT? **Compare and contrast** thermoplastic and thermosetting polymers.

_____

_____

_____

_____

Discuss recycling by completing the following paragraph.

Americans are not efficient at recycling their plastics. Currently, only

_____ of plastic waste is recycled. This low rate of _____

_____ is due in part to the _____.

Plastics must be _____ according to _____,

which is _____ and _____. The plastic

industry has _____ that indicate the

_____of each plastic product to make the process easier

on individuals.

Describe what the code of recycling polymers does. Give an example of the code from the textbook.

_____

_____

_____

REAL-WORLD CONNECTION
Describe some common polymers that you use every day.

_____

_____

_____

_____

5 Polymers (continued)

REVIEW IT!

22. Draw the structure for the polymer that could be produced from each of the following monomers by the method stated.

a. Addition

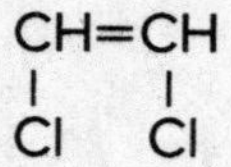

$$CH=CH$$
$$|\quad\ |$$
$$Cl\quad Cl$$

b. Condensation

$$NH_2 - CH_2CH_2 - \overset{\overset{\displaystyle O}{\|}}{C} - OH$$

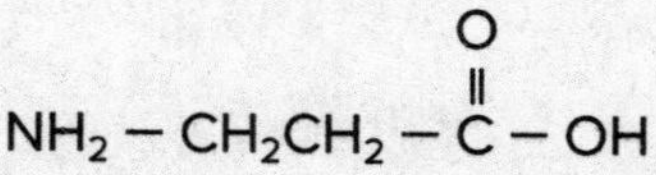

23. Label the polymerization reaction at right as addition or condensation. Explain your answer.

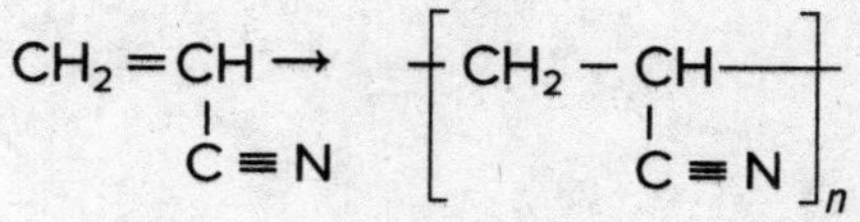

$$CH_2=CH \rightarrow \left[CH_2 - CH \right]_n$$
$$\qquad\quad |\qquad\qquad\qquad |$$
$$\qquad\quad C\equiv N\qquad\qquad\ C\equiv N$$

_____

_____

24. Identify Synthetic polymers often replace stone, wood, metals, wool, and cotton in many applications. Identify some advantages and disadvantages of using synthetic materials instead of natural materials.

_____

_____

_____

25. Predict the physical properties of the polymer that is made from the monomer at right. Mention solubility in water, electrical conductivity, texture, and chemical reactivity. Do you think it will be thermoplastic or thermosetting? Give reasons for your predictions.

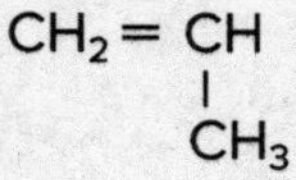

$$CH_2 = CH$$
$$\qquad\quad |$$
$$\qquad\quad CH_3$$

_____

_____

22 The Chemistry of Life

ESSENTIAL QUESTION

Write the Essential Question for this chapter.

_____

_____

_____

Use the "What I Know" column to list the things you know about the Essential Question. Then list the questions you have about the Essential Question in the "What I Want to Find Out" column. As you read the chapter, fill in the "What I Learned" column.

K _What I Know_	W _What I Want to Find Out_	L _What I Learned_

22 The Chemistry of Life

1 Proteins

BUILD TO THE ESSENTIAL QUESTION

Read the items under Build to the Essential Question at the beginning of the lesson. Restate each in your own words.

_____

_____

REVIEW VOCABULARY

polymer

Recall the definition of the Review Vocabulary term.

polymer _____

_____

NEW VOCABULARY

protein

amino acid

peptide bond

peptide

denaturation

enzyme

substrate

active site

Define each New Vocabulary term.

protein _____

_____

amino acid _____

_____

peptide bond _____

_____

peptide _____

_____

denaturation _____

_____

enzyme _____

substrate _____

_____

active site _____

_____

Draw and label a general amino acid with a variable side chain, an amino group, and a carboxyl group.

Describe the structure of a dipeptide and its functional units.

Rewrite each of the following statements, making each true.

To function properly, each protein must be flat.

_____

_____

A dipeptide consists of an amino acid with two side chains.

_____

_____

Complete the following statements about peptide bonds.

When a peptide bond is formed, _____ is released in the

process. This type of reaction is known as a _____ reaction.

GET IT? **Explain** how an amide functional group forms.

_____

_____

_____

Identify the peptide bond between the following amino acids.

$$\underset{\underset{H}{|}}{\overset{\overset{H}{|}}{N}} - \underset{\underset{H}{|}}{\overset{\overset{R_1}{|}}{C}} - \underset{\underset{O}{\parallel}}{C} - \underset{\underset{H}{|}}{\overset{\overset{H}{|}}{N}} - \underset{\underset{H}{|}}{\overset{\overset{R_2}{|}}{C}} - \underset{\underset{O}{\parallel}}{C} - OH$$

GET IT? **Explain** why Gly-Phe and Phe-Gly are different dipeptides.

_____

_____

_____

Explain why Gly-Phe is a different molecule than the Phe-Gly.

_____

_____

GET IT? **Calculate** the possible number of sequences for a peptide chain comprised of four amino acids.

_____

1 Proteins (continued)

Describe three changes in the environment that will uncoil or otherwise denature a protein.

1. _____

2. _____

3. _____

Draw an enzyme/substrate complex with the enzyme and substrates labeled.

GET IT? **Describe** in your own words how an enzyme works.

_____

_____

_____

_____

1 Proteins (continued)

Describe how the following functions affect living organisms by giving an example from your text.

Enzymes: _____

_____

Transport proteins: _____

_____

Structural proteins: _____

_____

Hormones: _____

_____

_____

Review the statements below and revise to make them correct.

1. Substrates bind to an enzyme site.

_____

2. An active site changes shape a great deal to accommodate the substrate.

_____

_____

3. An enzyme-substrate complex changes the enzyme, and it becomes part of the new molecule.

_____

_____

1 Proteins (continued)

REVIEW IT!

1. **Describe** three proteins and identify their functions.

_____

_____

2. **Compare** the structures of amino acids, dipeptides, polypeptides, and proteins. Which has the largest molecular mass? The smallest?

_____

_____

_____

3. **Draw** the structure of the dipeptide Gly-Ser, circling the peptide bond.

```



```

4. **Evaluate** How do the properties of proteins make them such useful catalysts? How do they differ from other catalysts you have studied?

_____

_____

5. **Explain** how a change in temperature might affect a protein's function.

_____

_____

6. **Categorize** Identify an amino acid from **Table 1** that can be classified into each of the categories in the following pairs.

   a. nonpolar side chain v. polar side chain

   b. aromatic v. aliphatic

   c. acidic v. basic

_____

_____

22 The Chemistry of Life

2 Carbohydrates

BUILD TO THE ESSENTIAL QUESTION

Read the items under Build to the Essential Question at the beginning of the lesson. Restate each in your own words.

_____

_____

_____

REVIEW
VOCABULARY

stereoisomers

Recall the definition of the Review Vocabulary term.

stereoisomers _____

_____

NEW VOCABULARY

carbohydrate

monosaccharide

disaccharide

polysaccharide

Define each New Vocabulary term.

carbohydrate _____

_____

monosaccharide _____

_____

disaccharide _____

_____

polysaccharide _____

_____

Copyright © McGraw-Hill Education

Science Notebook • The Chemistry of Life

400

2 Carbohydrates (continued)

Draw the cyclic and open-chain structures of the monosaccharide glucose.

GET IT? **Explain** the differences among a monosaccharide, a disaccharide, and a polysaccharide.

_____

_____

_____

Describe the structure and the composition of the following types of carbohydrates by completing this table.

Carbohydrate	Example	Structure and composition
starch		
cellulose		
glycogen		
glucose		

2 Carbohydrates (continued)

REVIEW IT!

7. **Explain** the functions of carbohydrates in living things.

_____

_____

8. **Describe** the structures of monosaccharides, disaccharides, and polysaccharides. Which has the largest molecular mass? The smallest?

_____

_____

_____

9. **Compare and contrast** the structures of starch and cellulose. How do the structural differences affect our ability to digest these two polysaccharides?

_____

_____

_____

10. **Calculate** If a carbohydrate has 2^n possible isomers, where n is equal to the number of chiral carbon atoms in the structure, calculate the number of possible isomers for the following monosaccharides: galactose, glucose, and fructose.

11. **Interpret Scientific Illustrations** Copy the illustration of sucrose on a separate sheet of paper, and circle the ether functional group that bonds the monomer sugars together.

_____

22 The Chemistry of Life

3 Lipids

BUILD TO THE ESSENTIAL QUESTION

Read the items under Build to the Essential Question at the beginning of the lesson. Restate each in your own words.

_____

_____

_____

REVIEW VOCABULARY

nonpolar

Recall the definition of the Review Vocabulary term.

nonpolar

_____

NEW VOCABULARY

lipid

fatty acid

triglyceride

saponification

phospholipid

wax

steroid

Define each New Vocabulary term.

lipid

_____

fatty acid

_____

triglyceride

_____

saponification

_____

phospholipid

_____

wax

_____

steroid

_____

_____

3 Lipids (continued)

Describe how a lipid differs from a protein or carbohydrate.

_____

_____

Compare and contrast saturated and unsaturated fatty acids. Give an example of each.

_____

_____

_____

_____

_____

Explain the reactions that form triglycerides. Give the type of reaction as well as the substrates.

_____

_____

_____

_____

3 Lipids (continued)

GET IT? **Describe** the difference between fatty acids and triglycerides.

_____

_____

Describe how waxes are made and what their specific properties include.

_____

_____

Describe a lipid that is not composed of fatty acid chains. Give an example.

_____

_____

_____

SYNTHESIZE
List the important functions for each of the following types of lipids.

triglycerides _____

phospholipids _____

waxes _____

steroids _____

_____

3 Lipids (continued)

REVIEW IT!

12. **Describe** the function of lipids.

_____

13. **Describe** the structures of fatty acids, triglycerides, phospholipids, and steroids.

_____

_____

_____

14. **List** an important function of each of these types of lipids.

    a. triglycerides

    b. phospholipids

    c. waxes

    d. steroids

_____

_____

_____

15. **Identify** two reactions that fatty acids undergo.

_____

16. **Describe** the structure and function of cell membranes.

_____

_____

17. **Compare and contrast** the structures of a steroid, a phospholipid, and a wax.

_____

_____

_____

3 Lipids (continued)

18. **Write** the equation for the complete hydrogenation of the polyunsaturated fatty acid linoleic acid, $CH_3(CH_2)_4CH = CHCH_2CH = CH(CH_2)_7COOH$.

_____

_____

19. **Interpret Scientific Illustrations** Draw the general structure of a phospholipid. Label the polar and nonpolar portions of the structure.

22 The Chemistry of Life

4 Nucleic Acids

3 Lipids (continued)

BUILD TO THE ESSENTIAL QUESTION

Read the items under Build to the Essential Question at the beginning of the lesson. Restate each in your own words.

_____

_____

REVIEW
VOCABULARY

genetic information

Recall the definition of the Review Vocabulary term.

genetic information
_____

_____

NEW VOCABULARY

nucleic acid

nucleotide

Define each New Vocabulary term.

nucleic acid
_____

_____

nucleotide
_____

_____

4 Nucleic Acids (continued)

Draw a diagram of a nucleotide. Label all of the parts: sugar, phosphate group, and nitrogen-containing base.

Sequence the events of DNA replication. The first one has been done for you.

_____ Hydrogen bonds form between new nitrogen bases and the existing strand.

_____ Two nucleotide strands unzip.

_____ Nitrogen bases pair adenine with thymine, cytosine with guanine.

_____ An enzyme breaks the hydrogen bonds between the nitrogen bases.

_____ The nucleotide strands separate to expose the nitrogen bases.

_____ Free nucleotides are delivered by enzymes from the surrounding environment.

Predict the complimentary base pairing given the following strand of nucleotides.

A T C T A T C G G A T A T C T G

_____

GET IT? **Describe** what forms the teeth of the DNA zipper.

_____

4 Nucleic Acids (continued)

Identify differences in DNA and RNA.

	DNA	**RNA**
Sugar		
Nitrogen Bases		
Function		
Form of strand		

State whether you would find each of the following in DNA, RNA, both, or neither. Explain your answer.

A-A	
A-T	
C-G	
G-A	
A-U	
U-A	

REAL-WORLD CONNECTION

Suppose you are an assistant to a forensic scientist who has found an unknown sample of DNA at a crime scene. Upon analysis, he finds it contains 22% thymine molecules. A DNA sample that contains 40% guanine is obtained from a suspect who is brought in. You ask for the suspect's release. Explain your reasoning based on the bonding patterns of DNA nucleotides.

4 Nucleic Acids (continued)

REVIEW IT!

20. **Explain** the primary function of RNA and DNA.

_____

_____

21. **Identify** the specific structural components of both RNA and DNA.

_____

_____

22. **Relate** the function of DNA to its structure.

_____

_____

_____

23. **Relate** the function of RNA to its structure.

_____

_____

24. **Analyze** the structure of nucleic acids to determine what structural feature makes them acidic.

_____

_____

25. **Predict** what might happen if the DNA that coded for a protein contained the wrong base sequence.

_____

_____

22 The Chemistry of Life

5 Metabolism

BUILD TO THE ESSENTIAL QUESTION

Read the items under Build to the Essential Question at the beginning of the lesson. Restate each in your own words.

_____

_____

REVIEW VOCABULARY

redox process

Recall the definition of the Review Vocabulary term.

redox process _____

_____

NEW VOCABULARY

metabolism

catabolism

anabolism

ATP

photosynthesis

cellular respiration

fermentation

Define each New Vocabulary term.

metabolism _____

catabolism _____

_____

_____

anabolism _____

_____

ATP _____

_____

ACADEMIC VOCABULARY

conceptualize

photosynthesis _____

_____

cellular respiration _____

_____

fermentation _____

_____

Define the following term.

conceptualize _____

_____

5 Metabolism (continued)

Explain the relationship between metabolism, catabolism, and anabolism.

_____

_____

_____

Explain how ATP is able to store and release energy in the cells of organisms.

_____

_____

_____

GET IT? **Explain** how the terms *metabolism, catabolism,* and *anabolism* are related.

_____

_____

_____

_____

_____

GET IT? **Describe** what occurs when ATP becomes ADP.

_____

_____

Write the reaction of photosynthesis. Label the individual molecules.

Identify the redox process that occurs during photosynthesis.

_____

_____

Write the reaction of cellular respiration. Be sure to label the individual molecules.

Identify the redox process that occurs during cellular respiration.

_____

_____

_____

Summarize the relationship between photosynthesis and cellular respiration.

_____

_____

_____

_____

_____

_____

_____

Compare and contrast alcoholic fermentation and lactic acid fermentation.

_____

_____

_____

_____

_____

_____

_____

5 Metabolism (continued)

REVIEW IT!

26. Explain why metabolism is important to living cells.

_____

_____

27. Compare and contrast the processes of anabolism and catabolism.

_____

_____

_____

_____

28. Explain the role of ATP in the metabolism of living organisms.

_____

_____

29. Compare and contrast the processes of photosynthesis, cellular respiration, and fermentation.

_____

_____

_____

_____

_____

30. Determine whether each process is anabolic or catabolic.

   a. photosynthesis

   b. cellular respiration

   c. fermentation

_____

_____

5 Metabolism (continued)

31. Evaluate Why is it necessary to use sealed casks when making wine?

_____

_____

32. Calculate How many moles of ATP would a yeast cell produce if 6 mol of glucose were oxidized completely in the presence of oxygen? How many moles of ATP would the yeast cell produce from 6 mol of glucose if the cell were deprived of oxygen?

_____

_____

23 Nuclear Chemistry

ESSENTIAL QUESTION

Write the Essential Question for this chapter.

_____

_____

_____

Use the "What I Know" column to list the things you know about the Essential Question. Then list the questions you have about the Essential Question in the "What I Want to Find Out" column. As you read the chapter, fill in the "What I Learned" column.

K _What I Know_	W _What I Want to Find Out_	L _What I Learned_

Copyright © McGraw-Hill Education

23 Nuclear Chemistry

1 Nuclear Radiation

BUILD TO THE ESSENTIAL QUESTION

Read the items under Build to the Essential Question at the beginning of the lesson. Restate each in your own words.

_____

_____

_____

REVIEW VOCABULARY

nucleus

Recall the definition of the Review Vocabulary term.

nucleus _____

_____

_____

_____

NEW VOCABULARY

radioisotope

X-ray

penetrating power

Define each New Vocabulary term.

radioisotope _____

X-ray _____

penetrating power _____

Contrast chemical and nuclear reactions.

Chemical Reactions	Nuclear Reactions
bonds are and formed	nuclei emit
atoms are , though they may be rearranged	s are converted into atoms of another element
reaction rate by pressure, temperature, concentration, and catalyst	reaction rate by pressure, temperature, concentration, or catalyst
involve only valence	may involve protons,
energy changes	energy changes

1 Nuclear Radiation (continued)

Summarize the discovery of radioactivity. Review the dates on the timeline below. Use your text to fill in the important achievements in radioactive research on those dates.

1895 Roentgen _____

_____

1895 Becquerel _____

_____

1898 The Curies _____

_____

1903 The Curies and Becquerel _____

1911 Marie Curie _____

GET IT? **Explain** what Marie and Pierre Curie concluded about the darkening of the photographic plates.

_____

_____

Identify the common type of radiation signified by each symbol.

α _____

β _____

γ _____

Explain how Rutherford determined whether each of the three types of radiation had a positive or negative charge or was unchanged.

_____

_____

_____

1 Nuclear Radiation (continued)

Differentiate between each of the subatomic radiation particles mentioned in the chapter.

Radiation Type	Charge	Mass	Relative Penetrating Power
Alpha			
Beta			
Gamma			

Describe what happens when a radioactive nucleus emits an alpha particle.

_____

_____

Describe beta particles by completing the following statements.

A beta particle is a very fast-moving _____ To represent its

insignificant mass, beta particles have a superscript of _____.

A subscript of –1 denotes the _____ charge of beta particles.

Beta particles have greater _____ than alpha particles.

Describe what the subscript and superscript of zero tell you about gamma particles.

_____

_____

GET IT? **Compare and contrast** X-rays and gamma rays.

_____

_____

_____

1 Nuclear Radiation (continued)

REVIEW IT!

1. List the different types of radiation and their charges.

_____

_____

2. Compare the subatomic particles involved in nuclear and chemical reactions.

_____

_____

_____

3. Explain how you know whether the reaction is chemical or nuclear when an atom undergoes a reaction and attains a more-stable form.

_____

_____

_____

_____

4. Calculate Table 2 gives approximate energy values in units of MeV. Convert each value into joules using the following conversion factor: $1 MeV = 1.6 \times 10^{-13}$ J.

_____

_____

_____

5. Summarize Make a time line that summarizes the major events that led to the understanding of alpha, beta, and gamma radiation.

_____

_____

_____

23 Nuclear Chemistry

2 Radioactive Decay

BUILD TO THE ESSENTIAL QUESTION

Read the items under Build to the Essential Question at the beginning of the lesson. Restate each in your own words.

REVIEW
VOCABULARY

radioactivity

Recall the definition of the Review Vocabulary term.

radioactivity

NEW VOCABULARY

transmutation

nucleon

strong nuclear force

band of stability

positron emission

positron

electron capture

radioactive decay
series

half-life

radiochemical dating

Define each New Vocabulary term.

transmutation

nucleon

strong nuclear force

band of stability

positron emission

positron

electron capture

radioactive decay series

half-life

radiochemical dating

2 Radioactive Decay (continued)

Contrast the properties of isotopes by imagining two eggs as models. One isotope would be created using hard-boiled eggs as building blocks, the other using raw eggs as building blocks. Explain which model would be more stable, and which would be more typical of known isotopes.

_____

_____

_____

Summarize how the strong nuclear force helps to keep protons in a nucleus.

_____

_____

Describe the neutron-to-proton (n/p) ratio in nuclear stability.

The number of protons compared to the number of _____ in a

ratio identifies the nuclear ratio. To some degree, the _____ of

a nucleus can be correlated with its _____

ratio. As atomic number _____, more _____ are needed

to balance the _____ forces. Plotting the

number of neutrons versus the number of _____ for all

stable nuclei illustrates the _____.

GET IT? **Explain** why the neutron-to-proton ratio of stable nuclei increases as the atomic number increases.

_____

_____

_____

Copyright © McGraw-Hill Education

2 Radioactive Decay (continued)

GET IT? **Define** the band of stability and relate it to the value of the neutron-to-proton ratio.

_____

_____

_____

_____

Analyze the relative stability of radioisotopes. Use Figure 7 as a guide.

1. a radioisotope with too many neutrons relative to its protons

_____

2. a radioactive isotope _____

3. a nucleus with more than 83 protons _____

4. a nucleus with a high atomic number and a neutron-to-proton ratio of 1:5:1. _____

GET IT? **Explain** why radioisotopes above the band of stability are unstable.

_____

_____

GET IT? **Calculate** how the neutron-to-proton ratio changes when polonium-210 decays into lead-206.

_____

2 Radioactive Decay (continued)

GET IT? List the decay processes that result in an increased neutron-to-proton ratio and a decreased neutron-to-proton ratio.

_____

_____

Compare positron emission with electron capture.

Positron emission is _____ that involves the emission

of a _____ (particle with the same mass as an electron but

opposite charge) from a nucleus. During this process, a

_____ in the nucleus is converted into a neutron and a

positron, and then the _____ is emitted.

Electron capture is _____ that decreases the

number of _____ in unstable nuclei lying below the

_____. This occurs when the nucleus of an atom draws in

a surrounding _____, usually from the lowest energy

level. The captured electron combines with a _____ to

form a _____.

Contrast balanced chemical equations with balanced nuclear equations.

Balanced chemical equations conserve _____

_____.

Balanced nuclear equations conserve _____

_____.

2 Radioactive Decay (continued)

Solve Read Example Problem 1 in your text.

YOU TRY IT

Problem

Write a balanced nuclear equation for the alpha decay of uranium-238 $\left({}_{92}^{238}\text{U} \right)$

1. Analyze the Problem

Known: _____

decay type: _____

Unknown: _____

2. Solve for the Unknown

Using each particle's mass number, make sure the mass number is conserved on each side of the reaction arrow.

Mass number: $238 = X +$ _____ $X = 238 - 4$

Mass number of $X =$ _____

Using each particle's atomic number, make sure the atomic number is conserved on each side of the reaction arrow.

Atomic number: $92 =$ _____ $X = 92 -$ _____

Atomic number of $X =$ _____

Use the periodic table to identify the unknown element.

_____

Write the balanced nuclear equation.

_____

2 Radioactive Decay (continued)

Describe a radioactive decay series by completing the following paragraph.

A radioactive decay series is a series of _____ that begins with a(n) _____ nucleus and ends in the formation of a stable _____. Both alpha decay and _____ are involved in the process.

GET IT? List each step in the decay of uranium-238. Include the type of decay and the resulting product.

_____

_____

_____

_____

_____

Describe how Ernest Rutherford's early experiments in inducing nuclear reactions led to modern particle accelerators.

Rutherford discovered that particles must move at extremely _____ _____ to overcome electrostatic _____ and affect a target nucleus. Scientists have built on this to develop methods to accelerate particles to extreme speed using _____ and _____ fields. Particle accelerators use conventional and _____ magnets to force particles to move at high speeds.

GET IT? Define the term half-life.

_____

_____

GET IT? Infer how much strontium remains after 1.5 half-lives.

_____

2 Radioactive Decay (continued)

Solve Read Example Problem 2 in your text.

YOU TRY IT

Problem

Determine the amount of an original sample of 2.0 grams of thorium-234 after 49 days. The half-life of thorium-234 is 24.5 days.

1. Analyze the Problem

Known:

Initial amount = _____

Elapsed time (t) = _____

Half-life (T) = _____

Unknown:

Amount remaining = ? g

2. Solve for the Unknown

Number of half-lives (n) = Elapsed time/Half-life

$n = 49/24.5 = $ _____

Amount remaining = _____

Amount remaining = _____

Amount remaining = _____

Amount remaining = _____

3. Evaluate the Answer

After 49 days, _____ half-lives of thorium-234 have elapsed. The number of half-lives is equivalent to (1/2)(1/2) or _____. The answer, _____ is equal to _____ the original quantity.

Write the balanced nuclear equation for carbon dating.

_____

2 Radioactive Decay (continued)

REVIEW IT!

12. Describe what happens to unstable nuclei.

_____

_____

13. Explain how you can predict whether or not an isotope is likely to be stable if you know its number of neutrons and protons.

_____

_____

_____

14. Describe the forces acting on the particles within a nucleus and explain why neutrons are the glue holding the nucleus together.

_____

_____

_____

_____

15. Predict the nuclear equation for the alpha decay of radium-226 used on the tips of older lightning rods.

_____

_____

16. Calculate how much of a 10.0-g sample of americium-241 remains after four half-lives. Americium-241 is a radioisotope commonly used in smoke detectors and has a half-life of 430 _y_.

_____

_____

_____

_____

17. **Calculate** After 2.00 y, 1.986 g of a radioisotope remains from a sample that had an original mass of 2.000 g.

    a. Calculate the half-life.

    b. How much of the radioisotope remains after 10.00 y?

    _____

    _____

    _____

    _____

18. **Graph** A sample of polonium-214 originally has a mass of 1.0 g. Express the mass remaining as a percent of the original sample after a period of one, two, and three half-lives. Graph the percent remaining versus the number of half-lives. Approximately how much time has elapsed when 20% of the original sample remains?

23 Nuclear Chemistry

3 Nuclear Reactions

BUILD TO THE ESSENTIAL QUESTION

Read the items under Build to the Essential Question at the beginning of the lesson. Restate each in your own words.

_____

_____

REVIEW
VOCABULARY

mass number

Recall the definition of the Review Vocabulary term.

mass number _____

_____

NEW VOCABULARY

induced transmutation

transuranium element

mass defect

nuclear fission

critical mass

breeder reactor

nuclear fusion

thermonuclear reaction

Define each New Vocabulary term.

induced transmutation _____

_____

transuranium element _____

_____

mass defect _____

_____

nuclear fission _____

_____

critical mass _____

_____

breeder reactor _____

_____

nuclear fusion _____

thermonuclear reaction _____

ACADEMIC
VOCABULARY

generate

Define the following term.

generate _____

Sequence the steps in Rutherford's induced transformation of nitrogen-14 into oxygen.

1   2   3   4

1. _____

2. _____

3. _____

4. _____

Write Einstein's equation. Be sure to include the measurement units.

_____

Identify the three things you need to know to calculate mass defects.

a. _____

b. _____

c. _____

GET IT? Describe how the binding energy varies as a function of the mass number.

_____

_____

Organize the steps in a nuclear fission reaction involving uranium.

1. A neutron _____

2. The uranium _____

3. The nucleus _____

_____

GET IT? Explain why heavy atoms undergo nuclear fission.

_____

_____

_____

Explain why a fissionable material must have sufficient mass before a sustained reaction can take place.

_____

_____

Explain why a fissionable material must not have an excess of mass.

_____

_____

Compare subcritical mass and critical mass.

_____

_____

_____

3 Nuclear Reactions (continued)

Describe how a nuclear reactor produces electrical energy. Include how the environment is protected from nuclear waste.

Nuclear fission produces _____.

A common fuel is _____

_____. A neutron-emitting

source _____ and control rods absorb

virtually all of the _____ produced in the reaction.

Heat from a reaction is used to power _____,

which generate electricity.

GET IT? **Infer** how the storage of nuclear wastes affects the environment.

_____

_____

Describe nuclear fusion by completing the following paragraph.

Nuclear fusion is the combining of atomic _____. Nuclear

fusion reactions are capable of _____.

Because of the energy requirements, fusion reactions are also known

as _____.

Explain why fusion reactions are not yet a practical source of everyday energy.

_____

_____

_____

_____

3 Nuclear Reactions (continued)

REVIEW IT!

22. Compare and contrast nuclear fission and nuclear fusion reactions. Describe the particles that are involved in each type of reaction and the changes they undergo.

_____

_____

_____

23. Describe the process that occurs during a nuclear chain reaction and explain how to monitor a chain reaction in a nuclear reactor.

_____

_____

_____

_____

_____

24. Explain how nuclear fission can be used to generate electric power.

_____

_____

_____

25. Formulate an argument supporting or opposing nuclear power as your state's primary power source. Assume the primary source of power currently is the burning of fossil fuels.

_____

_____

_____

_____

_____

_____

3 Nuclear Reactions (continued)

26. Calculate What is the energy change (ΔE) associated with a change in mass (Δm) of 1.00 mg?

_____

_____

_____

27. Interpret Graphs Use the graph in **Figure 14** to answer the following questions.

a. Why is the isotope $^{56}_{26}$Fe highest on the curve?

b. Are more stable isotopes located higher or lower on the curve?

c. Compare the stability of Li-6 and He-4.

_____

_____

_____

23 Nuclear Chemistry

4 Applications and Effects of Nuclear Reactions

4 Applications and Effects of Nucle...

BUILD TO THE ESSENTIAL QUESTION

Read the items under Build to the Essential Question at the beginning of the lesson. Restate each in your own words.

_____

_____

_____

Copyright © McGraw-Hill Education

REVIEW VOCABULARY

isotope

Recall the definition of the Review Vocabulary term.

isotope

_____

_____

NEW VOCABULARY

ionizing radiation

radiotracer

Define each New Vocabulary term.

ionizing radiation

_____

_____

radiotracer

_____

_____

4 Applications and Effects of Nuclear Reactions (continued)

List and describe three methods of detecting radiation.

1. _____

_____

2. _____

_____

3. _____

_____

GET IT? **Summarize** how a scintillation detector works.

_____

_____

_____

_____

_____

_____

Describe how a radiotracer works.

A radiotracer is a _____ that emits _____

and is used to signal the presence of _____ or

specific substance. The fact that all of an element's isotopes have the

same _____ makes the use of radioisotopes

possible.

GET IT? **Define** *radiotracer.*

_____

Copyright © McGraw-Hill Education

4 Applications and Effects of Nuclear Reactions (continued)

Discuss a common radiotracer that is used in medicine.

Iodine-131 is commonly used to detect _____ associated with

the _____ A doctor will give the patient a drink containing a

small amount of iodine-131. The iodine-containing _____ is

then used to monitor the function of the thyroid gland.

Identify three factors that affect the possible damage to the body
caused by ionizing radiation discussed in the textbook.

1. _____

2. _____

3. _____

Discuss genetic and somatic damage caused by ionizing radiation.

Somatic damage affects _____

_____

Genetic damage can affect _____

_____

_____

_____

REVIEW IT!

28. Explain one way in which nuclear chemistry is used to diagnose or treat disease.

_____

_____

Copyright © McGraw-Hill Education

4 Applications and Effects of Nuclear Reactions (continued)

29. Describe several methods used to detect and measure radiation.

_____

_____

_____

_____

_____

30. Compare and contrast somatic and genetic biological damage.

_____

_____

_____

_____

31. Explain why it is safe to use radioisotopes to diagnose medical problems.

_____

_____

_____

32. Calculate A lab worker receives an average radiation dose of 21 mrem each month. Her allowed dose is 5,000 mrem/y. On average, what fraction of her yearly dose does she receive?

_____

_____

33. Interpret Data Look at the data in **Table 7**. Suppose someone is exposed to the maximum values listed for average annual radiation from the ground, from buildings, and from the air. What fraction would the person receive of the minimum short-term dose (25 rem) that causes a temporary decrease in white blood cell population?

_____

_____

_____

A Dictionary of

Food and Nutrition

THIRD EDITION

DAVID A. BENDER

OXFORD
UNIVERSITY PRESS

OXFORD

UNIVERSITY PRESS

Great Clarendon Street, Oxford OX2 6DP

Oxford University Press is a department of the University of Oxford.
It furthers the University's objective of excellence in research, scholarship,
and education by publishing worldwide in

Oxford New York

Auckland Cape Town Dar es Salaam Hong Kong Karachi
Kuala Lumpur Madrid Melbourne Mexico City Nairobi
New Delhi Shanghai Taipei Toronto

With offices in

Argentina Austria Brazil Chile Czech Republic France Greece
Guatemala Hungary Italy Japan Poland Portugal Singapore
South Korea Switzerland Thailand Turkey Ukraine Vietnam

Oxford is a registered trade mark of Oxford University Press
in the UK and in certain other countries

Published in the United States
by Oxford University Press Inc., New York

Text © A. E. Bender and D. A. Bender 1995

Text © D. A. Bender 2005

Text © D. A. Bender 2009

British Library Cataloguing in Publication Data

Data available

Library of Congress Cataloging in Publication Data

Data available

Typeset by SPI Publisher Services, Pondicherry, India
Printed in Great Britain
on acid-free paper by
Clays Ltd., St Ives plc

ISBN 978-0-19-923487-5

1 3 5 7 9 10 8 6 4 2

A Dictionary of
Food and Nutrition

SEE WEB LINKS

Many entries in this dictionary have recommended web
links. When you see the above symbol at the end of an entry
go to the dictionary's web page at http://www.oup.com/uk/
reference/resources/foodandnutrition, click on **Web links** in
the Resources section and locate the entry in the
alphabetical list, then click straight through to the relevant
websites.

David A. Bender teaches nutrition and biochemistry to
students of medicine, biochemistry, and human sciences at
University College London. His publications include
Introduction to Nutrition and Metabolism, *Nutritional
Biochemistry of the Vitamins*, and jointly with his late father
Nutrition: A Reference Handbook, *Food Tables and Labelling*,
and *Benders' Dictionary of Nutrition and Food Technology*.

Oxford Paperback Reference

The most authoritative and up-to-date reference books for both students and the general reader.

*forthcoming

Contents

Introduction

This book is intended for all who have an interest in food and nutrition, be it as consumers concerned about the health of their diets, and the safety of foods, as cooks, food manufacturers, and salespeople, concerned about what they produce and sell, or as journalists and broadcasters, and students of nutrition, dietetics, food science, health and human sciences, who must understand, interpret, and communicate information to others.

The consumer is faced with dietary advice ranging from government publications to magazines, newspapers, and radio and TV programmes, not to mention food labels that almost require a training in chemistry and physiology to be understood, scare stories in the press, and claims and counter-claims in advertising. Many of the terms used are technical, and few people can understand all of them. This dictionary is intended to help such understanding. It provides clear authoritative definitions of some 7500 terms associated with all aspects of food and nutrition, diet, and health that may be encountered on food labels, in advertising and in the media, as well as culinary terms that may be encountered in menus, cookery books, novels, and films.

To help make decisions about which foods are nutritionally valuable, there are notes on those that are good sources of major nutrients. These are based on the percentage of the reference intake shown on food labels that is provided by an average serving. A rich source of a nutrient provides at least 30%, good sources 20–30%, and sources 10–20% of this reference intake. Foods that are not listed as sources of nutrients, because they supply less than 10% of the reference intake in a serving, may nevertheless make a significant contribution to an overall diet.

Where a word is *starred in the text, this means that you can find further information under that entry.

abalone A *shellfish (mollusc), *Haliotus* spp., also known as ormer, paua, or sea ear. A 100-g portion is a rich *source of protein and niacin; a source of iron and vitamin B_1; supplies 130 kcal (550 kJ).

abboccato Italian; medium sweet wines.

ABC protein ATP-binding cassette proteins; a family of cell membrane transport proteins that bind and hydrolyse ATP, linked to active uptake into, or efflux from, the cell of various compounds. *See also* TRANSPORT, ACTIVE.

abdug Iranian; drink made from *yoghurt with *soda water, and sometimes also vodka.

abetalipoproteinaemia Rare genetic disease involving failure of synthesis or assembly of plasma lipoproteins that contain apo-protein B (*chylomicrons, VLDL and LDL); characterized by severe *vitamin E deficiency, leading to serious neurological damage.

abiu The fruit of *Pouteria caimito*, with caramel flavoured, white translucent flesh. *See also* SAPOTE.

abocada Spanish; medium sweet wines.

absinthe A herb *liqueur flavoured with wormwood (*Artemisia absinthium*). Originally imported from Switzerland (where it was a patent medicine) to France in 1797 by Henri Louis Pernod; sale outlawed in USA in 1912, and in France and other countries in 1915, because of the toxicity of α-thujone. Now available in the EU with an upper limit of 10 ppm thujone.

absolute alcohol Pure ethyl *alcohol.

AC Appellation contrôlée. *See* WINE CLASSIFICATION, FRANCE.

acarbose A group of complex *carbohydrates (oligosaccharides) which inhibit the *enzymes of *starch and *disaccharide digestion; used experimentally to reduce the digestion of starch. It has been marketed for use in weight-reducing diets as a 'starch blocker', with little evidence of efficacy.

acaricides Pesticides used to kill mites and ticks (family Acaridae) which cause animal diseases and the spoilage of flour and other foods in storage.

ACAT Acyl CoA cholesterol acyl transferase, the *enzyme that catalyses esterification of *cholesterol by transfer of fatty acids from fatty acyl CoA. *See also* LCAT.

accelase A mixture of *enzymes that hydrolyse *proteins, used to shorten the maturation time of cheeses and intensify the flavour of processed cheese.

accelerated freeze drying *See* DRYING, FREEZE.

Acceptable Daily Intake (ADI) The amount of a food *additive that could be taken daily for an entire life-span without appreciable risk. Determined by measuring the highest dose of the substance that has no effect on experimental animals, then dividing by a safety factor of 100. Substances that are not given an ADI are regarded as having no adverse effect at any level of intake. *See also* NO EFFECT LEVEL.

accoub Mediterranean edible thistle *Goundelia tournefortii*. The cooked flower buds have a flavour resembling that of *asparagus or globe *artichoke; the shoots can be eaten in the same way as asparagus and the roots as *salsify.

accra Caribbean; heavy batter fritters with salt cod; also known as stamp-and-go, bacalaítos.

accuncciata Corsican; goat, lamb, or mutton stew with potatoes.

ACE Angiotensin converting enzyme, in the blood vessels of the lungs, which activates *angiotensin. Many of the drugs for treatment of *hypertension are ACE inhibitors.

acerola *See* CHERRY, WEST INDIAN.

acesulphames (acesulfames) A group of non-nutritive or intense *sweeteners. The potassium salt acesulphame-K is some 200 times as sweet as *sucrose. It is not metabolized, and is excreted unchanged.

acetanisole A synthetic flavouring agent (*p*-methoxyacetophenone) with a hawthorn-like odour.

acetic acid One of the simplest organic *acids, systematically ethanoic acid, CH_3COOH. The acid of *vinegar, it is formed, together with *lactic acid, in the fermentation of foods. *See* PICKLING.

acetoacetate One of the *ketone bodies formed in *fasting.

Acetobacter A genus of bacteria that oxidize ethyl *alcohol to *acetic acid, used in the manufacture of *vinegar. They also grow as a film on the surface of beer wort, pickle brine, and fruit juices, when they are commonly known as 'mother of vinegar'.

aceto dolce Italian; pickles eaten as an appetizer.

acetoin A precursor of the compound *diacetyl, one of the constituents of the flavour of *butter, produced by bacteria during ripening.

acetomel Sweet-sour syrup of vinegar and honey used to preserve fruit; also known as agrodolce.

acetomenaphthone Synthetic compound with *vitamin K activity; vitamin K_3, or menaquinone-0.

acetone One of the *ketone bodies formed in *fasting, dimethyl ketone (propan-2-one). It is formed by non-enzymic decarboxylation of acetoacetate and is poorly metabolized; detection of acetone in blood, urine, or breath may be clinically useful in cases of *diabetes, as a means of detecting ketosis. Also used as a solvent, e.g. in varnishes and lacquer.

acetylated monoglyceride An emulsifier manufactured by *interesterification of fats with glyceryl triacetate (triacetin) or by acetylation of monoacylglycerols with acetic anhydride. Characterized by sharp melting point and stability to oxidative rancidity.

acetylcholine The acetyl derivative of *choline, produced at cholinergic nerve endings both in the brain, where it acts as a chemical transmitter, and at the junctions between nerves and muscles, where it stimulates muscle contraction.

acetylene Hydrocarbon gas that acts as a plant growth regulator and can be used to control ripening of fruits; systematic name ethyne. *See also* CLIMACTERIC.

acha Alternative name for hungry rice. *See* RICE, HUNGERY.

achalasia Difficulty in swallowing due to disturbance of the normal muscle activity of the *oesophagus. Also known as cardiospasm.

achene Botanical term for small, dry, one-seeded fruit that does not open to liberate the seed, e.g. a nut.

ACH index Arm, chest, hip index. A method of assessing nutritional status by measuring the arm circumference, chest diameter, and hip width. *See also* ANTHROPOMETRY.

achira The edible canna, *Canna edulis*, related to the ornamental *C. indica*. The starchy rhizome is eaten as a vegetable in South America; it is grown in Vietnam to make transparent noodles, and in Australia as a commercial starch crop (Queensland arrowroot).

achlorhydria Failure to secrete hydrochloric acid in gastric juice. *See also* ANAEMIA; GASTRIC ACIDITY.

acholia (acholic) Absence or deficiency of *bile secretion.

achromotricia Loss of hair colour. One of the signs of *pantothenic acid deficiency in animals, but there is no evidence that pantothenic acid affects hair colour in human beings.

acid Compounds that dissociate (ionize) in water to give rise to hydrogen ions (H^+); they taste sour. *See also* ALKALI; AMINO ACIDS; BUFFERS; ESTERS; FATTY ACIDS; ORGANIC ACIDS; pH; SALT.

acid, gastric The acid in the *gastric secretion is hydrochloric acid; *see also* ACHLORHYDRIA; GASTRIC ACIDITY.

acid drops Boiled sweets with sharp flavour from tartaric acid (originally called acidulated drops); known as sourballs in the USA.

acid foods (basic foods) These terms refer to the residue of the *metabolism of foods. The *mineral salts of *sodium, *potassium, *magnesium, and *calcium are base-forming, while *phosphorus, *sulphur, and *chlorine are acid-forming. Which of these predominates in foods determines whether the residue is acidic or basic (alkaline); meat, cheese, eggs, and cereals leave an acidic residue, while milk, vegetables, and some fruits leave a basic residue. Fats and sugars have no mineral content and so leave a neutral residue. Although fruits have an acid taste due to organic acids and their salts, the acids are completely oxidized and the sodium and potassium salts form an alkaline residue.

acidity *See* pH.

acidity regulators *See* BUFFERS.

acid number (acid value (of a fat)) A measure of *rancidity due to *hydrolysis, releasing free *fatty acids; it serves as an index of the efficiency of refining since the fatty acids are removed during refining and increase with deterioration during storage.

acidophilin *See* ACIDOPHILUS THERAPY; MILK, ACIDOPHILUS.

acidophilus therapy A treatment for *constipation based on the consumption of milk containing a high concentration of viable *Lactobacillus acidophilus*, although the milk itself is unfermented. The effect is believed to be due to the implantation of the organisms in the intestine. *See also* MILK, ACIDOPHILUS; PROBIOTICS.

acidosis An increase in the acidity of *blood plasma to below the normal range of *pH 7.35–7.45. Respiratory acidosis is due to impaired exhalation of carbon dioxide; metabolic acidosis is due to overproduction of acids. *See also* ALKALOSIS; KETOACIDOSIS; LACTIC ACIDOSIS.

acids, fruit *Organic acids such as citric, malic, tartaric, etc., which give the sharp or sour flavour to fruits; often added to processed foods for taste.

acidulants Organic acids used as flavouring agents, preservatives, chelating agents, buffers, gelling, and coagulating agents. Citric, fumaric, malic, and tartaric acids are general purpose acidulants, other acids have more specialist uses.

ackee (akee) The fruit of the Caribbean tree *Blighia sapida*. The fruit is toxic when unripe because it contains the toxin hypoglycin.

acne Inflammatory pustular skin eruption occurring around sebaceous glands, especially around the time of puberty. Not known to be caused or exacerbated by diet, although a low-fat diet is sometimes recommended. Severe persistent acne may be treated by topical application of synthetic *retinoids.

acorn Fruit of the oak tree (*Quercus* spp.), used both for animal feed and (especially in Spain) to make a flour for baking. Roasted acorns have been used as a coffee substitute. Used in Korea to produce an edible starch gel known as mook. *See also* SUGAR, ACORN.

ACP 1. Acid calcium phosphate; *see* PHOSPHATES. **2.** Acyl carrier protein, part of the fatty acid synthetase multi-enzyme complex.

acrodermatitis enteropathica Skin lesions associated with *zinc deficiency, due either to failure to absorb zinc (probably as a result of genetic defect of an intestinal transport protein) or to inadequate intake.

acrodynia Dermatitis seen in *vitamin B_6 deficient animals. There is no evidence for a similar dermatitis in deficient human beings.

acrolein (acraldehyde) An aldehyde formed when *glycerol is heated to a high temperature. It is responsible for the acrid odour and lachrymatory (tear-causing) vapour produced when fats are overheated.

ACTH *See* ADRENOCORTICOTROPHIC HORMONE.

actin *See* MUSCLE.

actinidain (actinidin) Proteolytic *enzyme in *kiwi fruit with specificity similar to that of *papain.

activators Compounds that increase the activity of *enzymes.

actometer An instrument for measuring movement in three dimensions, so as to provide an indication of physical activity and hence energy expenditure.

acute phase proteins A variety of serum proteins synthesized in increased (or sometimes decreased) amounts in response to trauma and infection, so confounding their use as indices of nutritional status.

acyl CoA Fatty acid esterified to *coenzyme A by a thioester linkage.

acylglycerol One or more fatty acids esterified to glycerol; hence monoacylglycerol (also known as monoglyceride), diacylglycerol (diglyceride), and triacylglycerol (triglyceride). Triacylglycerols are the major constituent of fats and oils; mono- and diacylglycerols are used as *emulsifying agents.

ADA American Dietetic Association, founded Cleveland, Ohio, 1917.

(⊕) SEE WEB LINKS

● ADA's homepage.

adai Indian; pancakes made from ground rice and legumes; the dough is left to undergo lactic acid bacterial fermentation before frying.

adaptogens Name coined for the active ingredients of *ginseng and other herbs that are reputed to be anti-stress compounds.

additive Any compound not commonly regarded or used as a food, which is added to foods as an aid in manufacturing or processing, or to improve the keeping properties, flavour, colour, texture, appearance, or stability of the food, or as a convenience to the consumer. The term excludes *vitamins, *minerals, and other nutrients added to enrich or restore nutritional value. Herbs, spices, hops, salt, yeast, or protein hydrolysates, air, and water are usually excluded from this definition. Additives may be extracted from natural sources, may be synthesized in the laboratory to be chemically the same as the natural materials (and hence known as nature-identical), or may be synthetic compounds that do not occur in nature.

In most countries only additives from a permitted list of compounds that have been extensively tested for safety may legally be added to foods. The additives used must be declared on food labels, using either their chemical names or their numbers in the EU list of permitted additives (*E-numbers). *See* APPENDIX VIII.

See also ACCEPTABLE DAILY INTAKE.

adenine A *nucleotide, one of the purine bases of the *nucleic acids (DNA and RNA). The compound formed between adenine and *ribose is the nucleoside adenosine, and can form four phosphorylated derivatives important in metabolism: adenosine monophosphate (AMP, also known as adenylic acid); adenosine diphosphate (ADP); adenosine triphosphate (ATP); and cyclic adenosine monophosphate (cAMP). *See also* ATP; ENERGY METABOLISM.

adenosine *See* ADENINE.

adequate intake Where there is inadequate scientific evidence to establish requirements and *reference intakes for a nutrient for which deficiency is rarely, if ever, seen, the observed levels of intake are assumed to be greater than requirements, and thus provide an estimate of intakes that are (more than) adequate to meet needs.

ADHD Attention deficit hyperactivity disorder, a behavioural problem of children, sometimes associated with food intolerance. *See* FOOD, ADVERSE REACTIONS.

ADI *See* ACCEPTABLE DAILY INTAKE.

adipectomy Surgical removal of subcutaneous fat.

adipocyte A fat-containing cell in *adipose tissue.

adipocytokines (adipokines) *Cytokines secreted by *adipose tissue.

adiponectin A small protein, secreted by *adipocytes, that enhances insulin action, stimulates glucose and fatty acid metabolism, and increases energy expenditure by induction of *uncoupling proteins. Its secretion is inversely proportional to adipose tissue mass, so circulating levels are low in *obesity.

adiponutrin Intracellular *lipase in *adipose tissue; unlike *desnutrin, its activity increases on refeeding after a period of fasting, suggesting that its main role is in esterification to form triacylglycerol rather than lipolysis.

adipophilin One of the proteins that coats lipid droplets in *adipose tissue; in macrophages it increases storage of *triacylglycerol by stimulation of biosynthesis and inhibition of β-oxidation.) *See also* PERILIPIN.

adipose tissue Body fat—the cells that synthesize and store *fat, releasing it for *metabolism in *fasting. Also known as white adipose tissue, to distinguish it from the metabolically more active brown adipose tissue (*see* ADIPOSE TISSUE, BROWN). Much of the body fat reserve is subcutaneous; in addition there is essential (as opposed to storage) adipose tissue around the organs, which serves to protect them from physical damage. In lean people, 15–25% of body weight is adipose tissue, increasing with age; the proportion is greater in people who are *overweight or *obese. Adipose tissue contains 82–88% fat, 2–2.6% protein, and 10–14% water. The energy yield of adipose tissue is 34–38 MJ (8000–9000 kcal) per kg or 15–17 MJ (3600–4000 kcal) per pound.

adipose tissue, brown Metabolically highly active adipose tissue, which is involved in heat production to maintain body temperature, as opposed to white *adipose tissue, which is storage fat and has a low rate of metabolic activity. *See also* THERMOGENESIS.

adiposis Presence of an abnormally large accumulation of fat in the body—also known as liposis. *See also* OBESITY.

adiposity The proportion of fat in the body, and hence more useful as an indicator of *obesity than weight or *body mass index.

adipostat Control of body *adiposity, and hence body weight, by signals from *adipose tissue to control appetite and energy expenditure (especially *leptin).

adipsia Absence of thirst.

adipsin A *protease secreted by adipose tissue, and also expressed in macrophages, that is involved in the activation of complement; secretion is reduced in *obesity.

adjunct culture Bacterial culture used in cheese and yoghurt making, together with the *starter culture, to produce a specific benefit, e.g. texture, flavour, or nutrient content.

adlay The seeds of a wild grass (Job's tears, *Coix lachryma-jobi*), botanically related to *maize, growing wild in parts of Africa and Asia and eaten especially in the south-east Pacific region.

ad libitum Feeding as much food as the subject or experimental animal will eat, as opposed to restricting intake, e.g. by *pair feeding.

adoucir French; to reduce the bitterness of food by prolonged cooking, or to dilute a dish with milk, stock, or water to make it less salty.

ADP Adenosine diphosphate. *See* ADENINE; ATP.

adrenaline Also known as epinephrine. A *hormone secreted by the medulla of the adrenal gland, especially in times of stress or in response to fright or shock, and in response to *hypoglycaemia. Its main actions are to increase blood pressure and to mobilize tissue reserves of *glycogen (leading to an increase in the blood glucose concentration) and fat, in preparation for flight or fighting. Derived from the *amino acid *tyrosine.

adsorbent Compounds used to adsorb, and hence remove, unwanted materials in foods and beverages that affect food safety or quality. *See also* ADSORPTION.

adsorption (adsorb) The binding of compounds to the surface of a solid.

adulteration The addition of substances to foods etc. in order to increase the bulk and reduce the cost, with intent to defraud the purchaser. Common adulterants are starch in spices, water in milk and beer, etc. The British Food and Drugs Act (1860) was the first legislation to prevent such practices.

advocaat Dutch; liqueur made from brandy and eggs.

aerobic 1. Aerobic micro-organisms (aerobes) are those that require oxygen for growth; obligate aerobes cannot survive in the absence of oxygen. The opposite are anaerobic organisms, which do not require oxygen for growth; obligate anaerobes cannot survive in the presence of oxygen. **2.** Aerobic exercise is physical activity which requires an increase in heart rate and respiration to meet the increased demand of muscle for oxygen, as contrasted with maximum exertion or sprinting, when muscle can metabolize anaerobically, producing *lactic acid, which is metabolized later, creating a need for increased respiration after the exercise has ceased (so-called oxygen debt).

Aeromonas hydrophila A food-borne pathogen associated with seafood, snails, and drinking water, causing diarrhoea, vomiting, mild fever, and abdominal cramps.

aerosporin *See* POLYMYXINS.

aeruginosin *Mycotoxin produced by *Microcystis aeruginosa*.

AFD Accelerated freeze drying; *see* DRYING, FREEZE.

aflata West African; part of a fermented dough that is boiled, then mixed with the remaining dough to make *akpiti or *kenkey.

aflatoxins A group of *mycotoxins produced by *Aspergillus* spp. (*A. flavus*, *A. parasiticus*, *A. nomius*, *A. ochraceoroseus*), which can grow on *peanuts and cereal grains when they are stored under damp and warm conditions. In addition to being acutely toxic, many, especially aflatoxin B_1, are potent *carcinogens. Fungal spoilage of foods with *A. flavus* is a common problem in many tropical areas, and aflatoxin is believed to be the cause of much primary liver cancer in parts of Africa. Aflatoxins can be secreted in milk, so there is strict control of the level in cattle feed.

aftertaste A flavour, often unpleasant, that lingers in the mouth after a food has been swallowed.

agalactia Failure of the mother to secrete enough milk to feed a suckling infant.

agar Dried extracts from various seaweeds, including *Gelidium* and *Gracilaria* spp.; a partially soluble *non-starch polysaccharide composed of *galactose units. It swells with water to form a *gel, and is used in soups, jellies, ice cream, and meat products. It is also used as the basis of bacteriological culture media, as an adhesive, for sizing silk, and as a stabilizer for emulsions. Also called agar-agar, Macassar gum, vegetable gelatine. Danish agar is *furcellaran.

agave nectar A bulk *sweetener from the blue agave (*Agave tequilana*). Mainly *fructose, 30% sweeter than *sucrose.

ageing **1.** As wines age, they develop bouquet and a smooth mellow flavour, associated with slow oxidation and the formation of *esters, as well as losing the harsh yeasty flavour of young wine. **2.** The ageing of meat by hanging in a cool place for several days results in softening of the muscle tissue, which stiffens after death (*rigor mortis). This stiffening is due to anaerobic metabolism leading to the formation of lactic acid when the blood flow ceases. **3.** Ageing of wheat flour for bread making is due to oxidation, either by storage for some weeks after milling or by chemical action. Freshly milled flour produces a weaker and less resilient dough, and hence a less 'bold' loaf, than flour which has been aged.

ageusia Loss or impairment of the sense of *taste.

agglomeration The process of producing a free-flowing, dust-free powder from substances such as dried milk powder and wheat flour, by moistening the powder with droplets of water and then redrying in a stream of air. The resulting agglomerates can readily be wetted.

agglutination The clumping together of cells, such as bacteria or red blood cells, due to cross-linking by proteins such as antibodies or *lectins found in *legumes. The basis of immunological techniques for detecting and identifying bacteria.

agglutinins *See* LECTINS.

agidi West African; thick gruel prepared by soaking maize, then grinding and leaving to undergo lactic acid bacterial fermentation before the paste (koko) is cooked.

aglycone The non-sugar moiety of a *glycoside.

agnelotti Italian; envelopes of *pasta, stuffed with minced meat, cheese, or vegetables, cut into a half-moon shape, unlike *ravioli, which are cut into squares.

agneshka chorba Bulgarian; whole spring lamb stuffed with rice, offal, and raisins, then roasted. A traditional Easter dish.

AGORA Access to Global Online Research in Agriculture.

((⊕)) SEE WEB LINKS

• AGORA's homepage.

agouti mouse A genetically obese mouse; the agouti gene is normally expressed only in hair follicles, and only during hair growth, when it antagonizes melanocortin receptors. In the obese yellow mutant the gene is expressed in all tissues, and at all times; it antagonizes the melanocortin receptors in the hypothalamus that normally inhibit feeding. Expression of the agouti gene is variable, depending on maternal nutrition; this is an *epigenetic event, linked to failure of methylation of *CpG islands in *DNA.

Agrobacterium tumefaciens A bacterium that transforms plant cells into tumorous crown galls by introducing bacterial *DNA into the host cell. Widely exploited as a means of creating transgenic plants. *See also* GENETIC MODIFICATION.

agrodolce Italian; sweet and sour. *See* ACETOMEL.

agroecology The application of ecological principles to the design, development, and management of sustainable agricultural systems, with low external input and considerable reliance on available farm labour.

aguardiente Spanish; *see* MARC.

aguja Spanish; slightly sparkling wines.

AI *See* ADEQUATE INTAKE.

AIDS wasting syndrome *Cachexia associated with acquired immune deficiency syndrome (AIDS) due to human immunodeficiency virus (HIV) infection.

aiele *See* OLIVE, AFRICAN.

aigre-doux French; sweet and sour. *See* ACETOMEL.

aiguillette A thin strip or slice of cooked poultry, meat, or fish.

aiguiser French; to sharpen a *sauce by adding lemon juice or citric acid.

aileron French; wing tip of poultry.

aillade French; sauce prepared with garlic.

aïoli Garlic-flavoured mayonnaise used in Provençal cooking. *See also* SALAD DRESSING.

aitchbone Cut of *beef from the upper part of the leg. Sometimes incorrectly called the edgebone.

ajada Spanish; sauce made from bread steeped in water and garlic.

aji South American chilli *peppers, the fruit of *Capsicum* spp.

Ajinomoto *See* MONOSODIUM GLUTAMATE.

ajowan Thyme-flavoured seed of *Carum ajowan* (syn. *Trachylospermum amni*), used in Indian and Middle Eastern cuisine.

ajwain Alternative name for *lovage.

akamu Nigerian; cereal products produced by boiling the starchy extract from fermented *maize, *millet, or *sorghum, used especially for infant feeding.

akara West African snack food or side dish; deep-fried paste made from cowpeas (*see* BEAN, BLACK-EYED), seasoned with peppers, onions, and salt. Steamed cowpea paste is moinmoin.

akee *See* ACKEE.

akkra Caribbean (originally West African); fritter made from *black-eyed beans or *soya beans. Also known as calas or samsa.

akni Indian; *bouillon, made from water and herbs, used for cooking rice and vegetables.

akpiti West African; fried doughnuts made from maize (sometimes plantain) flour; the dough is left to undergo a lactic acid bacterial fermentation. Part of the fermented dough is boiled (aflata), mixed with the remainder, and fried. Awule bolo is similar, but made with rice flour, banku from sorghum, millet, or barley.

akutok Inuit; strips of dried caribou meat; the outer part has a crust, but the inside is only partially dry.

akvavit *See* AQUAVIT.

ala *See* BULGUR.

alactasia Partial or complete deficiency of the *enzyme *lactase in the small intestine, resulting in an inability to digest the sugar *lactose in milk, and hence intolerance of milk. *See also* DISACCHARIDE INTOLERANCE.

alanine A non-essential *amino acid, found in all proteins. β-Alanine is an *isomer in which the amino group is attached to carbon-3 rather than carbon-2; it is important as part of *pantothenic acid, *carnosine, and *anserine.

alant starch *See* INULIN.

Alaska, baked *See* BAKED ALASKA.

albacore *See* TUNA FISH.

albedo The white pith (mesocarp) of the inner peel of citrus fruits, accounting for between 20 and 60% of the whole fruit. It consists of sugars, *cellulose, and *pectins, and is used commercially as a source of pectin.

albert French name for English hot *horseradish sauce.

albigeoise, à l' French; garnish for meat consisting of stuffed tomatoes and potato croquettes.

albion French; **1.** Fish soup made with lobster *quenelles and truffles. **2.** Chicken broth with truffles, asparagus, chicken liver quenelles, and cocks' combs.

albondigas Spanish (Castilian); meat balls or dumplings.

albumin (albumen) A group of relatively small *proteins that are soluble in water and readily coagulated by heat. Ovalbumin is the main protein of egg-white, lactalbumin occurs in milk, and plasma or serum albumin is one of the major blood proteins. Serum albumin concentration is sometimes measured as an index of *protein-energy malnutrition.

Often used as a non-specific term for proteins (e.g. albuminuria is the excretion of proteins in the urine).

albumin index A measure of the quality or freshness of an egg—the height : width ratio of the albumin when the egg is broken on to a flat surface. As the egg deteriorates, so the albumin spreads further, i.e. the albumin index decreases. Also known as Haugh score. *See also* EGG PROTEINS; EGG-WHITE.

albumin milk *See* PROTEIN MILK.

albuminuria *See* ALBUMIN.

albumin water Beverage made from lightly whisked egg-white and cold water, seasoned with lemon juice and salt.

alcohol Chemically alcohols are compounds with the general formula $C_nH_{(2n+1)}OH$. The alcohol in *alcoholic beverages is ethyl alcohol (ethanol, C_2H_5OH); pure ethyl alcohol is also known as absolute alcohol. The *energy yield of alcohol is 7 kcal (29 kJ)/gram.

The strength of alcoholic beverages is most often shown as the percentage of alcohol by volume (sometimes shown as % v/v or % ABV). This is not the same as the percentage of alcohol by weight (% w/v) since the density of alcohol is 0.793 that of water: 5% v/v alcohol = 3.96% by weight (w/v); 10% v/v = 7.93% w/v; and 40% v/v = 31.7% w/v. *See also* PROOF SPIRIT.

alcohol, denatured Drinkable alcohol is subject to tax in most countries, and for industrial use it is denatured to render it unfit for consumption by the addition of 5% methyl alcohol (methanol, CH_3OH, also known as wood alcohol), which is poisonous. This is industrial rectified spirit. For domestic use a purple dye and pyridine (which has an unpleasant odour) are also added; this is methylated spirit.

alcoholic beverages Drinks made by fermenting fruit juices, sugars, and fermentable carbohydrates with *yeast to form *alcohol. These include *beer, *cider, and *perry, 4–6% alcohol by volume; *wines, 9–13% alcohol; *spirits (e.g. *brandy, *gin, *rum, *vodka, *whisky) made by distilling fermented liquor, 38–45% alcohol; *liqueurs made from distilled spirits, sweetened and flavoured, 20–40% alcohol; and fortified wines (apéritif wines, *Madeira, *port, *sherry) made by adding spirit to wine, 18–25% alcohol. *See also* ALCOHOL; PROOF SPIRIT.

alcoholism Physiological addiction to *alcohol, associated with persistent heavy consumption of *alcoholic beverages. In addition to the addiction, there may be damage to the liver (cirrhosis), stomach (gastritis), and pancreas (pancreatitis), as well as behavioural changes and peripheral nerve damage. *See also* WERNICKE–KORSAKOFF SYNDROME; VITAMIN B_1.

alcohol units For convenience in calculating intakes of alcohol, a unit of alcohol is defined as 8g (10mL) of absolute alcohol; this is the amount in ½ pint (300mL) of beer, a single measure of spirit (25mL), or a single glass of wine (100mL).

In England and Wales, the Royal College of Physicians set upper limits of prudent consumption of alcohol as 21 units (= 168g alcohol) per week for men and 14 units (= 112g alcohol) per week for women; the UK Department of Health set a daily limit of 4 units for men and 3 for women.

alcool blanc French; white spirit (silent spirit) or eau-de-vie. Distilled *spirits from fermented fruit juice.

al dente Italian (literally 'to the tooth'); firm to the bite, applied to pasta and cooked vegetables.

alderman's walk The name given in London to the longest and finest cut from the haunch of venison or lamb.

alditols *Sugar alcohols produced by reduction of an *aldose sugar, e.g. *sorbitol, *mannitol, *xylitol.

aldose Sugars containing an aldehyde group, which are therefore chemically reducing sugars (e.g. glucose, mannose), as opposed to *ketose sugars.

aldosterone A *steroid hormone secreted by the adrenal cortex that acts on the distal kidney tubule to stimulate reabsorption of sodium, and hence also water.

ale *See* BEER.

aleatico A *grape variety widely used for *wine making, not one of the classic varieties; makes fragrant sweet red wines.

alecost An aromatic herbaceous plant, *Tanacetum* (*Chrysanthemum*) *balsamita*, related to *tansy, used in salads and formerly used to flavour ale.

aleurone layer The single layer of large cells under the bran coat and outside the endosperm of *cereal grains. About 3% of the weight of the grain, and rich in protein, as well as containing about 20% of the *vitamin B_1, 30% of the *vitamin B_2, and 50% of the *niacin of the grain. Botanically the aleurone layer is part of the endosperm, but in milling it remains attached to the inner layer of the *bran. *See also* FLOUR, EXTRACTION RATE.

alewives River herrings, *Pomolobus* (*Alosa*) *pseudoharengus*, commonly used for canning after salting.

alexander A cocktail; usually gin, crème de cacao, and cream, although other spirits may be used.

alexanders A herb, black lovage (*Smyrnium olisatrum*), with a celery-like flavour.

alfalfa *See* LUCERNE.

algae Simple plants that do not show differentiation into roots, stems, and leaves. They are mostly aquatic—either *seaweeds or pond and river-weeds. Some seaweeds, such as *dulse and *Irish moss, have long been eaten, and a number of unicellular algae, including *Chlorella*, *Scenedesmus*, and *Spirulina* spp., have been grown experimentally as novel sources of food (50–60% of the dry weight is protein).

algérienne **1.** Garnish for steak consisting of tomatoes and peppers simmered in oil. **2.** Fried eggs served with a purée of tomatoes, peppers, and aubergines. **3.** Salad of courgettes, tomatoes, and cooked sweet potatoes. **4.** Sautéed chicken and aubergines with tomato, garlic, and onion sauce. **5.** Cream soup made from sweet potatoes and filbert nuts.

algin Gum derived from alginic acid. *See* ALGINATES.

alginates Salts of alginic acid found in many seaweeds as calcium salts or the free acid. Chemically, alginic acid is a *non-starch polysaccharide composed of mannuronic acid units.
    Iron, magnesium, and ammonium salts of alginic acid form viscous solutions and hold large amounts of water. They are used as thickeners, stabilizers, and gelling, binding, and emulsifying agents in food manufacture, especially in *ice cream and synthetic cream. Trade name Manucol.

alginic acid *See* ALGINATES.

aligoté A *grape variety widely used for *wine making, not one of the classic varieties. Burgundy's second-ranking white grape.

alimentary canal *See* GASTRO-INTESTINAL TRACT.

alimentary pastes *See* PASTA.

alioli (allioli) Spanish (Catalan); oil and garlic sauce prepared by pounding garlic in olive oil.

alitame Synthetic intense *sweetener, chemically an amide of aspartyl D-alanine. *See also* ASPARTAME.

alkali (base) A compound that takes up hydrogen ions and so raises the *pH of a solution; *see also* ACID; BUFFERS; SALT.

alkali formers *See* ACID FOODS.

alkaline phosphatase An *enzyme with an alkaline optimum *pH that hydrolyses phosphate esters. It is measured in milk as an index of the efficacy of *pasteurization, since it has a similar D value (*see* DECIMAL REDUCTION TIME) to heat-resistant pathogens. It is measured in blood as a marker of bone and liver disease; its activity is elevated in *rickets.

alkaline tide The small increase in blood *pH after a meal as a result of the secretion of gastric acid.

alkali reserve *See* BUFFERS.

alkaloids Naturally occurring organic bases normally containing nitrogen in a heterocyclic ring; most are derivatives of amino acids, with marked pharmacological actions. Many are found in plant foods, including potatoes and tomatoes (the *Solanum* alkaloids), or as the products of fungal action (e.g. *ergot), although they also occur in animal foods (e.g. tetrodotoxin in *puffer fish, tetramine in *shellfish). *See also* PROTOALKALOIDS; PSEUDOALKALOIDS.

alkalosis An increase in the alkalinity of *blood plasma to above the normal range of *pH 7.35–7.45. Respiratory alkalosis is due to excessive exhalation of carbon dioxide; metabolic alkalosis is due to overproduction of bases. *See also* ACIDOSIS.

alkannet (alkanet, alkannin, alkanna) A colouring obtained from the root of *Anchusa* (*Alkanna*) *tinctoria*. It is blue in alkali (or in the presence of lead), crimson with tin, and violet with iron. Used for colouring fats, cheese, and essences. Also known as orcanella.

allantoin The oxidation product of *uric acid which is the end-product of *purine metabolism in most animals apart from human beings and apes, which excrete uric acid.

allele One of two or more alternative forms of a *gene at a given position (locus) on a *chromosome.

allemande, à l' German style; dishes finished or garnished with German specialities such as sauerkraut, smoked sausage, or pickled pork.

allemande sauce Classic French *sauce, *velouté blended with egg yolks and cream. Also known as sauce blonde or parisienne. Named for its light colour, as opposed to *espagnole sauce, which is dark.

allergen A chemical compound, commonly a protein, which causes the production of antibodies, and hence an immune (allergic) reaction. *See also* ALLERGY; FOOD, ADVERSE REACTIONS.

allergy Adverse reaction to foods (*see* FOOD, ADVERSE REACTIONS) caused by the production of antibodies. The main food allergens are *peanuts, tree *nuts, *soy, *milk, *eggs, crustacea, *fish, and *wheat. Regulations in many countries require that food labelling includes a note of the presence of common allergens, or the possibility of the presence of traces of allergens from cross-contamination in manufacture.

alliance French; *sauce made from reduced (partially concentrated) white wine with tarragon vinegar and egg yolk.

allicin A sulphur-containing compound partly responsible for the flavour of *garlic, formed by the action of alliinase on alliin (*S*-(2-propenyl)-L-cysteine sulphoxide) when the cells are disrupted, releasing the enzyme to act on the substrate. Has antibacterial properties.

alligator pear *See* AVOCADO.

allotriophagy An unnatural desire for abnormal foods; also known as cissa, cittosis, and pica.

alloxan Synthesized in the 19th century as a precursor for synthesis of the purple dyestuff murexide; it is cytotoxic to β-islet cells of the *pancreas, and is used to produce an animal model of type I *diabetes mellitus.

allspice Dried fruits of the evergreen shrub *Pimenta officinalis* (syn. *P. dioica*), also known as pimento (as distinct from *pimiento) or Jamaican pepper. The name allspice derives from the aromatic oil, which has an aroma similar to a mixture of *cloves, *cinnamon, and *nutmeg. Used to flavour meat and in baking.

allumettes, pommes French; potatoes cut into thin 'matchsticks' and fried, also known as straw potatoes. Also used sometimes for narrow fingers of pastry.

allura red Water-soluble red colourant, *FD&C red 40.

almond A nut, the seeds of *Prunus amygdalus* var. *dulcis*. All varieties contain the *glycoside *amygdalin, which forms hydrogen cyanide when the nuts are crushed. The bitter almond, used for *almond oil (*P. amygdalus* var. *amara*), may yield dangerous amounts of cyanide.

A 60-g portion (36 nuts) is a rich *source of protein, copper, niacin, and vitamins B_2, E; a good source of iron and zinc; a source of vitamin B_1; contains 35 g of fat, of which 10% is *saturated and 70% mono-unsaturated; provides 8.4 g of dietary fibre; supplies 370 kcal (1550 kJ).

almond oil Essential oil (*see* OILS, ESSENTIAL) from the seeds of either the *almond tree (*Prunus amygdalus*) or more commonly the *apricot tree (*Prunus armeniaca*), containing benzaldehyde, hydrogen cyanide, and benzaldehyde cyanohydrin. After removal of the cyanide, used as a flavour and in perfumes and cosmetics.

almond paste *See* MARZIPAN.

almorta Spanish; flour made from seeds of common vetch or tare, *Vicia sativa*.

aloo Hindi; prepared with potatoes.

alpine strawberry *See* STRAWBERRY.

alsacienne, choucroute Sauerkraut dish garnished with smoked sausages, ham, and peas.

Alström syndrome A very rare genetic disease characterized by congenital heart failure due to dilated cardiomyopathy and photophobia (fear of bright lights). Affected babies and young children gain weight quickly, leading to *obesity and hyperinsulinemia, which may progress to type II *diabetes mellitus.

alum Aluminium sulphate and aluminium potassium sulphate, used in pickles and to prevent discolouration of potatoes.

aluminium (aluminum) The third most abundant element in the earth's crust (after oxygen and silicon), with no known biological function. Present in small amounts in many foods but only a small proportion is absorbed. Aluminium salts are found in the abnormal nerve tangles in the brain in Alzheimer's disease, and it has been suggested that aluminium poisoning may be a factor in the development of the disease, although there is little evidence.

Aluminium is used in cooking vessels (the first aluminium saucepan was produced in Cleveland, Ohio, by Henry Avery in 1890) and as foil for wrapping food, as well as in cans and tubes. Aluminium cans were first used for food and beverages in 1960; tab-opening aluminium cans for beverages were first introduced 1962. It is a soft flexible metal, resistant to oxidation and deterioration, although it is dissolved by alkalis. The 'silver' beads used to decorate confectionery are coated with either silver foil or an alloy of aluminium and *copper.

*Baking powders containing sodium aluminium sulphate as the acid agent were used at one time (alum baking powders), and aluminium hydroxide and silicates are commonly used in *antacid medications.

AMA American Medical Association.

(((●))) SEE WEB LINKS

• The AMA's homepage.

amabile Italian; wines intermediate between medium sweet (abboccato) and sweet (dolce).

Amadori compounds Intermediates of the *Maillard reaction of reducing sugars with amino groups in proteins.

amadumbe See TARO.

amala Nigerian; dark brown paste made by reconstituting *yam meal with boiling water; sometimes fortified with legume meal. Eaten with soups.

amaranth A burgundy red colour, stable to light (E123).

Amaranthus A genus of originally Central American plants cultivated for their leaves and seeds. The leaves of *A. tricolor* (Chinese spinach) are promoted in South-East Asia as a good source of *carotene. Paste made from the seeds from *A. hypochondriachus* and *A. cruentus* was widely eaten in Central America and used in religious ceremonies by the Aztecs; *A. caudatus* is also known as Inca wheat.

amaretti Italian; *see* MACAROON.

amaretto Italian; almond-flavoured *liqueur made by infusion of apricot kernels.

amarwa *See* ORUBISI.

amazone French garnish for meat; lentil fritters, hollowed out and stuffed with morel mushrooms and chestnut purée.

ambali Indian; sour millet and rice cake; the dough is left to undergo a lactic acid bacterial fermentation before cooking.

ambarella Fruit of the Polynesian deciduous tree *Spondias cytherea*, also known as hog plum.

ambigu French; cold collation or substantial snack eaten between meals or after midnight.

amchur (amchoor) Indian subcontinent; spice made from sun-dried unripe *mango (*Mangifera indica*), sometimes mixed with *turmeric.

AMDR Acceptable (i.e. healthy) macronutrient distribution ranges: 10–15% of energy from protein, 25–30% from fat, and 45–65% from carbohydrate.

amenorrhoea Cessation of menstruation, normally occurring between the ages of 40 and 55 (the menopause), but sometimes at an early age, especially as a result of severe undernutrition (as in *anorexia nervosa) when body weight falls below about 45 kg.

américaine, à l' French; various methods of preparing meat, game, fish, vegetables, and eggs, the best-known example being homard à l'américaine, lobster in a sauce based on tomato, onion, and herbs, cooked in wine or brandy.

Ames test An *in vitro* test for the ability of chemicals, including potential food *additives, to cause mutation in bacteria (the mutagenic potential). Commonly used as a preliminary screening method to detect substances likely to be carcinogenic.

amides Organic nitrogen compounds containing the $C{=}O.NH_2$ group; the *amino acids *asparagine and *glutamine are amides.

amines Formed by the decarboxylation of *amino acids. Amines in foods are normally inactivated by the *enzyme *monoamine oxidase in the liver, but some drugs used as antidepressant medication (monoamine oxidase inhibitors) inhibit the enzyme; patients receiving such drugs must avoid foods that contain relatively large amounts of amines.

See also AMINES, BIOGENIC.

amines, biogenic Biologically active *amines that may cause adverse reactions, synthesized by microbial decarboxylation of *amino acids (e.g. *histamine, *tyramine, *tryptamine, *phenylethylamine). They are found in ripened cheese, chocolate, yeast, wines, and fermented foods; they stimulate the sympathetic nervous system and can increase blood pressure. In sensitive people they are one of the dietary causes of migraine. *See also* FOOD, ADVERSE REACTIONS; MONOAMINE OXIDASE.

amino acid, limiting The essential amino acid present in least amount relative to the requirement for that amino acid. The ratio between the amount of the limiting amino acid in a protein and the requirement provides a chemical index of the nutritional value (*see* PROTEIN QUALITY) of the protein, the chemical score. Most cereal proteins are limited by *lysine, and most animal and other vegetable proteins by the sum of *methionine + *cysteine (*see* AMINO ACIDS, SULPHUR). In whole diets it is usually the sulphur amino acids that are limiting.

amino acid disorders A number of extremely rare *genetic diseases, occurring in 1–80 per million live births, that affect the metabolism of individual *amino acids; if untreated, many result in mental retardation. Screening for those conditions that can be treated is carried out in most countries shortly after birth. Treatment is generally by feeding specially formulated diets providing minimal amounts of the amino acid involved. *See also* ARGININAEMIA; ARGININOSUCCINIC ACIDURIA; CITRULLINAEMIA; CYSTINURIA; CYSTATHIONINURIA; HARTNUP DISEASE; HOMOCYSTINURIA; HYPERAMMONAEMIA; MAPLE SYRUP URINE DISEASE; PHENYLKETONURIA.

amino acid profile The *amino acid composition of a *protein.

amino acids The basic units from which *proteins are made. Chemically compounds with an amino group ($-NH_2$) and a carboxyl group ($-COOH$) attached to the same carbon atom.

Twenty amino acids are incorporated into proteins during synthesis on the *ribosome. A number of other amino acids also occur in proteins as a result of post-synthetic modification, including hydroxyproline, hydroxylysine, γ-carboxyglutamate, and methylhistidine, but are nutritionally unimportant since they cannot be reutilized for protein synthesis. Other amino acids occur as intermediates in metabolic pathways but are not required for protein synthesis, and are nutritionally unimportant, although they may occur in foods. These include *homocysteine, citrulline, and ornithine.

See also AMINO ACIDS, ESSENTIAL; AMINO ACIDS, NON-ESSENTIAL.

amino acids, acidic Two amino acids have an acidic carboxylic acid (–COOH) group in the side-chain: glutamic acid (glutamate) and aspartic acid (aspartate).

amino acids, aromatic Three amino acids—phenylalanine, tyrosine, and tryptophan—have an *aromatic side-chain.

amino acids, basic Three amino acids—lysine, arginine, and histidine—have a basic side-chain.

amino acids, branched-chain Three amino acids—leucine, isoleucine, and valine—have a branched side-chain. These three have very similar metabolism, and a rare genetic disease affecting their metabolism results in *maple syrup urine disease.

amino acids, dispensable *See* AMINO ACIDS, NON-ESSENTIAL.

amino acids, essential Nine amino acids cannot be synthesized in the body at all and so must be provided in the diet; they are called the essential or indispensable amino acids—histidine, isoleucine, leucine, lysine, methionine, phenylalanine, threonine, tryptophan, and valine. In addition, arginine may be essential for infants, since their requirement is greater than their ability to synthesize it. Two of the non-essential amino acids are made in the body from essential amino acids: cysteine (and cystine) from methionine, and tyrosine from phenylalanine.

amino acids, glucogenic Those amino acids that can be utilized for *gluconeogenesis. *See also* AMINO ACIDS, KETOGENIC.

amino acids, ketogenic Those amino acids that give rise to *ketone bodies or *acetate when they are metabolized. Only leucine and lysine are purely ketogenic; isoleucine, phenylalanine, tyrosine, and tryptophan give rise to both ketogenic and glucogenic fragments; the remainder are purely glucogenic. *See also* AMINO ACIDS, GLUCOGENIC.

amino acids, non-essential Eleven of the amino acids involved in proteins can be synthesized in the body, and so are called non-essential or dispensable amino acids, since they do not have to be provided in the diet. They are alanine, arginine, aspartic acid, asparagine, cysteine, glutamic acid, glutamine, glycine, proline, serine, and tyrosine.

amino acids, sulphur Two amino acids—methionine and cysteine—contain sulphur in the side-chain; although cysteine is not an essential amino acid, it can only be synthesized from methionine, and it is conventional to consider the sum of methionine plus cysteine (the sulphur amino acids) in respect to *protein quality.

aminoaciduria Excretion of abnormal amounts of one or more *amino acids in the urine, usually as a result of a genetic disease. *See also* AMINO ACID DISORDERS.

aminogram A diagrammatic representation of the *amino acid composition of a *peptide or *protein. A plasma aminogram is the composition of the free amino acid pool in blood plasma.

amino group The CH–NH$_2$ group of *amino acids and *amines, among other compounds. The amino acid *lysine also has an amino group in its side-chain.

aminopeptidase An *enzyme secreted in the *pancreatic juice that removes amino acids sequentially from the free amino terminal of a peptide or protein (i.e. the end that has a free amino group exposed), until the final product is a *dipeptide. Since it works at the end of the peptide chain, it is an *exopeptidase.

aminostatic mechanism of appetite control Control of appetite, hunger, and satiety by changes in circulating *amino acids, especially *tryptophan and the ratio of tryptophan to other large neutral amino acids that compete with tryptophan for uptake into the central nervous system and other tissues.

amino sugars Aminated derivatives of monosaccharides, e.g. glucosamine, galactosamine.

aminotransferase Any *enzyme that catalyses the reaction of *transamination.

amla Indian gooseberry, *Emblica officinalis Gaertn* (syn. *Phyllanthus emblica*), also known as aonla. Important in Ayurvedic medicine and reported to reduce *hypercholesterolaemia. An extremely rich source of vitamin C (600 mg/100 g). The raw fruit is acidic and astringent; usually used to make pickles.

amlou *See* ARGAN.

amoebiasis (amoebic dysentery) Infection of the intestinal tract with pathogenic amoeba (commonly *Entamoeba histolytica*) from contaminated food or water, causing profuse diarrhoea, intestinal bleeding, pain, jaundice, anorexia, and weight loss.

amomum A group of tropical plants, including *cardamom and melegueta *pepper, which have pungent and aromatic seeds.

amontillado, amoroso *See* SHERRY.

amour (parfait amour) Purple-coloured liqueur, flavoured with citrus fruits and violets.

amourettes French; marrow from calves' bones, normally cooked as a garnish.

AMP Adenosine monophosphate; *see* ADENINE.

amphetamine Also known as benzidrine. A chemical at one time used as an appetite suppressant; addictive, and a common drug of abuse ('speed'), its use is strictly controlled by law.

Amtlicher Prüfungsnummer (AP) German; batch number on labels of quality wines. *See* WINE CLASSIFICATION, GERMANY.

amur, white *See* CARP.

amydon A traditional starchy material made by steeping wheat flour in water, then drying the starch sediment in the sun, used for thickening broths, etc.

amygdalin **1.** A *glycoside in *almonds and apricot and cherry stones which is hydrolysed by the *enzyme emulsin to yield glucose, hydrocyanic acid, and benzaldehyde. It is highly poisonous, although it has been promoted, with no evidence, as a nutrient, *laetrile or so-called vitamin B_{17}. Unfounded claims have been made for its value in treating cancer. **2.** French pharmaceutical term meaning made with almonds.

amylases *Enzymes that hydrolyse *starch and *glycogen. α-Amylase (dextrinogenic amylase or diastase) acts to produce small *dextrin fragments from starch, while β-amylase (maltogenic amylase) liberates maltose, some free glucose, and isomaltose from the branch points in *amylopectin.

Salivary amylase (sometimes called by its obsolete name of ptyalin) and pancreatic amylase are both α-amylases. Fungal α-amylase from *Aspergillus oryzae* is used to increase *diastatic activity of flour. *See also* Z-ENZYME.

amyli Dried *tamarind.

amylin A *peptide that is secreted together with *insulin from the β-islet cells of the *pancreas during and after food intake; it has a potent anorectic (appetite suppressant) action.

amylodyspepsia An inability to digest starch.

amyloins Carbohydrates that are complexes of dextrins with varying proportions of maltose.

amylopectin The branched-chain form of *starch. About 75–80% of most starches; the remainder is *amylose.

amylopeptic A general term for enzymes that are able to split *starch to give soluble products.

amylose The straight-chain form of *starch. About 20–25% of most starches; the remainder is *amylopectin.

amylum Roman; starch used to thicken sauces, made by soaking wheat grains in water, then straining the liquid and pouring on to a tiled floor to thicken in the sun.

anabolism The process of building up or synthesizing. *See* METABOLISM.

anacard Brazilian; vinegar made by fermentation of the pulp surrounding the *cashew nut.

anaemia A shortage of red *blood cells, leading to pallor and shortness of breath, especially on exertion. Most commonly due to a dietary deficiency of *iron, or excessive blood losses resulting in iron losses greater than can be met from the diet. Other dietary deficiencies can also result in anaemia, including deficiency of *vitamin B_{12} or *folic acid (megaloblastic anaemia; *see* ANAEMIA, MEGALOBLASTIC; ANAEMIA, PERNICIOUS), *vitamin E (haemolytic anaemia; *see* ANAEMIA, HAEMOLYTIC), and rarely *vitamin C or *vitamin B_6.

anaemia, haemolytic *Anaemia caused by premature and excessive destruction of red blood cells; not normally due to nutritional deficiency, but can occur as a result of *vitamin E deficiency in premature infants.

anaemia, megaloblastic Release into the circulation of immature precursors of red *blood cells, due to deficiency of either *folic acid or *vitamin B_{12}. *See also* ANAEMIA, PERNICIOUS.

anaemia, pernicious *Anaemia due to deficiency of *vitamin B_{12}, most commonly as a result of failure to absorb the vitamin from the diet. There is release into the circulation of immature precursors of red *blood cells, the same type of megaloblastic anaemia as is seen in *folic acid deficiency. There is also progressive damage to the spinal cord (sub-acute combined degeneration), which is not reversed on restoring the vitamin. The underlying cause of the condition may be the production of *antibodies against either the *intrinsic factor that is required for absorption of the vitamin or the cells of the gastric mucosa that secrete intrinsic factor. *Atrophy of the gastric mucosa with ageing also impairs vitamin B_{12} absorption and causes pernicious anaemia. Dietary deficiency of vitamin B_{12}, leading to a similar anaemia with spinal cord degeneration, occurs in strict *vegetarians.

anaerobes Micro-organisms that grow in the absence of oxygen. Obligate anaerobes cannot survive in the presence of oxygen; facultative anaerobes normally grow in the presence of oxygen but can also grow in its absence. *See also* AEROBIC (1).

anaerobic threshold The level of exercise at which the rate of oxygen uptake into muscle becomes limiting and there is an increasing proportion of anaerobic metabolism to yield lactate. *See also* AEROBIC (2).

analysis, proximate *See* PROXIMATE ANALYSIS.

ananas *See* PINEAPPLE.

anardana Dried seeds of the *pomegranate (*Punica granatum*). Used in India as an acidulant in chutneys and curries.

anastomosis A connection between two blood vessels, or surgical joining of two segments of the intestine, commonly as a bypass for much of the absorptive small intestine, as a treatment for gross *obesity.

anatto *See* ANNATTO.

ancho A flat, heart-shaped chilli *pepper, the fruit of *Capsicum annuum*, widely used in Mexican cuisine.

anchoveta Small fish (*Engraulis ringens*) found in the Pacific off the western coast of South America; commercially important as a source of *fish meal and fish oils (*see* OIL, FISH).

anchovy Small oily fish (*Engraulis* spp; *see* FISH, OILY). European anchovy is *E. encrasicolus*, northern anchovy is *E. mordax*, and Japanese anchovy is *E. japonica*. Usually semi-preserved with 10–12% salt and sometimes *benzoic acid. Anchovy butter is prepared from pounded fillets of anchovy mixed with butter as a savoury spread, anchovy paste from pounded fillets of anchovy mixed with vinegar and spices.

anchoyade French (Provençal); anchovies puréed with garlic and olive oil.

ancienne, à l' Literally, 'old-style'. Usually a dish with a mixed garnish of beans, cooked lettuce, and hard-boiled egg.

andalouse **1.** Dishes with rice and tomatoes. **2.** French sauce based on mayonnaise with tomato purée and diced peppers. **3.** Garnish of tomatoes stuffed with rice, aubergine, and tomatoes. **4.** Clear chicken soup garnished with tomatoes, rice, ham, and beaten egg.

andouille French sausage made from pork meat and intestines (chitterlings); smaller versions are andouillettes.

andruty Polish; *waffle.

aneurine Obsolete name for *vitamin B_1.

aneurysm Local dilatation (swelling and weakening) of the wall of a blood vessel, usually the result of *atherosclerosis and *hypertension; especially serious in the aorta, when rupture may prove fatal.

angelica Crystallized young stalks of the southern European umbelliferous herb *Angelica archangelica* (*A. officinalis*). They are bright green in colour, and are used to decorate and flavour confectionery. The roots are used together with *juniper berries to flavour *gin, and the seeds are used in *vermouth and *Chartreuse. Essential oils (*see* OILS, ESSENTIAL) are distilled from the roots, stem, and leaves. The root of *A. sinensis* is dong quai, a traditional Chinese medicine.

angel's hair (Spanish: *cabello de ángel*) Jam made from the fibrous part of mature pumpkin or squash, preferably kept from the previous year's harvest.

angels on horseback Oysters wrapped in bacon, skewered, and grilled. *See also* DEVILS ON HORSEBACK.

anghiti Indian; *charcoal brazier used for grilling *kebabs.

angina (angina pectoris) Paroxysmal thoracic pain and choking sensation, especially during exercise or stress, due to partial blockage of a coronary artery (blood vessel supplying the heart), as a result of *atherosclerosis.

angiotensin A potent vasoconstrictor that acts to raise blood pressure. It is a glycoprotein secreted by the liver as inactive angiotensinogen and converted to angiotensin I in the kidneys by the enzyme renin, then to the active angiotensin II in the lungs by angiotensin converting enzyme (*see* ACE).

angkak Red pigment produced by fermentation of rice with *Monascus* spp. Used as a food colour in Asia.

anglaise **1.** Plainly cooked in stock or water. **2.** Coating of eggs on foods that are then dipped in breadcrumbs and fried. **3.** Garnish for boiled salt beef consisting of boiled vegetables.

anglerfish *See* MONKFISH.

Angostura The best known of the *bitters, widely used in cocktails; a secret blend of herbs and spices, including the bitter aromatic bark of either of two trees of the orange family (*Galipea officinalis, Cusparia felorifuga*). Invented in 1818 by Dr Siegert in the town of Angostura (now Ciudad Bolivar) in Venezuela, originally as a medicine, and now made in Trinidad. A few drops of Angostura in *gin makes a 'pink gin'.

Ångstrom A unit of length equal to 10^{-8} cm (10^{-10} m) and hence = 10 nm; not an official SI unit, but commonly used in structural chemistry and crystallography.

angular stomatitis A characteristic cracking and fissuring of the skin at the angles of the mouth, a symptom of *vitamin B_2 deficiency, but also seen in other conditions.

animal charcoal *See* CHARCOAL.

anion A negatively charged *ion.

anisakiasis (anisakidosis) Infection caused by the larval stage of the parasitic nematode *Anisakis simplex*, usually as a result of eating contaminated raw or undercooked seafoods. *Pseudoterranova* larvae have also been implicated as causative organisms.

anise (anis) *Liqueur made by infusion of *aniseed berries in *spirit; may be sweet or dry. French sweet anise liqueur is anisette. *Pastis is prepared by distillation of anise and liquorice rather than infusion.

anise, star A spice, the seeds of *Illicium verum*, widely used in Chinese cooking. Distinct from *aniseed.

aniseed (anise) The dried fruit of *Pimpinella anisum*, a member of the parsley family, which is used to flavour baked goods, meat dishes, and drinks, including *anise, *anisette, *arak, and *ouzo. *See also* ANISE, STAR.

anisette *See* ANISE.

ann (an) Japanese; bean jams made by boiling and pounding adzuki beans (*see* BEANS, ADZUKI), then adding syrup to form a paste. Other beans may also be used.

annata Year of vintage on Italian wine labels. *See* WINE CLASSIFICATION, ITALY.

annatto (anatto) Also known as bixin, butter colour, or rocou; an orange colouring (E160(b)) extracted from the fruit of the tropical shrub *Bixa orellana*. The main component is the *carotenoid bixin, which is fat-soluble. It is used to colour cheese, dairy produce, and baked goods. The seeds are used for flavouring in Caribbean and Latin American foods.

annona *See* CUSTARD APPLE.

anorectic drugs (anorexigenic drugs) Drugs that depress the appetite, used as an aid to weight reduction. Apart from *rimonabant and *sibutramine, most have been withdrawn from use; diethylpropion and mazindol are available but not recommended.

anorexia Lack of appetite.

anorexia nervosa An *eating disorder in which low body weight is an essential diagnostic criterion. There is some degree of overlap with *bulimia nervosa, and some authorities subdivide anorexia nervosa into binge-purging and pure restricting subtypes. Characterized by loss of appetite, leading to severe energy deficit. The result is a very considerable loss of weight, with tissue *atrophy and a fall in *basal metabolic rate. It is especially prevalent among adolescent girls; when body weight falls below about 45 kg there is a cessation of menstruation. A number of studies implicate impaired hypothalamic function (neuroendocrine stress response and serotoninergic systems) rather than peripheral energy signalling deficits. *See also* BINGE-EATING DISORDER; BULIMIA NERVOSA.

anosmia Lack or impairment of the sense of smell.

anserine A *dipeptide of β-alanine and *methylhistidine found in *muscle and other tissues, of unknown function.

Antabuse Trade name for the drug disulfiram, used in the treatment of *alcoholism. It inhibits the further metabolism of acetaldehyde arising from the metabolism of alcohol, and so causes headache, nausea, vomiting, and palpitations if alcohol is consumed.

antacids *Bases that neutralize acids, used generally to counteract excessive *gastric acidity and to treat *indigestion. Antacid preparations generally contain sodium bicarbonate, aluminium hydroxide, magnesium carbonate, or magnesium hydroxide.

anthelmintics Drugs used to treat infestation by parasitic worms (nematodes and cestodes).

anthocyanins Violet, red, and blue water-soluble colours extracted from flowers, fruits, and leaves (E163). They can react with *iron or *tin, and so may cause discoloration in canned foods.

anthoxanthins Alternative name for *flavonoids.

anthropometry Body measurements used as an index of physiological development and nutritional status; a non-invasive way of assessing body composition. Weight for age provides information about the overall nutritional status of children; weight for height is used to detect acute malnutrition (wasting) and height for age to detect chronic malnutrition (stunting). Mid-upper-arm circumference provides an index of muscle wastage in undernutrition. *Skinfold thickness is related to the amount of subcutaneous fat as an index of over- or undernutrition. *See also* BODY MASS INDEX; CRISTAL HEIGHT; STUNTING; WETZEL GRID.

anthroponotic transmission Person to person transmission of organisms associated with *food-borne diseases; especially important for foods that are intended to be consumed raw, or for those that are handled after being cooked.

antibiotics Substances produced by living organisms that inhibit the growth of other organisms. The first antibiotic to be discovered was penicillin, which is produced by the *mould *Penicillium notatum* and inhibits the growth of sensitive bacteria. Many antibiotics are used to treat bacterial infections in human beings and animals. Small amounts of antibiotics added to animal feed (a few grams/tonne) result in improved growth, possibly by controlling mild infections or changing the population of intestinal bacteria and so altering the digestion and absorption of food; their use as growth promoters is banned in the EU.

antibodies A class of proteins formed in the body in response to the presence of *antigens (foreign proteins and other compounds); they bind to the antigen, inactivating it. Immunity to infection is due to the production of antibodies against specific proteins of pathogenic organisms, and immunization is the process of giving these marker proteins, generally in an inactivated form, to stimulate the production of antibodies. Adverse reactions to foods (food allergies) may be due to the production of antibodies against specific food proteins. Antibodies form a class of proteins known as the γ-globulins or immunoglobulins. *See also* FOOD, ADVERSE REACTIONS.

anti-caking agents Compounds added in small amounts to powdered foodstuffs to prevent clumping or caking—e.g. anhydrous disodium hydrogen phosphate is added to salt and icing sugar, aluminium calcium silicate or calcium or magnesium carbonate to table salt, calcium silicate to *baking powder.

anticarcinogen Any compound that protects against the development of cancer, including *antioxidant nutrients and various non-nutrient compounds in plant foods, among them *flavonoids, allyl sulphur compounds, glucosinolates, and isoprenoids.

anticoagulants Compounds that prevent or slow the process of blood clotting or coagulation, either in samples of blood taken for analysis or in the body.

People at risk of thrombosis are often treated with Warfarin and similar compounds as an anticoagulant, to reduce the risk of intravenous blood clot formation. These act by antagonizing the action of *vitamin K in the synthesis of blood clotting proteins, and people taking anticoagulants should not take supplements containing vitamin K. It is unlikely that the vitamin K in foods would be enough to have any significant effect.

anticodon A triplet of bases in tRNA that binds to the *codon on mRNA during protein synthesis on the *ribosome.

antidiarrhoeal Drug used to treat *diarrhoea by absorbing water from the intestine, altering intestinal motility, or adsorbing toxins.

antidiuretic Drug used to reduce the excretion of urine and so conserve fluid in the body. *See also* WATER BALANCE.

antiemetic Drug used to prevent or alleviate nausea and vomiting.

antienzymes Substances that specifically inhibit the action of enzymes. Many that inhibit digestive enzymes are present in raw legumes. Most are proteins, and are therefore inactivated by heat.

antifoaming agents Compounds used to reduce foaming caused by the presence of dissolved protein.

antigen Any compound that is foreign to the body (e.g. bacterial, food, or pollen protein, or some complex carbohydrates) which, when introduced into the circulation, stimulates the formation of an *antibody. *See also* FOOD, ADVERSE REACTIONS.

anti-grey-hair factor Deficiency of the *vitamin *pantothenic acid causes loss of hair colour in black and brown rats, and at one time the vitamin was known as the anti-grey-hair factor. It is not related to the loss of hair pigment in human beings.

antihaemorrhagic vitamin *See* VITAMIN K.

antihistamine Drug that antagonizes the actions of *histamine; those that block histamine H_1 receptors are used to treat allergic reactions; those that block H_2 receptors are used to treat peptic *ulcers.

antihypertensive Drug, diet, or other treatment used to treat *hypertension by lowering blood pressure.

antilipidaemic Drug, diet, or other treatment used to treat *hyperlipidaemia by lowering blood lipids.

antimetabolite Compound that inhibits a normal metabolic process, acting as an analogue of a normal metabolite. Some are useful in chemotherapy of cancer, others are naturally occurring toxins in foods, frequently causing vitamin deficiency diseases by inhibiting the normal metabolism of the vitamin. *See also* ANTIVITAMINS.

antimicrobial agents Compounds used to preserve food by preventing growth of micro-organisms (bacteria and fungi).

antimicrobial agents, indigenous Various compounds occurring naturally in foods that inhibit the growth of micro-organisms. These include essential oils (*see* OILS, ESSENTIAL) such as eugenol in *cloves, allicin in *garlic, cinnamic aldehyde and eugenol in *cinnamon, allyl isothiocyanate in *mustard, eugenol and thymol in *sage, and carvacrol, isothymol, and thymol in *oregano. A number of plants have antibacterial and antifungal activity due to hydroxycinnamic acid derivatives, such as ferulic, caffeic, and chlorogenic acids. Cruciferous plants contain glucosinolates in intracellular vacuoles; when disrupted the glucosinolates are hydrolysed by myrosinase, forming isothiocyanates, which have antifungal and antibacterial activity.

antimony Toxic metal of no known metabolic function, and therefore not a dietary essential. Antimony compounds are used in treatment of some parasitic diseases.

antimotility agents Drugs used to reduce gastro-intestinal motility, and hence reduce the discomfort associated with *diarrhoea.

anti-mould agents *See* ANTIMYCOTICS.

antimutagen Compound acting on cells and tissues to decrease initiation of mutation by a *mutagen.

antimycotics Substances that inhibit the growth of *moulds and *fungi.

antineuritic vitamin Obsolete name for *vitamin B_1.

antioxidant A substance that retards the oxidative *rancidity of fats in stored foods. Many fats, and especially vegetable oils, contain naturally occurring antioxidants, among them *vitamin E, which protect them against rancidity for some time. Synthetic antioxidants include propyl, octyl, and dodecyl gallates, butylated hydroxyanisole (BHA), and butylated hydroxytoluene (BHT). *See also* ANTIOXIDANT NUTRIENTS; INDUCTION PERIOD.

antioxidant nutrients Highly reactive oxygen *radicals are formed during normal oxidative *metabolism and in response to infection and some chemicals. They cause damage to *fatty acids in cell membranes, and the products of this damage can then cause damage to proteins and *DNA. The most widely accepted theory of the biochemical basis of much *cancer, and also of *atherosclerosis and possibly *kwashiorkor, is that the key factor in precipitating the condition is tissue damage by radicals. A number of different mechanisms are involved in protection against, or repair after, oxygen radical damage, including a number of nutrients, especially *vitamin E, *carotene, *vitamin C, and *selenium. Collectively these are known as antioxidant nutrients.

antioxidant paradox Although epidemiological studies show a protective effect of *antioxidant nutrients against cardiovascular disease and cancer, intervention trials with *vitamin E and *carotene have generally shown increased mortality. One explanation is that antioxidants act by forming relatively stable *radicals that persist long enough to undergo reaction to non-radical products; they are therefore also capable of perpetuating radical damage deeper into tissues and plasma *lipoproteins.

antipasto Italian; dishes served before the main meal, hors d'œuvre.

antiracchitic Preventing or curing *rickets.

antiscorbutic Preventing or curing scurvy; the antiscorbutic vitamin is *vitamin C.

antisialagogues Substances that reduce the flow of *saliva.

anti-spattering agents Compounds such as *lecithin, sucrose esters of *fatty acids, and sodium sulpho-acetate derivatives of *mono- and *diglycerides, which are added to oils and fats used for frying to prevent potentially dangerous spattering. They function by preventing the coalescence of water droplets.

anti-staling agents Substances that retard the *staling of baked products and soften the crumb, e.g. sucrose stearate, polyoxyethylene monostearate, glyceryl monostearate, stearoyl tartrate.

antivitamins Substances that interfere with the normal metabolism or function of *vitamins, or destroy them. Dicoumarol in spoiled sweet clover antagonizes the function of *vitamin K, thiaminase in raw fish destroys *vitamin B_1, the drug methotrexate antagonizes *folic acid metabolism (this is part of its mechanism of action in treating cancer), the drug isoniazid antagonizes the action of *vitamin B_6.

antixerophthalmic vitamin Obsolete name for *vitamin A.

anu *See* ULLUCO.

AOAC Originally the Association of Official Agricultural Chemists, formed in 1884 to adopt uniform methods of analysis of fertilizers; the name was changed in 1965 to the Association of Official Analytical Chemists. Its main purpose is to promote validation and quality assurance in analytical science, and to develop new methods.

(⊕) SEE WEB LINKS
• The AOAC's homepage.

AOC Appellation d'origine contrôlée; *see* WINE CLASSIFICATION, FRANCE.

aortic aneurysm *See* ANEURYSM.

AP Amtlicher Prüfungsnummer, German; batch number on labels of quality wines. *See* WINE CLASSIFICATION, GERMANY.

apastia Refusal to take food, as an expression of a psychiatric disturbance. *See also* ANOREXIA NERVOSA.

aperient *See* LAXATIVE.

apéritif (apéritif wines) *See* WINE, APÉRITIF.

apfelstrudel *See* STRUDEL.

APHA American Public Health Association.
(⊕) SEE WEB LINKS
• The APHA's homepage.

aphagia Inability to swallow. Difficulty in swallowing is dysphagia.

aphagosis Inability to eat.

apiculture Bee keeping for *honey production; from the Latin name of the honey bee, *Apis mellifera*.

apio Root vegetable from the legume *Apios tuberosa*, eaten like potatoes.

aplasia Complete failure of development of an organ or tissue. *See also* HYPOPLASIA.

apo-carotenal *See* CAROTENE.

apoenzyme The *apoprotein of an *enzyme that requires a tightly or covalently bound *prosthetic group for activity, and has no catalytic activity without the prosthetic group. *See also* COENZYMES; ENZYME ACTIVATION.

apokreo Greek: literally 'fast from meat'; the three weeks of abstinence from meat ordained by the Greek Orthodox Church during Lent.

apolipoprotein The protein of *lipoproteins without the associated lipid. *See also* LIPIDS, PLASMA.

apoprotein 1. When an *enzyme or other protein has a *prosthetic group, the apoprotein is the protein without the prosthetic group. **2.** With reference to the plasma *lipoproteins, the individual proteins that surround the lipid core.

apoptosis Programmed cell death, as opposed to *necrosis, which is accidental.

aposia Absence of sensation of thirst.

apositia Aversion to food.

appellation contrôlée (AC; appellation d'origine contrôlée (AOC)) *See* WINE CLASSIFICATION, FRANCE.

appendix (vermiform appendix) A residual part of the intestinal tract, a small sac-like process extending from the caecum, some 4–8 cm long. Acute inflammation, caused by an obstruction (appendicitis), can lead to perforation and peritonitis if surgery is not performed in time. *See also* GASTRO-INTESTINAL TRACT.

appenzeller Swiss hard cheese, washed with white wine and herbs while maturing.

appertization Term of French origin for the process of destroying all the micro-organisms of significance in food, i.e. 'commercial sterility'; a few organisms remain alive but quiescent. Named after Nicholas Appert (1752–1841), a Paris confectioner who invented the process of *canning; he opened the first vacuum-bottling factory in 1804.

appestat *See* APPETITE CONTROL.

appetite control Hunger centres in the lateral hypothalamus initiate feeding; satiety centres in the ventromedial hypothalamus signal satiety. *See also* AMINOSTATIC MECHANISM OF APPETITE CONTROL; ANOREXIC DRUGS; GLUCOSTATIC MECHANISM OF APPETITE CONTROL; LIPOSTATIC MECHANISM OF APPETITE CONTROL.

apple Fruit of the tree *Malus sylvestris* and its many cultivars and hybrids; there are more than 2000 varieties in the British *National Fruit Collection. The first apple seeds in North America are believed to have been planted in 1629 in Massachussetts Bay by Gov. John Endecott. Crab apples are grown mainly for decoration and for pollination of fruit-bearing trees, although the sour fruit can be used for making jelly. Cooking apples are generally sourer varieties than dessert apples, and have flesh that crumbles on cooking; cider apples are sour varieties especially suited to the making of *cider. One apple (110g) provides 2.2g of dietary fibre and supplies 40kcal (165kJ).

apple, liquid American; apple juice with pulverized apple pulp in suspension.

apple, Malay (mountain apple) Fruit of the Malaysian and Indian tree *Syzygium malaccense*. Also known as pomerac.

apple, rose Fruit of the Caribbean evergreen tree *Eugenia jambos* (syn. *Syzygium jambos*). Also called jambos, Malabar plum, and pomarrosa. Java rose apple (or wax apple) is *A. samarangense*, also known as wax jambu.

apple, sodom Tropical plant, *Calotropis procera*; the fruit is inedible, but the leaves are used in West Africa as a source of proteolytic milk-clotting enzymes in *cheese production.

apple, wax *See* APPLE, ROSE.

apple brandy *Spirit made by distillation of *cider, known in France as calvados. *See also* APPLE JACK.

apple butter Apple that has been boiled in an open pan to a thick consistency; similar to *apple sauce, but darker in colour due to the prolonged boiling.

apple jack American name for *apple brandy, normally distilled, but traditionally prepared by leaving *cider outside in winter, when the water froze out as ice crystals, leaving the alcoholic spirit.

apple mint A herb, *Mentha rotundifolia*. *See also* MINT.

apple nuggets Crisp granules of apple of low moisture content, used commercially for manufacture of *apple sauce.

apple-pear Not a cross between apple and pear but a distinctive varietal type of pear-shaped fruit with apple texture. Also called Japanese pear, pear-apple, and shalea or chalea.

apple sauce Pulped stewed apple; in the UK it is made from sour apples, as an accompaniment to pork and goose; in the USA also stewed apple as a dessert.

apricot Fruit of the deciduous tree *Prunus armeniaca*. Apricot kernels are used to prepare *almond oil. One apricot (60g) is a *source of vitamins A (as carotene) and C; provides 1.2g of dietary fibre and supplies 18kcal (75kJ).

apricot, wild Fruit of the African shrub *Dovyalis caffra*, also known as kei-apple.

APUD cells Amine precursor uptake and decarboxylating cells; cells of the *gastro-intestinal tract that secrete peptide *hormones, including *cholecystokinin, *gastrin, GIP (*see* GASTRIC INHIBITORY PEPTIDE), *GLP, *motilin, *neurotensin, *pancreatic polypeptide, and *secretin.

aquaculture The farming of aquatic organisms—fish, molluscs, crustaceans, echinoderms (sea urchins), cephalopods (octopus, squid, cuttlefish), reptiles (alligators, sea turtles, freshwater turtles), amphibians (frogs), and aquatic plants. Includes fresh-, salt-, and brackish-water cultivation. Cultivation in salt water is mariculture.

aquamiel *See* PULQUE.

aquaporins Trans-membrane proteins that permit transport of water and *glycerol across cell membranes. Aquaporin-7 occurs in adipocytes, and is important in the efflux of glycerol from the cell. Deficiency in experimental animals is associated with increased activity of glycerol kinase and lipogenesis and with late-onset *obesity.

aquavit (akvavit, akavit) Scandinavian; spirit flavoured with herbs (commonly caraway, cumin, dill, or fennel). Also known as snaps, and in Germany as schnapps.

arabinogalactan *Gum extracted from sap of larch trees (*Larix* spp.), also known as larch gum.

arabinoxylans Polysaccharides of arabinose and *xylose; part of the *pentosan fraction in cereals.

arabitol *Sugar alcohol produced by reduction of arabinose.

araboascorbic acid *See* ERYTHORBIC ACID.

arachidonic acid A long-chain polyunsaturated *fatty acid (C20:4 ω6). Not strictly an essential fatty acid, since it can be formed from *linoleic acid, but three times more potent than linoleic acid in curing the signs of essential fatty acid deficiency. Found in animal tissues, especially fish, eggs, liver, and brain.

arachis oil *See* PEANUT OIL.

a

arak (arack, araq) Arabic; *anise- and *liquorice-flavoured spirit. Also used generally in the Middle and Far East to mean any one of a variety of spirits, often distilled from fermented dates or palm wine. Similar to the Greek ouzo and the Turkish raki.

ARAT Acyl CoA:retinol acyltransferase.

árbol, chile de Pungent fruit of *Capsicum annuum*, similar to Thai or bird chillies.

Arbroath smokie Smoked haddock; differs from *finnan haddock in that it is not split but smoked whole.

arbute Fruit of the southern European strawberry tree (*Arbutus unedo*) with a grainy texture and little taste.

archaea Formerly classified as bacteria, then archaebacteria, now recognized as a separate type of prokaryotic organism, genetically distinct from bacteria; they are chemo-autrophic *extremophiles, surviving at very high or very low temperatures.

archiduc, à l' Dishes seasoned with paprika and blended with cream.

Arcobacter **spp.** *See* CAMPYLOBACTER.

arctic cisco Freshwater fish, *Coregonus autumnalis*, also known as pollan.

ard bhoona *See* BHOONA.

areca nut *See* BETEL.

arepas Colombian name for *tortillas.

argan Fruit of the North African tree *Argania spinosa*. The seed oil is 80% unsaturated fatty acids (43% oleic acid, 37% linoleic acid), and the paste remaining after oil extraction (known as amlou) is mixed with honey as a traditional Berber dish.

argemone oil Oil derived from seeds of the North American and Caribbean prickly poppy, *Argemone* spp.

argentines Sea fish, species of the family *Argentinidae*.

argininaemia A genetic disease affecting the metabolism of the *amino acid arginine, and hence the normal formation of urea as the end-product of protein metabolism. Depending on the severity of the condition, affected infants may become comatose and die after a moderately high intake of protein. Treatment is by severe restriction of protein intake. Sodium benzoate may be given to increase the excretion of nitrogenous waste as hippuric acid. *See also* BENZOIC ACID.

arginine A basic *amino acid. Not a dietary essential for adult human beings, but infants may not be able to synthesize enough to meet the high demands of growth so may require some in their diet.

argininosuccinic aciduria A genetic disease affecting the formation of urea as the end-product of protein metabolism. Depending on the severity of the condition, affected infants may become comatose and die after a moderately high intake of protein. Treatment is by restriction of protein intake and feeding supplements of the amino acid arginine, which permits elimination of nitrogenous waste as argininosuccinic acid. Sodium benzoate may be given to increase the excretion of nitrogenous waste as hippuric acid. *See also* BENZOIC ACID.

argol Crust of crude *cream of tartar (potassium acid tartrate) which forms on the sides of wine vats, also called wine stone. It consists of 50–85% potassium hydrogen tartrate and 6–12% calcium tartrate, and will be coloured by the grapes, so white argol comes from white grapes and red argol from red grapes. Used in *vinegar fermentation, in the manufacture of *tartaric acid, and as a mordant in dyeing.

ariboflavinosis Deficiency of riboflavin (*vitamin B_2) characterized by swollen, cracked, bright red lips (cheilosis), an enlarged, tender, magenta-red tongue (glossitis), cracking at the corners of the mouth (angular stomatitis), congestion of the blood vessels of the conjunctiva, and a characteristic dermatitis with filiform (wire-like) excrescences.

arkshell (ark clam) Marine bivalve molluscs, *Arcidae* spp.

arlésienne, à l' French garnishes: **1.** aubergine, onions, and tomatoes; **2.** fried small whole tomatoes and pickled chicory hearts; **3.** tomatoes stuffed with rice and large olives stuffed with minced chicken.

armagnac *Brandy made from white wine from one of three defined areas of France: Bas-Armagnac, Haut-Armagnac, or Ténarèze. *See also* COGNAC.

Armenian bole Ferric oxide (iron oxide), either occurring naturally as haematite or prepared by heating ferrous sulphate and other iron salts. Used in metallurgy, polishing compounds, paint pigment, and as a food colour (E172).

aromatic In chemistry, cyclic organic compounds with delocalized conjugated double bonds; the parent compound is benzene. Also used, more generally, to mean compounds providing aroma in foods.

aronia berry *See* CHOKEBERRY.

Aros *See* P.4000.

arracacha Also know as Peruvian carrot or parsnip; Andean (Colombian) root vegetable from the legume *Arracacia xanthorriza*, eaten like potatoes or used to make flour.

arrowhead Aquatic plant (*Sagitaria sagittifolia*); both leaves and root are used in Chinese cooking. Also known as tule potato or wappato.

arrowroot Tuber of the Caribbean plant *Maranta arundinacea*, mainly used to prepare a particularly pure form of starch which contains only a trace of protein (0.2%) and is free from vitamins. It is used to thicken sauces and in bland, low-salt, and protein-restricted diets. Queensland arrowroot is from the rhizome of *achira.

arroz fermentado (arroz amarillo) *See* RICE, FERMENTED.

arsenic A toxic metal, which may have some metabolic functions, although deficiency is unknown and there are no estimates of possible requirements. Organic arsenic derivatives (arsenicals) have been used as pesticides. Arsenic can accumulate in crops treated with arsenical pesticides, and in fish and shellfish living in arsenic-polluted water.

arteriosclerosis Thickening and calcification of the arterial walls, leading to loss of elasticity, occurring with ageing and especially in *hypertension. *See also* ATHEROMA; ATHEROSCLEROSIS.

artichoke, Chinese Tubers of *Stachys affinis* (syn. *S. sieboldii*), similar to Jerusalem artichoke but smaller.

artichoke, globe Young flower heads of *Cynara scolymus*; the edible parts are the fleshy bracts and the base; the choke is the inedible filaments. A 110-g portion (two artichoke hearts) is a *source of vitamin C; provides 1.1 g of dietary fibre; supplies 17 kcal (70 kJ).

artichoke, Japanese Tubers of the perennial plant *Stachys sieboldi*, similar to Jerusalem artichoke.

artichoke, Jerusalem Tubers of *Helianthus tuberosus* introduced into Europe from Canada by Samuel de Champlain in the 17th century and originally called Canadian artichoke; the origin of the name Jerusalem is from the Italian *girasole* (sunflower). A 170-g portion is a good *source of copper; a source of vitamin B_1; provides 1.7 g of dietary fibre; supplies 30 kcal (125 kJ). Much of the carbohydrate is the *non-starch polysaccharide *inulin.

artophites Roman; leavened bread baked in a mould.

asafoetida A resin extracted from the oriental umbelliferous plant *Narthex asafoetida* (syn. *Ferula assafoetida*) with a bitter flavour and pungent odour, used widely in oriental and Middle Eastern cooking and in small amounts in sauces and pickles. The flavour on its own is extremely unpleasant, like concentrated rotten garlic. When cooked, it adds an onion-like flavour.

(The strength of its aroma is suggested by its French and German names: respectively, *merde du diable* and *Teufelsdreck*.)

ascites Abnormal accumulation of fluid in the peritoneal cavity, occurring as a complication of cirrhosis of the liver, congestive heart failure, cancer, and infectious diseases. Depending on the underlying cause, treatment may sometimes consist of a high-energy, high-protein, low-sodium diet, together with diuretic drugs and fluid restriction.

ascorbic acid *Vitamin C, L-xyloascorbic acid, to distinguish it from the *isomer D-araboascorbic acid (isoascorbic acid or erythorbic acid), which has only slight vitamin activity. Both ascorbic acid and erythorbic acid are strong reducing agents, and are used as *antioxidants in foods, to preserve the red colour of fresh and preserved meats, and in the curing of hams.

ascorbic acid oxidase An *enzyme in plant tissues that oxidizes ascorbic acid to dehydro-ascorbic acid; it is released only when the plant wilts or is cut. To preserve the vitamin in cooked vegetables, it is generally recommended that they be plunged into boiling water, to *denature and therefore inactivate the enzyme, as soon as possible after cutting.

ascorbin stearate An ester of *ascorbic acid and *stearic acid; a fat-soluble form of *vitamin C which is used as an *antioxidant.

ascorbyl palmitate An ester of *ascorbic acid and *palmitic acid, used as an *anti-staling compound in bakery goods.

aseptic filling The filling of cans or other containers with food that has already been sterilized, the process thus having to be carried out under aseptic conditions. Continuous sterilization as the food passes along narrow pipes (followed by aseptic filling) allows more rapid heating, with less effect on the quality of the food, than sterilization by heating after *canning.

aseptic processing Heat sterilization of foods before filling into pre-sterilized (aseptic) containers.

ash The residue left behind after all organic matter has been burnt off, a measure of the total content of mineral salts in a food.

ASN American Society for Nutrition.

(∰) SEE WEB LINKS
• The ASN's homepage.

ASO Association for the Study of Obesity.

(∰) SEE WEB LINKS
• The ASO's homepage.

asopao Creole; rice soup containing chicken and seafood.

aspalathin *See* TEA, ROOIBOS.

asparagine A non-essential *amino acid, the β-amide of *aspartic acid.

asparagus The young shoots of the plant *Asparagus officinalis*, originally known in England as sparrow grass (17th century). A 110-g portion (four spears) is a rich *source of folate; a source of vitamin C and copper; provides 1.1 g of dietary fibre; supplies 8 kcal (33 kJ).

aspartame An artificial *sweetener, aspartyl-phenylalanine methyl ester, some 200 times as sweet as sucrose. Stable for a limited time (a few months) in solution, when it gradually breaks down. Used in soft drinks, dessert mixes, and as a 'table top sweetener'. The major trade names are Canderel, Equal, Nutrasweet, and Sanecta.

Because aspartame contains *phenylalanine, it is specifically recommended that children with *phenylketonuria avoid consuming it, although the amounts that would normally be consumed are very small.

aspartic acid (aspartate) A non-essential *amino acid.

aspartyl-phenylalanine methyl ester *See* ASPARTAME.

ASPEN American Society for Parenteral and Enteral Nutrition.

(((⊕))) SEE WEB LINKS

• The ASPEN's homepage.

***Aspergillus* spp.** Filamentous fungi, long employed as a source of *enzymes for use in food manufacture, and now widely utilized as an expression system for production of enzymes and other products as a result of *genetic modification. Because of their long history of use, products of *Aspergillus* spp. are classified as *GRAS (generally regarded as safe) for use in foods.

Some *Aspergillus* spp. produce *aflatoxins. Most strains of *A. parasiticus* are aflatoxigenic, but only about 35% of strains of *A. flavus* produce aflatoxins. Some strains of *A. flavus* have been used to produce *koji, and the more widely used *A. oryzae* (grown commercially as a source of *takadiastase) is probably a domesticated strain of *A. flavus*.

aspic A clear jelly made from fish, chicken, or meat stock, sometimes with added *gelatine, flavoured with lemon, tarragon, vinegar, sherry, peppercorns, and vegetables, used to glaze foods such as meat, fish, and game. The name may be derived from the herb espic or spikenard.

assiette anglaise French (literally 'English plate'); plate of cold assorted meats.

assize of bread English; courts to prosecute bakers selling underweight or over-priced bread (established 1266, abolished 1815).

astaxanthin One of the *carotenoids, the pink colour of salmon and trout muscle; not *vitamin A active.

asti spumante Italian; sparkling wines (generally sweet) made from muscat grapes.

astringency The action of unripe fruits and cider apples, among other foods, to cause contraction of the epithelial tissues of the tongue (literally astringency means 'a drawing together'). The result of loss of the lubricant properties of *saliva because of precipitation by *tannins.

atemoya See CUSTARD APPLE.

atherogenic Compounds that promote the development of *atherosclerosis.

atheroma The fatty deposit composed of various lipids, complex carbohydrates, and fibrous tissue that forms on the inner wall of blood vessels in *atherosclerosis.

atherosclerosis Degenerative disease of the arteries in which there is accumulation in the inner wall of lipids, together with complex carbohydrates and fibrous tissue, called *atheroma. This leads to narrowing of the lumen of the arteries. When it occurs in the coronary artery it can lead to failure of the blood supply to the heart muscle (ischaemia). See also ARTERIOSCLEROSIS.

athletae Roman; unleavened bread mixed with curd cheese.

atholl brose Scottish beverage made from malt whisky, honey, cream, and oatmeal.

atomic absorption spectroscopy (spectrophotometry) A technique for measuring mineral elements by the absorption of light by atoms in a flame or plasma stream.

atomic emission spectroscopy A technique for measuring mineral elements by the emission of light by excited atoms in a flame or plasma stream.

atomization The process of converting a liquid or slurry into a fine spray suitable for spray drying.

atomizer Apparatus for *atomization of liquids or slurries.

atopy The production of *antibodies (IgE) in response to environmental *allergens, including foods, leading to symptoms such as asthma, rhinitis, conjunctivitis, eczema, or dermatitis. In nonatopic disease, patients do not have elevated total serum IgE and show negative skin prick tests, although it has been suggested that such subjects may produce IgE locally against allergens. See also FOOD, ADVERSE REACTIONS.

ATP Adenosine triphosphate, the coenzyme that acts as an intermediate between energy-yielding (catabolic) *metabolism (the oxidation of *metabolic fuels) and *energy expenditure in physical work and in synthetic (anabolic) reactions. ADP (adenosine diphosphate) is phosphorylated to ATP linked to

a

oxidation; in energy expenditure ATP is hydrolysed to ADP and phosphate ions.

ATPases *Enzymes that catalyse the hydrolysis of *ATP, commonly linked to the transport of ions or molecules across cell membranes (*see* TRANSPORT, ACTIVE) or *muscle contraction.

ATP bioluminescence assay A method for rapid estimation of the extent of bacterial contamination of foods, or monitoring cleaning of work surfaces, by measuring the content of *ATP (present only in metabolically active cells) by the light emitted when reacted with the enzyme *luciferase.

atrogin A protein expressed specifically in skeletal muscle, and induced in starvation; probably responsible for the muscle *atrophy seen in *diabetes mellitus, cancer *cachexia, and renal failure.

atrophy Tissue wasting, or decrease in size of a tissue or organ, as a result of disease, injury, or lack of use. Prolonged bed rest leads to considerable muscle atrophy.

atta Indian; wholewheat flour, or dough made from it, for preparation of *chapattis.

attelet (hâtelet) French; ornamental skewers used to decorate cold meats and fish.

aubergine The fruit of *Solanum melongena*, a native of South-East Asia, widely cultivated and eaten as a vegetable, also known as brinjal, egg-plant, and (in West Africa) field egg. Half a medium-sized aubergine (140g) is a *source of folate and vitamin C; provides 2.8g of dietary fibre; supplies 20kcal (85kJ).

AUDIT Alcohol Use Disorders Identification Test, a questionnaire to screen for alcohol abuse.

audit ale Strong *beer originally brewed at Oxford and Cambridge universities to be drunk on 'audit days'.

Auerbach's plexus *See* MYENTERIC PLEXUS.

aurantiamarin A *glucoside present in the *albedo of the bitter orange, which is partly responsible for its flavour.

aurora sauce Danish; *béchamel sauce with tomato purée.

aurore, à l' Dishes served with tomato-flavoured aurora sauce or yellow-coloured garnishes, suggesting the rising sun.

aurum potabile Italian liqueur (literally 'drinkable gold'), made from brandy coloured with saffron, flavoured with oranges, orange zest, and herbs; probably the forerunner of *goldwasser.

ausbruch *See* WINE CLASSIFICATION, GERMANY.

auslese *See* WINE CLASSIFICATION, GERMANY.

autoclave A vessel in which high temperatures can be achieved by using high pressure; the domestic pressure cooker is an example. At atmospheric pressure, water boils at 100°C; at 5lb (35kPa) above atmospheric pressure the boiling point is 109°C; at 10lb (70kPa), 115°C; at 15lb (105kPa), 121°C; and at 20lb (140kPa), 126°C.

Autoclaves have two major uses. In cooking, the higher temperature reduces the time needed. At these higher temperatures, and under moist conditions, bacteria are destroyed more rapidly, so permitting sterilization of foods, surgical dressings and instruments, etc.

autocrine A compound secreted by a cell that acts on the cell that secreted it. *See also* ENDOCRINE GLANDS; HORMONE; JUXTACRINE; PARACRINE.

autoimmune diseases Conditions in which antibodies are raised against normal tissue proteins, leading to destruction of tissue. Examples include type I *diabetes mellitus and some forms of pernicious anaemia (*see* ANAEMIA, PERNICIOUS).

autolysis The process of self-digestion by the enzymes naturally present in tissues. For example, the tenderizing of *game while *hanging is due to autolysis of *connective tissue. *Yeast extract is produced by autolysis of yeast.

autopyron Roman; coarse unleavened bread made from bran and only a little flour, fed mainly to slaves.

autosomal In genetics, a trait carried on any of the *chromosomes other than the sex (X and Y) chromosomes.

autotrophes Organisms that can synthesize all the compounds required for growth from simple inorganic salts, as distinct from heterotrophes, which must be supplied with complex organic compounds. Plants are autotrophes, whereas animals are heterotrophes. Bacteria may be of either type; heterotrophic bacteria are responsible for food spoilage and disease.

autoxidation *Radical chain reaction leading to oxidation of unsaturated *fatty acids in fats and oils, forming hydroperoxides that decompose to form off-flavours (secondary oxidation products).

Autrichienne, à l' French; used synonymously with à la Hongroise for dishes seasoned with paprika, fennel, and sour cream.

auvergnate French; soup made from pig's head broth with lentils, leeks, and potatoes.

auxotrophe Mutant strain of micro-organism that requires one or more nutrients for growth that are not required by the parent organism. Commonly used for microbiological assay of vitamins, amino acids, etc.

availability (bioavailability, biological availability) In some foodstuffs, nutrients that can be demonstrated chemically to be present may not be available, or may be only partially available, when they are eaten. This is because the nutrients are chemically bound in a form that is not susceptible to enzymic digestion, although it is susceptible to the strong acid or alkali *hydrolysis used in chemical analysis. For example, the *niacin in cereal grains, *calcium bound to *phytate, and *lysine combined with sugars in the *Maillard complex, are all biologically unavailable. In some cases low availabity may be because nutrients are not accessible to digestive enzymes. *See also* BIOACCESSIBILITY; BIOCONVERSION; BIOEFFICACY; LYSINE.

available carbon dioxide *See* BAKING POWDER; FLOUR, SELF-RAISING.

available nutrients *See* AVAILABILITY.

avenalin, avenin *Proteins present in *oats.

avern jelly Scottish; jelly made from wild strawberries.

aversion to foods *See* FOOD, ADVERSE REACTIONS.

avgolemono Greek; egg and lemon soup or sauce.

Avicel Trade name for microcrystalline cellulose that has been partially hydrolysed with acid and reduced to a fine powder, used as a *fat replacer. It disperses in water and has the properties of a *gum. It is used in oily foods such as *cheese and *peanut butter, as well as in *syrups and *honey, sauces, and dressings.

avidin A protein in raw egg-white that binds *biotin, preventing its absorption. People who consume abnormally large amounts of uncooked egg (several dozen eggs per week) have been reported to show biotin deficiency. Avidin is *denatured on cooking, and does not combine with biotin; indeed cooked egg is a rich *source of available biotin.

avitaminosis Absence or deficiency of a vitamin; may be used specifically, as, for example, avitaminosis A, or generally, to mean a vitamin deficiency disease.

avocado Fruit of the tree *Persica* (*Persea*) *americana*, also known as the avocado pear or alligator pear, because of its rough skin and pear shape, although it is not related to the *pear. It is unusual among fruits for its high fat content (17–27%), of which 7–14% is *linoleic acid, and also for the fact that it does not ripen until after it has been removed from the tree.

Half an avocado (130g) is a rich *source of vitamin C and copper; a good source of vitamin B_6; a source of protein and iron; contains 26g of fat, of which 20% is saturated; provides 2.6g of dietary fibre; supplies 265kcal (1110kJ).

avron *See* CLOUDBERRY.

a_w *See* WATER ACTIVITY.

awule bolo *See* AKPITI.

aye A *catfish, *Sperata aor*.

ayu North-western Pacific fish, *Plecoglossus altivelis*, that migrates between the sea and fresh water; farmed in several Asian countries.

azeotrope A mixture of two liquids that boils at a constant temperature; the composition of the vapour is the same as that of the liquid. Also known as a constant boiling mixture.

azienda Italian; estate or vineyard on wine labels. *See* WINE CLASSIFICATION, ITALY.

azodicarbonamide A dough conditioner used in ageing and bleaching flour.

azorubin(e) A red colour, carmoisine (E122).

azotaemia Raised blood concentration of *urea and other nitrogenous compounds as a result of renal failure.

baba A French cake supposedly invented by King Stanislas I of Poland and named after Ali Baba. 'Rum baba' is flavoured with rum; a French modification using a 'secret' syrup was called brillat-savarin or savarin.

babaco The seedless fruit of the tree *Carica pentagona*, related to the *papaya, a hybrid between the mountain papaya (*C. pubescens*) and *C. stipulata*, discovered in Ecuador in the 1920s, introduced into New Zealand in 1973, and more recently into the Channel Islands. A 100-g portion is a rich *source of vitamin C.

babassu oil (babaçu oil) Edible oil from nuts of the wild Brazilian palms *Orbignya* spp. and *Attalea* spp., similar in fatty acid composition to *coconut oil, and used for food and in soaps and cosmetics.

Babcock test For the fat content of milk; invented by Wisconsin agricultural chemist Stephen Moulton Babcock, 1890.

babka 1. Russian; yeast cake with grated carrot or potato and flour. **2.** Polish; conical yeast cake traditionally eaten for festivals, similar to Italian *panettone.

baby foods General term to include *infant formula milk and *weaning foods.

bacalaítos *See* ACCRA.

bacalao Spanish and South American name for dried salted cod; Portuguese is bacalhau. *See* KLIPFISH.

bacha Freshwater fish, *Eutropiichthys vacha*.

Bacillus cereus Spore-forming bacterium in cereals (especially rice), a cause of *food-borne disease. Two different toxins are produced, one causing vomiting when present preformed in foods, and the other causing diarrhoea when the organisms multiply in the gastro-intestinal tract. Recovery usually complete within 24–48 hours.

backerbsen German; garnish for soup, batter mixture poured through a colander into hot oil and fried to resemble dried peas.

bäckerei German for baked goods; Austrian name for a variety of different types of biscuit made with baking powder.

baclava *See* BAKLAVA.

bacon Cured (and sometimes smoked) meat from the back, sides, and belly of a pig; variety of cuts with differing fat contents. Gammon is bacon made from the top of the hind legs; green bacon has been cured but not smoked.

A 100-g portion of boiled collar joint is a rich *source of protein, niacin, and vitamin B_1, a source of vitamin B_2 and iron; contains 30g of fat, of which 40% is saturated; supplies 320kcal (1345kJ). A 100-g grilled gammon rasher is exceptionally rich in vitamin B_1 (0.9mg); a rich source of protein and niacin; a good source of iron; a source of vitamin B_2; contains 12g of fat, of which 40% is saturated; supplies 230kcal (970kJ). A 100-g portion of fried streaky bacon is a rich source of protein, niacin, and vitamin B_1; a source of vitamin B_2 and iron; contains 45g of fat, of which 40% is saturated; supplies 500kcal (2100kJ). Also a source of zinc, copper, and selenium.

bacoreta A variety of *tuna fish with dark flesh.

bacteria Unicellular micro-organisms, ranging between 0.5 and 5μm in size. They may be classified on the basis of their shape: spherical (coccus), rodlike (bacilli), spiral (spirillum), comma-shaped (Vibrio), corkscrew-shaped (spirochaetes), or filamentous. Other classifications are based on whether or not they are stained by Gram stain; *aerobic or *anaerobic; and *autotrophic or *heterotrophic. Some form spores that are resistant to heat and sterilizing agents.

Bacteria are responsible for much food spoilage, and for disease (pathogenic bacteria), but they are also made use of, for example in the *pickling process and in *fermentation of milk, as well as in the manufacture of *vitamins and *amino acids and a variety of *enzymes and *hormones.

Between 45 and 85% of the dry matter of bacteria is protein, and some can be grown on petroleum residues or methanol for use in animal feed.

bacteria, planktonic In terms of food processing hygiene, *bacteria that are floating freely on a surface, as opposed to those that have attached to the surface and formed a *biofilm.

bacterial count *See* PLATE COUNT.

bacterial filter A filter fine enough to prevent the passage of *bacteria (0.5–5μm in diameter), which permits removal of bacteria from solutions. *Viruses are considerably smaller, and will pass through a bacterial filter.

bacteriocins *Antibiotic *peptides coded for in bacterial *plasmids that kill or inhibit closely related species or even different strains of the same species. Two main classes: *lantibiotics, and small, heat-stable, nonlantibiotics.

bacteriophage *Viruses that attack *bacteria, commonly known as phages. They pass through *bacterial filters, and can be a cause of considerable problems in bacterial cultures (for example milk *starter cultures).

bacteriostat A compound that inhibits the growth and multiplication of *bacteria, but does not kill them.

Bacterium aceti *See* ACETOBACTER.

bactometer A device for the estimation of bacterial contamination within a few hours, based on measuring the early stages of breakdown of nutrients by the bacteria through changes in the electrical impedance of the medium.

bacuri Fruit of the Amazonian forest trees *Platonia insignis* and *P. esculenta*, with a leathery shell enclosing creamy white flesh. Similar to *mangosteen.

badam pak *See* BARFI.

badderlocks Edible *seaweed (*Alaria esculenta*) found on northern British coasts and around the Faroe Islands. Known in Scotland as honeyware.

badminton A drink prepared with *claret, sugar, and *soda water.

bael Thick-shelled fruit of the Indian tree *Aegle marmelos*, a rich source of vitamin C. Used as a treatment for dysentery. Also known as Bengal or Indian quince.

bagaciera *See* MARC.

bagasse The residues from sugar-cane milling, consisting of the crushed stalks from which the juice has been expressed; it consists of 50% *cellulose, 25% *hemicelluloses, and 25% *lignin. It is used as a fuel, for cattle feed, and in the manufacture of paper and fibre board. The name is sometimes also applied to the residues of other plants, such as *beet, which is sometimes incorporated into foods as a source of *dietary fibre.

bagel A circular bread roll with a hole in the middle, made from fermented wheat flour dough (including egg), which is boiled before being baked. A Jewish speciality; the first recorded mention of *beygls* was in Krakow (Poland) in 1610, in regulations that stated they were to be given as a gift to women in childbirth.

bagna cauda Italian (Piedmontese); sauce made from olive oil and butter flavoured with garlic and anchovy. Small pieces of raw vegetables are dipped into the hot sauce.

bagoong Filipino; fermented salted fish paste, usually made from an anchovy-like fish called dilis (*Stolephorus indicus*) or from young herring.

baguette A French *bread, a thin loaf (about 60 cm long) and weighing 250 g, with a crisp crust.

baharat North African spice mix used to season lamb; the name means spice in Arabic.

bain-marie A double saucepan named after the medieval alchemist Maria de Cleofa.

baiser French; two small meringues joined together with cream or jam.

bajoa *See* MILLET.

baked Alaska Dessert of ice cream on a sponge base and covered with meringue, baked in a hot oven for a very short time, so that the meringue is cooked but the ice cream remains frozen. Earlier called omelette norvégienne or Norwegian omelette. Invented by chef Charles Ranhofer at Delmonico's restaurant in New York, 1867.

baked apple berry *See* CLOUDBERRY.

baker's cheese *See* CHEESE, COTTAGE.

baker's yeast glycan The dried cell walls of yeast, *Saccharomyces cerevisiae*, used as an emulsifier and thickener.

bakes Caribbean (Trinidadian); fried biscuits made with baking powder dough. *See also* FLOATS.

Bakewell tart An open pastry tart with an almond-flavoured cake filling, originally made in Bakewell in Derbyshire, England.

baking *Cooking in an oven by dry heat.

baking additives Materials added to flour products for a variety of purposes, including bleaching the flour, *ageing, slowing the rate of staling, and improving the texture of the finished product.

baking blind A pastry case for a tart or flan, which is baked empty and then filled.

baking powder A mixture that liberates carbon dioxide when moistened and heated. The source of carbon dioxide is sodium bicarbonate, and an acid is required. This may be *cream of tartar (in fast-acting baking powders which liberate carbon dioxide in the dough before heating) or calcium acid phosphate, sodium pyrophosphate, or sodium aluminium sulphate (in slow-acting powders, which liberate most of the carbon dioxide during heating).

Legally, baking powder must contain not less than 8% available, and not more than 1.5% residual, carbon dioxide. Golden raising powder (formerly known as egg substitute) is similar, but is coloured yellow, and must contain not less than 6% available, and not more than 1.5% residual, carbon dioxide.

baking soda (bicarbonate of soda) Sodium bicarbonate (sodium hydrogen carbonate, $NaHCO_3$), the source of carbon dioxide in *baking powder.

baklava (baclava) Middle Eastern; sweet made from phyllo *pastry filled with nuts and honey, baked and served drenched with syrup.

balance With reference to diet, positive balance is a net gain to the body and negative balance a net loss from the body. When intake equals excretion, the body is in equilibrium or balance with respect to the nutrient in question. Used in reference to nitrogen (protein), mineral salts, and energy. A balanced diet is one containing all nutrients in appropriate amounts.

balanced plate *See* EATWELL PLATE; *see also* FOOD PYRAMID.

ballekes Belgian; croquettes of minced pork simmered in white wine or beer.

ball mill A vessel in which material is ground by rolling with heavy balls, used especially for hard materials.

ballottine A kind of *galantine of meat, poultry, game, or fish, boned, stuffed, and rolled into a bundle; also small balls of meat or poultry.

balm A perennial herb, *Melissa officinalis*, with hairy leaves and a lemon scent, therefore often known as lemon balm. Used for its flavour in fruit salads, sweet or savoury sauces, etc., as well as for preparation of herb teas. Claimed to have calming medicinal properties; it is rich in tannins.

balmain bug A variety of *lobster found in Australia.

balsamic vinegar *See* VINEGAR.

balsam pear *See* GOURD, BITTER.

balsam peru oil A flavouring agent with a sweet balsamic odour, extracted from Peruvian balsam (*Myroxylon pereirae*).

balti Pakistani, Kashmiri; spiced meat or vegetable dishes cooked and served in a conical metal vessel, a karahi.

bamboo, water *Zizania latifolia* or *Z. aquatica*. The edible portion is the succulent stem; stem enlargement is due to the fungus *Ustilago esculenta*, which prevents floral initiation; it must be harvested before the fungus enters the reproductive phase when the spores form black *smut. Closely related to American wild rice; *see* RICE, WILD.

bamboo shoots Thick, pointed young shoots of *Bambusa vulgaris*, *Phyllostachys pubescens*, and *Dendrocalamus* spp., eaten as a vegetable in Eastern Asia. A 100-g portion is a *source of vitamin B_1; supplies 27 kcal (115 kJ).

bamboo tea Chinese; bitter black *tea, so called because it is encased in bamboo leaves.

bamies (bamya) *See* OKRA.

bami goreng (bahmi goreng) Malaysian, Indonesian, Dutch; noodles with fried shredded vegetables, served with diced pork, chicken or prawns, topped with strips of omelette.

banaba The leaves of *Lagerstroemia speciosa* used to make a herbal tea in the Philippines and Japan. The leaf extracts have a hypoglycaemic action and may be useful in treating *diabetes mellitus.

banana Fruit of the genus *Musa*; cultivated varieties are sterile hybrids, and so cannot be given species names. Dessert bananas have a high sugar content (17–19%) and are eaten raw; *plantains (sometimes known as green bananas) have a higher starch and lower sugar content and are picked when too hard to be eaten raw.

One medium banana (100g) is a good *source of vitamin A; a source of vitamins B_6 and C, and copper; contains 0.3g of fat, of which 33% is saturated; provides 3g of dietary fibre; supplies 86kcal (360kJ). The sodium content is low (1.2mg/100g) so bananas are used in low-sodium diets.

banana, Abyssinian *See* BANANA, FALSE.

banana, baking American name for *plantain.

banana, false Ensete, the fruit of *Ensete ventricosum*, related to the banana. The fruits are small and, unlike bananas, contain seeds. The rhizome and inner tissue of the stem form a major part of the diet in southern Ethiopia. Also known as Abyssian banana.

banana figs Bananas that have been split longitudinally and sun-dried without treating with *sulphur dioxide. The product is dark in colour and sticky.

Banbury cake Flat oval cake of flaky pastry filled with dried fruit; originated in Banbury, Oxfordshire, England.

bangers Colloquial English term for *sausages. When served with mashed potatoes, the dish is known as bangers and mash.

banian days Historical; days on which no meat was served; named after Banian (Hindu) merchants who abstained from eating meat.

bànitsa Bulgarian; tarts made from phyllo pastry (*see* PASTRY, PHYLLO) filled with nuts and cream, cheese, or spinach.

banku *See* AKPITI.

bannock A flat round cake made from oat, rye, or barley meal and baked on a hearth or griddle. Pitcaithly bannock is a type of almond *shortbread containing *caraway seeds and chopped peel.

banspata Freshwater fish, a member of the *carp family, *Danio devario*.

Bantu beer *See* BEER, SORGHUM.

baobab Fruit of the African tree *Adansonia digitata*; the edible pulp (known as monkey bread) is used in foods and beverages. The leaves are also edible and the seeds are ground to produce a meal (frequently mixed with millet) or used for production of baobab oils.

bap Traditionally a soft, white, flat, flour-coated Scottish breakfast roll. The term is now also used for any relatively large soft-crusted roll made from white, brown, or wholemeal flour.

BAPEN British Association for Parenteral and Enteral Nutrition.

(((●))) SEE WEB LINKS
- The BAPEN's homepage.

bara brith *See* BARM BRACK.

barack pálinka Hungarian; dry apricot *brandy.

bara lawr *See* LAVER.

Barbados cherry *See* CHERRY, WEST INDIAN.

barbecue Originally Caribbean (native American) name for a wooden frame used to smoke and dry meat over a slow, smoky fire; the whole animal was placed on a spit over burning coals. Now outdoor cooking of meat, sausages, etc., on a *charcoal or gas fire; also the fire on which they are cooked.

barbecue sauce Chopped onions fried in butter, made into a sauce with tomato paste and seasoned, served with barbecued meat and sausages.

barbel Freshwater fish, a member of the *carp family, *Barbus barbus*.

barbera A *grape variety widely used for *wine making, not one of the classic varieties; makes the dark, fruity, and often sharp red wines of northern Italy.

barberry *See* BERBERRY.

barberry fig *See* PRICKLY PEAR.

Barcelona nut Spanish variety of *hazelnut.

Bardet–Biedl syndrome A very rare genetic disease leading to obesity, pigmentary retinopathy, polydactyly, mental retardation, hypogonadism, and renal failure.

barding To cover the breast of a bird with slices of fat before roasting in order to prevent the flesh from drying. *See also* LARDING.

barfi (burfi) Indian sweet made from condensed milk, cooked with sugar until it solidifies; flavoured varieties include kesri pedha, flavoured with *saffron; kaju katli, flavoured with cashew; pista barfi, flavoured with *pistachio; and badam pak, flavoured with *rose water and *almonds. Besan barfi is made with *gram flour.

bariatrics The medical and surgical specialities concerned with the treatment of overweight and *obesity.

barium A metal of no known metabolic function, and hence not a dietary essential. Barium sulphate is opaque to X-rays and a suspension is used (a barium meal) to allow examination of the shape and movements of the stomach for diagnostic purposes and (a barium enema) for X-ray investigation of the lower intestinal tract.

Barker hypothesis *See* PROGRAMMING, METABOLIC.

barley Grain of *Hordeum vulgare*, one of the hardiest of the *cereals; mainly used for animal feed and brewing beer. The whole grain with only the outer husk removed (pot, Scotch, or hulled barley) requires several hours' cooking. Pot barley has undergone three *pearlings, which remove all of the hull and most of the bran layer; further pearlings produce pearl barley. Barley flour is ground pearl barley; barley flakes are the flattened grain. A 150-g portion of cooked pearl barley (50 g dry cereal) is a *source of niacin, vitamin B_6, folate, zinc, copper, and iron; provides 9 g of dietary fibre; supplies 180 kcal (750 kJ).

barley, malted *See* MALT.

barleycorn An obsolete measure of length; the size of a single grain of barley; ⅓ inch (0.85 cm).

barley sugar *Sugar confectionery made by melting and cooling sugar, originally by boiling with a decoction of barley.

barley water A drink made by boiling pearl barley with water, commonly flavoured with orange or lemon.

barley wine Fermented malted barley, stronger than *beer (8–10% *alcohol by volume), bottled under pressure, so sparkling.

Barlow's disease Infantile *scurvy, also known as Moeller's disease and Cheadle's disease.

barm An alternative name for *yeast or leaven, or the froth on fermenting malt liquor. Spon (short for spontaneous) or virgin barm is made by allowing wild yeast to fall into sugar medium and multiply.

barm brack Irish; yeast cake made with butter, egg, buttermilk, and dried fruit, flavoured with caraway seed. Similar Welsh cake is bara brith.

barquette Small boat-shaped pastry cases, used for savoury or sweet mixtures.

barracuda Pelagic predatory marine fish (*Sphyraena* spp.); widely distributed in warmer regions of the Atlantic and Pacific oceans.

barramundi Fast-growing fish (*Lates calcarifer*) from coastal waters, estuaries, and lagoons in the south-west Pacific region, farmed in Thailand, Indonesia, and Australia.

barrel A standard barrel contains 36 gallons (36 imperial gallons (UK) = 163.6L; 36 US gallons = 113.7L).

bartail flathead Bottom-dwelling fish (*Platycephalus indicus*) found in coastal waters and estuaries in South Pacific and Indian Ocean regions; also introduced into the eastern Mediterranean, and farmed in Japan.

basa Freshwater fish, *Pangasius* spp., also called basa *catfish.

basal metabolic rate (BMR) The *energy cost of maintaining the metabolic integrity of the body, nerve and muscle tone, respiration, and circulation. It depends on the amount of metabolically active body tissue, and can be calculated from body weight, height, and age:

$$\text{MJ/day} = 0.0418 \times \text{weight (kg)} + 0.026 \times \text{height (cm)} - 0.0209 \times \text{age (y)} - 0.674$$
$$\text{(for males) or} - 0.0291 \text{ (for females)}$$

$$\text{kcal/day} = 9.99 \times \text{weight (kg)} + 6.25 \times \text{height (cm)} - 5 \times \text{age (y)} - 161 \text{ (males)}$$
$$\text{or} - 5 \text{ (females).}$$

For children the BMR also includes the energy cost of growth. Experimentally, BMR is measured as the heat output from the body, or the rate of oxygen consumption, under strictly standardized conditions, 12–14 hours after the last meal, completely at rest (but not asleep) and at an environmental temperature of 26–30°C, to ensure thermal neutrality. Measurement of metabolic rate under less rigorously controlled conditions gives the resting metabolic rate (RMR).

For people with a sedentary life-style and relatively low physical activity, BMR accounts for about 70–80% of total energy expenditure. The energy costs of different activities are generally expressed as the physical activity ratio, the ratio of energy expenditure in the activity to BMR.

base *See* ALKALI.

Basedow's disease *See* THYROTOXICOSIS.

base formers *See* ACID FOODS.

basil An aromatic herb, *Ocimum basilicum* and *O. minimum*; other members of the genus *Ocimum* are also used as seasoning.

basmati Long-grain Indian variety of *rice; much prized for its delicate flavour (the name means 'fragrant' in Hindi).

bass A variety of marine and freshwater fishes. European sea bass is *Dicentrarchus labrax*, striped bass is *Morone saxatilis*, white bass is *M. chrysops*, Japanese sea bass is *Lateolabrax japonicus*, spotted sea bass is *Dicentrarchus punctatus*, southern rock bass is *Paralabrax callaensis*.

baste To ladle hot fat (or other liquid) over meat, poultry, etc., at intervals while it is baking or roasting, in order to improve the texture, flavour, and appearance.

BAT Brown adipose tissue. *See* ADIPOSE TISSUE, BROWN.

batashi Freshwater fish, *Pseudeutropius atherinoides*.

batata *See* POTATO, SWEET.

Bath bun A small English cake made from milk-based yeast dough, with dried fruit and a topping of sugar crystals, attributed to Dr W. Oliver of Bath (18th century).

Bath chap The cheek and jawbones of the pig, salted and smoked. Originated in Bath (England).

Bath cheese A small English *cheese, made from cow's milk with the subsequent addition of cream.

Bath Oliver A biscuit made with yeast, attributed to Dr W. Oliver of Bath (18th century).

Battenberg cake A two-coloured sponge cake, baked in an oblong tin, usually covered with almond paste; named in honour of the marriage of Queen Victoria's granddaughter to Prince Louis of Battenberg, 1884.

batter Thick liquid mixture of flour, milk, and eggs, used to coat fish before frying, fried alone to make pancakes or griddle cakes, or baked to make Yorkshire pudding.

bauernschmaus Austrian; pork loin chops, bacon, and sausages cooked in beer with *sauerkraut, grated raw potato, and seasoning.

bauernspeck Austrian; pork cured in brine with juniper berries and smoked.

bavarois(e) **1.** A hot drink made from eggs, milk, and tea, sweetened and flavoured with a liqueur; 17th-century Bavarian. **2.** French; (*crème bavaroise*) a cold dessert made from egg custard with gelatine and cream. **3.** *Hollandaise sauce with *crayfish garnish.

bay (bay leaf) A herb, the leaf of the Mediterranean sweet bay tree *Lauris nobilis*, with a strong characteristic flavour. Rarely used alone, but an important component of *bouquet garni, and used with other herbs in *marinades, pickles, stews, and stuffing. Indonesian bay or salam is *Szyzgium polyanthum*.

bayberry Root bark of the tree *Myricia cerifera*, containing *flavonoids, *tannins, and *terpenes, claimed to possess antipyretic, circulatory stimulant, emetic, and mild diaphoretic (sweat-inducing) properties.

bay lobster (Moreton Bay bug) A variety of sand lobster found in Australia.

BDA British Dietetic Association.

(⊕) SEE WEB LINKS

• The BDA's homepage.

bdelygmia An extreme loathing for food.

bean, adzuki Also known as aduki or feijoa bean, the seed of the Asian adzuki plant *Phaseolus* (*Vigna*) *angularis*. Sweet tasting, the basis of Cantonese red bean paste used to fill *dim sum. Also ground to a flour and used in bread, pastry, and sweets or eaten after sprouting as *bean sprouts. A 100-g portion is a *source of protein, iron, zinc, vitamin B_1, and niacin; provides 5 g of *dietary fibre; supplies 125 kcal (525 kJ).

bean, asparagus Seeds and pods of *Vigna sesquipedalis*, known in the Caribbean as yard-long bean. Young leaves and stems are also eaten.

bean, black *See* CHESTNUT, AUSTRALIAN.

bean, black-eyed Also known as black-eyed pea or cowpea, *Vigna sinensis* or *V. unguiculata*; creamy white bean with a black mark on one edge.

bean, borlotti Italian variety of *Phaseolus vulgaris*, haricot or common bean. *See* BEAN, HARICOT.

bean, broad Also known as fava or horse bean, *Vicia faba*. A 75-g portion is a good *source of copper; a source of niacin, folate, and vitamin C; contains 0.5 g of fat, of which 16% is saturated; provides 3 g of dietary fibre; supplies 35 kcal (145 kJ). *See also* FAVISM.

bean, butter Several large varieties of *Phaseolus vulgaris* or *P. lunatus*, also known as lima, curry, Madagascar, and sugar bean. A 100-g cooked portion is a *source of protein, copper, iron; provides 5 g of dietary fibre; supplies 80 kcal (335 kJ).

bean, djenkol Seed of the South-East Asian plant *Pithecellobium lobata*. Contains djenkolic acid, a sulphur-containing amino acid derived from *cysteine. It is metabolized but, being relatively insoluble, any that is not metabolized crystallizes in the kidney tubules causing renal stones.

bean, French Unripe seeds and pods of *Phaseolus vulgaris*; ripe seeds are haricot beans (*see* BEAN, HARICOT). A 100-g portion is a rich *source of folate; a source of vitamin A (as carotene) and copper; provides 3g of dietary fibre; supplies 7kcal (30kJ).

bean, frijole Mexican haricot, tepary, or pinto bean, *Phaseolus acutifolius*, a drought-hardy crop.

bean, haricot Ripe seed of *Phaseolus vulgaris*. Also known as navy, string, pinto, or snap bean. A 100-g portion of dried haricot beans is a good *source of copper; a source of protein, vitamin B_1, and iron; contains 0.5g of fat, of which 20% is saturated; provides 7g of dietary fibre; supplies 100kcal (420kJ). *See also* BEAN, FRENCH.

bean, hyacinth Also known as lablab bean, *Lablab purpureus*.

bean, jack *Canavalia ensiformis*, grown mainly as a fodder crop, although immature pods and seeds are eaten. The ripe beans are the main commercial source of the *enzyme urease.

bean, jugo *See* GROUNDNUT, BAMBARRA.

bean, lima *See* BEAN, BUTTER.

bean, mung Whole or split seed of *Vigna radiata* (*Phaseolus aureus*, *P. radiatus*), green gram or urd bean. A 150-g portion is a rich source of folate, copper, and selenium; a good *source of vitamin B_6, iron, and zinc; a source of protein and vitamin B_1; provides 3g of dietary fibre; supplies 90kcal (380kJ). *See also* BEAN SPROUTS.

bean, pinto *Phaseolus acutifolius*, also known as frijole, Mexican haricot, or tepary bean; drought hardy.

bean, red kidney Ripe seed of *Phaseolus vulgaris*. A 100-g portion of dried raw beans is a rich *source of protein, vitamin B_1, folate, iron, copper, and selenium; a good source of vitamin B_6 and zinc; a source of vitamin B_2, niacin, and calcium; contains 1.7g of fat, of which 11% is saturated; provides 25g of dietary fibre; supplies 280kcal (1180kJ).

bean, runner *Phaseolus multiflorus* or *P. coccineus*. A 100-g portion is a rich *source of folate; contains 0.2g of fat, of which 50% is saturated; provides 3g of dietary fibre; supplies 20kcal (85kJ).

bean, soya *See* SOYA BEAN.

bean, string Either runner beans or French beans that have a climbing habit; the name derives from the method of growing them up strings.

bean, tonka Seed of the South American tree *Dipteryx odorata*, with a sweet, pungent smell, used like *vanilla for flavouring.

bean, urd *See* BEAN, MUNG.

bean, winged *Psophocarpus tetragonolobus.*

bean, yard-long *See* BEAN, ASPARAGUS.

bean curd *See* TOFU.

bean curd skin *See* YUBA.

beans Seeds of the family *Leguminosae*, eaten as food. Dried beans contain toxic *lectins; uncooked or partially cooked beans cause vomiting, diarrhoea, and serious damage to the intestinal mucosa. The lectins are inactivated by boiling for about 10 minutes, but not by cooking below boiling point.

beans, baked Usually mature haricot beans, small variety of *Phaseolus vulgaris*, cooked in sauce; often canned with tomato sauce and starch with added sugar (or sweetener) and salt. The first canned baked beans were produced in Portland, Maine, 1875. A 225-g portion (small can) is a good *source of protein; a source of vitamin B_1, niacin, calcium, and iron; contains about 700 mg of sodium; 8 g of dietary fibre; supplies 160 kcal (670 kJ).

beans, refried *See* FRIJOLES.

bean sprouts Any of a number of peas, beans, and seeds that can be germinated and the sprouts eaten raw or cooked. The sprouting causes the synthesis of vitamin C. One of the commonest sprouts is that of the mung bean, but *alfalfa and adzuki beans are also used. An 80-g portion is a good *source of folate; provides 2.4 g of dietary fibre; supplies 7 kcal (30 kJ).

bearberry Fruit of the wild Arctic bush *Arctostaphylos uva-ursi*, similar in size to currants, with a tough skin and mealy white pulp containing hard seeds.

béarnaise sauce A thick French *sauce made with egg yolk, butter, wine vinegar or white wine, and chopped *shallots, named after Béarn in south-west France.

beat **1.** To agitate an ingredient or a mixture by vigorously turning it over and over with an upward motion, in order to introduce air, using a spoon, fork, whisk, or electric mixer. **2.** Raw meat is beaten by hitting it briskly all over the surface to break down the fibres and make it more tender when cooked.

Beaujolais Red *wine from the Beaujolais region of France, made from Gamay grapes. Beaujolais nouveau is the new season's wine, drunk young. It is 'officially' available on the third Thursday of November.

béchamel sauce Also known as white *sauce. One of the basic French sauces, made with milk, butter, and flour. Named after Louis de Béchamel, of the court of Louis XIV of France. He invested heavily in Newfoundland fisheries, and invented the sauce in 1654 to mask the flavour of dried cod he shipped across the Atlantic.

bêche-de-mer *See* SEA CUCUMBER.

BED *See* BINGE-EATING DISORDER.

beechwood sugar *See* XYLOSE.

beef Flesh of the ox (*Bos taurus*); flesh from young calves is *veal. A 150-g portion of most cuts is a rich *source of protein, niacin, iron, and vitamin B_{12}; a good source of vitamin B_2 and copper; a source of vitamins B_1, B_6, and selenium; contains 20–30 g of fat, of which half is *saturated (lean part is 5% fat); supplies 350–500 kcal (1470–2100 kJ).

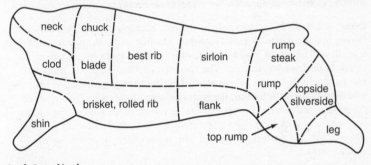

Beef. Cuts of beef

beef, baron of The pair of sirloins of *beef, left uncut at the bone.

beef, bully The name given by troops during the First World War to corned beef (*see* BEEF, CORNED).

beef, corned In the UK, a canned product made from low-quality beef that has been partially extracted with hot water to make *meat extract; the traditional tapered can was patented by Arthur Libby in 1875. A 150-g portion is an exceptionally rich *source of protein, niacin, and iron; a good source of vitamin B_2; contains 18 g of fat, of which half is saturated; and supplies 330 kcal (1390 kJ). In the USA and elsewhere corned beef means pickled beef (in the UK this is called salt beef).

beef, pressed *See* BEEF, SALT.

beef, salt Boned brisket beef that has been salted, cooked, and pressed. Also known as pressed beef and, in the USA, corned beef.

beefalo A cross between the domestic cow (*Bos taurus*) and the buffalo (*Bubalus* spp.) which can be fattened on range grass rather than requiring cereal and protein supplements.

beef bourguignon *See* BOURGUIGNON.

beefburger *See* HAMBURGER.

beef olives Thin strips of beef filled with savoury stuffing, braised in stock.

beefsteak fungus Large edible fungus (*Fistulina hepatica*) with a stringy, meat-like texture and deep red juice. *See* MUSHROOMS.

beef stroganoff Thin strips of beef, fried and served in a sour cream and mushroom sauce.

beef tea An extract of stewing beef, formerly used for invalids, since the extractives stimulate appetite. *See also* MEAT EXTRACT.

beer *Alcoholic beverage made by the fermentation of *cereals; traditionally barley, but also maize, rice, and sorghum. The first step is the malting of barley: it is allowed to sprout, when the *enzyme *amylase hydrolyses some of the starch to dextrins and maltose. The sprouted (malted) barley is dried, then extracted with hot water (the process of mashing) to produce wort. After the addition of *hops for flavour, the wort is allowed to ferment. Two types of *yeast are used in brewing: top-fermenting yeasts, which float on the surface of the wort, and bottom or deep fermenters. Most traditional British beers (ale, bitter, stout, and porter) are brewed with top-fermenting yeasts. *See also* BARLEY WINE.

UK beers, brown ale, and stout: around 3% alcohol by volume, 2–4% carbohydrate, 75–110 kcal (315–460 kJ) per 300 mL (half pint). Strong ale is 6.6% alcohol, 6% carbohydrate, 210 kcal (880 kJ) per 300 mL (half pint). Ale is a light-coloured beer, relatively high in alcohol content, and moderately heavily hopped. Bitter beers are darker and contain more hops. Porter and stout are almost black in colour; they are made from wort containing some partly charred malt; milk stout is made from wort containing added *lactose. Porter was first brewed in London in 1722, as a low cost beer for market porters.

Lager is the traditional mainland European type of beer, sometimes called Pilsner lager or Pils, since the original lager was brewed in Pilsen in Bohemia. It is brewed by deep fermentation.

Lambic, geuze, and weisse are strong sour beers made from barley or wheat, mainly in Belgium and Germany. Krieken lambic is cherry flavoured.

beer, kaffir *See* BEER, SORGHUM; POMBÉ.

beer, lite Beer that has been allowed to ferment until virtually all the carbohydrate has been converted to alcohol, and so it is low in carbohydrate and high in alcohol.

beer, low alcohol May be made either by fermentation of a low carbohydrate wort or by removal of much of the alcohol after fermentation (de-alcoholized beer).

beer, sorghum African; made from sorghum, and also millet, maize, or plantain, a thick sour beverage consumed while still fermenting. Also known by numerous local names, kaffir beer, bouza, *pombé, Bantu beer. 3–8% alcohol, 3–10% carbohydrate, a rich source of vitamin B_1 per 300mL portion.

beer, spruce Western Canadian; branches, bark, and cones of black spruce (*Picea mariana*) boiled for several hours, then put in a cask with molasses, hops, and yeast, and allowed to ferment.

beerenauslese *See* WINE CLASSIFICATION, GERMANY.

bees' royal jelly *See* ROYAL JELLY.

beestings The first milk given by the cow after calving, the colostrum, rich in immunoglobulins.

beeswax Wax from the honeycomb of the bee, used to glaze confectionery, in chewing gum, and as a flavouring agent.

beet, common (beet, red) *See* BEETROOT.

beet, fructan Genetically modified sugar beet (*see* BEET, SUGAR) that converts ≈90% of the sucrose to short-chain *fructans because it has been modified with the gene for sucrose:sucrose fructosyl transferase from Jerusalem *artichoke.

beet, leaf (sea kale beet; silver beet; spinach beet; white leaf beet) *See* CHARD, SWISS.

beet, sugar *Beta vulgaris* var. *vulgaris*, a biennial plant related to *beetroot but with white, conical roots; the most important source of *sugar (*see* SUCROSE) in temperate countries; contains 15–20% sucrose. *See also* BEET, FRUCTAN.

beetroot The root of *Beta vulgaris* var. *esculenta*, eaten cooked or pickled. Known simply as beet in North America. The violet-red pigment, betanin, is used as a food colour (E162). One small beetroot (40g) is a good *source of folate; provides 1.6g of dietary fibre; supplies 18kcal (75kJ).

beeturia Excretion of red-coloured urine after eating *beetroot, due to excretion of the pigment betanin. It occurs, not consistently, in about one person in eight.

bee wine Wine produced by the usual fermentation of sugar, but using *yeast in the form of a clump of yeast and lactic bacteria; the clump rises and falls with the bubbles of carbon dioxide formed during fermentation, hence the name 'bee'.

behenic acid Very long-chain saturated *fatty acid (C22:0).

beignets French; *fritters, especially deep-fried *choux pastry.

beikost Any additional food used in infant feeding other than human milk and infant milk formula; weaning foods.

belching *See* ERUCTATION.

belegte brote German; open *sandwiches.

beli sir Yugoslavian soft cheese, brine ripened and pressed into moulds.

belle hélène **1.** Garnish of mushrooms stuffed with cooked tomatoes or green peas. **2.** Pears poached in vanilla-flavoured syrup, served in vanilla ice cream with a chocolate sauce.

bell pepper *See* PEPPER.

bel paese Italian soft cheese.

beluga Russian name for the white sturgeon (*Acipenser huro*), whose roe forms the most prized *caviar.

Benedictine A French *liqueur invented in about 1510 by the monks of the Benedictine Abbey of Fécamp in France. The abbey was closed, and the recipe lost after the French Revolution, then rediscovered about 1863. It is based on double-distilled *brandy, flavoured with some 75 herbs and spices; it contains 40% (by volume) alcohol and 30% sugar; 300 kcal (1.3 MJ)/100 mL.

benniseed *See* SESAME.

bentonite *See* FULLER'S EARTH.

bento no tomo Japanese seasoning consisting of dried fish, salt, soy sauce, and *monosodium glutamate.

benzedrine *See* AMPHETAMINE.

benzoates Salts of *benzoic acid.

benzoic acid A preservative normally used as the sodium, potassium, or calcium salts and their derivatives, especially in acid foods such as pickles and sauces. It occurs naturally in a number of fruits, including *cranberries, *prunes, *greengages, and *cloudberries, and in *cinnamon. Cloudberries contain so much benzoic acid that they can be stored for long periods of time without bacterial or fungal spoilage. Benzoic acid and its derivatives are excreted from the body conjugated with the *amino acids glycine (forming hippuric acid) and alanine. Because of this, benzoic acid is sometimes used in the treatment of *argininaemia, *argininosuccinic aciduria, and *citrullinaemia, permitting excretion of nitrogenous waste from the body as these conjugates.

benzoyl peroxide Used as a bleaching agent for flour. *See* AGEING.

beolas Jewish; fritters made from *matzo meal, flour, and eggs.

berberry Fruit of *Berberis vulgaris*. Ripe fruits are edible, but unripe berries contain toxic alkaloids. Also known as barberry.

bercy *Sauce made from white wine, light stock, shallots, and herbs.

bergamot 1. A pear-shaped orange, *Citrus bergamia*, grown mainly in Calabria, Italy, for its peel oil. **2.** An ornamental perennial herb, *Monarda didyma*, also know as bee balm, the dried leaves of which were used to make Oswego tea, a native American traditional remedy. **3.** A type of *pear, *Pyrus persica*.

beriberi The result of severe and prolonged deficiency of *vitamin B_1, still occasionally a problem in parts of South-East Asia, where the diet is high in carbohydrate and poor in vitamin B_1. In developed countries vitamin B_1 deficiency is associated with alcohol abuse; while it may result in beriberi, more commonly the result is central nervous system damage, the *Wernicke–Korsakoff syndrome. In beriberi there is degeneration of peripheral nerves, starting in the hands and feet and ascending the arms and legs, with a loss of sensation and deep muscle pain. There is also enlargement of the heart, which may lead to *oedema (wet beriberi), and death results from heart failure. Fatal heart failure may develop without the nerve damage being apparent (Shoshin or sudden beriberi). The name is derived from the Bahasa-Malay word for sheep, to describe the curious sheep-like gait adopted by sufferers.

berry Botanical term for fleshy juicy fruits with one or more seeds and not having a stone, e.g. grape, gooseberry, tomato, blackcurrant, cranberry.

besan (bessan) Indian; *chickpea flour.

best before *See* DATE-MARKING.

beta-carotene (β-carotene) *See* CAROTENE.

beta-glucans *See* GLUCANS.

betalaines (betanins) Red-purple pigments of *beetroot.

Betatene Trade name for mixed *carotenoids from the alga *Dunaliella salina*.

betel 1. Leaf of the creeper *Piper betel*, which is chewed in some parts of the world for its stimulating effect on account of the presence of the *alkaloids arecoline and guvacoline. The leaves are chewed with the nuts of the areca palm (called pinang in Malaysia), *Arecha catechu*, which is therefore often called the betel palm, and the nut is called betel nut. The Indian delicacy pan is based on betel leaf and areca nut, together with aromatic spices and herbs; it is chewed as a digestive and stimulant. **2.** Leaves of *Piper sermentosum*, used in South-East Asian cuisine as wrapping for spiced minced meat.

beurre, au Cooked or served with butter.

beurre manié Butter with an equal amount of flour blended in, used for thickening sauces.

beurre noir *See* BUTTER, BLACK.

beutelwurst German; blood sausage made from pork offal (including intestine and brain), encased in pig intestines.

bezoar (phytobezoar) A hard ball of undigested food, sometimes together with hair, which forms in the stomach or intestine and can cause obstruction. Foods with a high content of indigestible *pectin, such as orange pith, can form bezoars if swallowed without chewing. The name is derived from the Arabic, meaning 'protection against poison', since bezoars were formerly believed to have protective properties.

BFMIRA *See* LEATHERHEAD FOOD INTERNATIONAL.

BHA *See* BUTYLATED HYDROXYANISOLE.

bhaji 1. Chinese spinach (*Amaranthus gangeticus*), also known as *callaloo. **2.** Also bhajia, Indian; vegetable fritters, normally made with gram (lentil) flour.

bhatura Indian; deep-fried flat bread; the dough is leavened with yoghurt (dahi *puri) or curds (khamiri puri) and fermented overnight before cooking.

bhoona Indian term for frying. Sukha bhoona is a simple sauté. Dumned bhoona is a pot roast, or steam-fried dish; marinated meat is seared, moistened, and cooked in a tightly closed vessel in the oven. Ard bhoona is a dry pot roast; the meat is seared then cooked in a tightly closed vessel in the oven with butter but no water.

BHT *See* BUTYLATED HYDROXYTOLUENE.

bhujia Indian; vegetable dishes, highly spiced. In the final stage of cooking they are fried in *ghee which has been heated with onions, chillies, garlic, and ginger.

bianco Italian; white wines.

BIBRA The British Industrial Biological Research Association.

(⊕) SEE WEB LINKS
• The BIBRA's homepage.

bicarbonate of soda *See* SODIUM BICARBONATE.

BIE *See* BIO-ELECTRICAL IMPEDANCE.

bierschinken German; ham sausage containing coarsely cut pieces of meat.

bierwurst German; chunky, tubular, dark red, cooked and smoked sausages made from chopped seasoned beef and pork. The sausages are cooked at high temperature and smoked. They are usually sliced and served cold in *sandwiches.

bifidobacteria *See* PROBIOTICS.

bifidogenic Promoting the growth of (beneficial) bifidobacteria in the intestinal tract; *see* PREBIOTICS.

bienmesabe Caribbean (Puerto Rico); custard made with coconut milk and eggs.

biersuppe German; soup made from light beer, thickened with potato flour and flavoured with cinnamon and lemon peel.

biffins Apples that have been peeled, partly baked, then pressed and dried.

bifidus factor A variety of *prebiotic *oligosaccharides in human milk that stimulate the growth of (beneficial) bifidobacteria in the intestinal tract. These organisms lower the *pH of the intestinal contents and suppress the growth of pathogenic *bacteria.

bigarade (bigaradier) *See* ORANGE, BITTER.

bigarade, à la French; with orange or orange sauce.

big eye Marine fish, *Priacanthus* spp.

bigos Polish; casserole of *sauerkraut, cooked meat, game, sausages, ham, etc., with vodka and wine.

biguanides Oral hypoglycaemic agents used in treatment of type II *diabetes mellitus; they potentiate *insulin action and inhibit *gluconeogenesis and *glycogenolysis.

bijon South-East Asian; noodles made from fermented maize kernels and cornflour.

bilberry The berry of wild shrubs, *Vaccinium* spp., not generally cultivated. Variously known as whortleberry, blaeberry, whinberry, huckleberry. A 110-g portion is a rich *source of vitamin C; a source of copper; provides 7.7 g of dietary fibre; supplies 60 kcal (250 kJ).

bile Fluid produced by the liver and stored in the gall bladder before secretion into the small intestine (duodenum) via the bile duct; some 0.6–1 L secreted daily. It contains the *bile salts, which function in the emulsification and absorption of fats, bile pigments (bilirubin and biliverdin, the result of breakdown of the haemoglobin of red blood cells), phospholipids, and *cholesterol. It is alkaline, and neutralizes the *acid from the stomach as the food reaches the small intestine. Relatively large amounts of *vitamin B_{12} and *folic acid are secreted in the bile and then reabsorbed from the small intestine. Most of the cholesterol and bile salts are also reabsorbed from the small intestine. *See also* GALL STONES; GASTRO-INTESTINAL TRACT; JAUNDICE.

bile salts (bile acids) Salts of cholic and deoxycholic acid and their glycine and taurine conjugates, secreted in the *bile.

bilimbi Sour fruit of the South-East Asian tree *Averrhoa bilimbi*, also known as camias or cucumber tree, mainly used in pickles and curries.

bilirubin, biliverdin The *bile pigments, formed by catabolism of *haemoglobin. *See also* JAUNDICE.

biltong South African; strips of dried meat, salted, spiced, and dried in air for ten to fourteen days.

bind To add liquid, fat, or egg to a mixture to hold it together. *See also* PANADA.

binge-eating disorder An *eating disorder characterized by over-eating and excessive weight gain, in the absence of food restriction. There may be imbalance between orexigenic and anorexigenic pathways in the hypothalamus, favouring positive energy balance. *See also* ANOREXIA NERVOSA; BINGE–PURGE SYNDROME; BULIMIA NERVOSA.

binge–purge syndrome A feature of the *eating disorder *bulimia nervosa, characterized by the ingestion of very large amounts of food and the excessive use of *laxatives.

bio Commonly used to indicate *probiotic *yoghurt containing live bacterial culture.

bioaccessibility The extent to which nutrients in foods are accessible to digestive enzymes when they are contained within cells in the food. A factor in the *availability of nutrients.

bioassay Biological assay; measurement of biologically active compounds (e.g. vitamins and essential amino acids) by their ability to support growth of micro-organisms or animals.

bioavailability *See* AVAILABILITY.

biocides Chemicals used to kill unwanted organisms: herbicides, insecticides, fungicides.

bioconservation The preservation of food by use of micro-organisms (as in traditional fermented foods), as opposed to chemical preservatives. May be achieved by adding bacteria that produce antagonistic compounds or by adding the purified antagonistic substances. Some *lactic acid bacteria produce a variety of inhibitory substances, including *diacetyl, CO_2, hydrogen peroxide, and *bacteriocins.

biocontrol *See* BIOLOGICAL CONTROL.

bioconversion The proportion of the absorbed precursor of a nutrient (e.g. *carotene as a precursor for *vitamin A) that is converted into the active form. *See also* AVAILABILITY; BIOEFFICACY.

biocytin *Biotin esterified to the *amino acid *lysine, the main form of the *vitamin in most foods.

biodeterioration Deterioration or spoilage as a result of biological (usually microbial) activity. May cause foods to be less palatable and sometimes toxic, and can involve alterations in flavour, aroma, appearance, or texture. The organisms involved are typically bacteria and fungi, and their activity depends on the nutrients present, available water (*see* WATER, AVAILABLE), *pH, temperature, and presence or absence of oxygen.

bioefficacy The product of the *availability of a nutrient × its *bioconversion to the active form.

bio-electrical impedance (BIE) A method of measuring the proportion of fat in the body by the difference between fat and lean tissue in resistance to passage of an electric current.

biofilm Bacteria that have attached to a surface and produced extracellular fibrils, forming a matrix that encourages the growth and subsequent attachment of more bacteria, other microbes, and debris, creating a film that is difficult to remove and resistant to cleaning and sanitization.

bioflavonoids *See* FLAVONOIDS.

biofortification Food fortification achieved by plant breeding or *genetic modification to give a higher content of nutrients. *See also* HARVESTPLUS.

biolistic transformation Technique for introducing *DNA into plants, to create genetically modified plants, by bombarding cells with heavy metal particles coated with the required DNA.

biological control Deliberate exploitation of one species of organism to control another, e.g. the introduction into the environment of parasites, insects, or pathogens that can infect and kill or disable particular insect pests or weeds. Also known as biocontrol.

biological oxygen demand (BOD) A way of assessing bacterial contamination of water, milk, etc., by aerobic micro-organisms that take up oxygen.

Biological Value (BV) A measure of *protein quality.

bioluminescence Emission of light by reaction of the enzyme *luciferase with *ATP. Exploited as a rapid and sensitive way of detecting living bacteria (and other cells) in milk and other foods, since all viable cells contain ATP.

biomarkers Metabolic, chemical, or functional changes that can be measured in response to nutritional, drug, or other interventions. Sometimes regarded as surrogate end-points, since they respond more rapidly, and more sensitively, than clinical disease or overt signs of toxicity.

biopterin The *coenzyme for a number of enzymes, including phenylalanine, tyrosine, and tryptophan hydroxylases. Not a dietary requirement, since it can readily be synthesized in the body. Rare patients with a variant form of *phenylketonuria cannot synthesize biopterin, and have to receive supplements.

biosensor An analytical probe in which a biochemical interaction at the probe surface is translated into a quantifiable physical signal. The biochemical signal is from an immobilized enzyme, antibody, DNA, or cell organelle.

biotin A *vitamin, sometimes known as vitamin H, required for the synthesis of fatty acids and glucose, among other reactions, and in the control of gene expression and cell division. Biotin is widely distributed in foods such as liver, kidney, egg yolk, yeast, vegetables, grains, and nuts; dietary deficiency is unknown. There is no evidence on which to base *reference intakes other than to state that current average intakes (between 15–70 µg/day) are obviously more than adequate to prevent deficiency; the US/Canadian *adequate intake is 30 µg. *See also* AVIDIN; BIOCYTIN.

biphenyl *See* DIPHENYL.

birch beer A non-alcoholic carbonated beverage flavoured with oil of wintergreen or oils of sweet birch and *sassafras.

bird's nest soup Chinese; made from the dried gelatinous coating of the nest of various species of southern Asian swifts, with chicken broth, ham, egg-white, and spring onion.

biriani (biryani) Indian; highly spiced rice dish flavoured with saffron and layered with meat. *See also* PILAU.

birnbrot Swiss; bread with filling of dried pears and other fruits.

biscuit A baked flour confectionery dried down to low moisture content. The name is derived from the Latin *bis coctus*, meaning cooked twice. A 100-g portion provides 400–500 kcal (1680–2100 kJ). Known as cookie in the USA, where 'biscuit' means a small cake-like bun.

biscuit check The development of splitting and cracking in *biscuits immediately after baking.

bishop A medieval beverage of hot, spiced, sweetened wine (commonly *port).

bisque Thick rich soup made from fish or *shellfish.

bitki Polish, Russian; meatballs made from raw minced beef with fried onions, grilled or fried.

Bitot's spots Irregularly shaped foam-like plaques on the conjunctiva of the eye, characteristically seen in *vitamin A deficiency, but not considered to be a diagnostic sign without other evidence of deficiency.

bitter Traditional British *beer with a bitter flavour due to its content of *hops.

bitterballen Dutch; fried meatballs flavoured with Worcestershire sauce and nutmeg.

bitterness One of the five senses of *taste.

bitterroot Roots of *Lewisia rediviva* (purslane family), North American vegetable.

bitters Extracts of herbs, spices, roots, and bark, steeped in, or distilled with, *spirits. Originally prepared for medicinal use (tinctures or alcoholic extracts of the natural products); now used mainly to flavour spirits and cocktails, or as apéritifs. *See also* ANGOSTURA; WINE, APÉRITIF.

biuret test A chemical test for proteins based on the development of a violet colour when alkaline copper sulphate reacts with a peptide bond.

bixin A *carotenoid pigment found in the seeds of the tropical plant *Bixa orellana*; the crude extract is the colouring agent *annatto (E160).

blackberry Fruit of the bramble, *Rubus fruticosus*. A 100-g portion is a good *source of vitamin C; a source of folate and copper; provides 7.5g of dietary fibre; supplies 25kcal (105kJ).

black bun *See* SCOTCH BUN.

black butter *See* BUTTER, BLACK.

blackcock *See* GROUSE.

blackcurrant Fruit of the bush *Ribes nigra*, of special interest because of its high vitamin C content (150–230mg/100g). The British *National Fruit Collection has 105 varieties. A 100-g portion is a rich *source of vitamin C; a source of iron and copper; provides 9g of dietary fibre; supplies 35kcal (145kJ).

black-eyed bean (black-eyed pea) *See* BEAN, BLACK-EYED.

black fungus (wood-ears) Edible wild fungus, *Auricularia polytricha; see* MUSHROOMS.

black jack See CARAMEL.

black PN A black food colour, also known as Brilliant Black BN.

black pudding Also known as blood pudding. Traditional European dish made with sheep or pig blood and suet, together with oatmeal, liver, and herbs, stuffed into membrane casings shaped like a horseshoe. Although it is already cooked, it is usually sliced and fried. In Germany and France it is made without cereal. A 100-g portion is an exceptionally rich *source of iron; a rich source of protein; a good source of niacin and copper; a source of vitamin B₁; contains 22g of fat, of which 40% is saturated; supplies 300kcal (1260kJ).

blackthorn See SLOE.

black tongue disease A sign of *niacin deficiency in dogs, the canine equivalent of *pellagra, historically important in the isolation of the *vitamin.

black velvet Mixture of equal parts of sparkling wine and stout (see BEER); traditionally Guinness stout.

blaeberry See BILBERRY.

blanc, au Cooked in a white stock or served with a white *sauce.

blanc de blancs French; white *wine made from white grapes. By contrast, blanc de noirs is white wine made from black grapes; the skins are removed before fermentation.

blanching A partial precooking by plunging the food into hot water (82–95°C) for ½–5 minutes. Also known as scalding, a preferred term, since the original reason for blanching was to whiten food, but the process is also used to preserve colour. Fruits and vegetables are blanched before canning, drying, or freezing, to soften the texture, remove air, denature *enzymes that may cause spoilage when frozen, and remove undesirable flavours. Blanching is also performed to remove excess salt from preserved meat, and to aid the removal of skin, e.g. from almonds and tomatoes. There can be a loss of 10–20% of the sugars, salts, and protein, as well as some of the vitamins B₁, B₂, and niacin, and up to one-third of the vitamin C.

blancmange powder Usually a *cornflour base with added flavour and colour, mixed with hot milk to make a dessert.

blanco Spanish; white wines.

blanquette French; white stew of chicken, veal, lamb, or sweetbreads, with a rich cream sauce.

blätterteig German (literally 'leaf dough'); puff pastry.

blawn fish Scottish (Orkney); fresh fish, rubbed with salt and hung in a windy passage for a day, then grilled.

bleaching The removal or destruction of colour. In the context of food it usually refers to the refining of flour (*see* AGEING) or oils. Bleaching is a stage in the refining of oils in which dispersed impurities and natural colouring materials are removed by activated *charcoal or *fuller's earth.

bleu, au Fish such as trout, cooked immediately after they are caught, by simmering in white wine with herbs, or in water containing salt and vinegar.

blewits Edible wild fungus, *Tricholoma* (*Lepista*) *saevum*, also known as bluetail; also wood blewits, *T. nudum*. See MUSHROOMS.

blind, baking *See* BAKING BLIND.

blind staggers Acute *vitamin B_1 deficiency in horses and other animals, caused by eating *bracken, which contains *thiaminase, which destroys the vitamin.

blinis Russian; small yeast pancakes made from buckwheat flour, traditionally served with salt herring, smoked salmon, or caviar, and sour cream.

blintzes Middle-European Jewish; pancakes, stuffed with either curd cheese (and then served with soured cream) or minced meat.

bloaters Salted, cold-smoked *herrings.

blood Various *blood cells suspended in plasma. Blood carries nutrients and oxygen to tissues and removes metabolic products. Oxygenated blood travels from the heart in arteries, while deoxygenated blood returns in veins; in the tissues the blood from the arteries enters smaller vessels, the arterioles, then capillaries, which drain first into venules and then the veins. *See also* BLOOD PLASMA.

blood cells Three main types of cell are present in blood: erythrocytes or red cells, *leucocytes or white cells, and platelets. Red blood cells contain the protein *haemoglobin, which is responsible for the transport of oxygen from the lungs to tissues, and of carbon dioxide from tissues to the lungs. White blood cells are generally concerned with protection against invading micro-organisms, and platelets with coagulation to prevent excessive blood loss through bleeding.

blood clotting The process by which the soluble protein fibrinogen in *blood plasma is converted to insoluble fibrin, thus preventing blood loss through cuts, etc. *Vitamin K is required for synthesis of the clotting proteins, and deficiency is characterized by excessive bleeding.

Thrombosis is the inappropriate formation of blood clots in the blood vessels, and can be a cause of serious illness and death when blood vessels are blocked. Antagonists of vitamin K, including Warfarin, are commonly used as *anticoagulants to reduce clotting in patients at risk of thrombosis.

blood plasma The liquid component of blood, accounting for about half the total volume. Plasma is a solution of nutrients and various proteins, mainly albumin and various globulins, including the immunoglobulins, which are responsible for much of the body's defence against infection and some adverse reactions to foods. When blood has clotted (*see* BLOOD CLOTTING), the resultant fluid is known as serum. *See also* FOOD, ADVERSE REACTIONS; LIPIDS, PLASMA.

blood pressure When the heart contracts (systolic pressure) the normal blood pressure of females is 120 mm mercury at the age of twelve, rising to 175 at the age of 70. In males it is 120 rising to 160. When the heart relaxes (diastolic pressure) the normal range for females is 70 rising to 95; males 70 to 85. Diastolic blood pressure above 105 is moderate, and above 115 severe, *hypertension.

blood sausage *See* BLACK PUDDING.

blood serum *See* BLOOD PLASMA.

blood sugar *Glucose; normal concentration is between 3.5–6.0 mmol/L, and is maintained in the fasting state by mobilization of tissue reserves of *glycogen and synthesis from *amino acids. Only in prolonged starvation does it fall below about 3.5 mmol/L. If it falls to 2 mmol/L there is loss of consciousness (hypoglycaemic coma).

After a meal the concentration of glucose rises, but this rise is limited by the hormone *insulin, which is secreted by the β-islet cells of the pancreas to stimulate the uptake of glucose into tissues. *Diabetes mellitus is the result of failure of the insulin mechanism.

blood volume The average blood volume is 5.3 L (78 mL/kg body weight, 9 pints) in males and 3.8 L (56 mL/kg body weight, 6.5 pints) in females.

bloom Fat bloom is the whitish appearance on the surface of chocolate which sometimes occurs on storage. It is due either to a change in the form of the fat at the surface or to fat diffusing outwards and being deposited as crystals on the surface. Sugar bloom is less common; it is due to the deposition of sugar crystals on the surface.

blotting Transfer of nucleic acids or proteins from an electrophoretic gel on to a chemically reactive matrix (e.g. nitrocellulose) to permit their detection by binding labelled nucleic acids or antibodies. Southern blotting is for DNA, northern blotting for RNA, and western blotting for proteins.

blowing (late blowing) A defect of cheese that leads to gas formation and development of abnormal flavours during ripening. Caused by butyric acid fermentation by *Clostridium tyrobutyricum*, a pasteurization-resistant organism that can contaminate milk when animals have been fed silage.

blueberry Fruit of *Vaccinium corymbosum* (the high-bush blueberry) or *V. augustifolium* (low-bush blueberry). Common blueberry or bilberry is *V. myrtillus*.

blue cheese *See* CHEESE, BLUE.

bluefish Atlantic marine fish *Pomatmus saltatrix*, a game fish, and also farmed; also known as taylor.

bluetail *See* BLEWITS.

blush wine Californian term for rosé *wines.

BMAST Brief Michigan Alcoholism Screening Test, a questionnaire to screen for *alcohol abuse.

BMC Bone mineral content.

BMD Bone mineral density.

BMI *See* BODY MASS INDEX.

BMNES British Meat Nutrition Education Service.

(((🌐))) SEE WEB LINKS
• The BMNES's homepage.

BMR *See* BASAL METABOLIC RATE.

BMS Breast milk substitute. *See* INFANT FORMULA.

BNF British Nutrition Foundation.

(((🌐))) SEE WEB LINKS
• The BNF's homepage.

boal A *catfish, *Wallago attu*.

boar, wild Meat of *Sus scrofa*. Wild boar are hunted in parts of Europe, farmed on small scale in UK. A 150-g portion is a rich *source of protein; contains 4.5 g of fat, of which one-third is saturated; and supplies 160 kcal (670 kJ).

bocadillo Spanish; a *sandwich made by slicing a long crusty loaf or roll lengthways.

bocal French; wide-mouthed glass jar used for bottling or pickling fruit and vegetables.

bockwurst German; mildly flavoured sausage made from veal and pork, with chives, chopped parsley, eggs, and milk. Traditionally served with bock beer.

BOD *See* BIOLOGICAL OXYGEN DEMAND.

body-building food A term used indiscriminately, but generally referring to proteins.

body density Body fat has a density of 0.90, while the density of fat-free body mass is 1.10. Determination of density by weighing in air and in water, or by measuring body volume and weight, permits calculation of the proportions of fat and lean body tissue.

body fluid *See* WATER BALANCE.

bodying agents Additives used to impart body, viscosity, and consistency to foods.

body mass index (BMI) An index of fatness and obesity. The weight (in kg) divided by the square of height (in m). The acceptable (desirable) range is 20–25. Above 25 is *overweight, and above 30 is *obesity. BMI below the lower end of the acceptable range indicates undernutrition and wasting. Also called Quetelet's index, after the Belgian statistician L. A. J. Quetelet (1796–1874), who first developed it. *See also* OBESITY; WEIGHT, DESIRABLE.

body surface area Heat loss from the body is related to surface area, and *basal metabolic rate and energy expenditure are sometimes expressed per unit body surface area. The surface area of adults is about $18000 \, cm^2$ (men) or $16000 \, cm^2$ (women). Two formulae are commonly used:

$$\text{Du Bois: area (cm}^2) = 71.84 \times \text{weight}^{0.425} \text{ (kg)} \times \text{height}^{0.725} \text{ (cm)}$$

$$\text{Meeh: area (cm}^2) = 11.9 \times \text{weight}^{2/3} \text{ (kg)}.$$

bog myrtle A wild plant (*Myrica gale*) with a strong resinous flavour. The leaves and seeds are used to flavour soups and stews.

bogue Marine fish *Boops boops*, found in the eastern Atlantic, the Mediterranean, and the Black Sea.

bole *See* ARMENIAN BOLE.

boletus Edible wild *mushroom, *Boletus edulis* or *B. granulatus*, also known as the yellow mushroom or cep.

boller Danish, Norwegian; dumplings.

bologna *See* POLONY.

bolti *See* TILAPIA.

bolus The soft mass of chewed food ready to be swallowed.

Bombay duck Indian fish, *Harpodon nehereus* or *Saurus ophiodon*, eaten either fresh or after salting and curing. The name is a corruption of the local name of the fish, bombil.

Bombay halva Indian dessert made from semolina, almonds, and pistachio nuts. *See also* HALVA.

Bombay mix *See* CHEVDA.

bomb calorimeter *See* CALORIMETER.

bombe A mould with a tight-fitting lid, used to shape ice cream and sometimes fruit. Bombe glacée is a hemispherical frozen dessert made from two separate layers of different ice creams.

bombesin A peptide secreted by nerves throughout the *gastro-intestinal tract that increases gastric acid secretion and stimulates *gall bladder contraction, possibly acting through increased secretion of *gastrin.

bombil *See* BOMBAY DUCK.

Bommerlunder A German schnapps; *see* AQUAVIT.

Bonal *See* WINES, APÉRITIF.

bonbon General term for *sugar confectionery.

bondiola Italian (Parma); cured shoulder of pork.

bondon French (Normandy); soft cheese shaped in the form of a bun.

bone Bones consist of an organic matrix composed of *collagen and other proteins and crystalline mineral, mainly hydroxyapatite (calcium phosphate and calcium hydroxide), together with magnesium phosphate, fluorides, and sulphates. *See also* BONE, CORTICAL; BONE, TRABECULAR; BONE MARROW; CALCIUM.

bone, cancellous *See* BONE, TRABECULAR.

bone, cortical Dense or compact bone, found mainly in the shafts (diaphyses) of long bones, accounting for about 80% of total body bone. *See also* BONE, TRABECULAR.

bone, trabecular (cancellous bone) The spongy bone, consisting of a structural mesh of trabeculae forming an internal scaffold, found mainly at the ends of long bones, in vertebral bodies, and flat bones, accounting for some 20% of total body bone. The spaces between the trabeculae are filled with red and yellow marrow (*see* BONE MARROW). Although only 20% of total bone in the body, it accounts for most of bone turnover because it has a larger surface area than cortical bone (*see* BONE, CORTICAL).

bone broth Prepared by prolonged boiling of bones to break down the *collagen and extract it as *gelatine. Of little nutritional value, since it consists of 2–4% gelatine, with a little calcium. *See also* STOCK.

bone charcoal *See* CHARCOAL.

bone diseases *See* OSTEOMALACIA; OSTEOPOROSIS; RICKETS.

bone marrow The soft tissue in the interior of bones. Red marrow (myeloid tissue) is the site of production of red *blood cells, platelets, and most white blood cells. Yellow marrow, which is richer in fat, is the site of production of other white blood cells. Almost all marrow is red at birth; the proportion of yellow marrow increases with age, and accounts for about 50% of marrow in adults.

bone-meal Prepared from degreased bones and formerly used as a supplement in both animal and human foods as a source of calcium and phosphate; no longer used because of the risk of transmitting *BSE. Also used as a plant fertilizer as a slowly released source of phosphate.

bongkrek Indonesian; fermented coconut *presscake. *Rhizopus oligosporus* and *Neurospora sitophila* are the fermenting fungi. If the *pH is above 6, it can be infected with *Pseudomonas cocovenenans*, which produces the toxins bongkrekic acid and toxoflavin.

boniatillo Caribbean (Cuban); creamed dessert made from sweet potato and eggs.

bonito Various species of *tuna: *Sarda*, *Auxis*, and *Euthynnus* spp.

bonnag Manx; soda bread.

bonne-bouche Small savoury appetizers.

bonne femme French; cooked in a simple or 'housewifely' style, with a garnish of fresh vegetables or herbs, usually including mushrooms. Applied especially to fish dishes and cream soups.

boonchi Caribbean name for yard-long beans or asparagus beans, *Vigna sesquipedalis*.

boondi Indian snack food; deep-fried fritters made from Bengal *gram.

boquerones Spanish; fresh anchovies, floured and joined together by making a small incision at the tail of one and slipping the tails of three or four others through. Fried in the shape of a fan.

boracic acid *See* BORIC ACID.

borage A herb, *Borago officinalis*. The flowers and leaves have a cucumber-like flavour and are used to flavour drinks, salads, and cheese. Contains potentially toxic alkaloids. The seed oil is a rich source of *γ-linolenic acid.

  Indian borage is *Plectranthus amboinicus*, also known as oregano in the Philippines and broad-leaved thyme in the West Indies.

borax The sodium salt of *boric acid.

borborygmos (pl. borborygmi) Audible abdominal sound produced by excessive intestinal motility.

Bordeaux Red and white wines produced in the Bordeaux region of France; red Bordeaux wines are called claret in the UK.

Bordeaux mustard *See* MUSTARD.

bordelaise, à la French; dish with a red wine sauce and ceps (*boletus mushrooms).

borderline substances Foods that may have characteristics of medication in certain circumstances, and which may then be prescribed under the National Health Service in UK.

bordure, en Dish with a border of cooked vegetables.

borecole *See* KALE.

börek Turkish; fried or baked phyllo pastry (*see* PASTRY, PHYLLO) with a savoury filling, generally cheese. The Greek equivalent is bourekia.

boric acid H_3BO_4; it has been used in the past as a preservative in bacon and margarine, but *boron accumulates in the body.

Borneo tallow *See* BUTTER, VEGETABLE.

boron An element, known to be essential for plant growth, but not known to have any function in human beings or animals. Suggested to modify the actions and metabolism of *oestrogens, and sometimes used in preparations to alleviate pre-menstrual syndrome, although there is little evidence of efficacy; toxic in excess. Occurs mainly as salts of *boric acid.

borscht (borshch) Russian, Polish (barszcz); beetroot soup, served hot or cold. Shav borscht is made with *sorrel.

Boston brown bread An American spiced pudding, steamed in the can.

botargo A relish or dip prepared from fish roe (usually mullet or *tuna); *see also* TARAMOSALATA.

boti kabab Indian; small pieces of meat, marinated and cooked rapidly under intense heat, basted with butter or *ghee.

bottle The traditional wine bottle holds 700, 720, or 750 mL of wine, depending on the variety; within the EU wine bottles are standardized at 700 mL.

A two-bottle size is a magnum, four is a Jeroboam or double magnum, six a Methuselah, twelve a Salmanzar, and twenty a Nebuchadnezzar.

bottle feeding *See* INFANT FORMULA.

bottle house An old English term for a manufacturer of glass containers (bottles and jars) as distinct from tableware.

bottlers' sugar *See* SUGAR.

botulinum cook The degree of heat required to ensure destruction of (virtually) all spores of *Clostridium botulinum*, the causative organism of *botulism, which are the most resistant of bacterial spores.

botulism A rare form of *food-borne disease caused by the extremely potent neurotoxins produced by *Clostridium botulinum* (isolated in 1895 by Belgian bacteriologist Emile Pierre-Marie van Ermengem). At least seven different toxins have been identified; they can be inactivated by heating at 80°C for 10 minutes, but in foods are more resistant to heat. Although rare, it is often fatal unless the antitoxin is given. Some strains of other *Clostridia* may also produce the toxin, e.g. *C. butyricum, C. barati.*

The name is derived from *botulus*, for sausage, since the disease was originally associated with sausages in Germany (the first recorded outbreak was in 1735). A wide range of foods have been involved, including meat, fish, milk, fruits, and vegetables which have been incorrectly preserved or treated, so that competing micro-organisms have been destroyed; spores of *C. botulinum* are extremely resistant to heat, and dangerous amounts of toxins can accumulate in contaminated foods without any apparent spoilage.

boucanning A Caribbean process by which meat was preserved by sun-drying and smoking while resting on a wooden grid known as a boucan. *See also* BARBECUE.

bouchée French; small open pastry case (vol-au-vent) filled with chopped meat, game, or fish, served hot with a thick sauce. Bouchées à la reine are filled with chicken or calves' sweetbreads, blended in a thick white sauce with mushrooms.

bouchet *See* CABERNET FRANC.

boudin noir French *black pudding.

bouillabaisse French; fish stew or soup flavoured with saffron, spices, and herbs; speciality of the Mediterranean region. So named because it is repeatedly boiled. *See also* BOURRIDE.

bouillon A plain, unclarified beef or veal broth; also used synonymously with *stock. Bouillon granules were first introduced by Fabrique des Produits Maggi in 1892, followed by cubes (stock cubes) in 1906.

boula boula American (originally Seychellois); *turtle soup mixed with puréed fresh green peas.

boulangère, à la Originally French for any dish baked in the oven. Nowadays it means potatoes and onions cooked with meat in stock.

bouquet garni A small bundle of parsley, thyme, marjoram, and bay leaves, tied together with cotton and added to the dish being cooked. Now also the same mixture of herbs in a porous paper sack. Also known as a faggot.

bourbon American *whiskey made by distilling fermented *maize mash. Sour mash bourbon is made from mash that has yeast left in it from a previous fermentation.

bourbonal Ethylvanillin; *see* VANILLA.

bourekia *See* BÖREK.

bourgeoise, à la Family-style dish, homely but appetizing cookery. Also means garnished with carrots, onions, and diced lean bacon.

bourguignon (bourguignonne, à la) French; dish with a garnish incorporating mushrooms, onions, and grilled bacon and cooked in or served with red wine sauce.

bourride French (Marseilles region); fish soup similar to *bouillabaisse but without saffron, flavoured with aïoli (garlic mayonnaise).

Boursin French; trade name of a soft triple cream cheese (75% fat); may be flavoured with garlic, herbs or crushed peppercorns.

bouza *See* BEER.

bovine offal, specified Those parts of the animal thought to have the highest likelihood of carrying the *BSE agent, which have been banned from the human food chain.

bovine spongiform encephalopathy *See* BSE.

Bovril Trade name for a preparation of *meat extract, hydrolysed beef, beef powder, and yeast extract, used as a beverage, a flavouring agent, and for spreading on bread. A 10-g portion is a good *source of vitamin B_2 and a source of niacin.

Bowman–Birk inhibitor One of the *trypsin inhibitors found in legumes; denatured and hence inactivated by heat. The other is the Kunitz inhibitor.

boxthorn, Chinese A woody shrub, *Lycium chinense*; both the leaves and the fruit are eaten.

boysenberry Fruit similar to *loganberry, a hybrid of blackberry, raspberry, and loganberry developed by Rudolph Boysen (1920). Rediscovered in 1933 by Walter Knott, who made it the basis of Knott's Berry Farms in Anaheim, California. Originally the farm sold Mrs Cordelia Knott's home-made jams; it is now a theme park.

boza Balkan; a thick sweet-sour fermented beverage made from various cereals (commonly *bulgur wheat or *millet), cooked in water and then crushed before fermenting with yeast.

bozbash Armenian, Azerbaijani; mutton soup.

brachyose *See* ISOMALTOSE.

bracken Young unopened leaves (fronds) and rhizomes of bracken (*Pteridium* spp.), eaten as a vegetable and regarded as a delicacy in the Far East. Known as fiddleheads in Canada. The leaves contain an antagonist of vitamin B_1—cattle and horses eating large amounts suffer from *blind staggers due to acute vitamin B_1 deficiency—and also a number of known or suspected *carcinogens. The rhizomes may be eaten as a vegetable or used to prepare a starchy flour. *See also* GOFLO.

bradycardia An unusually slow heartbeat, less than 60 beats/minute. Such a low rate may be normal in trained athletes.

bradyphagia Eating very slowly.

brain Traditionally the brains of sheep and calves are stewed and eaten; this is probably not advisable because of the risk of transmitting the agents responsible for various degenerative brain diseases, including scrapie and bovine spongiform encephalopathy (*see* BSE).

brain sugar Obsolete name for *galactose.

braise A method of cooking in a closed container, with very little liquid, normally in an oven.

bramble Wild *blackberry.

bran The outer layers of cereal grain, which are largely removed when the grain is milled (i.e. in the preparation of white flour or white rice). The germ is discarded at the same time, and there is a considerable loss of iron and other minerals, and particularly of the B vitamins, as well as of dietary fibre. A 30-g portion of wheat bran is a rich *source of niacin, iron, and zinc; a good source of vitamin B_1; a source of vitamin B_2; provides 12g of dietary fibre; supplies 70kcal (295kJ). *See also* FLOUR, EXTRACTION RATE; WHEATFEED.

branched-chain amino acids *See* AMINO ACIDS, BRANCHED-CHAIN.

branco Portuguese; white wines.

brandade Southern French dish of salt cod flavoured with garlic.

brander Scottish name for gridiron or grill.

brandy A *spirit distilled from wine, and containing 37–44% (most usually 40%) alcohol by volume. The name is derived from the German *brandtwein*, meaning burnt wine, corrupted to brandy wine. First produced in 1300 at the Montpellier medical school by Arnaud de Villeneuve.

The age of brandy is generally designated as three-star (three to five years old before bottling); VSOP (very special old pale, aged four to ten or more years, the name indicating that it has not been heavily coloured with caramel); Napoleon (premium blend aged six to twenty years); XO, Extraordinary Old (Extra or Grand Reserve, possibly 50 years old). *Cognac and *armagnac are brandies made in defined regions of France.

Fruit brandies are either distilled from fruit wines (e.g. plum and apple brandies) or are prepared by soaking fruit in brandy (e.g. cherry and apricot brandies). *See also* EAU-DE-VIE; MARC.

brandy butter Hard sauce made from butter, caster sugar, and *brandy, traditionally served with Christmas pudding and mince pies.

brandy sauce English; sauce made from egg yolk, cream, sugar, and *brandy, traditionally served with Christmas pudding.

brandy snaps Crisp toffee-like biscuits made from flour, butter, syrup, and powdered ginger, baked, then rolled into cylinders while still warm and pliable.

Brassica Genus of vegetables that includes broccoli, Brussels sprouts, cabbage, cauliflower, kale, kohl rabi, mustard, and swedes.

brat *See* SAUSAGES, EMULSION.

bratwurst German; pork *sausage with many regional specialist varieties; may be served boiled, grilled, or fried.

brawn Made from pig meat, particularly the head, boiled with peppercorns and herbs, minced and pressed into a mould. Mock brawn (head cheese) differs in that other meat by-products are used. A 150-g portion is a rich *source of protein; a good source of niacin and iron; contains 18 g of fat; supplies 230 kcal (960 kJ).

Brazil nut From wild trees of *Bertholletia excelsa*. The related sapucaia or paradise nut is the fruit of *Lecythis zabucajo*. A 60-g portion (eighteen nuts) is an exceptionally rich *source of selenium; a rich source of vitamins B_1 and E; a good source of protein, niacin, and calcium; a source of iron; contains 40 g of fat, of which 25% is *saturated and 40% mono-unsaturated; provides 5.5 g of dietary fibre; supplies 400 kcal (1680 kJ).

brazzein Sweet-tasting thermostable protein from the West African plant *Pentadiplandra brazzeana*.

bread Baked dough made from cereal flour, usually wheat, although rye, barley, and other cereals are also used. Normally leavened by fermentation of the dough with yeast, or addition of sodium bicarbonate.

Wholemeal bread is baked with 100% extraction flour, i.e. containing the whole of the cereal grain. White bread is made from 72% extraction flour. Brown bread is made with flour of extraction rate intermediate between that of white bread and wholemeal. A loaf may not legally be described as brown unless it contains at least 0.6% *fibre on a dry weight basis. Black bread is a coarse wholemeal wheat or rye bread leavened with sourdough.

The white loaf in the UK has added iron, vitamin B_1, niacin and folic acid, but not to the level of wholemeal bread, and white but not wholemeal is enriched with calcium. In some countries *riboflavin but not calcium is added.

There is a wide variety of different types of bread, with loaves baked in different shapes, or with various additions to the dough. *See also* CHORLEYWOOD BREAD PROCESS; FLOUR, EXTRACTION RATE; QUICKBREADS.

bread, Adirondack American baked product made from ground *maize, butter, wheat flour, eggs, and sugar.

bread, aerated Bread made from dough containing water saturated with carbon dioxide under pressure, rather than being leavened with yeast. The aim was to produce an aerated loaf without the loss of carbohydrate involved in a yeast fermentation (7% of the total ingredients). The resultant loaf was insipid in flavour and the method went out of use.

bread, Allinson A wholewheat bread named after Allinson, who advocated its consumption in England at the end of the 19th century, as did Graham in the USA (*see* BREAD, GRAHAM). Now a trade name for a wholemeal loaf.

bread, bank holiday Bread made with extra fat to soften the crumb so that it would last over a long (bank holiday) weekend.

bread, batch The moulded pieces of dough touch each other in the oven, so that when baked and separated only the top and bottom of the loaf have crusts.

bread, blaanda Shetland; unleavened bread made from barley and oatmeal, with milk and butter, baked slowly on a griddle.

bread, bleeding A bacterial infection with *Bacillus prodigiosus*, which stains the bread bright red. Under warm and damp conditions the infection can appear overnight, and contamination of shewbread in churches has led to accusations and riots against religious minorities over the centuries.

bread, Cornell Bread, originally developed at Cornell University, with increased nutritional value from the addition of 6% soya flour and 8% skimmed milk solids.

bread, flower pot Old English; wheatmeal bread baked in terracotta plant pots that have been seasoned by coating in oil and heating in an oven.

bread, French Traditionally made with soft-wheat flour, it has an open texture and crisp crust. It is generally baked as a *baguette, a long thin loaf. It does not keep well, and usually needs to be eaten on the day it is purchased.

bread, Graham Wholewheat bread in which the bran is very finely ground. Named after Sylvester Graham (1794–1851), a miller who advocated its use in the USA and published *Treatise on Bread and Bread Making* (1837) and *Lectures on the Science of Life* (1839), in which he advocated vegetarianism and unsifted wholemeal flour. Graham cakes are made from wholemeal flour and milk. *See also* BREAD, ALLINSON.

bread, horse Medieval English; bread made with any cereal to hand, as well as peas and beans.

bread, Italian Foccacia is white bread made with olive oil (9%) and herbs; ciabatta is a flat rectangular loaf of white bread made with olive oil (5%).

bread, lactein Bread made with added milk, usually about 6% milk solids (3–4% milk solids are often added to the ordinary loaf in the USA).

bread, monkey *See* BAOBAB.

bread, prebaked (part-baked bread) Bread that has been either partially baked, then allowed to cool, or frozen, for final baking later, to produce a freshly baked loaf.

bread, rye Bread baked wholly or partially with rye flour, of varying extraction rate, so that it can vary from very light to grey or black. It is commonly a sourdough bread and may contain caraway seeds.

bread, soda Irish; bread made from flour and whey, or buttermilk, using sodium bicarbonate and acid in place of yeast.

bread, sourdough White or wholemeal wheat or rye bread that has been leavened with sourdough (*sauerteig*); dough that has been left to ferment overnight, and contains a mixture of fermenting micro-organisms, including peptonizing bacteria that turn the dough to a more plastic state, yeast, and lactic or acetic bacteria that produce the sour flavour.

bread, starch-reduced Bread is normally 9–10% protein and about 50% starch; if the starch is reduced, either by some of it being washed out of the dough or by extra protein being added, the bread is referred to as starch-reduced, and is often claimed to be of value in slimming and diabetic diets. Legally, the name 'starch-reduced bread' may be applied only to bread containing less than 50% carbohydrate, and claims for its value as a slimming aid are strictly controlled.

bread, Sussex Old English; loaf made from wheat and rye flour mixed with grains; originally given to servants, now revived.

bread, unleavened Flat bread made by baking dough that has not been leavened with yeast or baking powder. *Matzo is baked to a crisp texture, while *pitta and *chapattis have a softer texture.

bread, victory American; recipe for bread containing *soya flour to spare wheat, in a circular published by the US Secretary of Agriculture in 1918.

bread, Vienna Loaf with a very crisp, thin, highly glazed crust, with cuts on the upper surface, coarser than ordinary bread and with gas holes. It is baked in an oven which retains the steam.

breadfruit Large spherical, starchy fruit of the tree *Artocarpus communis*, *A. incisa*, or *A. altilis*, discovered in 1688 in the Pacific island of Guam by William Dampier. Staple but seasonal food in the Caribbean, eaten roasted whole when ripe, or boiled in pieces when green. The seeds, known as breadnuts, are also eaten. A 200-g portion is a rich *source of vitamin C; a source of iron and vitamin B_1; supplies 220 kcal (925 kJ).

breadfruit, African Seeds of the tree *Treculia africana*, eaten roasted as nuts or ground into meal which is used to prepare a porridge.

bread sauce Thick white sauce made from bread and milk in which an onion has been boiled; a traditional accompaniment to poultry.

breadspreads General term for fats used to spread on bread, including *butter, *margarine, and low-fat spreads that may not legally be called margarine. Sometimes called yellow fats.

breadstick See GRISSINI.

breakfast cereal (breakfast food) Legally defined as any food obtained by the swelling, roasting, grinding, rolling, or flaking of any cereal.

break middlings See DUNST.

break rolls See MILLING.

bream Freshwater fish *Abramis brama*, distributed across Europe and parts of Asia; a member of the carp family. Bluegill bream is *Leponis macrochinus*.

bream, sea Marine fish, members of the family *Sparidae*. See also POMFRET.

bream, threadfin Marine fish, *Nemipterus* spp.

breast-feeding See LACTATION.

breathing Of red *wine, opening the bottle some time before serving to allow oxidation and development of the full mature flavour.

breath test, ethane and pentane Oxidative damage to polyunsaturated *fatty acids leads to production of small amounts of ethane and pentane, which are exhaled in the breath. Measurement of these gases permits estimation of whole body *radical burden.

breath test, hydrogen Intestinal bacterial fermentation of undigested carbohydrates leads to production of small amounts of hydrogen; this diffuses from the intestine into the bloodstream and is exhaled on the breath. Measuring the increased hydrogen in breath provides a sensitive way of detecting, e.g., *lactose intolerance, using a very much smaller amount of lactose than the traditional method of measuring the increase in blood glucose after a test dose of lactose.

brem Indonesian; sweet or sweet-sour starchy rice paste produced by fermenting cooked rice with moulds and yeasts for several days, then boiling down and sun drying.

brenza (brinza) Eastern European soft cheese made from goat's or sheep's milk.

bresaola Italian; moist, lean, air-dried cured beef (or sometimes horse). A similar Swiss product is called bundnerfleisch or viande des Grisons.

bretonne, à la Dish with a garnish of cauliflower.

bretonne sauce Used with fish, made with onions or leeks and white wine.

bretzels *See* PRETZELS.

brevetoxins (brevitoxins) Potent neurotoxins responsible for shellfish poisoning produced by the unicellular dinoflagellate protozoan *Ptychodiscus brevis*.

brewers' grains Cereal residue from brewing, containing about 25% protein; used as animal feed.

brewing The process of making *beer.

brie Soft white cheese originally from the Brie region of France, made from cow's milk and moulded into a flat disc; it has a white rind, is ripened for three to four weeks, and deteriorates rapidly. A 30-g portion is a rich *source of vitamin B_{12}; a source of protein and vitamin A; contains 8 g of fat, of which 70% is saturated, 200 mg sodium, and 160 mg calcium; supplies 100 kcal (400 kJ).

brill A marine flatfish, *Scopthalmus rhombus*, distributed along the European Atlantic coast and Mediterranean.

brilliant acid green BS *See* GREEN S.

brilloli (brioli) Corsican; chestnut meal, prepared in the same way as *polenta.

brimstone *See* SULPHUR.

brine Salt solutions of varying concentrations used in *pickling. 'Fresh' brine may have added nitrite; 'live' brine contains micro-organisms that convert nitrate to nitrite (pickling salts). *See also* PICKLING.

brining The process of soaking vegetables in *brine before *pickling in vinegar, in order to remove some of the water and retain a crisp texture. Dry brining is when the vegetables are covered with dry salt rather than being immersed in a salt solution.

brinjal *See* AUBERGINE.

brinza (brenza) Eastern European soft cheese made from goat's or sheep's milk.

brioche French; sweet bread or yeast cake, sometimes containing currants and candied fruit, or chocolate chips.

brioli (brilloli) Corsican; chestnut meal, prepared in the same way as *polenta.

brisket The meat covering the breast bone of the animal. *See* BEEF.

brislings Name for young sprats, *Clupea sprattus*, when canned. A 100-g portion is an extremely rich *source of vitamin D and a rich source of vitamin A.

British Farm Standard Voluntary labelling of foods with a red tractor logo, meaning that the requirements of specific farm quality assurance schemes have been met. Under EU legislation the mark cannot be restricted to British produce, but may be used for produce of other EU countries providing it meets the required standards.

broa Portuguese; yellow bread made from maize and wheat flour, with egg.

broasting A cooking method in which the food is deep fried under pressure, which is quicker than without pressure, and the food absorbs less fat.

broccoli, Chinese (Chinese kale) *Brassica oleracea* var. *alboglabra*; similar to *calabrese and purple sprouting *broccoli.

broccoli, sprouting Member of the cabbage family, *Brassica oleracea* var. *italica* group, with purple and white clusters of flower buds (which turn green when boiled) and smaller heads than *calabrese. Originally known in France as Italian asparagus (17th century; Italian *broccoli* means 'little shoots'). A 100-g portion, boiled, is a rich *source of vitamin C; a source of vitamin A (500 µg carotene); provides 3g of dietary fibre; supplies 25 kcal (105 kJ).

broche (brochette), en French; roasted or grilled on a spit or skewer.

broiler chicken Fast-growing *chicken developed by the *USDA at Beltsville, Maryland, and first produced commercially in 1930.

broiling Cooking by direct heat over a flame, as in a *barbecue; American term for grilling. Pan broiling is cooking through hot dry metal over direct heat.

bromatology The science of foods, from the Greek *broma*, food.

bromelains *Enzymes in the *pineapple, and related plants of the family *Bromelidaceae*, which hydrolyse proteins. They are available as by-products from commercial pineapple production, usually from the stems, and are used to tenderize meat, to treat sausage casings, and to chill-proof beer (*see* HAZE). Similar enzymes are found in figs (*ficin) and *papaya (*papain).

brominated oils *See* OILS, BROMINATED.

bromine An element, chemically related to *iodine, *chlorine, and *fluorine, not known to have any function in the body, and not a dietary essential.

bronze diabetes *See* HAEMOCHROMATOSIS.

brooklime A wild plant (*Veronica beccabunga*) that grows in wet marshy conditions. The large, round, fleshy leaves can be added to salads.

broonie Orkney; gingerbread made with oatmeal.

brose A Scottish dish made by pouring boiling water on to oatmeal or barley meal; fish, meat, and vegetables may be added.

broth Thick soup.

broussiko Greek sweet fortified wine from the Cyclades.

brown adipose tissue (brown fat) *See* ADIPOSE TISSUE, BROWN.

brown betty American; pudding made from apple and breadcrumbs; similar to apple *charlotte.

brown colours Three brown colours are used in foods: Brown FK, synthetic, which is used to colour *kippers; Chocolate-brown HT, synthetic; and *caramel.

brown fat *See* ADIPOSE TISSUE, BROWN.

brown heart Internal browning of the flesh of apples and pears, originating in or near the core, but not detectable externally. It is thought to result from injury caused by carbon dioxide.

brownie American cake made with chocolate. Unleavened; probably originated when a cook forgot to add *baking powder; the first published recipe appeared in 1897.

browning, gravy *See* GRAVY BROWNING.

browning, non-enzymic *See* MAILLARD REACTION.

browning reactions Chemical reactions in foods which result in the formation of a brown colour. *See* MAILLARD REACTION; PHENOL OXIDASES.

brucellosis Infection with *Brucella* spp. Commonly acquired by close association with infected cows (*B. abortus*), sheep and goats (*B. melitensis*), and pigs (*B. suis*), so affecting mainly farmers and slaughterhouse workers. It can also be acquired by consumption of milk and milk products. Acute symptoms, which may not develop for up to two months after infection, include malaise, chills, sweats, fatigue and weakness, muscle and joint pain, and weight loss.

brühwurst German; frankfurter-type sausages which are heat treated during preparation.

brugnon Hybrid fruit, a cross between a *plum and a *peach. It resembles a *nectarine, and the name is sometimes used in France for nectarines.

brûlé Literally 'burnt'; food grilled or otherwise heated sufficiently to give it a brown colour. *See also* CRÈME BRÛLÉE.

brunch Combination meal of breakfast and lunch, a hearty late breakfast; first used in *Punch* magazine in 1896.

Brunner's glands Mucus-secreting glands in the *duodenum.

brunoise Mixture of diced or shredded vegetables used as base for a soup, sauce, or garnish.

bruschetta Italian; toasted bread moistened with olive oil (and optionally also garlic).

Brussels sprouts Leaf buds of *Brassica oleracea* var. *gemmiferra*. Nine sprouts (90 g) are a rich *source of folate and vitamin C; a source of vitamin B_6; provide 2.7 g of dietary fibre; supply 16 kcal (65 kJ).

brut Dry wines. *See* WINE SWEETNESS.

BS 5750 British Standard of excellence in quality management; originally an engineering standard but applicable to food companies, hospitals, etc.; incorporates the EU equivalent ISO 9002.

BSE Bovine spongiform encephalopathy, a degenerative brain disease in cattle, transmitted by feeding slaughterhouse waste from infected animals. Commonly known as 'mad cow disease'. The infective agent is a *prion; it can be transmitted to human beings, causing early-onset variant Creutzfeld–Jakob disease.

BST *See* SOMATOTROPIN, BOVINE.

bual *See* MADEIRA WINES.

bubble and squeak English; originally cold boiled beef fried with cooked potatoes and cabbage (the name comes from the sound made as it cooks). More commonly a fried mixture of left-over cabbage and potatoes. Colcannon is a similar Irish dish.

buccellatum Roman; biscuit or dried bread.

buchu oil Aromatic oil extracted from the leaves of the African shrubs *Agathosma betulina*, *A. crenulata*, and *Barosma* spp., used in artificial fruit flavours.

buckling A hot-smoked *herring (the *kipper is cold-smoked).

buck rarebit *See* WELSH RAREBIT.

buck's fizz Sparkling wine mixed with orange juice; known in the USA as a mimosa.

buckwheat A pseudocereal, the fruit of the herb *Fagopyrum esculentum*, which is not a grass; also known as Saracen corn and, when cooked, as kasha (Russian). Siberian or kangra buckwheat (tatary) is *F. tataricum*. Buckwheat is unsuitable for bread making, and is eaten as the cooked grain or a porridge, or baked into pancakes. A 100-g portion is a good *source of protein, niacin, and vitamin B_1; a source of vitamin B_2; supplies 350kcal (1470kJ).

budino Italian name for (usually cooked) puddings, often containing cheese, fruit, or nuts.

budu Malay, Thai; fermented fish sauce produced from salted *anchovy.

buffalo berry North American yellow berry, the fruit of *Shepherdia argentea*.

buffalo currant Two varieties of North American currant: *Ribes odoratum*, which has a distinctive smell, and *R. aureum*, the golden or Missouri currant.

buffers Substances that prevent a change in the *pH when *acid or *alkali is added. A mixture of a weak acid or base and its salt acts as a buffer by donating or taking up protons; buffers are commonly used to control the acidity of foods. Amino acids and proteins also act as buffers. The pH of blood is maintained by physiological buffers including phosphates, bicarbonate, and proteins.

bulgogi Korean; paper-thin slices of meat, marinated and grilled over charcoal, then wrapped in salad leaves.

bulgur The oldest processed food known. Prepared precooked wheat, originally from the Middle East. Wheat is soaked, cooked, and dried, then lightly milled to remove the outer bran and cracked. It is eaten in soups and cooked with meat (when it is known as kibbe). Also called ala, burghul, cracked wheat, and American rice.

b

bulimia nervosa An *eating disorder in which binge-eating is a necessary diagnostic criterion. Characterized by periods of over-eating, often followed by purging (self-induced vomiting and the abuse of laxatives and diuretics). *See also* ANOREXIA NERVOSA; BINGE-EATING DISORDER.

buljol Caribbean; salad of salt cod, chilli, tomato, and avocado.

bulking agents Non-nutritive substances (commonly *non-starch polysaccharides) added to foods to increase the bulk and hence sense of *satiety, especially in foods designed for weight reduction.

bulk sweeteners *See* SWEETENERS.

bullace Fruit of the wild damson, *Prunus insititia*; similar to *sloe (*P. spinosa*) and very acidic.

bullnose pepper *See* PEPPER.

bullock's heart *See* CUSTARD APPLE.

bull's eye Cushion-shaped, mint-flavoured boiled sweet, with dark and light stripes.

bulrush A wild plant common in ponds and marshes (correctly the false bulrush or common reedmace, *Typha latifolia*). The young sprouts and shoots can be eaten in salads, the pollen is used as a flavouring, and the roots and unripe flower heads may be boiled as a vegetable.

bun Sweetened bread roll; correctly made with yeast dough, although sometimes applied to small cakes made with baking powder, or to cream buns, which are made with choux pastry. Also applied to the rolls used for *hamburgers (burger buns).

bunderfleisch Swiss; beef that has been brined, rubbed with spices, and air-dried. *See also* BRESAOLA.

buni Coffee beans left in the field to dry; generally hard and of poor quality.

bunt *See* SMUT.

burbot Freshwater fish *Lota lota*, widely distributed in Europe and the USA, but rare in Great Britain.

burdock Wild thistle-like plant (*Arctium lappa* or *A. majus*); the leaves are used in salads and to flavour a traditional carbonated beverage (dandelion and burdock); the root contains *inulin rather than *starch, and is eaten in Japan, where it is called gobo.

burfi *See* BARFI.

burger *See* HAMBURGER.

burghul *See* BULGUR.

Burgundy Red and white wines produced in the Burgundy region of France (Bourgogne).

burnet Salad burnet, a wild perennial herb (*Poterium sanguisorba* syn. *Sanguisorba minor*) growing in grassland on chalky soil. The leaves, which have the flavour of cucumber, can be used to flavour fruit *wines, vinegar, and butter, and are used in salads. Also called pimpernel. Greater or garden burnet is *S. (P.) officinalis.*

burning foot syndrome Nutritional melalgia (neuralgic pain): severe aching, throbbing, and burning pain in the feet, associated with nerve damage, observed in severely under nourished prisoners of war in the Far East. It results from long periods on a diet poor in protein and B *vitamins, and may (doubtfully) be due specifically to a deficiency of *pantothenic acid.

burstin Orkney, historical; barley grains toasted by placing in a pot beside the fire, then ground and used to make a porridge.

busa *See* MILK, FERMENTED.

bushel A traditional dry measure of capacity, equivalent to 80 lb of distilled water at 17°C with a barometer reading of 30 inches, i.e. 8 imperial gallons (36.4 L); used as a measure of corn, potatoes, etc. The American (Winchester) bushel is 3% larger.

The weight of a bushel varies with the product: wheat 27 kg, maize and rye 25 kg, barley 22 kg, paddy rice 20 kg, oats 14.5 kg.

butifarra Spanish (Catalan and Mallorquin); spiced pork sausage containing pine nuts, almonds, cumin seed, and cinnamon. Butifarrones are smaller.

butt A cask for beer or wine, containing 108 imperial gallons (491 L).

butter Made from separated *cream by churning (sweet cream butter); legally not less than 80% fat (and not more than 16% water) of which around 60% is *saturated, a small proportion (3%) polyunsaturated, the rest being mono-unsaturated. Lactic butter is made by ripening the cream with a bacterial culture to produce lactic acid and increase the flavour (due to diacetyl). This is normally unsalted or up to 0.5% salt added. Sweet cream butter may be salted up to 2%. Butter supplies 72 kcal (300 kJ) per g; a 40-g portion (as spread on four slices of bread) is a rich *source of vitamin A and contains 32 g of fat, of which two-thirds is saturated; supplies 300 kcal (1 260 kJ).

butter, black Butter that has been browned by heating, then vinegar and seasonings are added.

butter, bog Norsemen, Finns, Scots and Irish used to bury *firkins of butter in bogs to ripen and develop a strong flavour.

butter, bush Fruit of the African tree *Dacryodes edulis*, also known as African plum tree. The bitter flesh must be boiled to make it tender enough to eat; the large seed is fed to livestock.

butter, clarified Butter fat, prepared by heating butter and separating the fat from the water. It does not become *rancid as rapidly as butter. Also known as ghee or ghrt (India) and samna (Egypt).

butter, devilled Butter mixed with lemon juice, cayenne and black pepper, and curry powder.

butter, drawn Melted butter used as a dressing for cooked vegetables.

butter, Goa *See* KOKUM.

butter, green Butter mixed with chopped herbs and other seasonings to produce a savoury spread.

butter, herb A mixture of butter and mayonnaise blended with parsley, tarragon, dill, watercress, thyme, green pepper, garlic, and other herbs, used as a savoury spread on biscuits or bread.

butter, mowrah *See* BUTTER, VEGETABLE.

butter, ravigote Butter creamed with chopped fresh aromatic herbs (tarragon, parsley, chives, chervil), usually served with grilled meat.

butter, renovated (process butter) Butter that has been melted and rechurned with the addition of milk, cream, or water.

butter, vegetable Naturally occurring fats that melt sharply because they contain mainly a single *triacylglycerol. Cocoa butter is from the *cocoa bean, used in *chocolate; Borneo tallow or green butter from the Malaysian and Indonesian plant *Shorea stenopiera* resembles cocoa butter; shea butter from the African plant *Butyrospermum parkii* is softer than cocoa butter. Mowrah fat or illipé butter is from the Indian plant *Bassia longifolia*.

butter, whey (serum butter) Butter made from the small amount of fat left in *whey; it has a slightly different *fatty acid composition from ordinary butter.

butterbur The large soft leaves of *Petasites japonicus* were formerly used to wrap butter, and are eaten as a vegetable in Korea and Japan.

butterfish Marine oily fish *Brama brama*; also known as pomfret, widely distributed in the Atlantic, Pacific and Indian oceans. In the USA, the marine fish *Peprilus triacanthus* is also known as butterfish.

butterine *See* MARGARINE.

buttermilk The residue left after churning butter, 0.1–2% fat, with the other constituents of milk proportionally increased. It is slightly acidic, with a distinctive flavour due to the presence of *diacetyl and other substances. Also made by adding lactic bacteria to skimmed milk; 90–92% water, 4% lactose with acidic flavour from lactic acid, it is similar to skimmed milk in composition. Dried buttermilk is used in bakery products and ice cream.

butternockerln *See* KNÖDELN.

butternut White *walnut, fruit of the native North American tree *Juglans cinerea*.

butterscotch *See* TOFFEE.

butylated hydroxyanisole (BHA) An *antioxidant used in fats and fatty foods; it is stable to heating, and so is useful in baked products.

butylated hydroxytoluene (BHT) An *antioxidant used in fats and fatty foods.

butyric acid A short-chain saturated *fatty acid (C4:0). It occurs as the *triacylglycerol in 5–6% of butter fat, and in small amounts in other fats and oils. Also formed by intestinal bacterial fermentation of resistant *starch, when it is possibly protective against the development of colo-rectal cancer.

buzuri A *catfish, *Mystus tengara*.

BV Biological Value, a measure of *protein quality.

CA Controlled atmosphere. *See* STORAGE, MODIFIED GAS.

cabbage Leaves of *Brassica oleracea* var. *capitata*. A 100-g portion (boiled) is a rich *source of vitamin C; a good source of folate; a source of vitamin B$_1$; provides 2g of dietary fibre; supplies 15kcal (65kJ). *See also* COLLARD; SAUERKRAUT; SAVOY; SPRING GREENS.

cabbage, Chinese Name given to two oriental vegetables: *Brassica pekinensis* (pe-tsai, Pekin cabbage, snow cabbage), pale green compact head resembling lettuce, and *B. chinensis* (pak choi, Chinese greens, Chinese chard), loose bunch of dark green leaves and thick stalks; a 50-g portion is an exceptionally rich *source of vitamin C; a rich source of *folate; a source of vitamin A (as carotene); supplies 15kcal (65kJ).

cabbage, swamp *See* SPINACH, WATER.

cabbage palm Several types of palm tree that have edible inner leaves, terminal buds, or inner part of the stem (heart of palm). *See also* PEJIBAYE.

cabbie-claw Scottish (Shetland); fresh codling, salted and hung in the open air for one to two days, then simmered with horseradish. The name derives from the Shetland dialect name for young *cod, kabbilow.

cabello de ángel *See* ANGEL'S HAIR.

cabernet franc A *grape variety widely used for *wine making, not one of the classic varieties. Also known as bouchet.

cabernet sauvignon One of the nine 'classic' *grape varieties used for *wine making, used for some of the great red wines of Bordeaux, and widely grown throughout the world.

cabinet pudding Moulded pudding made from bread and butter or sponge cake, with custard; sometimes glacé cherries and egg are added.

caboc Scottish; double cream cheese (60% fat), rolled in oatmeal.

cabrales Spanish; queso de cabrales is goat's or sheep's milk hard cheese.

cacao butter *See* COCOA BUTTER.

cacciatora, alla Italian; in the hunter's style, generally game or poultry with onions, herbs, and tomatoes in a wine sauce.

cacciatore Small Italian *salami.

cacen-gri Welsh; soda scones made with currants and *buttermilk.

cachama Freshwater fish, *Colossoma macroponum*, also known as tambaqui.

cachelos Spanish (Galician); dish of potatoes, cabbage, ham, and chorizo (spiced sausage).

cachexia The condition of extreme emaciation and wasting seen in patients with advanced diseases such as cancer and AIDS. Due partly to an inadequate intake of food and mainly to the effects of the disease in increasing *metabolic rate (hypermetabolism) and the breakdown of tissue protein. *See also* PROTEIN-ENERGY MALNUTRITION.

cachou Small scented tablets for sweetening the breath.

CaCo2 cells A human colon adenocarcinoma line; in cell culture the cells develop many of the features of differentiation of small intestine epithelial cells; widely used in studies of intestinal absorption.

cacogeusia An unpleasant taste in the mouth; may be a side-effect of medication in some cases.

cactus apple *See* PITAYA.

cactus pear *See* PRICKLY PEAR.

cadmium A mineral of no known function in the body, and therefore not a dietary essential. It accumulates in the body throughout life, reaching a total body content of 20–30 mg (200–300 μmol). It is toxic, and cadmium poisoning is a recognized industrial disease. In Japan cadmium poisoning was implicated in itai-itai disease, a severe and sometimes fatal loss of calcium from the bones, that occurred in an area where rice was grown on land irrigated with contaminated waste water. Accidental contamination of drinking water with cadmium salts also leads to kidney damage, and enough cadmium can leach out from cooking vessels with cadmium glaze to pose a hazard.

caecum The first part of the large intestine, separated from the small intestine by the ileo-colic sphincter. It is small in carnivorous animals and very large in herbivores, since it is involved in the digestion of cellulose. In omnivorous animals, including human beings, it is of intermediate size. *See also* GASTRO-INTESTINAL TRACT.

caerphilly Welsh; hard cheese with sour flavour and crumbly texture.

cafestol Diterpene in coffee oil, associated with reversible hypercholesterolaemia and hypertriglyceridaemia, and also possibly an anticarcinogenic effect by enhancement of phase II metabolism (*see* METABOLISM, PHASE II) of foreign compounds. Released into the beverage only when coffee is boiled for a prolonged period of time. *See also* KAHWEOL.

caffeine An *alkaloid (trimethylxanthine) found in coffee and tea (when it is sometimes called theine). It raises blood pressure, has a diuretic action, and temporarily averts fatigue and tiredness, so has a stimulant action. It can also be a cause of insomnia in some people, and decaffeinated coffee and tea are commonly available.

Coffee beans contain about 1% caffeine, and the beverage contains about 70 mg/100 mL. Tea contains 1.5–2.5% caffeine, about 50–60 mg/100 mL of the beverage. Cola drinks contain 12–18 mg/100 mL, and some *energy drinks may contain more.

See also COFFEE, DECAFFEINATED; THEOBROMINE; XANTHINE.

caffeol A volatile oil in coffee beans, giving the characteristic flavour and aroma.

cafiroleta Caribbean (Cuba); dessert made from *boniatillo (creamed sweet potato) and *coquimol (coconut milk custard).

CAGE Questionnaire to screen for *alcohol abuse—'cut down, annoyed, guilty, eye-opener'.

caja Fruit of the South American tree *Spondias lutea* (syn. *S. mombin*), also known as yellow mombin and hog, gulley, or Spanish plum.

cake Baked from flour with added fat (butter or margarine), sugar, and eggs. Plain cakes are made by rubbing the fat and sugar into the flour, with no egg; sponge cakes by whipping with or without fat; rich cakes contain dried fruit.

caking Undesirable agglomeration of powders as a result of exposure to humidity. *See* ANTI-CAKING AGENTS.

calabasa West Indian or green *pumpkin or *squash, with yellow flesh.

calabash *See* GOURD.

calabrese An annual plant (*Brassica oleracea* var. *italica*), a variety of *broccoli which yields a crop in the same year as it is sown. Also called American, Italian, or green sprouting broccoli. A 75-g portion is a rich *source of vitamin A (as carotene), folate, and vitamin C; provides 3g of dietary fibre; supplies 25 kcal (105 kJ).

calamary Spanish: *calamares*; Italian: *calamari*. Mediterranean squid (*Lodogo vulgaris*).

calamondin A *citrus fruit resembling a small tangerine, with a delicate pulp and a lime-like flavour.

calas American (New Orleans); rice fritters. *See* AKKRA.

calbindins Intracellular calcium binding proteins that are synthesized in response to *vitamin D action.

calcidiol The 25-hydroxy-derivative of *vitamin D, also known as 25-hydroxycholecalciferol, the main storage and circulating form of the vitamin in the body.

calciferol Used at one time as a name for ercalciol (ergocalciferol or vitamin D_2), made by the ultraviolet irradiation of ergosterol. Also used as a general term to include both *vitamers of *vitamin D (vitamins D_2 and D_3).

calciol The official name for cholecalciferol, the naturally occurring form of *vitamin D (vitamin D_3).

calcionetta Italian; dessert made from fried ravioli filled with spiced sweetened chestnut purée.

calcinosis Abnormal deposition of *calcium salts in tissues. May be due to excessive intake of *vitamin D.

calcitetrol The 1,24,25-trihydroxy-derivative of vitamin D, an inactivation product of *calcitriol and intermediate in the catabolism of the vitamin.

calcitonin Peptide *hormone secreted by the parafollicular or C cells of the *thyroid gland; opposes the hypercalcaemic action of *parathyroid hormone. Alternative splicing of the same gene expressed in other tissues yields the calcitonin gene-related peptide (CGRP), which is a neurotransmitter and has vasodilatory actions.

calcitriol The 1,25-dihydroxy-derivative of *vitamin D, also known as 1,25-dihydroxycholecalciferol; the active metabolite of the vitamin in the body.

calcium The major inorganic component of bones and teeth; the total body content of an adult is about 1–1.5kg (15–38mol). The small amounts in blood plasma (2.1–2.6mmol/L, 85–105mg/L) and in tissues play a vital role in the excitability of nerve tissue, the control of muscle contraction, and the integration and regulation of metabolic processes.

The absorption of calcium from the intestinal tract requires *vitamin D, and together with parathyroid hormone, vitamin D also regulates calcium balance, mobilizing it from the bones to maintain the plasma concentration within a very narrow range. An unacceptably high plasma concentration of calcium is *hypercalcaemia.

Loss of calcium from bones occurs as a normal part of the ageing process, and may lead to *osteoporosis.

The richest *sources of calcium are milk and cheese; in some countries it is added to flour. Other rich sources include haggis, canned pilchards and sardines, spinach, sprats, and tripe.

calcium acid phosphate Also known as monocalcium phosphate and acid calcium phosphate or ACP, $Ca(H_2PO_4)_2$. It is used as the acid ingredient of *baking powder and self-raising flour, since it reacts with bicarbonate to liberate carbon dioxide.

caliciviruses RNA-containing viruses, including *Norwalk and Norwalk-like viruses, which are responsible for acute gastroenteritis; transmitted by the faecal–oral route via contaminated water and foods, especially shellfish and salads.

calculi (calculus) Stones formed in tissues such as the gall bladder (biliary calculus or *gallstone), kidney (renal calculus), or ureters. Renal calculi may consist of *uric acid and its salts (especially in *gout) or *oxalic acid salts. Oxalate calculi may be of metabolic or dietary origin, and people at metabolic risk of forming oxalate renal calculi are advised to avoid dietary sources of oxalic acid and its precursors. Other renal calculi may be formed from *cystine, *xanthine, calcium phosphate, or magnesium ammonium phosphate.

caldereta Spanish; stewed fish or meat, named from the *caldera* or cauldron in which it is cooked.

caldo Portuguese, Spanish; broth.

calf's foot jelly Stock made by boiling calves' feet in water; it sets to a stiff jelly on cooling. It consists largely of water and *gelatine, so is of little nutritional value.

calipash The green fat attached to the upper shell (carapace) of the *turtle; the yellow fat attached to the lower shell is calipee.

calipee *See* CALIPASH.

calisay Spanish (Catalan); liqueur made from chinchona (cinchona) bark, aged in oak casks.

callaloo (calaloo, calilu, calalou, callau) Caribbean name for leaves of both *taro and Chinese spinach (*Amaranthus gangeticus*), and for the soup made from them.

calorie A unit of *energy used to express the *energy yield of foods and energy expenditure by the body. Name coined by Atwater in 1895. One calorie (cal) is the amount of heat required to raise the temperature of 1 g of water through 1 °C (from 14.5–15.5 °C). Nutritionally the kilocalorie (1 000 calories) is used (the amount of heat required to raise the temperature of 1 kg of water through 1 °C), and to avoid confusion with the cal is abbreviated as either kcal or Cal.

The calorie is not an SI unit, and correctly the *joule is used as the unit of energy, although kcal are widely used. 1 kcal = 4.18 kJ; 1 kJ = 0.24 kcal.

calorie-free In US law, providing less than 5 kcal (21 kJ) per serving.

calories, empty A term used to describe foods that provide energy but little, if any, of the nutrients.

calorimeter (bomb calorimeter) An instrument for measuring the amount of oxidizable *energy in a substance, by burning it in oxygen and measuring the heat produced. The energy yield of a foodstuff in the body is equal to that obtained in a bomb calorimeter only when the metabolic end-products are the same as those obtained by combustion. Thus, proteins liberate 5.65 kcal (23.64 kJ)/g in a calorimeter, when the nitrogen is oxidized to the dioxide, but only 4.4 kcal (18.4 kJ)/g in the body, when the nitrogen is excreted as urea (which has a heat of combustion equal to the 'missing' 1.25 kcal (5.23 kJ)).

calorimetry The measurement of energy expenditure by the body. Direct calorimetry is the direct measurement of heat output from the body, as an index of energy expenditure, and hence energy requirements. The subject is placed inside a small, thermally insulated room, and the heat produced is measured.

Indirect calorimetry is a means of estimating energy expenditure by either measurement of the rate of oxygen consumption, using a *spirometer (each litre of oxygen consumed is equivalent to 20 kJ energy expenditure), or estimation of the total production of carbon dioxide over a period of 7–10 days, after consumption of dual isotopically labelled water (i.e. water labelled with both ^{2}H and ^{18}O; *see* WATER, DOUBLE LABELLED).

calpain Proteolytic *enzyme involved in tissue protein turnover, and also meat tenderization during storage and deterioration of fish proteins gels. Regulated by intracellular calcium concentration and the regulatory protein calpastatin.

caltrops *See* CHESTNUT.

calvados French; apple brandy made by distillation of *cider. Appellation contrôlée calvados is from the Calvados region in Normandy, and is double distilled.

calzone Italian; crescent-shaped turnover of leavened dough, filled with ham and cheese; may be fried or baked. Sometimes called pizza calzone.

camash *See* QUAMASH.

Cambridge sauce English; substitute for mayonnaise, made with oil, vinegar, and pounded yolk of hard-boiled eggs, flavoured with capers, anchovies, and herbs. *See also* SALAD DRESSING.

camembert A soft, French *cheese made from cow's milk, originating from Auge, Normandy, France. It is covered with a white mould (*Penicillium candidum* or *P. camembertii*) which participates in the ripening process.

It contains 50% water and 25% fat (= '50% fat in dry matter'); a 30-g portion is a rich *source of vitamin B_{12}; a source of protein, vitamins A, B_2, and niacin; contains 8g of fat, 100mg of calcium, and 200mg of sodium; supplies 90kcal (370kJ). Also made with '30% fat in dry matter' (= 13% of total), '40', '45', and '60% fat in dry matter' (= 18% of total).

camias *See* BILIMBI.

camomile (chamomile) Either of two herbs, *Anthemis nobilis* or *Matricaria recutica*. The essential oil (*see* OILS, ESSENTIAL) is used to flavour *liqueurs; camomile tea is a *tisane prepared by infusion of the dried flower heads, and the whole herb can be used to make a herb beer.

Campden process The preservation of food by the addition of sodium bisulphite, which liberates sulphur dioxide. Also known as cold preservation, since it replaces heat *sterilization.

Campden tablets Tablets of sodium bisulphite used for sterilization of bottles and other containers and in the preservation of foods (the *Campden process).

campesterol A plant *sterol.

Campylobacter Food-borne pathogens (esp *C. jejuni* and *C. coli*) causing, sometimes severe, diarrhoea, and long-term health problems in 2–10% of cases. Now correctly classified as *Arcobacter* spp. The main sources of infection are raw milk and undercooked poultry. Highly virulent with an infectious dose of a few hundred organisms.

campylobacteriosis *See* CAMPYLOBACTER.

camu-camu Fruit of the Peruvian bush *Myrciaria paraensis*; burgundy red in colour, weighing 6–14g and about 3cm in diameter; contains 3000mg vitamin C/100g pulp.

cananga oil A lipid-soluble flavouring agent, obtained by distillation of flowers of *Cananga odorato*.

canapés Small rectangular slices of bread, toasted or fried, spread with meat or fish pâté; originally served as an accompaniment to winged game, and spread with forcemeat made from the entrails of the birds. The name derives from the French *canapé*, 'sofa', since these were traditionally eaten in the drawing room before dinner was served in the dining room.

canary grass Mediterranean annual grass *Phalaris canariensis*; the grain is used to feed caged birds, but is also consumed by human beings.

canavanine Toxic amino acid (an analogue of *arginine in which the final methylene group is replaced by oxygen), originally isolated from the jack bean, *Canavalia ensiformis*, and also found in a variety of other plants, including especially alfalfa bean sprouts. It is incorporated into proteins in place of arginine, and also inhibits nitric oxide synthetase.

canbra oil (canola oil) Oil extracted from selected strains of *rapeseed containing not more than 2% *erucic acid.

cancer A wide variety of diseases characterized by uncontrolled growth of tissue. Dietary factors may be involved in the initiation of many cancers, and a high-fat diet has been especially implicated. There is evidence that *antioxidant nutrients such as *carotene, *vitamins C and *E, and the mineral *selenium may be protective. *See also* CARCINOGEN.

Patients with advanced cancer are frequently malnourished, the condition of *cachexia.

candelilla wax A hydrocarbon wax from the candelilla plant (*Euphorbia cerifera*). Used as a lubricant and surface finishing agent in chewing gum and hard candy.

Candida Genus of yeasts that inhabit the gut. *C. albicans* can, under some circumstances, cause candidiasis (thrush).

candidate gene One or more genes that have been implicated in the pathophysiology of a complex disease involving interactions between genotype and diet and/or other environmental factors, based on genetic, physiological, or pharmacological evidence.

candied peel Preserved peel, commonly of *citrus fruits, used in confectionery and cake making. It is prepared by softening the peel, then boiling with sugar syrup.

candlenut Fruit of the South-East Asian tree *Aleurites moluccana*, mainly a source of oil (candlenut or lambang oil), but also eaten roasted and as a paste in Malaysian and Indonesian curries. The raw nuts are toxic, but the toxin is denatured on cooking.

candy 1. Crystallized sugar made by repeated boiling and slow evaporation. 2. USA; a general term for *sugar confectionery. *See also* TOFFEE.

candy doctor *See* SUGAR DOCTOR.

cane sugar *See* SUGAR CANE.

canihua Seeds of *Chenopodium pallidicaule*, grown in the Peruvian Andes; nutritionally similar to wheat and other cereals.

canistel Fruit of the American tree *Pouteria campechiana*, also known as egg-fruit or yellow *sapote, with a mealy texture.

cannelloni *See* PASTA.

canners' alkali A mixture of sodium hydroxide and carbonate used to remove the skin from fruit before canning.

canning The process of preserving food by sterilization and cooking in a sealed metal can, which destroys bacteria and protects from recontamination. If foods are sterilized and cooked in glass jars which are then closed with hermetically sealed lids, the process is known as bottling. Canned foods are sometimes known as tinned foods, because the cans were made using tin-plated steel. More commonly now they are made of lacquered steel or aluminium. In aseptic canning, foods are pre-sterilized at a very high temperature (150–175°C) for a few seconds, and then sealed into cans under sterile (aseptic) conditions. The flavour, colour, and retention of vitamins are superior with this short-time, high-temperature process compared with conventional canning.

canola A variety of *rape that is low in glucosinolates. Canola oil (*canbra oil) contains less than 2% *erucic acid.

cantal French *Cheddar-type cheese.

cantaloup A variety of *melon.

canthaxanthin A red *carotenoid pigment which is not a precursor of *vitamin A. It is used as a food colour, and can be added to the diet of broiler *chickens to colour the skin and shanks, and to the diet of farmed *trout and *salmon to produce the same colour as is seen in wild fish, which is derived from carotenoids in natural foodstuffs. It is also used to maintain the plumage colour of flamingos kept in captivity.

CAP **1.** Common Agricultural Policy of the European Union. **2.** Controlled atmosphere packaging; *see* PACKAGING, MODIFIED ATMOSPHERE.

Cape gooseberry *See* PHYSALIS.

capelin Marine fish *Mallotus villosus* found in the north Atlantic, the north Pacific, and adjoining regions of the Arctic.

caper Unopened flower buds of the subtropical shrub *Capparis spinosa* or *C. inermis* with a peppery flavour; used in pickles and sauces. Unripe seeds of the nasturtium (*Tropaeolum majus*) may be pickled and used as a substitute.

capercaillie (capercailzie) A large *game bird (*Tetrao urogallus*), also known as wood grouse or cock of the wood.

capillariasis Infestation with the larvae of the parasitic nematodes *Capillaria philippinensis* and *C. hepatica*, causing abdominal pain, nausea, vomiting, diarrhoea, and anorexia; potentially fatal. Transmitted by eating raw fish contaminated with the larvae.

capillary fragility A measure of the resistance to rupture of the small blood vessels (capillaries), which leads to leakage of red blood cells into tissue spaces. Deficiency of *vitamin C can lead to increased capillary fragility, and there is some evidence that *flavonoids reduce capillary fragility.

capocollo Italian; dried, cured, and seasoned pork sausage, a speciality of the Parma region.

capon A castrated cockerel (male chicken), which has a faster rate of growth, and more tender flesh, than the cockerel. Surgery has generally been replaced by chemical caponization, the implantation of pellets of oestrogen.

caponata Sicilian; fried aubergine, in a tomato sauce containing capers, olives, celery, and anchovy, garnished with slices of tuna, crawfish, etc.

cappelletti Italian; small hat-shaped pasta envelopes stuffed with minced meat, etc.; a variant of *ravioli.

cappuccino Italian; coffee with a head of frothy milk or whipped cream.

caprenin Poorly absorbed fat, two medium-chain fatty acids (*capric and *caprylic) and one very long-chain fatty acid (*behenic) esterified to glycerol; used as a *fat replacer. Provides 20 kJ (5 kcal)/g because caprylic and capric acids are metabolized less efficiently than longer-chain fatty acids, and behenic acid is only partially absorbed. Its melting profile is similar to that of *cocoa butter.

capretto Meat from goat kids fed on milk up to five months of age.

capric acid A medium-chain *fatty acid (C10:0), found in coconut oil and in goat and cow butter.

caproic acid A short-chain *fatty acid (C6:0), found in coconut oil and goat and cow butter.

caprylic acid A medium-chain *fatty acid (C8:0), found in goat and cow butter, coconut oil, and human fat.

capsaicin An alkylamide found in *Capsicum* spp.; the pungent compound in chilli peppers.

capsicum *See* PEPPER.

carambola (star fruit) Long (8–12 cm) ribbed fruit of *Averrhoa carambola*; a 50-g portion is a rich *source of vitamin C.

caramel Brown material formed by heating carbohydrates in the presence of acid or alkali; also known as burnt sugar. It can be manufactured from various sugars, starches, and starch hydrolysates and is used as a flavour and colour in a wide variety of foods.

caramel cream A dessert made either by gently heating eggs in milk and allowing to cool (egg *custard) or by using *cornflour and milk, topped with a caramel sauce. Also known as crème caramel and (in Spain) as flán.

caramels Sweets similar to *toffee but boiled at a lower temperature; may be soft or hard. *See also* FUDGE.

caraway Dried ripe fruit of the herb *Carum carvi*, an aromatic spice, used to flavour the liqueur *kümmel, some types of *aquavit, on bread and rolls, and in *seed cake. Black caraway is *kalonji.

carbohydrate Carbohydrates are the major metabolic fuels, the sugars and starches. They are composed of carbon, hydrogen, and oxygen in the ratio $C_n : H_{2n} : O_n$. The basic carbohydrates are the *monosaccharide *sugars, of which glucose, fructose, and galactose are the most important nutritionally.

Disaccharides consist of two monosaccharides: nutritionally the important disaccharides are sucrose (a dimer of glucose + fructose), lactose (a dimer of glucose + galactose), and maltose (a dimer of two glucose units).

A number of oligosaccharides occur in foods, consisting of 3–9 monosaccharide units; in general these are not digested, and should be considered among the unavailable carbohydrates (*see* CARBOHYDRATE, UNAVAILABLE).

Larger polymers of carbohydrates are known as polysaccharides or complex carbohydrates. Nutritionally two classes of polysaccharides can be distinguished: i) starches, which are polymers of glucose units, either as a straight chain (amylose) or with a branched structure (amylopectin), and are digested; and ii) a variety of other polysaccharides which are collectively known as *non-starch polysaccharides (NSP), and are not digested by human digestive enzymes.

The reserve of carbohydrate in the liver and muscles is glycogen, a glucose polymer with a similar structure to the amylopectin form of starch, but more branched.

Carbohydrates form the major part of the diet, providing between 50 and 70% of the energy intake, largely from starch and sucrose. The metabolic energy yield of carbohydrates is 4 kcal (17 kJ)/g. More precisely, monosaccharides yield 3.74 kcal (15.7 kJ), disaccharides 3.95 kcal (16.6 kJ), and starch 4.18 kcal (17.6 kJ)/g. *Glycerol is a 3-carbon sugar alcohol, and classified as a carbohydrate; it yields 4.32 kcal (18.1 kJ)/g.

See also STARCH; SUGAR; SUGAR ALCOHOLS.

carbohydrate by difference Historically it was difficult to determine the various carbohydrates present in foods, and an approximation was made by subtracting the measured *protein, *fat, *ash, and water from the total weight. Carbohydrate by difference is the sum of nutritionally available carbohydrates (dextrins, starches, and sugars), nutritionally unavailable carbohydrate (pentosans, pectins, hemicelluloses, and cellulose), and non-carbohydrates such as organic acids and *lignins.

carbohydrate loading Practice of some endurance athletes (e.g. marathon runners) in training for a major event; it consists of exercising to exhaustion, so depleting muscle *glycogen, then eating a large carbohydrate-rich meal so as to replenish glycogen reserves with a higher than normal proportion of straight-chain glycogen, which is mobilized more slowly than highly branched glycogen.

carbohydrate metabolism *See* GLUCOSE METABOLISM.

carbohydrate, parietal Those *non-starch polysaccharides that make up plant cell walls. *See also* CELLULOSE.

carbohydrate, unavailable A general term for those carbohydrates present in foods that are not digested, and are therefore excluded from calculations of energy intake, although they may be fermented by intestinal bacteria and yield some energy. The term includes resistant *starch, indigestible *oligosaccharides, and the various *non-starch polysaccharides. *See also* FATTY ACIDS, VOLATILE.

carbon dioxide, available *See* BAKING POWDER; FLOUR, SELF-RAISING.

carbon dioxide storage *See* STORAGE, MODIFIED GAS.

carbonnade Stewed or braised meat, often with beer in the sauce; originally the French term for meat grilled over hot coals.

γ-carboxyglutamate A derivative of the *amino acid glutamate whose formation in post-synthetic modification of precursor proteins requires *vitamin K. It is found in *prothrombin and other enzymes involved in *blood clotting, and in osteocalcin and matrix Gla protein in *bone, where it has a function in ensuring the correct crystallization of bone mineral.

carboxymethylcellulose *See* CELLULOSE DERIVATIVES.

carboxypeptidase An *enzyme secreted in the *pancreatic juice that removes amino acids sequentially from the free carboxyl terminal of a peptide or protein (i.e. the end that has a free carboxyl group exposed), until the final product is a *dipeptide. Since it works at the end of the peptide chain, it is an *exopeptidase.

carboxypeptidase E The enzyme that catalyses the cleavage of pro-insulin to *insulin, and catalyses post-synthetic modification of pro-opiomelanocortin and other peptide *hormone precursors.

carcinogen A substance that can induce *cancer; carcinogenesis is the process of induction of cancer.

carciofi Italian; tender globe *artichokes, eaten whole.

cardamom The seeds and dried, nearly ripe, fruit of *Elettaria cardamomum* (syn. *Amomum cardamomum*), a member of the ginger family. An aromatic spice used as a flavouring in sausages, bakery goods, *sugar confectionery, and whole in mixed pickling spice. It is widely used in Indian cooking (the Hindi name is elaichi), and as one of the ingredients of *curry powder. Arabic coffee (similar to Turkish *coffee) is flavoured with ground cardamom seeds.

cardinal, à la Dish with a scarlet effect, as when a fish dish is served with a *coral or lobster sauce dusted with paprika or cayenne.

cardiomyopathy Any chronic disorder affecting the muscle of the heart. May be associated with *alcoholism and *vitamin B_1 deficiency.

cardiospasm *See* ACHALASIA.

cardoon Leafy vegetable (*Cynara cardunculus*); both the fleshy root and the ribs and stems of the inner (blanched) leaves are eaten. Extracts from the dried flowers are used as vegetable *rennet in cheese making. Sometimes called chard, although distinct from true *chard or spinach beet.

carey encebollabo Creole; sea turtle steak with onions.

caries Dental decay caused by attack on the tooth enamel by acids produced by bacteria that are normally present in the mouth. Sugars in the mouth promote bacterial growth and acid production; *sucrose specifically promotes *plaque-forming bacteria, which cause the most damage. A moderately high intake of *fluoride increases the resistance of tooth enamel to acid attack. *See also* SWEETS, TOOTH-FRIENDLY.

carignan A *grape variety widely used for *wine making, not one of the classic varieties; a prolific cropper, producing reputedly uninspiring wines.

cariogenic Causing tooth decay (*see* CARIES) by stimulating the growth of acid-forming bacteria on the teeth. The term is applied to sucrose and other fermentable carbohydrates.

carmine Brilliant red colour derived from *cochineal (E120).

carminic acid *See* COCHINEAL.

carmoisine A red colour, also known as azorubine, synthetic azo-dye, E122.

carnatz Romanian; croquettes of seasoned minced beef and pork, served with a tomato sauce.

carnauba wax A hard wax from the buds and leaves of the Brazilian wax palm *Copernicia cerifera*, used in candy glaze.

carnitine A derivative of the *amino acid *lysine, required for the transport of fatty acids into *mitochondria for oxidation. There is no evidence that it is a dietary essential for human beings, since it can readily be formed in the body, although there is some evidence that increased intake may enhance the work capacity of muscles. It is a dietary essential for some insects, and was at one time called vitamin B_T.

carnosine A dipeptide, β-alanyl-histidine, found in the muscle of most animals. Its function is not known, although it has antioxidant actions and may inhibit *glycation of proteins.

carob Seeds and pod of the tree *Ceratonia siliqua*, also known as locust bean and St John's bread. It contains a sweet pulp which is rich in sugar and gums, as well as containing 21% protein and 1.5% fat. It is used as animal feed, to make confectionery (as a substitute for chocolate), and in the preparation of *carob gum. The African locust is *Parkia filicoidea* and the locust bean is *P. biglobosa*, an important food in the Caribbean.

carob gum The *gum extracted from the *carob, used as an emulsifier and a stabilizer as well as in cosmetics and as a size for textiles. Also known as locust bean gum or tragasol.

caroenum Roman; very sweet cooking wine, reduced to one-third its volume by boiling, and mixed with honey.

caroline French; small choux pastry filled with purée of meat or pâté.

carotene The red and orange pigments of many plants, obvious in carrots, red palm oil, and yellow maize, but masked by *chlorophyll in leaves. Three main types of carotene in foods are important as precursors of *vitamin A: α-, β-, and γ-carotene, which are also used as food colours. Plant foods contain a considerable number of other carotenes, most of which are not precursors of vitamin A.

Some carotene is converted into vitamin A (*retinol) in the intestinal mucosa, and some is absorbed unchanged (and may be converted to retinol in the liver). It is generally considered that 6 µg of β-carotene, and 12 µg of other provitamin A carotenoids, is nutritionally equivalent to 1 µg of preformed *vitamin A, but feeding studies suggest that as much as 26 µg or more of β-carotene from yellow and red fruits is required to form 1 µg of retinol. About 30% of the vitamin A in Western diets, and considerably more in diets in less-developed countries, comes from carotene.

In addition to their role as precursors of vitamin A, carotenes are *antioxidant nutrients, and there is evidence that they provide protection against *ischaemic heart disease and some forms of *cancer. There is no evidence on which to base *reference intakes of carotene other than as a precursor of vitamin A.

carotenoids A general term for the wide variety of red and yellow compounds chemically related to *carotene that are found in plant foods, some of which are precursors of *vitamin A, and hence known as provitamin A carotenoids.

carotinaemia Presence of abnormally large amounts of *carotene in blood plasma. Also known as xanthaemia.

carp Freshwater fish, all members of the family *Cyprinidae*. Common carp (the main farmed carp) is *Cyprinus carpio*, crucian carp is *Carassius carassius*, grass carp or white amur is *Ctenopharyngodon idella*, silver carp is *Hypophthalmicthys molitrix*, and bighead carp is *H. nobilis*.

carpaccio Italian; thinly sliced raw beef fillet, served as an antipasto or hors d'œuvre.

carpal tunnel syndrome Painful disorder of wrist and hand due to compression of the median nerve in the carpal tunnel. Claimed to be relieved by high intakes of *vitamin B_6, some 50–100 times the *reference intake, but there is little evidence.

carrageen Edible *seaweed, *Chondrus crispus*, also known as Iberian moss or Irish sea moss, and *Gigartina stellata*; stewed in milk to make a jelly or blancmange. A source of *carrageenan.

carrageenan A *polysaccharide extracted from red seaweeds, especially *Chondrus crispus* (Irish moss) and *Gigartina stellata*. One of the plant *gums, it binds water to form a gel, increases viscosity, and reacts with proteins to form emulsions. It is used as an emulsifier and stabilizer in milk drinks, processed cheese, low-energy foods, etc.

carrot The root of *Daucus carota*, commonly used as a vegetable. A 100-g portion is a rich source of vitamin A (5–10 mg carotene); provides 2.5 g of dietary fibre; and supplies 35 kcal (145 kJ). Peruvian carrot is *arracache.

carte, à la Meal chosen from a list of foods and dishes available rather than from a set menu or meal.

carthamin A yellow to red colourant from safflower flowers, *Carthemus tinctorius*, chemically a chalcone.

cartilage The hard connective tissue of the body, composed mainly of *collagen, together with chondromucoid (a protein combined with chondroitin sulphate) and chondroalbuminoid (a protein similar to *elastin). New *bone growth consists of cartilage on which calcium salts are deposited as it develops.

carubinose *See* MANNOSE.

carvie Scottish name for *caraway.

CAS Controlled atmosphere storage. *See* STORAGE, MODIFIED GAS.

case control study Epidemiological study in which people with the clinical condition of interest are compared with disease-free control subjects matched as closely as possible for ethnicity, gender, occupation, and other potentially confounding factors.

casein A group of twelve to fifteen different proteins in milk, about 80% of the total; those proteins that are precipitated when milk is acidified to *pH 4.6 at 20°C. They are phosphorylated proteins, and bind calcium. The proteins that remain soluble under these conditions are mainly *whey proteins or serum proteins.

Acid casein is produced by acidification of skimmed milk using hydrochloric or sulphuric acid, lactic casein by acidification by bacterial fermentation, rennin casein by enzymic coagulation using *pepsin and *chymosin.

caseinate Neutralized precipitates of acid or lactic *casein, by sodium, potassium, ammonium, or calcium hydroxide.

caseinogen Obsolete name for the micellar form in which *casein is present in solution in milk; when it was precipitated it was then called casein.

caseinophosphopeptides Phosphorylated peptides derived from *casein by partial enzymic hydrolysis that bind *calcium and increase its intestinal absorption. Potentially valuable as a functional food ingredient (*see* FOOD, FUNCTIONAL) as a means of increasing calcium absorption.

cashew nut From the tropical tree *Anacardium occidentale*, usually eaten roasted and salted. The nut hangs from the true fruit, a large fleshy but sour apple-like fruit, which is very rich in vitamin C and can be eaten raw or processed into jams, jellies, and ices. Cashews are also fermented to produce juices and liqueurs. A 30-g portion of roasted salted nuts (30 nuts) is a *source of protein, niacin, iron, and zinc; contains 15 g of fat, of which 20% is saturated and 60% mono-unsaturated; provides 180 kcal (755 kJ).

cassareep Caribbean; boiled-down juice squeezed from grated *cassava root, flavoured with cinnamon, cloves, and brown sugar; used as a base for sauces. It can also be fermented with *molasses.

cassata Italian; ice cream made in a mould with layers of diced fruit, nuts, and macaroons. Cassata Siciliana is sponge cake containing layers of ricotta cheese, grated chocolate, and crystallized fruit.

cassava (manioc) The tuber of the tropical plant *Manihot utilissima* syn. *M. esculenta*. It is the dietary staple in many tropical countries, although it is an extremely poor source of protein; the plant grows well even in poor soil, and is extremely hardy, withstanding considerable drought; introduced into Africa by slave ships returning from Brazil in 1569. It is one of the most prolific crops, yielding up to 13 million kcal/acre, compared with *yam, 9 million, and *sorghum or *maize, 1 million. A 150-g portion is a rich *source of vitamin C; a source of iron and vitamin B$_1$; supplies 150 kcal (600 kJ).

Cassava root contains cyanide, and before it can be eaten it must be grated and left in the open to allow the cyanide to evaporate. The leaves can be eaten as a vegetable, and the tuber is the source of *tapioca. *See also* CASSAREEP.

casserole Lidded container designed for slow cooking of meat or fish and vegetables in the oven; also the food so cooked.

cassia The inner bark of the Asian tree *Cinnamomum* spp., used as a flavouring, similar to *cinnamon. Indian cassia is *C. tamala*, Indonesian or padang cassia is *C. burmanni*. The buds of *C. cassia* resemble *cloves. The dried leaves of *C. tamala* are the Indian spice tejpat.

cassina A tea-like beverage made from cured leaves of a holly bush, *Ilex cassine*, containing 1–1.6% *caffeine and 8% *tannin.

cassis (crème de cassis) French; extract of *blackcurrants; about 15% alcohol by volume, sweetened with sugar. Mixed with about 10 parts of white wine to make kir, or with champagne to make kir royal.

cassolette Individual dish containing a single portion of a savoury mixture; sometimes lined with potato or puff pastry.

cassoulet French; stew of haricot beans with assorted meats. The name is derived from the earthenware vessel in which it is cooked, a *cassole d'Issel*.

castagnacci Corsican; fritters made from chestnut flour.

caster sugar *See* SUGAR, CASTER.

castor oil Oil from the seeds of the castor oil plant, *Ricinus* spp. The oil itself is not irritating, but in the small intestine it is hydrolysed by *lipase to release ricinoleic acid, which is irritant to the intestinal mucosa and therefore acts as a purgative. The seeds also contain the toxic *lectin, ricin.

CAT Computerized Axial Tomography, a scanning X-ray technique that permits visualization of soft tissues in a 'slice' through the body. Also known as computerized tomography, CT.

catabolism Those pathways of *metabolism concerned with the breakdown and oxidation of fuels and hence provision of metabolic energy. People who are undernourished or suffering from *cachexia are sometimes said to be in a catabolic state, in that they are catabolizing their body tissues without replacing them.

catadromous fish Fish such as eels that live in fresh water and go to sea to spawn.

catalane, à la Dish with a garnish of aubergine and rice.

catalase An *enzyme that splits hydrogen peroxide to yield oxygen and water; an important part of the body's antioxidant defences.

catalyst An agent that participates in a chemical reaction, speeding the rate, but itself remains unchanged. Catalysts are used, for example, in the *hydrogenation of vegetable oils. *Enzymes and *coenzymes are biological catalysts.

catchup See KETCHUP.

catechin tannins See TANNINS.

catecholamines Three compounds derived from the *amino acid *tyrosine: *adrenaline, dopamine, and *noradrenaline. All three are neurotransmitters; adrenaline and noradrenaline are also *hormones.

catfish Freshwater fish that have barbels resembling a cat's whiskers, species of the families *Clariidae*, *Siluridae*, *Bigridae*, and *Pimelodidae*. *Anarhichas* spp. are also known as rockfish or wolffish. Sea catfish is a species of the family *Ariidae*; channel catfish, *Ictalurus punctatus*, is farmed in the USA; *Clarius* spp. are important food fish in Africa and *Silurus* spp. in Asia.

cathartic See LAXATIVE.

cathepsins (kathepsins) A group of intracellular enzymes in animal tissues which hydrolyse proteins. They are involved in the normal turnover of tissue protein and in the softening of meat when *game is hung.

cation Chemical term for a positively charged *ion.

catmint The wild catmint (*Nepeta cataria*) is distinct from the cultivated catmint (*Nepeta* spp.) of gardens; both have a minty smell which is liked by cats. The leaves are used to prepare *herb teas and may be added to stews; young shoots can be eaten raw in salads.

catsup See KETCHUP.

caudle Hot spiced wine, *mulled wine thickened with eggs.

caul Membrane enclosing the fetus; that from sheep or pig is used to cover meat while roasting.

cauliflower The edible flower of *Brassica oleracea* var. *botrytis*, normally creamy-white in colour, although some cultivars have green or purple flowers. Horticulturally, varieties that mature in summer and autumn are called cauliflower and those that mature in winter *broccoli, but commonly both are called cauliflower. A 90-g portion is a rich *source of vitamin C; a good source of folate; a source of vitamin B_6; provides 1.8 g of dietary fibre; and supplies 8 kcal (33 kJ).

cava Spanish; sparkling wines made by the méthode champenoise. *See also* CHAMPAGNE.

caveached fish *See* ESCABECHE.

caviar(e) The salted hard *roe of the sturgeon, *Acipenser* spp.; three main types, named for the species of sturgeon: sevruga, asetra (ocietre), and *beluga, the prime variety.

Roe of bream, carp, coalfish, cod, herring, mullet, pike, and tuna may also be used, including the name of the fish, e.g. cod caviar. Mock caviar (also known as German, Danish, or Norwegian caviar) is the salted hard roe of the lumpfish (*Cyclopterus lumpus*), and may be red or dyed black. Botargo caviar is made from mullet roe.

cayenne pepper *See* PEPPER.

CBE *See* COCOA BUTTER EQUIVALENTS.

CCK *See* CHOLECYSTOKININ.

cDNA Complementary *DNA, a single-stranded DNA molecule that is complementary to a molecule of mRNA, from which it is produced using *reverse transcriptase. cDNA libraries represent the information encoded in the mRNA of a particular tissue or organism.

cecil Old name for fried meat balls.

CED Chronic energy deficiency; *see* PROTEIN-ENERGY MALNUTRITION.

Celacol Trade name for methyl, hydroxyethyl, and other *cellulose derivatives.

celeriac A variety of *celery with a thick root which is eaten grated in salads or cooked as a vegetable, *Apium graveolens* var. *rapaceum*, also known as turnip-rooted or knob celery. A 40-g portion provides 1.2g of dietary fibre and supplies 5kcal (21kJ).

celery Edible stems of *Apium graveolens* var. *dulce*. A 100-g portion (two sticks) is a *source of vitamin C; provides 2g of dietary fibre; supplies 8kcal (34kJ). The seeds are used as a flavouring, and may be ground and mixed with pepper or salt to form a condiment. *See also* CELERIAC.

celiac disease *See* COELIAC DISEASE.

cellobiose A disaccharide of glucose units linked 1,4-β, which is not hydrolysed by mammalian digestive enzymes (as distinct from the 1,4-α linkage of maltose); a product of the hydrolysis of *cellulose.

Cellofas Trade name for derivatives of *cellulose: Cellofas A is methyl-ethylcellulose, Cellofas B is sodium carboxymethylcellulose.

Cellophane Trade name for the first of the transparent, non-porous films, made from wood pulp (*cellulose), patented in 1908 by the Swiss chemist Jacques-Edwin Brandenberger; waterproof cellophane for food wrapping was developed by Du Pont in 1926. Still widely used for wrapping foods and other commodities.

cellulase An *enzyme that hydrolyses *cellulose to its constituent monosaccharide (glucose) and disaccharide (*cellobiose) units. It is present in the digestive juices of some wood-boring insects and in various micro-organisms, but not in mammals.

cellulose A *polysaccharide of *glucose linked 1,4-β which is not hydrolysed by mammalian digestive enzymes; the main component of plant cell walls. It is digested by the bacterial *enzyme *cellulase, and only *ruminants and animals that have a large *caecum have an adequate population of intestinal bacteria to permit them to digest cellulose to any significant extent. There is little digestion of cellulose in the human large intestine; nevertheless, it serves a valuable purpose in providing bulk to the intestinal contents, and is one of the major components of dietary fibre (*see* FIBRE, DIETARY; NON-STARCH POLYSACCHARIDES).

cellulose, microcrystalline Partially hydrolysed *cellulose used as a filler in slimming and other foods.

cellulose derivatives A number of chemically modified forms of cellulose are used in food processing for their special properties, including i) carboxymethylcellulose, which is prepared from the pure cellulose of cotton or wood. It absorbs up to 50 times its own weight of water to form a stable colloidal mass. It is used, together with stabilizers, as a whipping agent, in ice cream, confectionery, jellies, etc., and as an inert filler in 'slimming aids'; ii) methylcellulose, which differs from carboxymethylcellulose (and other *gums) since its viscosity increases rather than decreases with increasing temperature. Hence it is soluble in cold water and forms a gel on heating. It is used as a thickener and emulsifier, and in foods formulated to be low in *gluten; iii) other cellulose derivatives used as emulsifiers and stabilizers— hydroxypropylcellulose, hydroxypropyl-methylcellulose, and ethyl-methylcellulose.

celtuce Stem lettuce, *Lactuca sativa*; enlarged stem eaten raw or cooked, with a flavour between celery and lettuce; the leaves are not palatable.

centrifuge A machine that exerts a force many thousand times that of gravity, by spinning. Commonly used to clarify liquids by settling the heavier solids in a few minutes, a process that might take several days under gravity. Liquids of different density can also be separated by centrifugation, e.g. cream from milk.

cep Edible wild fungus, *Boletus edulis*, also known as boletus. *See* MUSHROOMS.

cephalic phase of eating Stimulation of the parasympathetic nervous system leading to gastric secretion in response to the sight, aroma, and anticipation of food.

cephalins *See* KEPHALINS.

cephalopods Cuttlefish (*Sepia officinalis*), *squid, *octopus.

cephalosporins *Antibiotics; those with an *N*-methylthiotetrazole side-chain inhibit hepatic *vitamin K epoxide reductase, and may cause functional vitamin K deficiency.

cereal Any grain or edible seed of the grass family which may be used as food, e.g. *wheat, *rice, *oats, *barley, *rye, *maize, and *millet. Collectively known in the UK as corn, although in the USA corn is specifically maize. Cereals provide the largest single foodstuff in almost all diets; in some less-developed countries up to 90% of the total diet may be cereal, and in the UK *bread and *flour provide 25–30% of the total energy and protein of the average diet. *See also* FLOUR, EXTRACTION RATE.

cereal coffee Beverages prepared from roasted cereal grains.

cereals, breakfast Legally defined as any food obtained by the swelling, roasting, grinding, rolling, or flaking of any *cereal.

cereals, puffed Whole grains, grain parts, or a shaped dough, expanded by subjecting to heat and pressure to produce a very light and airy product.

cerebrose Obsolete name for *galactose.

cerebrosides *See* GALACTOLIPIDS.

cerebrovascular accident (CVA) *See* STROKE.

cerelose A commercial preparation of *glucose containing about 9% water.

ceriman *See* MONSTERA.

ceroid pigment Age spots or liver spots. Patches of brown pigment under the skin, increasing with age, believed to be due to accumulation of the products of oxidation of fatty acids and protein.

ceruloplasmin A copper-containing protein in *blood plasma, the main circulating form of *copper in the body.

cervelat Smoked, uncooked, mildly seasoned sausage made from chopped pork or a mixture of pork and beef; originally made with brain. Soft cervelat is semi-dry; dry cervelat is dried slowly to a hard texture. Also known as summer sausage.

cestode Alternative name for *tapeworm.

cevapcici Yugoslavia, Balkans; highly spiced meat products, sometimes considered to be fresh sausages without casings, made from beef and/or pork mixed with fresh herbs.

ceviche Raw fish marinated in lime or lemon juice with olive oil, spices, and sometimes onions, green peppers, or tomatoes.

CF *See* CITROVORUM FACTOR.

CFSAN Center for Food Safety and Applied Nutrition of the US Food and Drug Administration.

(⊕) SEE WEB LINKS
• The CFSAN's homepage.

cfu Colony-forming units, a measure of viable bacteria by counting the number of colonies formed on culture.

CGIAR Consultative Group on International Agricultural Research; the group that led the development of high-yielding crops, the basis of the *green revolution of the 1960s and 1970s.

(⊕) SEE WEB LINKS
• The CGIAR's homepage.

CGRP Calcitonin gene related peptide; *see* CALCITONIN.

chabichou French; goat's milk cheese.

chafing dish Metal dish on a trivet over a spirit lamp or a gas flame, used for heating or cooking at the table.

chalasia Abnormal relaxation of the cardiac sphincter muscle of the stomach so that gastric contents reflux into the oesophagus, leading to regurgitation.

challa *See* CHOLLA.

chalva *See* HALVA.

chamak *See* TARKA.

chambré Red wines brought to room temperature (15–18°C, 59–65°F) before serving.

chamomile *See* CAMOMILE.

champagne Sparkling wine (*see* WINE, SPARKLING) from the Champagne region of north-eastern France, made by a second fermentation in the bottle. Pioneered by Benedictine cellar master Dom Pierre Pérignon at the Abbey d'Hautvilliers in the late 17th century. Sparkling wines from other regions, even when made in the same way, cannot legally be called champagne, but are known as being made by the méthode champenoise.

champignon French; *mushrooms; *champignons de Paris* are button mushrooms.

chanakhi Russian (Georgian); mutton casserole with potatoes, onions, green beans, tomatoes, aubergines, and peppers.

chanfaina Spanish; stew made from the *offal of goat or kid, cooked together with the head and feet, with artichokes, chard, lettuce, and peas.

channa *See* CHICKPEA.

chanterelle Edible wild fungus, *Cantharellus cibarius*; *see* MUSHROOMS.

chantilly, à la Dessert including or accompanied by sweetened, vanilla-flavoured whipped cream.

CHAOS Cambridge Heart Antioxidant Study; intervention trial in the 1990s of *vitamin E supplements in people with pre-existing cardiovascular disease.

chao shao roast pork Chinese (Cantonese); strips of pork marinated then roasted.

chaource French; aromatic soft cheese.

chapatti (chapati, chupatti) Indian; unleavened wholegrain wheat or millet bread, baked on an ungreased griddle. Phulka are small chapattis; roti are chapattis prepared with maize flour. Two chapattis (60g) are a *source of vitamin B_1 and copper; provide 4.2g of dietary fibre; if made with added fat contain 8g of fat; supply 210kcal (880kJ); if made without added fat contain 0.6g of fat; supply 130kcal (545kJ).

chapila Freshwater fish, *Gudusia chapra*.

chapon Crust of bread rubbed with garlic and added to salad for flavour, then removed.

chaptalization Addition of sugar to grape must during fermentation to increase the alcohol content of the final *wine.

char Various trout-like freshwater fish, *Salvelinus* spp. Arctic char is *S. alpinus*, brook trout is *S. fontinalis*, and lake trout is *S. namaycush*. *See also* TROUT.

charcoal Finely divided carbon, obtained by heating wood in a closed retort to carbonize the organic matter. It is used to purify solutions because it will absorb colouring matter and other impurities; wood charcoal is commonly employed as a fuel for *barbecues. Animal or bone charcoal is made by heating bone, leaving carbon deposited on a framework of calcium carbonate.

charcuterie French; pork butchery; shop where various cold meats are sold, also the meats.

chard, Chinese (bok choy, pak tsoi) *Brassica rapa* var. *chinensis*.

chard, Swiss The spinach-like leaves and broad midrib of *Beta vulgaris* var. *cicla*, also known as leaf beet, leaf chard, sea kale beet, silver beet, white leaf beet, spinach beet. A 100-g portion (boiled) is a rich *source of vitamin A (as carotene); a good source of vitamin C; a source of iron; supplies 18 kcal (72 kJ).

The name is also used for blanched summer shoots of globe *artichoke and for inner leaves of *cardoon, *Cynara cardunculus*.

chardonnay One of the nine 'classic' *grape varieties used for *wine making, widely grown throughout the world. Chardonnay wines are among the white wines best adapted to maturation in oak barrels; both oaked and unoaked chardonnays are produced.

charlotte Dessert made from stewed fruit encased in, or layered alternately with, bread or cake crumbs, e.g. apple charlotte. In charlotte russe there is a cream mixture in the centre, surrounded by cake. *See also* BROWN BETTY.

charolais Breed of cattle noted for the quality and leanness of the meat.

charoset(h) Jewish; sweet-sour sauce, a traditional part of the *Passover meal, derived from the Roman sauces that were used as a dip for raw bitter salad herbs eaten to refresh the palate.

charqui (charki) South American (especially Brazilian); dried meat, normally prepared from beef, but may also be made from sheep, llama, and alpaca. Strips of meat cut lengthways and pressed after salting, then air-dried. The final form is flat, thin, flaky sheets, so differing from the long strips of *biltong. Also called jerky.

Chartreuse A *liqueur invented in 1605 and still made by the Carthusian monks, named for the great charterhouse (*la grande Chartreuse*) which is the mother house of the order, near Grenoble in southern France. It is reputed to contain more than 200 ingredients. There are three varieties: green Chartreuse is 55%, yellow 43%, and white 30% *alcohol.

chasnidarh Indian; sweet-sour foods.

chasseur, à la In the hunter's style; dish with a garnish of mushrooms cooked with shallots and white wine. Chasseur sauce is a highly seasoned sauce based on white wine, with mushrooms and shallots, served with meat or game.

chastek paralysis Acute deficiency of vitamin B_1 in foxes and mink fed on diets high in raw fish, which contains *thiaminase.

chateaubriand Thick steak cut from *beef fillet. Named originally in 1822 in honour of the Comte de Chateaubriand.

chaud-froid Meat, fish, or poultry coated with a white sauce that jellifies when cooling down. The dish is served cold.

chaudron (chawdron) Medieval English; sauce served with roast swan, made from the giblets boiled in broth with its blood, vinegar, and spices.

chaumes French; soft cheese, 50% fat.

chausson French; turnover; pastry folded over jam or fruit before baking.

chaya Large tropical herb (up to 2m tall), *Cnidoscolus chayamansa*; the young leaves are eaten like *spinach.

chayote Tropical squash (originally Mexican), *Sechium edule*; prickly skin and a single edible seed. Also called cho-cho, christophene, or mirliton.

CHD Coronary heart disease; *see* HEART DISEASE.

cheat bread Medieval English; wholewheat bread with the coarse bran removed.

Cheddar Hard *cheese dating from the 16th century prepared by a particular method (*cheddaring); originally from the Cheddar area of Somerset, England; matured for several months or even years. Red Cheddar is coloured with *annatto; fat-reduced versions are now made. A 30-g portion is a rich *source of vitamin B_{12}, a source of protein, niacin, and vitamin A; contains 10g of fat, 200mg of calcium, 200mg of sodium; supplies 120kcal (500kJ).

cheddaring In the manufacture of *cheese, after coagulation of the milk, heating of the curd, and draining, the curds are piled along the floor of the vat, where they consolidate to a rubbery sheet of curd. This is the cheddaring process; for cheeses with a more crumbly texture the curd is not allowed to settle so densely.

cheese Prepared from the curd precipitated from milk by *rennet (containing the *enzyme *chymosin or rennin), purified chymosin, or lactic acid. Cheeses other than cottage and cream cheeses (*see* CHEESE, SOFT) are cured by being left to mature with salt, under various conditions that produce the characteristic flavour of each type of cheese. Although most cheeses are made from cow's milk, goat's and sheep's milk are used to make speciality cheeses, which are generally soft.

There are numerous variants, including more than a hundred from England and Wales alone (nine major regional cheeses: Caerphilly, *Cheddar, *Cheshire, Derby, Double *Gloucester, Lancashire, Red Leicester, *Stilton, and Wensleydale). Some varieties are regional specialities, and legally may be made only in a defined geographical area; others are defined by the process rather than the region of production. The strength of flavour of cheese increases as it ages; mild or mellow cheeses are younger, and less strongly flavoured, than mature or extra-mature cheeses.

Cheeses differ in their water and fat content and hence their nutrient and energy content, ranging from 50–80% water in soft cheeses (*mozzarella, *quark, Boursin, cottage; see CHEESE, SOFT) to less than 20% in hard cheese (*Parmesan, *Emmental, *Gruyère, *Cheddar; see CHEESE, HARD) with semi-hard cheeses around 40% water (Caerphilly, *Gouda, *Edam, Stilton). They retain much of the calcium of the milk and many contain a relatively large amount of sodium from the added salt. Blue-veined cheeses (Gorgonzola, *Stilton, Roquefort, etc.) derive the colour (and flavour) from the growth of the mould *Penicillium roquefortii*, during ripening. Holes (e.g. in Gouda, Emmental) arise during ripening from gases produced by bacteria.

cheese, Austrian Classified according to butterfat content as percentage of dry weight as: *doppelfett* (double cream) 65%, *üverfett* (extra cream) 55%, *vollfett* (full cream) 45%, *dreiviertelfett* 35%, *halbfett* 25%, *viertelfett* 15%, and *mager* under 15% fat.

cheese, colby American, semi-soft washed curd cheese.

cheese, filled Cheese made from skimmed milk with the addition of vegetable oil to replace the butterfat of whole milk.

cheese, hard Traditionally, hard cheeses must contain not less than 40% fat on a dry weight basis, and the fat must be milk fat. However, a number of low-fat variants of traditional hard cheeses are now made. A 40-g portion of hard cheese is a rich *source of vitamin B_{12} and calcium; a good source of protein and vitamin A; a source of vitamin B_2, iodine, and selenium; depending on type contains 9–16g of fat, of which 64–69% is saturated; provides 120–190kcal (500–800kJ).

cheese, processed Made by milling various hard cheeses with emulsifying salts (phosphates and citrates), whey, and water, then pasteurizing to extend its shelf life. Typically 40% water; a soft version with 50% water is used as a spread.

cheese, soft Cottage cheese is soft, uncured, white cheese made from pasteurized skimmed milk (or milk powder) by lactic acid starter (with or without added rennet), heated, washed, and drained (salt may be added). Contains more than 80% water. Also known as pot cheese, schmierkäse, and, in the USA, Dutch cheese. Baker's or hoop cheese is made in the same way as cottage cheese, but the curd is not washed, and it is drained in bags, giving it a finer grain. It contains more water and acid than cottage cheese.

Cream cheese is unripened soft cheese made from cream with varying fat content (20–25% fat or 50–55% fat); at 50% fat a 100-g portion is a rich *source of vitamins B_{12} and A and supplies 440kcal (1800kJ).

cheese, Swiss American name for any hard cheese, domestic or imported, that contains relatively large bubbles of air, like the Swiss Emmentaler and Gruyère cheeses.

cheese, vegetarian Cheese in which animal *rennet has not been used to precipitate the curd. Precipitation is achieved using lactic acid alone, or a plant *enzyme or biosynthetic *chymosin. Truly vegetarian cheese is made from vegetable protein rather than milk.

cheese, whey Made from *whey by heat coagulation of the proteins (lactalbumin and lactoglobulin).

cheese analogues Cheese-like products made from *casein or *soya and vegetable fat.

cheesecake A flan or tart filled with curd or cream cheese. Traditional Middle-European cheesecake is baked; most cheesecakes now sold are uncooked, set with gelatine, and topped with fruit.

cheilosis Cracking of the edges of the lips, one of the clinical signs of *vitamin B_2 (riboflavin) deficiency.

chelapata Freshwater fish, a member of the *carp family, *Salmostoma bacaila*.

chelating agents Chemicals that combine with metal ions and remove them from their sphere of action, also called sequestrants. They are used in food manufacture to remove traces of metal ions which might otherwise cause foods to deteriorate, and clinically to reduce absorption of a mineral, or to increase its excretion, e.g. citrates, tartrates, phosphates, and *EDTA.

Chelsea bun A yeast bun that originated in Chelsea, London, in the 18th century.

chemesthesis Chemical sensitivity of the skin and mucous membranes to compounds in foods, other than taste and aroma receptors, e.g. the pungency of chillies, horseradish, and mustard.

chemical caponization *See* CAPON.

chemical ice Ice containing a preservative, e.g. a solution of *antibiotics or other chemicals; used to preserve fish.

chemical score A measure of *protein quality based on chemical analysis of its *amino acid composition.

chenin blanc One of the nine 'classic' *grape varieties used for *wine making; the great white grape of the middle Loire valley.

chenopods Seeds of two species of *Chenopodium* eaten in the Peruvian Andes: *C. quinoa* (*quinoa) and *C. pallidicaule* (*canihua). Other species of *Chenopodium* have been considered for poultry feed, including Russian thistle, summer cypress, and garden orache.

cherimoya *See* CUSTARD APPLE.

chermoula North African (Moroccan); a mixture of *cumin, paprika (*see* PEPPER), and *turmeric with *onion, *parsley, *coriander, *garlic, and cayenne pepper used to marinade meat and fish.

cherry Fruit of *Prunus* spp.; the British *National Fruit Collection has almost 300 varieties. A 100-g portion (ten cherries weighed without stones) is a *source of vitamin C; provides 2 g of dietary fibre; supplies 50 kcal (210 kJ).

cherry, cornelian Fruit of the wild dogwood (*Cornus mas*).

cherry, glacé *Cherry preserved in a heavy syrup of sugar and glucose, generally also with added colour. Used in confectionery and fruit cakes. Little or none of the vitamin C remains.

cherry, ground *See* PHYSALIS.

cherry, maraschino Cherries preserved in the cherry *liqueur maraschino.

cherry, morello A sour cherry (*Prunus cerasus*) that cannot be eaten raw; used for cooking and making *liqueurs and jams.

cherry, Peruvian *See* PHYSALIS.

cherry, Surinam *See* PITANGA.

cherry, West Indian The fruit of a small bush native to the tropical and subtropical regions of America, *Malpighia punicifolia* syn. *M. glabra*. It is the richest known source of vitamin C; the edible portion of the ripe fruit contains 1000 mg, and the green fruit 3000 mg/100 g. Also known as Barbados or Antilles cherry, acerola.

chervil **1.** A herb, *Anthriscus cerefolium*, with parsley-like leaves, used as a garnish and, fresh or dried, to flavour salads and soups. **2.** Turnip-rooted chervil, *Chaerophyllum bulbosum*, is a hardy biennial vegetable cultivated for its roots.

chervil, sweet *See* SWEET CICELY.

Cheshire cheese Oldest English *cheese, dating from Roman Britain; crumbly, may be pale yellow, blue-veined, or coloured orange with *annatto; matured for two to six weeks; approx. 30% water, 24% protein, 30% fat. At one time the cheesemakers of Cheshire impressed the image of a grinning cat on the outside of the cheese; this is believed to be the origin of the Cheshire cat popularized in Lewis Carroll's *Alice in Wonderland*.

chestnut Fruit of trees *Castanea* spp., especially *C. sativa* (Spanish or sweet chestnut), *C. mollissima* (Chinese chestnut), and *C. crenata* (Japanese chestnut). Unlike other nuts it contains very little fat, being largely starch and water. Seven nuts (75 g) provide 5.3 g of dietary fibre and are a good *source of copper; a source of vitamins B_1 and B_6; contain 2 g of fat, of which 18% is saturated; supply 135 kcal (570 kJ).

chestnut, Australian Seeds of the endangered Australian tree *Castanospermum australe*. Poisonous when raw, but the toxins are denatured by heating. Contain castanospermine, which has antiviral activity *in vitro*. Also known as Moreton Bay chestnuts or black beans.

chestnut, Chinese water (matai, waternut) Tuber of the sedge *Eleocharis tuberosa* or *dulcis*; white flesh in a black, horned shell.

chestnut, Malabar Fruit of the tree *Pachira aquatica* syn. *Bombax glabrum*, also known as Guyana chestnut, saba nut, and French peanut.

chestnut, Moreton Bay *See* CHESTNUT, AUSTRALIAN.

chestnut, water Seeds of *Trapa natans* or *T. bicornis*, also called caltrops or sinharanut; eaten raw or roasted.

chevda (chewda) A dry and highly spiced mixture of deep-fried rice, *dahl, *chickpeas, and small pieces of chickpea batter, with peanuts and raisins, seasoned with sugar and salt; a common north Indian snack food, also known as Bombay mix.

chevon Alternative term for goat meat.

chewing gum Based on *chicle and other plant resins, with sugar or other sweetener, balsam of Tolu and various flavours.

chhana Indian; soft cheese (*see* CHEESE, SOFT) prepared by heating milk to nearly boiling, adding acid coagulants, and removing the whey by filtration. The basis of sweets such as *rasgulla.

chia Annual herbs, *Salvia hispanica* (true chia) and *S. columbariae* (golden chia); the seeds were a major food of the Aztecs in central Mexico, providing 20% protein, 34% oil, of which 64% is ω3-polyunsaturated fatty acids, 25% dietary fibre, mainly soluble.

chiao-tzu *See* WUNTUN.

chiaretto Italian; light red wines.

chicha Latin American; maize-based alcoholic beverage; both a lactic acid bacterial and a yeast fermentation.

chicharrones Caribbean; fried pork *crackling.

chichi (chicha) South American; effervescent sour alcoholic beverage made from maize, other starch crops or beans; both a lactic acid bacterial and a yeast fermentation.

chicken Domestic fowl, *Gallus domesticus*. A 150-g portion is a rich *source of protein and niacin; a good source of copper and selenium; a source of iron and vitamins B_1, B_2, and B_6. There are differences between the white (breast) and dark (leg) meat, the former being lower in fat but also lower in iron and vitamin B_2. Of a 150-g portion of boiled chicken, the white meat supplies 0.9 mg of iron, 0.09 mg of vitamin B_1, 0.18 mg of vitamin B_2, 7.5 g of fat, of which one-third is saturated; the dark meat supplies 3.8 mg of iron, 0.1 mg of vitamin B_1, 0.4 mg of vitamin B_2, 15 g of fat, of which one-third is saturated.

Poussin or spring chicken is a young bird, four to six weeks old, weighing 250–300 g.

chicken, broiler Fast-growing chicken developed by the USDA at Beltsville, Maryland, and first produced commercially in 1930.

chicken, mountain *See* CRAPAUD.

chicken cordon bleu Boned breast of chicken stuffed with cheese and ham, coated in batter or breadcrumbs, and baked.

chicken Kiev Boned breast of chicken stuffed with garlic butter, coated in batter or breadcrumbs, and baked.

chicken Marengo *See* MARENGO.

chicken Maryland Chicken fried in breadcrumbs or batter, served with fruit fritters.

chickoo *See* SAPODILLA; SAPOTE.

chickpea Also known as garbanzo; seeds of *Cicer arietinum*, widely used in Mediterranean and Middle Eastern stews and casseroles. Puréed chickpea is the basis of *hummus and deep-fried balls of chickpea batter are *felafel. A 90-g portion is a rich *source of copper; a good source of folate; a source of protein, vitamin A, and iron; contains 3 g of fat, of which 6% is saturated; provides 4.5 g of dietary fibre; supplies 130 kcal (545 kJ).

chickweed Common garden weed (*Stellaria media*); can be eaten in salads or cooked; a modest source of vitamin C.

chicle The partially evaporated milky latex of the evergreen sapodilla tree (*Manilkara zapote*, formerly *Achras sapota*); it contains gutta (which has elastic properties) and resin, together with carbohydrates, waxes, and tannins. The basis of *chewing gum. The same tree also produces the *sapodilla.

chicory Witloof or Belgian chicory (Belgian endive in the USA), *Cichorium intybus*; the root is harvested and grown in the dark to produce bullet-shaped heads of young white leaves (chicons). Also called succory; the red variety is radicchio. The leaves are eaten as a salad or braised as a vegetable, and the bitter root, dried and partly caramelized, is often added to coffee. A 50-g portion supplies 1 g of dietary fibre, a little vitamin C, and 5 kcal (20 kJ).

chief cells Cells in the stomach that secrete pepsinogen, the precursor of the *enzyme *pepsin.

chiffonnade French; shredded green vegetables.

chikuwa Japanese; grilled foods prepared from *surimi. *See also* KAMABOKO.

chilled foods Perishable products stored at temperatures between 0 and 7°C.

chill haze *See* HAZE.

chilli (chili) *See* PEPPER.

chilli con carne Minced beef stewed with onion, chilli, and red kidney beans; originally Mexican and south-western USA.

chilling Reduction of temperature to between –1 and 8°C.

chilling injury The physiological damage to many plants and plant products as a result of exposure to low temperatures (above freezing), including surface pitting, poor colour, failure to ripen, and loss of structure and texture.

chilli sauce (chili sauce) Piquant sauce made from tomatoes, with spices, onions, garlic, sugar, vinegar, and salt. Similar to tomato *ketchup but containing more cayenne, onion, and garlic.

chillproofing A treatment to prevent the development of haze or cloudiness due to precipitation of proteins when beer is chilled. Treatments include the addition of *tannins to precipitate proteins, materials such as *bentonite to adsorb them, and proteolytic *enzymes to hydrolyse them.

chiltepin *See* TEPIN.

china Italian; bitter apéritif wines containing *quinine.

chincona Spanish; bitter apéritif wines containing *quinine.

chine A joint of meat containing the whole or part of the backbone of the animal. *See also* CHINING.

Chinese cabbage *See* CABBAGE, CHINESE.

Chinese cherry *See* LYCHEE.

Chinese eggs *See* EGGS, CHINESE.

Chinese gooseberry *See* KIWI FRUIT.

Chinese keys The root of *Boesenbergia rotunda*, related to *ginger and *galangal, with a mild ginger-like aroma, used in fish dishes in Thai and Malay cuisine.

Chinese leaves *See* CABBAGE, CHINESE.

Chinese restaurant syndrome Flushing, palpitations, and numbness associated at one time with the consumption of *monosodium glutamate, and then with *histamine, but the cause of these symptoms after eating various foods is not known.

chining To sever the rib bones from the backbone by sawing through the ribs close to the spine. *See also* CHINE.

chino Spanish; small conical strainer used to sieve chopped vegetables to make *gazpacho.

chipolata Small pork *sausage.

chips Chipped potatoes; pieces of potato deep fried in fat or oil. Known in French as *pommes frites* or just *frites*; in the USA *potato crisps are known as chips, and chips are called French fries or just fries. A 200-g portion is a rich *source of vitamins C and B_1; a source of protein, niacin, and iron; fat content depends on the size of the chip and the process: commonly about 25 g, but can be 40 g in fine-cut chips and as little as 8 g in frozen, oven-baked chips. A 200-g portion with an average of 25 g of fat supplies 500 kcal (2100 kJ); with 40 g of fat supplies 700 kcal (2900 kJ); low-fat, oven-baked supplies 300 kcal (1260 kJ).

chirga Indian; skinned chicken rubbed with cayenne, paprika, and lime juice, coated with a sauce of ginger, onion, and pimiento in yoghurt, then roasted, basting with *ghee. It has a red colour.

chistorra Spanish (Basque); semi-cured long thin pork sausage.

chitin The organic matrix of the hard parts of the exoskeleton of insects and crustaceans, and also present in *mushrooms. It is an insoluble and indigestible *non-starch polysaccharide, of *N*-acetylglucosamine. Partial deacetylation results in the formation of *chitosan.

chitosan Polysaccharide derived from *chitin by partial deacetylation with a strong base. Marketed as a fat binder to reduce fat absorption and aid weight reduction, with little evidence of efficacy. Also used as protein-flocculating agents. It has antibacterial and antifungal properties, disrupting bacterial cell walls, and is used in active packaging of foods (*see* PACKAGING, ACTIVE) and as an edible protective coating, e.g. on fish, fruits, and vegetables (to prevent post-harvest spoilage), and to increase the shelf-life of eggs.

chitterlings The (usually fried) small intestine of ox, calf, or pig.

chive Small member of the onion family (*Allium schoenoprasum*); the thin hollow leaves are used as a garnish or dried as a herb; mild onion flavour.

chive, Chinese Young leaves and flower stalks of *Allium tuberosum*, with a garlic-like flavour. Unlike *chive, the leaves are flat and solid. Also known as garlic chives and oriental garlic.

chlorella *See* ALGAE.

chlorine An element found in biological tissues as the chloride *ion; the body contains about 100g (3mol) of chloride and the average diet contains 6–7g (0.17–0.2mol), mainly as sodium chloride (ordinary salt). Free chlorine is used as a sterilizing agent, e.g. for drinking water.

chlorine dioxide A flour improver; *see* AGEING.

chlorophyll The green pigment of plant materials which is responsible for the trapping of light energy for photosynthesis, the formation of carbohydrates from carbon dioxide and water. Both α- and β-chlorophylls occur in leaves, together with the *carotenoids xanthophyll and carotene. Chlorophyll has no nutritional value, although it does contain *magnesium as part of its molecule, and although it is used in breath-fresheners and toothpaste, there is no evidence that it has any useful action.

chlorophyllide The green colour found in the water after cooking some vegetables; it is a water-soluble derivative of *chlorophyll formed by either enzymic action (chlorophyllase in the vegetables) or alkaline hydrolysis.

chlorpropamide An oral hypoglycaemic agent used in the treatment of *diabetes mellitus; it stimulates secretion of *insulin.

cho-cho *See* CHAYOTE.

chocolate Made from cocoa nibs (husked, fermented, and roasted *cocoa beans) by refining and the addition of sugar, *cocoa butter, flavouring, *lecithin, and, for milk chocolate, milk solids. It may also contain vegetable oils other than cocoa butter. White chocolate contains cocoa butter, but no cocoa powder.

Originally from Central America, *xocoatl* is a cold drink made from cocoa flavoured with honey, spices, and vanilla; according to Aztec mythology the god of air, Quetzalcoatl, came to earth and taught human beings to cultivate various crops, including cacao. The first use of cocoa as a food rather than a beverage was developed by the Dutch cocoa merchant Conrad van Houten in 1815; the first milk chocolate for eating was invented in 1875, by adding sweetened condensed milk.

A 100-g portion of milk chocolate is a rich *source of copper; a good source of calcium; a source of protein, vitamin B_2, iron, and selenium; contains

30g of fat, of which 60% is saturated and 30% mono-unsaturated; supplies 540kcal (2270kJ). A 100-g portion of plain chocolate is a rich source of copper; a source of protein and iron; fat and energy as for milk chocolate.

chocolate, drinking Partially solubilized cocoa powder for preparation of a chocolate-flavoured milk drink, containing about 75% sucrose.

chokeberry, black Violet-black fruit of the North American shrub *Aronia melanocarpa*, also known as aronia berry, used in fruit juices and as a natural food colourant.

choke cherry Sour wild North American cherry, fruit of *Prunus virginiana* and *P. edmissa*.

cholagogue A substance that stimulates the secretion of *bile from the gall bladder into the duodenum.

cholangitis Bacterial infection of *bile in the bile duct. *See also* CHOLECYSTITIS.

cholecalciferol *See* VITAMIN D.

cholecystectomy Removal of the *gall bladder.

cholecystitis Bacterial infection of *bile in the *gall bladder. *See also* CHOLANGITIS.

cholecystokinin *Hormone secreted by the proximal small intestine that stimulates gall bladder and pancreatic secretion, sometimes known as pancreozymin, and abbreviated to CCK.

cholelithiasis *See* GALLSTONES.

cholent Traditional Jewish and Middle-European casserole of beans and beef, cooked extremely slowly (traditionally overnight beside the baker's oven). Also known as hamin.

cholera Traditionally associated with contaminated water, also a food-borne infection. *See* VIBRIO SPP.

cholestasis Failure of normal amounts of *bile to reach the intestine, resulting in obstructive *jaundice. May be caused by *gallstones, liver disease, or pancreatic cancer.

cholesterol The principal sterol in animal tissues, an essential component of cell membranes and the precursor for the formation of the *steroid hormones. It is transported in the plasma *lipoproteins. Not a dietary essential, since it is synthesized in the body. Eggs contain about 450mg, milk 14mg, cheese 70–120mg, brain 2.2mg, liver and kidney 300–600mg, poultry 70–100mg, and fish 50–60mg/100g.

An elevated plasma concentration of cholesterol is a risk factor for *atherosclerosis. *See also* CHYLOMICRONS; HDL; HMG CoA REDUCTASE INHIBITORS; HYPERCHOLESTEROLAEMIA; HYPERLIPIDAEMIA; IDL; LDL; LIPIDS, PLASMA; VLDL.

cholestyramine An ion exchange resin used to bind *bile salts in the intestinal lumen and increase their excretion, used to treat *jaundice (relieving the itching caused by bile salts in the circulation), and formerly to treat hypercholesterolaemia (by reducing the reabsorption of bile salts so that more must be synthesized from *cholesterol).

choline A derivative of the amino acid *serine; an important component of cell membranes. Phosphatidylcholine is also known as *lecithin, and preparations of mixed phospholipids rich in phosphatidylcholine are generally called lecithin, although they also contain other phospholipids; lecithin from *peanuts and *soya beans is widely used as an emulsifying agent. Choline released from membrane phospholipids is important for the formation of the neurotransmitter *acetylcholine, and choline is also important in the metabolism of methyl groups.

Choline is synthesized in the body, and it is a ubiquitous component of cell membranes and therefore occurs in all foods, so that dietary deficiency is unknown. Deficiency has been observed in patients on long-term total *parenteral nutrition, suggesting that the ability to synthesize choline is inadequate to meet requirements without some intake. There is no evidence on which to base estimates of requirements; the US/Canadian *adequate intake is 550 mg for men and 425 for women.

cholla (challa) A loaf of white bread made in a twisted form by plaiting together a large and small piece of dough. The dough is made from white flour, enriched with eggs and a pinch of saffron, and the loaf is decorated with poppy seed. Traditionally used for benediction of the Jewish sabbath and festivals.

chondroitin A *polysaccharide of galactosamine and glucuronic acid, a mucopolysaccharide. Chondroitin sulphate is a component of *cartilage and the organic matrix of *bone, and has been used in treatment of osteoarthritis, with some evidence of efficacy.

Chondrus crispus A *seaweed, the source of *carrageenan.

chop A slice of meat containing a part of the bone; commonly the rib, but also cut from the chump or tail end of the loin (chump chops) or neck (then called cutlets).

chopsuey Chinese dishes based on bean sprouts and shredded vegetables, cooked with shredded quick-fried meat, capped with a thin omelette. Not authentically Chinese, but an invention of Chinese restaurateurs reputedly in either New York or San Francisco in 1896, although it may derive from *tsap seui* from the Guangzhou region of China. Unlike true Chinese food, the flavours of a chopsuey are all mixed together; one translation is 'savoury mess'.

chorote *See* POZOL.

chorizo Spanish; coarse textured, red, spiced sausage.

Chorleywood bread process A method of preparing dough for *bread making by submitting it to intense mechanical working, so that, together with the use of oxidizing agents, the need for bulk fermentation of the dough is eliminated. This is a so-called no-time process and saves 1½–2 hours, permits use of an increased proportion of weaker flour, and produces a softer, finer loaf, which stales more slowly. Named after the British Baking Industries Research Association at Chorleywood in Hertfordshire.

choux pastry (chou pastry) *See* PASTRY, CHOUX.

chow-chow Chinese; preserve of ginger, orange peel, and fruit in syrup, or a mixed vegetable pickle containing mustard and spices.

chowder Thick soup made from shellfish (especially clams) or other fish, with pork or bacon. Originally French, now mainly New England and Newfoundland. The name derives from the French *chaudière*, the large cauldron in which it is prepared.

chow mein Chinese; dishes based on fried noodles.

chrane Jewish, Middle-European; condiment made from *beetroot and *horseradish.

christophene *See* CHAYOTE.

chromium A metallic element that is a dietary essential. It forms an organic complex with *nicotinic acid, known as the glucose tolerance factor, which facilitates the interaction of *insulin with receptors on cell surfaces. Deficiency results in impaired *glucose tolerance.

There is little evidence on which to base estimates of requirements; deficiency has been observed at intakes below 6 µg (0.12 µmol)/day; the US/Canadian *adequate intake is 35 µg for men and 25 µg for women. High intakes of inorganic chromium salts (in excess of 1–2 mg/day) are associated with kidney and liver damage.

chromoproteins Proteins conjugated with a metal-containing group, such as the haem group of *haemoglobin, which contains iron.

chromosome A large macromolecule of *DNA and associated histones and other proteins; the human *genome consists of twenty-two pairs of chromosomes and the sex chromosomes (XX in females, XY in males).

chub Freshwater fish *Leuciscus cephalus*, mainly a game fish, of little commercial importance.

chubeza(h) Palestinian Arab, now also Israeli; spiced fried leaves of mallow or *spinach.

chuck See BEEF.

chufa See TIGER NUT.

chulupa Fruit of the tropical vine *Passiflora maliformis*; see also PASSION FRUIT.

chump chop See CHOP.

chuño Traditional dried potato prepared in the highlands of Peru and Bolivia. The tubers of bitter potatoes are crushed, pressed, frozen during the night, then dried in the sunshine during the day, a process of freeze-drying. Papa seca is similar, but made from non-bitter potatoes.

chupatti See CHAPATTI.

churning In butter making, the process of agitating cream to break down the membrane surrounding the globules of fat, allowing them to coalesce into grains which separate from the *buttermilk.

churpi (dudh churpi) Indian; cooked curd prepared by coagulating partially defatted milk (commonly yak milk) with acid and heat; the partially dried product (prechurpi) is cooked or dipped in a milk-sugar solution, and dried.

churros Spanish; sausage-shaped, deep-fried doughnuts, dusted with sugar.

chutney Pickled fruits or vegetables, normally spiced, used as a relish; of Indian origin.

chyle See LYMPH.

chylomicrons Plasma lipoproteins containing newly absorbed fat, assembled in the small intestinal mucosa and secreted into the lymphatic system, circulating in the *lymph and bloodstream as a source of fat for tissues. The remnants are cleared by the liver. See also LIPIDS, PLASMA.

chymase Alternative name for *chymosin.

chyme The partially digested mass of food in the stomach.

chymosin *Enzyme in the abomasum of calves and the stomach of human infants which clots milk by precipitation of the *casein. Also known as rennin. Biosynthetic chymosin is used in cheese making (vegetable *rennet). See also CHEESE.

chymotrypsin An *endopeptidase secreted by the *pancreas that catalyses hydrolysis of the esters of aromatic amino acids. Secreted as the inactive precursor, chymotrypsinogen, which is activated by *trypsin.

chymotrypsinogen The inactive form (*zymogen) in which *chymotrypsin is secreted; activated by *trypsin.

ciabatta *See* BREAD, ITALIAN.

cibophobia Dislike of food.

cider (cyder) An *alcoholic beverage; fermented *apple juice (in the UK may include not more than 25% *pear juice). Dry cider has 2.6% sugars, 3.8% alcohol, and 110 kcal (460 kJ) per 300 mL. Sweet cider has 4.3% sugars and supplies 125 kcal (525 kJ) per 300 mL. Vintage cider has 7.3% sugars, 10.5% alcohol, and supplies 300 kcal (1260 kJ) per 300 mL (half pint).

In the USA cider or fresh cider is unfermented apple juice; the fermented product is called hard or fermented cider.

cieddu *See* MILK, FERMENTED.

ciguatera Poisoning from eating fish feeding in the region of coral reefs. The species of fish are normally edible, and appear to derive the toxins, ciguatoxins, from their diet. Reported in seafarers' tales in the 16th century. The toxins originate from several dinoflagellates that are common to coastal regions. Mainly a problem with marine fin fish, it causes gastroenteritis for one to two days, then general weakness for two to seven days, with paraesthesia lasting from two days to three weeks or longer. *See also* PHYCOTOXINS; RED TIDE; SHELLFISH POISONING.

ciguatoxins The toxins responsible for *ciguatera.

cilantro *See* CORIANDER.

CIMMYT Centro Internacional de Mejoramiento de Maíz y Trigo, the International Maize and Wheat Improvement Center, Texcoco, Mexico.

(⊕) SEE WEB LINKS
• The CIMMYT's homepage.

cinnamon The aromatic bark of various species of trees of the genus *Cinnamomum*; it is split from the shoots, cured, and dried, when it shrinks and curls into a cylinder or 'quill'. Used as a flavour in meat products, bakery goods, and confectionery, and may be available either as the whole quill or powdered ready for use.

cinsaut A *grape variety widely used for *wine making, not one of the classic varieties. The common bulk wine-producing grape of southern France.

cirrhosis Chronic inflammatory liver disease characterized by the replacement of normal tissue with fibrous tissue and the loss of functional liver cells.

cis- and *trans-*isomerism In compounds such as unsaturated *fatty acids, which have double bonds, the chain may continue on the same side of the double bond (*cis-*) or the opposite side (*trans-*). Most of the naturally occurring unsaturated fatty acids, and the desirable forms, have the *cis-*configuration; *trans-*unsaturated fatty acids are consided undesirable in the diet.

cissa An unnatural desire for foods; alternative terms are cittosis, allotriophagy, and pica.

citrange An American *citrus fruit resulting from a cross between the ordinary orange and the trifoliate orange, *Poncirus trifoliata*.

citric acid An organic *acid (a tricarboxylic acid) which is widely distributed in plant and animal tissues; it is an important metabolic intermediate, and yields 2.47 kcal (10.9 kJ)/g. It is used as a flavouring and acidifying agent, and its salts (citrates) are used as acidity regulators. Commercially it is either prepared by the fermentation of sugars by the mould *Aspergillus niger* or extracted from citrus fruits (lemon juice contains 5–8% citric acid).

citric acid cycle (Krebs's cycle) A central pathway for the *metabolism of fats, carbohydrates, and amino acids.

citrin A mixture of two *flavonones found in citrus pith, hesperidin and eriodictin. A constituent of what is sometimes called vitamin P.

citrinin Nephrotoxic *mycotoxin produced by *Penicillium citrinum*.

citron The first of the *citrus fruits to become known to Europeans, *Citrus medica*. The fruit has a very thick peel and sweet, acid-free pith with practically no juice. It is used for preparing *candied peel.

citronella *See* LEMON GRASS.

citronin A flavonone *glycoside from the peel of unripe Ponderosa lemons; *see* FLAVONOIDS.

citrovorum factor The name given to a growth factor for the micro-organism *Leuconostoc citrovorum*, now known to be one of the main forms of the vitamin *folic acid.

citroxanthin A yellow *carotenoid pigment in orange peel which has vitamin A activity. Also known as mutachrome.

citrullinaemia A genetic disease affecting the formation of urea as the end-product of protein metabolism. The defect may be mild, or so severe that affected infants become comatose and may die after a moderately high intake of protein. Treatment is usually by restriction of protein intake and feeding supplements of the amino acid arginine. Sodium benzoate may be given to increase the excretion of nitrogenous waste as hippuric acid. *See also* BENZOIC ACID.

citrulline An *amino acid formed as a metabolic intermediate, but not involved in proteins, and of no nutritional importance.

Citrus Genus of trees with fleshy, juicy fruits; there is considerable confusion over the names because of hybridization and mutations. Sweet orange *Citrus sinensis*; various cultivars, including Valencia, Washington navel, Shamouti. Sour, bitter, or Seville orange, *C. aurantium*, is too bitter to eat and is used for marmalade. Lemon, *C. limon*. Lime, *C. aurantifolia*. Citron, *C. medica*, has thick, white inner skin and is used mainly to make candied peel. Pomelo (shaddock), *C. grandis*, is the parent of the grapefruit. Grapefruit, *C. paradisi*, is a hybrid of pomelo and sweet orange. Tangerine, satsuma, mandarin, calamondin, and naartjie are small fruits with loose skins. Clementine, a hybrid of tangerine and bitter orange, is sometimes regarded as a variety of tangerine. Mineola is a hybrid of grapefruit and tangerine. Ortanique is a hybrid of orange and tangerine. Citrange is a hybrid of citron and orange. Tangors are hybrids of tangerine and sweet orange. Ugli fruit is a hybrid of grapefruit and tangerine. Tangelo is a hybrid of tangerine and pomelo. All are a rich *source of vitamin C and contain up to 10% sugars (glucose and fructose).

cittosis An unnatural desire for foods; alternative terms are cissa, allotriophagy, and pica.

CJD Creutzfeldt-Jakob disease, a rapidly progressing degenerative neurological disease; the classical or spontaneous disease affects people aged over 60. A variant form (vCJD) affects younger people, and is associated with *prions that may be transmitted by eating nervous tissue of cattle affected by *BSE.

CLA Conjugated linoleic acid. *See* LINOLEIC ACID, CONJUGATED.

clafoutis French; batter pudding with black cherries or other fruit.

clam bake American; beach picnic.

clam chowder *See* CHOWDER.

clams Various marine bivalve molluscs; large tropical clam is *Tridacna gigas*, quahog is *Mya arenaria*, native or grooved carpet shell clam or palourde is *Tapes decussates*, *Ruditapes decussates*, or *Venerupis decussa*, soft shell clam or gapers is *Mya* spp., surf clam is *Spisula* spp., amand clam or dog cockle is *Glycymeris glycymeris*, and otter shell clam is *Lutraria lutraria*. A 100-g portion of clams is an exceptionally rich *source of vitamin B$_{12}$; a good source of protein and niacin; contains 120 mg of sodium; supplies 60 kcal (250 kJ). *See also* SCALLOP.

clapshot Scottish (Orkney); mashed potato and turnip, seasoned with chives and bacon fat.

claret Name given in the UK to red wines from the Bordeaux region of France.

clarete Portuguese, Spanish; light red wines.

clarification The process of clearing a liquid of suspended particles. It may be carried out by filtration, *centrifugation, the addition of *enzymes to hydrolyse and solubilize particulate matter (proteolytic or pectolytic enzymes), or the addition of *flocculating agents.

clarifying Of fats, freeing the fat of water so that it can be used for frying, pastry-making, etc. Clarified fats are less susceptible to *rancidity on storage; ghee is clarified butterfat (*see* BUTTER, CLARIFIED). Also the process of filtering juices before making jellies, etc.

clementine A *citrus fruit, *Citrus nobilis* var. *deliciosa*; regarded by some as a variety of tangerine and by others as a cross between the tangerine and a wild North African orange.

climacteric 1. Post-harvesting increase in metabolic rate and production of carbon dioxide and ethylene associated with ripening in some (but not all) fruits. **2.** Clinically, the menopause in women, or declining sexual drive and fertility in men after middle age.

clofibrate Drug used to treat *hyperlipidaemia by lowering specifically low-density lipoproteins. *See also* LIPIDS, PLASMA.

cloning 1. The production of genetically identical cells (clones) from a single ancestor; achieved in plants by vegetative propagation. **2.** The use of various genetic techniques for producing copies of single genes or segments of DNA by insertion into *cloning vectors which can then be introduced into recipient cells and propagated.

cloning vectors *DNA molecules that are capable of autonomous replication (e.g. plasmids, viral genomes, and yeast artificial chromosomes) into which foreign DNA can be inserted, which can then be inserted into host cells, propagated, and expressed.

Clostridium botulinum A bacterium that is responsible for *botulism, a rare but often fatal form of *food-borne disease. It is widely distributed in soil; during growth in foods it synthesizes an extremely potent neurotoxin which is released into the food when the cell dies. The spores are extremely heat-resistant, and their thermal death time is used as a minimum standard for processing foods with *pH values higher than 4.5.

Clostridium perfringens Formerly *C. welchii*, a bacterium that is
a rare cause of *food-borne infection, causing severe abdominal pain,
flatulence, and diarrhoea, with recovery within about twenty-four hours.
Mainly acquired from cooked meat; the organism can multiply very rapidly
under favourable conditions, doubling in number every eight to ten minutes.

cloudberry Fruit of the arctic and sub-arctic creeping perennial *Rubus
chamaemorus*, orange-yellow and resembling a raspberry in shape. Known
as avron in Scotland and baked-apple berry in Canada. It is not cultivated
but harvested from wild plants. It is an extremely rich natural source of
*benzoic acid and will not ferment; it remains fresh for many months
without preservation.

clove The dried aromatic flower buds of *Caryophyllus aromaticus* (also
known as *Eugenia caryophyllus* syn. *E. caryophyllata*, *E. aromatica*,
Caryophyllus aromaticus, *Syzygium aromaticum*); mother of clove is the
ripened fruit, which is inferior in flavour. Used as a flavour in meat
products and baked goods.

club soda *See* SODA WATER.

club steak American name for *entrecôte steak.

cluster analysis Statistical technique to analyse data (e.g. from food
consumption records) by classifying into groups or clusters, so that the
degree of association is strong between members of the same cluster and weak
between members of different clusters. *See also* DIETARY PATTERN ANALYSIS.

CMC Carboxymethylcellulose; *see* CELLULOSE DERIVATIVES.

CMPI Cow's milk protein intolerance.

cns Central nervous system—the brain and spinal cord.

Co I, Co II Abbreviations of coenzymes I and II, now known as nicotinamide
adenine dinucleotide (*NAD) and nicotinamide adenine dinucleotide
phosphate (NADP), respectively.

CoA *See* COENZYME A.

coacervation The heat-reversible aggregation of the *amylopectin form
of *starch, which is believed to be one of the mechanisms involved in the
staling of bread.

coagel A *fat replacer; a network of monoacylglycerol that can contain
95% water but has a fat-like texture; used for 'zero fat' spreads (actually
contains 4% fat).

coagulation A process involving the *denaturation of proteins, the loss
of their native, soluble structure, so that they become insoluble; it may be
effected by heat, strong acids and alkalis, metals, and other chemicals.

Some proteins are coagulated by specific enzymic action; the action of
*chymosin in cheese making is to coagulate the proteins of milk.

The final stage in blood clotting is the precipitation of insoluble fibrin,
formed from the soluble plasma protein fibrinogen. The enzyme responsible
is prothrombin, which is normally inactive, but in response to injury is
activated by a cascade of events. *Vitamin K is required for the synthesis
of prothrombin, and clotting requires calcium ions. *See also* BLOOD PLASMA.

coalfish *See* POLLACK.

CoASH Free *coenzyme A.

cobalamin *See* VITAMIN B_{12}.

cobalophilin *Vitamin B_{12} binding protein secreted in saliva that binds
the vitamin in the stomach when it is released from dietary proteins by the
action of gastric acid and *pepsin.

cobalt A mineral whose main function is in *vitamin B_{12}, although there
are some cobalt-dependent *enzymes. There is no evidence of cobalt
deficiency in human beings, and no evidence on which to base estimates of
requirements for inorganic cobalt. 'Pining disease' in cattle and sheep is due
to cobalt deficiency (their intestinal micro-organisms synthesize vitamin B_{12})
and it is a growth factor for some animals. Cobalt salts are toxic in excess,
causing degeneration of the heart muscle, and habitual intakes in excess of
300 mg/day are considered undesirable.

cobamide A derivative of *vitamin B_{12}.

cobbler **1.** Sweetened cold drink made from fruit with wine or liqueur
and ice. **2.** Meat or fruit dishes topped with scone rounds.

cobia Marine fish, *Rachycentron canadum*.

cob nut *See* HAZELNUT.

coburg cakes Small cakes containing syrup and flavoured with spices.

cocarboxylase Obsolete name for thiamin diphosphate, the metabolically
active *coenzyme form of *vitamin B_1.

cocarcinogen A substance which, alone, does not cause the induction of
cancer, but potentiates the action of a *carcinogen.

cochineal A water-soluble red colour obtained from the female conchilla,
Dactilopius coccus (*Coccus cactus*), an insect found in Central America and
the Caribbean, which lives on the *nopal cactus *Opuntia cochenillefera*; 1 kg
of the colour is obtained from about 150 000 insects. Legally permitted in
foods in most countries. Contains carminic acid. Cochineal red A is an
alternative name for *Ponceau 4R, often used to replace cochineal.

cock-a-leekie Scottish; soup made from leeks and chicken.

cocket Medieval English; white bread.

cockles Marine bivalve molluscs, *Cerastoderma* spp.; commonly eaten species include *C. edulis* (common cockle), *Cardium corbis*, and *C. aculeatum* (spiny cockle), often sold preserved in brine or vinegar. Dog cockle or amand clam is *Glycymeris glycymeris*. A 50-g portion is a rich *source of iron, iodine, and selenium; a source of protein and copper; contains 0.2g of fat, of which 33% is saturated; supplies 25kcal (105kJ).

cock of the wood *See* CAPERCAILLIE.

cocktail Mixed alcoholic drink; there are many recipes based on a wide variety of spirits and liqueurs, with fruit juice, milk, or coconut milk, normally shaken with crushed ice.

cocoa Originally known as cacao, introduced into Europe from Mexico by the Spaniards in the early 16th century. The powder prepared from the seed embedded in the fruit of the cocoa plant, *Theobroma cacao*, also a milk drink prepared with cocoa powder. Used to prepare *chocolate. Contains the *alkaloid *theobromine.

cocoa, Dutch Cocoa treated with a dilute solution of alkali (carbonate or bicarbonate) to improve its colour, flavour, and solubility. The process is known as 'Dutching'.

cocoa butter The fat from the cocoa bean, used in *chocolate manufacture and in pharmaceuticals; it has a sharp melting point, between 31 and 35°C, so it melts in the mouth; mostly 2-oleopalmitostearin.

cocoa butter equivalents Also known as cocoa butter extenders; fats that are physically and chemically similar to *cocoa butter and can be mixed with it in chocolate manufacture. Some raise the melting point of the chocolate, making it more suitable for tropical regions. Borneo tallow (green butter) from the Malaysian and Indonesian plant *Shorea stenopiera*; dhupa from the Indian plant *Vateria indica*; illipe butter (mowrah fat) from the Indian plant *Bassia longifolia*; kokum from the Indian tree *Garcinia indica*; sal from the Indian plant *Shorea robusta*; shea butter from the African plant *Butyrospermum parkii*. *See also* COCOA BUTTER SUBSTITUTES.

cocoa butter extenders *See* COCOA BUTTER EQUIVALENTS.

cocoa butter substitutes Fats that are physically similar to *cocoa butter, but chemically different, used with defatted cocoa, to make substitute *chocolate or compound coatings for bakery. They cannot be mixed with cocoa butter, but some do not require tempering and can be cooled much more rapidly than cocoa butter. *See also* COCOA BUTTER EQUIVALENTS.

cocoa nibs Seeds of the cocoa plant, *Theobroma cacao*, are left to ferment, which modifies the bitterness, and their colour darkens. They are then roasted and separated from the husks as two halves of the seed known as cocoa nibs. They contain about 50% fat, part of which is removed in the preparation of chocolate and cocoa for beverages.

cocolait A form of *coconut 'milk' made by applying high pressure to coconuts and homogenizing the oil and water emulsion plus coconut water (coconut milk) obtained. Bottled and used in place of cow's milk.

cocona Orange-red fruit of the South American shrub *Solanum topiro* (syn. *S. sessiliflorum*), with pale yellow flesh, a source of iron, carotene, vitamin C, and niacin. The leaves are also cooked and eaten as a vegetable. Also known as peach tomato or orinoko apple.

coconut Fruit of the tropical palm, *Cocos nucifera*. The dried nut is copra which contains 60–65% coconut oil. The residue after extraction of the oil is used for animal feed. The hollow, unripe nut contains a watery liquid known as coconut milk, which is gradually absorbed as the fruit ripens. A 50-g portion is a rich *source of copper; contains 18g of fat, of which 90% is saturated; provides 7g of dietary fibre; supplies 175kcal (735kJ).

coconut oil Semi-solid oil extracted from copra (dried *coconut); contains 90% saturated fats.

cocotte, en Describes a dish cooked and served in a small casserole.

cocoyam West African names for *tannia (new cocoyam) and *taro (old cocoyam).

cocum *See* KOKUM.

cod (codling) A white fish, *Gadus morrhua*. Pacific cod is *G. macrocephalus*, Greenland cod is *G. ogac*, saffron cod is *Eleginus gracillis*, red cod is *Pseudophycis bachus*, blue cod is *Parapercis colias*. Poor cod is *Trisopterus minutus*.

coddle To cook slowly in water kept just below boiling point.

Codes of Practice In the area of food production these refer to standards of procedure which cannot be covered by exact specifications and serve as agreed guidelines. They may originate from government departments, trade organizations, the Institute of Food, Science and Technology, or individual companies.

Codex Alimentarius Originally Codex Alimentarius Europaeus; since 1961 part of the United Nations FAO/WHO Commission on Food Standards to simplify and integrate food standards for adoption internationally.

(((●))) SEE WEB LINKS

● Codex Alimentarius's homepage.

cod liver oil The oil from codfish liver; the classic source of vitamins A and D, used for its medicinal properties long before the vitamins were discovered; also a rich source of omega-3 polyunsaturated fatty acids. An average sample contains 120–1200 µg vitamin A and 1–10 µg vitamin D per gram.

codon A triplet of bases in *RNA that codes for an amino acid.

coeliac disease (celiac disease) Intolerance of the proteins of wheat, rye, and barley; specifically, the gliadin fraction of the protein *gluten. The villi of the small intestine are severely affected and absorption of food is poor. Stools are bulky and fermenting from unabsorbed carbohydrate, and contain a large amount of unabsorbed fat (steatorrhoea). As a result of malabsorption, affected people are malnourished and children suffer from growth retardation. Treatment is by exclusion of wheat, rye, and barley proteins (the starches are tolerated); rice, oats, and maize are generally tolerated. Manufactured foods that are free from gluten and hence suitable for consumption by people with coeliac disease are usually labelled as 'gluten-free'. Also known as gluten-induced enteropathy, and sometimes as non-tropical sprue.

coenzyme A *Coenzyme derived from the *vitamin *pantothenic acid and cysteamine (the *amine derived by decarboxylation of *cysteine); it forms thioesters with fatty acids (acyl CoA) for oxidation. The free coenzyme is usually written as CoASH, to show the free sulphydryl group that reacts with the fatty acid.

coenzyme Q10 *See* UBIQUINONE.

coenzymes Organic compounds required for the activity of some *enzymes; most are derived from vitamins. Coenzymes that remain tightly bound to the enzyme at all times are known as prosthetic groups; non-protein components of the enzyme molecule. Other coenzymes act to transfer groups from one enzyme to another, e.g. *coenzyme A transfers acetyl groups between enzymes, *NAD transfers hydrogen between enzymes in oxidation and reduction reactions.

An enzyme that requires a tightly bound coenzyme is inactive in the absence of its coenzyme; this can be exploited to assess *vitamin B_1, *B_2, and *B_6 *nutritional status, by measuring the activity of enzymes that require coenzymes derived from these vitamins (*see* ENZYME ACTIVATION ASSAYS).

cœur à la crème *See* FROMAGE À LA CRÈME.

coffee A beverage produced by roasting the beans from the berries of two principal types of shrub: *Coffea arabica* (arabica coffee) and *C. canephora* (robusta coffee); Liberian coffee (*C. liberica*) grows in tropical regions, but quality is inferior and it accounts for less than 1% of world coffee trade. Reputedly discovered in the 9th century in southern Ethiopia by a goatherd whose goats became frisky after eating the berries. *Niacin is formed during the roasting process, and coffee can contain 10–40 mg of niacin per 100 g, depending on the extent of roasting, thus making a significant contribution to average intakes of niacin.

Instant coffee (invented by Satori Kato of Chicago, 1901) is dried coffee extract which can be used to make a beverage by adding hot water or milk. It may be manufactured by spray-drying or *freeze-drying. Coffee essence is an aqueous extract of roasted coffee; usually about 400 g of coffee/L.

coffee, decaffeinated Coffee beans (or instant coffee) from which the *caffeine has been extracted with solvent (e.g. methylene or ethylene chloride), carbon dioxide under pressure (supercritical CO_2), or water. Coffee decaffeinated by water extraction is sometimes labelled as 'naturally' decaffeinated.

coffee, Irish Sweetened coffee, laced with Irish whiskey and with cream floated on top. It originated in the Buena Vista Café in San Francisco in 1953. Many restaurants offer a range of related speciality coffees laced with spirits such as rum or brandy, or liqueurs such as Tia Maria.

coffee, Viennese Ground coffee containing dried figs.

coffee whitener *See* CREAMER, NON-DAIRY.

cognac *Brandy made only in the Charentes region of north-west France, around the town of Cognac, from special varieties of grape grown on shallow soil and claimed to be distilled only in pot, not continuous, stills; first distilled by Jean Martell in 1715. Sometimes used (incorrectly) as a general name for brandy. *See also* ARMAGNAC.

Cohen syndrome Genetic disease leading to hypotonia, delayed mental development, characteristic facial features, slender hands and feet, and sometimes also obesity.

cohort study Prospective epidemiological study in which a group of people are followed for many years in order to elucidate dietary and other factors associated with disease. Also known as follow-up study.

Cointreau Orange-flavoured liqueur.

cola nuts (kola nuts) Fruit of the tropical rainforest trees *Cola nitida* and *C. acuminata*. Used in manufacture of cola beverages, and chewed as a stimulant because of its high content of *caffeine.

colcannon 1. Irish; potato mashed with kale or cabbage, often fried (*see also* BUBBLE AND SQUEAK). **2.** Scottish; cabbage, carrots, potatoes, and turnips mashed together.

colchicine An *alkaloid isolated from the meadow saffron or autumn crocus (*Colchicum* spp.). It is an old remedy for *gout. It inhibits cell division, and is used in experimental horticulture to produce plants with abnormal numbers of chromosomes.

cold preservation *See* CAMPDEN PROCESS.

cold-shortening (of meat) If the temperature of muscle is reduced below 10°C while the *pH remains above 6–6.2 (early in the post-mortem conversion of glycogen to lactic acid) the muscle contracts in reaction to cold and, when cooked, the meat is tough. Also known as cold contraction.

cold sterilization *See* IRRADIATION; STERILIZATION, COLD.

cold store bacteria *See* PSYCHROPHILIC BACTERIA.

cole (coleseed) *See* RAPE.

colectomy Surgical removal of all or part of the colon, to treat cancer or severe ulcerative *colitis.

coleslaw Salad made from finely shredded white cabbage dressed with cream or mayonnaise; other vegetables may be included.

colewort *See* COLLARD.

coley *See* SAITHE.

colic Waves of abdominal pain due to impaired or disordered *peristalsis.

coliform bacteria A group of aerobic, lactose-fermenting bacteria, of which *Escherichia coli* is the most important member. Most coliforms are not harmful, but since they arise from faeces they are useful as a test of faecal contamination, especially of water. Some strains of *E. coli* produce toxins, or are otherwise pathogenic, and are associated with *food-borne disease.

colipase Protein that is an essential cofactor for pancreatic *lipase action in fat digestion; it anchors lipase to lipid droplets in the small intestine.

colitis Inflammation of the large intestine, with pain, diarrhoea, and weight loss; there may be ulceration of the large intestine (ulcerative colitis). *See also* CROHN'S DISEASE; GASTRO-INTESTINAL TRACT; IRRITABLE BOWEL SYNDROME; MEGACOLON.

collagen Insoluble protein in *connective tissue, bones, tendons, and skin of animals and fish; converted by moist heat into the soluble protein *gelatine.

collagen sugar An old name for *glycine.

collard (collard greens) American name for varieties of cabbage (*Brassica oleracea*) which do not form a compact head. Generally known in the UK as greens or spring greens.

collared Pickled or salted meat which is rolled, boiled with seasonings, and served cold.

colloid Particles (the disperse phase) suspended in a second medium (the dispersion medium); can be solid, liquid, or gas suspended in a solid, liquid, or gas. Examples of gas-in-liquid colloids are beaten egg-white and whipped cream; of liquid-in-liquid colloids, emulsions such as milk and salad cream. *See also* EMULSIFYING AGENTS; STABILIZERS.

collop Scottish; originally a small boneless piece of meat (from the French *escalope*); now a savoury dish made from finely minced meat.

colocasia *See* TARO.

cologel Alternative name for methylcellulose; *see* CELLULOSE DERIVATIVES.

colon Also known as the large intestine or bowel, consisting of three anatomical regions: the ascending, the transverse, and the descending colon. The colon normally has a considerable population of bacteria, while it is rare to find a large bacterial population in the small intestine. The colon terminates at the rectum, where faeces are compacted and stored before voiding. *See also* GASTRO-INTESTINAL TRACT.

colon, spastic *See* IRRITABLE BOWEL SYNDROME.

colorimetry Analytical technique based on comparison of the intensity of the colour of a solution with that of a standard solution.

colostomy Surgical creation of an artificial conduit (a stoma) on the abdominal wall for voiding of intestinal contents following surgical removal of much of the colon and/or rectum. *See also* GASTRO-INTESTINAL TRACT.

colostrum The milk produced by mammals during the first few days after parturition; compared with mature milk, human colostrum contains more protein (2 compared with 1.3g/100mL), slightly less lactose (6.6 compared with 7.2g/100mL), considerably less fat (2.6 compared with 4.1g/100mL), and overall slightly less energy (56kcal (235kJ)/100mL compared with 69kcal (290kJ)). Colostrum is a valuable source of antibodies for the newborn infant. Animal colostrum is sometimes known as beestings and human colostrum as foremilk.

colours Widely used in foods to increase their aesthetic appeal; may be natural, *nature-identical, or synthetic. Natural colours include *carotenoids (yellow to orange-red in apricots, carrots, maize, tomatoes), some of which are vitamin A precursors. *Chlorophylls are the green pigments in leaves. *Anthocyanins are the red, blue, and violet pigments in beetroots, raspberries, and red cabbage. *Flavones are yellow pigments in leaves and flowers. *Caramel, used for both flavour and as a brown colour, is made by heating sugar.

In addition to all these there are various ingredients such as paprika, saffron, and turmeric that also provide colour.

colwick English soft cheese made in cylindrical shape.

colza *See* RAPE; colza oil is rapeseed oil.

COMA Committee on Medical Aspects of Food Policy; formerly a permanent Advisory Committee to the UK Department of Health.

comet assay Technique for rapid quantification of *DNA strand breaks in single cells by *electrophoresis.

comfrey Wild member of the *borage family, *Symphytum officinale.* Leaves may be cooked like spinach or fried in batter, but they contain alkaloids that cause liver damage.

comminuted Finely divided; used with reference to minced meat products and fruit drinks made from crushed whole fruit including the peel.

complementation Of proteins, when a relative deficiency of an essential *amino acid in one is compensated by a relative surplus from another protein consumed at the same time. The *protein quality is higher than the average of the separate values.

compote Fruit stewed with sugar; a single fruit or a mixture, served hot or cold. Also sometimes used for a stew of small birds such as pigeons.

conalbumin (ovotransferrin) A *glycoprotein in egg-white that binds di- and trivalent metal ions, comprising 12% of the total solids. It binds iron in a pink-coloured complex; this accounts for the pinkish colour resulting when eggs are stored in rusty containers.

concanavalin A A *lectin extracted from jack beans, *Canavalia ensiformis,* which binds *glycoproteins with α-glycoside or α-mannoside groups.

conching Part of the process of making *chocolate in which the mixture is subjected to severe mechanical treatment with heavy rollers to produce a uniform smooth consistency.

condé Dessert of creamed rice with fruit and red jam sauce. Also the name of a type of pâtisserie.

condiment Seasoning added to flavour foods, such as salt, or herbs and spices such as mustard, ginger, curry, pepper, etc. Although some are relatively rich in nutrients, they are generally used in such small quantities that they make a negligible contribution to the diet (but *see* CURRY POWDER).

conditioning, meat *See* MEAT CONDITIONING.

confectioner's glucose *See* SYRUP, CORN.

confectionery *Sugar confectionery is sweets, candies, chocolates, etc.; flour confectionery is cakes, pastries, etc. Originally a medicinal preparation made palatable with sugar, syrup, or honey.

confidence interval A range of values that will have the stated probability of including any data from a set (e.g. a 95% confidence interval will include 95% of the data points).

confit French; **1.** Fruit or vegetables preserved in brandy, vinegar, or sugar. **2.** Poultry meat or pork preserved in a vessel and covered with a layer of fat to exclude air.

confounding In epidemiology, any factor that may cause or prevent the outcome of interest and is also associated with the exposure of interest in a way that distorts the association between exposure and outcome.

congee Chinese soft rice soup or gruel; may be sweet or savoury. Commonly eaten for breakfast. *See also* CONGIE.

congeners Flavour substances in alcoholic *spirits that distil over with the alcohol; a mixture of higher alcohols and esters. Said to be responsible for many of the symptoms of *hangover after excessive consumption. *See also* FUSEL OIL.

congie (congee) The water from cooking rice, which contains much of the thiamin and niacin from the rice; used as a drink.

congress tart Small pastry case filled with ground almonds, sugar, and egg.

congris Caribbean (Cuban); casseroled red beans served with rice.

conjugase The enzyme (γ-glutamyl peptidase) that hydrolyses the poly-γ-glutamyl side-chain of *folic acid conjugates in the small intestine, permitting the absorption of free folate.

connective tissue Consists of the protein *collagen, which in fish is found between the muscle segments (myotomes); in meat it is spread through the muscle, uniting the muscle fibres into bundles and supporting the blood vessels (a kind of soft skeleton), and consists of both collagen and *elastin.

A high content of connective tissue results in tougher meat.

Collagen is insoluble; it is converted to soluble *gelatine by moist heat, so making the food more tender. Tough meat is softened to some extent by stewing, but roasting or frying has little effect. Elastin is unaffected by heating, and remains tough, elastic, and insoluble.

conophor nut Fruit of the West African tree *Tetracarpidium conophorum*; boiled nuts are a popular snack in West Africa, and also a source of oil.

consommé A clear soup made from meat or meat extract.

constipation Difficulty in passing stools or infrequent passage of hard stools. In the absence of intestinal disease, frequently a result of a diet low in *non-starch polysaccharide, and treated by increasing the intake of fruits, vegetables, and especially wholegrain cereal products.

contaminant, chemical Defined by *Codex Alimentarius as any substance not intentionally added to food, which is present as a result of the production (including operations carried out in crop husbandry, animal husbandry, and veterinary medicine), manufacture, processing, preparation, treatment, packing, packaging, transport, or holding of the food, or as a result of environmental contamination. For many such compounds there are limits to the amount that may legally be present in the food. *See also* ACCEPTABLE DAILY INTAKE.

controliran *See* WINE CLASSIFICATION, BULGARIA.

controlled atmosphere storage *See* STORAGE, MODIFIED GAS.

convicine A pyrimidine glucoside, one of the toxins in broad beans, responsible for the acute haemolytic *anaemia of *favism.

convolvulus, water *See* SPINACH, WATER.

coo-coo Caribbean; a cooked side dish of starchy vegetables such as breadfruit or corn meal with herbs and spices.

cook-chill A method of catering involving cooking followed by fast chilling and storage at –1 to +5°C, giving a storage time of a few days.

cooker, fireless *See* HAYBOX COOKING.

cook-freeze A method of catering involving cooking followed by rapid freezing and storage between –18 and –30°C, giving a storage time of several months.

cookie *See* BISCUIT.

cooking Required to make food more palatable, more digestible, and safer. There is breakdown of the *connective tissue in meat, softening of the *cellulose in plant tissues, and proteins are denatured by heating, so increasing their digestibility. *See also* BOILING; BROILING; CODDLE; DEVILLED; FRICASSÉE; FRYING; GRILLING; ROASTING; SAUTÉING; SIMMERING; STEAMING; STEWING.

cooking, loss of nutrients In general, water-soluble vitamins and minerals are lost into the cooking water, the amount depending on the surface area to volume ratio, i.e. greater losses take place from finely cut or minced foods. Fat-soluble vitamins are little affected except at frying temperatures. Proteins suffer reduction of available *lysine when they are heated in the presence of reducing substances, and further loss under extreme conditions of temperature. Dry heat, as in baking, results in some loss of vitamin B_1 and available lysine. The most sensitive nutrient by far is vitamin C, with vitamin B_1 next. Average losses from cereals are: boiling, 40% vitamins B_1, B_2, B_6, niacin, biotin, and pantothenic acid; 50% total folate; baking, 5% niacin, 15% vitamin B_2; 25% vitamins B_1, B_6, and pantothenic acid; 50% folate; with biotin being stable. In meat, losses are approximately 20% of all the vitamins for roasting, frying, and grilling and 20–60% for stewing and boiling.

cooking, waterless Cooking in a heavy pan with tightly fitting lid, with a steam vent; only a minimal amount of cooking liquid is needed, but the food is not cooked under pressure.

coon American *Cheddar-type cheese; manufacture includes scalding the milk.

coppa Italian; raw, fermented pork sausage, traditionally prepared from the neck muscles by fermentation with lactic acid bacteria and yeast.

copper A dietary essential trace metal, which forms the *prosthetic group of a number of *enzymes. The *Reference Nutrient Intake is 1.2 mg/day. It is toxic in excess, and it is recommended that not more than 2–10 mg/day should be consumed habitually. Rich *sources include meat, poultry, game, fish and shellfish, avocado, nuts, pulses, bread, chocolate, beer, cider, coconut, mushrooms. *See also* MENKES SYNDROME; WILSON'S DISEASE.

copra Dried *coconut used for production of oil for *margarine and soap manufacture.

coproducts In meat processing, everything except the dressed carcase; edible coproducts are *offal (organ meat), blood, tallow, and gelatine, inedible coproducts include blood charcoal, bone meal, bone charcoal, and feather meal.

coprolith Mass of hard faeces in colon or rectum due to chronic *constipation.

coprophagy Eating of faeces. Since B vitamins are synthesized by intestinal bacteria, animals that eat their faeces can make use of these vitamins, which are not absorbed to any significant extent from the large intestine, the site of bacterial action.

Co Q *See* UBIQUINONE.

coquille, en Normally a seafood dish, served in the shell, or made to resemble a shell.

coquille St-Jacques *See* SCALLOP.

coquimol Caribbean (Cuban); custard made with coconut milk and eggs.

coracan *See* MILLET.

coral The ovaries of female *lobsters, used as the basis for sauces; red-coloured when cooked.

cordial, fruit Originally a fruit *liqueur, and still used in this sense in the USA; in the UK a cordial is now used to mean any fruit drink, usually a concentrate to be diluted. *See* SOFT DRINKS.

cordon bleu First-class or gourmet cooking. Originally the blue sash worn by senior students at the Institut de Saint-Louis, founded in 1686 for the daughters of impoverished nobility; cookery was one of the subjects taught. The École de Cordon Bleu was founded in Paris in 1880 by Marthe Distel, and Le Petit Cordon Bleu cooking school and restaurant in New York in 1942.

coriander A herb, *Coriandrum sativum* (a member of the parsley family); the leaf (also known as cilantro or Chinese parsley) is used fresh or dried, and the dried fruit (dhanyia) as a spice in meat products, bakery goods, gin, and curry powder. Vietnamese coriander is *laksa.

Cori cycle The inter-organ cycling of lactate produced by anaerobic *glycolysis in red blood cells and exercising muscle to the liver, where it is a substrate for *gluconeogenesis, with release of glucose back into the circulation.

coring Removal of the pips and central membranes (the core) from apples, pears, etc.

corked Of wines, the development of an unpleasant flavour due to fungal contamination of the cork.

cork spots In apples and pears, large brown spots in the fruit flesh and fruit deformation, with a pitted appearance. Caused by calcium deficiency.

corm The thickened, underground base of the stem of plants, often called bulbs, as, for example, *taro and *onion.

corn Term used in the UK for *wheat, in the USA for *maize, and sometimes in Scotland and Ireland for *oats; originally any grain. Kaffir corn is *millet, kaffir manna corn is *sorghum.

corn, flour Flour corn is a variety of *maize with large, soft grains and very friable endosperm, making it easy to grind to flour.

corn, guinea (kaffir, corn) *See* SORGHUM.

corn, knocked Orkneys, historical; threshed barley lightly bruised in a mortar with warm water; the husks were floated off and the grains boiled.

corn fibre oil By-product of *maize processing, rich in plant *sterols.

cornflakes Breakfast cereal made from *maize, often enriched with vitamins.

cornflour Purified starch from *maize; in the USA called corn starch; used in custard, blancmange, and baking powders and for thickening sauces and gravies.

corn grits *See* HOMINY.

Cornish pasty *See* PASTY.

corn oil (maize oil) Extracted from maize germ, *Zea mays*; 13% saturates, 60% polyunsaturates.

corn pone Small corn (maize) cakes, a speciality of Alabama, USA.

corn salad Winter salad vegetable, *Valeriana olitoria*, also known as lamb's lettuce.

corn starch *See* CORNFLOUR.

corn starch hydrolysate *See* SYRUP, CORN.

corn steep liquor A by-product of preparing *cornflour, a brown, syrupy liquid containing lactic and phytic acids as well as amino acids, proteins, peptides, and carbohydrates. Used as a substrate for bacterial fermentation.

coronary heart disease *See* ISCHAEMIC HEART DISEASE.

coronary thrombosis *See* ATHEROSCLEROSIS.

corrinoids (corrins) The basic chemical structure of *vitamin B_{12} is the corrin ring; compounds with this structure, whether or not they have vitamin activity, are corrinoids.

cortisol A *glucocorticoid *hormone synthesized in the adrenal cortex that acts to increase *gluconeogenesis and the catabolism of *tryptophan and *tyrosine in the liver; also formed in *adipocytes, where it causes *insulin resistance and depresses production of *resistin.

cosecha Spanish; vintage of wine.

cos lettuce Long-leafed variety of *lettuce, known in the USA as romaine.

cossettes Thin chips of sugar beet shredded for hot-water extraction of the sugar.

costermonger Originally costard monger, late 14th-century London; person selling costard apples (the earliest cultivated variety) in the street. Now anyone selling fruit and vegetables from a barrow.

costmary *See* ALECOST.

cotechino Italian; pork sausage with white wine and spices.

cottage loaf Traditional English loaf consisting of a large round base with a smaller round topknot.

cottage pie *See* SHEPHERD'S PIE.

cottonseed Seed of *Gossypium* spp.; the oil is valuable as cooking oil or for margarine manufacture, and the protein residue is a valuable animal feed. The oil is 25% saturated and 50% polyunsaturated.

coulis Also cullis; originally the juices that run out of meat when it is cooked, now used to mean rich sauce or gravy made from meat juices, puréed shellfish, vegetables, or fruit. Most usually a sauce made from puréed and sieved fruit.

coulommiers French; soft cheese similar to *brie and *camembert.

coupe Dessert of ice cream and fruit, a sundae.

courgette Variety of *marrow developed to be harvested when small; also known as Italian marrow, Italian squash, or zucchini.

Courlose Trade name for sodium carboxymethylcellulose. *See* CELLULOSE DERIVATIVES.

court-bouillon Fish stock used in place of water to cook fish; may contain wine, vinegar, or milk.

couscous North African; millet flour, fine semolina, or crushed wheat, steamed until fluffy and usually served with stew.

cowberry *See* LINGONBERRY.

cow-heel Dish made from heel of ox or cow, stewed to a jelly; also known as neat's foot.

cow pea *See* BEAN, BLACK-EYED.

coypu Large semi-aquatic South American rodent, *Myocastor coypus*, both hunted and farmed for fur and meat. Also known as nutria.

CpG islands Small stretches of *DNA that are comparatively rich in CpG nucleotides (i.e. cytosine followed by guanine), frequently located within the promoter region of *genes. Methylation within the islands is associated with transcriptional inactivation of the gene, and is hence a mechanism of cell differentiation. Failure of methylation of CpG islands is associated with the initiation of cancer. *See also* EPIGENETICS.

crab *Shellfish; *Cancer* and *Carcinus* spp.; king crab is *Limulus polyphemus*, snow crab is *Chionoecetes* spp. A 100-g portion (500g with shell) is a rich *source of protein, niacin, zinc, copper, and selenium; a good source of iron; a source of vitamins B_2 and B_6; contains 400mg of sodium and 5g of fat, of which 13% is saturated; supplies 130kcal (545kJ).

crab apple Wild varieties of *apple (*Malus* spp.), normally very sour; used to make sweet-sour jelly as accompaniment to meat. Commonly grown as an ornamental plant, and to fertilize other apple trees.

crab stick *See* SEAFOOD STICK.

crackers Plain, thin biscuits such as water biscuits, cream crackers, and wholemeal crackers, made from wheat flour, fat, and bicarbonate as a raising agent. A 40-g portion (five biscuits) contains 3–6g of fat; provides 1–2g of dietary fibre and 160–280mg of sodium; supplies 170kcal (715kJ).

crackling Crisp rind of a joint of pork after baking or roasting.

cracknel 1. Plain biscuit made with paste which is boiled before baking so that it puffs up. **2.** Brittle *toffee filling for chocolates.

cran A traditional measure for herrings containing 37½ gallons (167L) or about 800 fish.

cranberry The fleshy, acid fruit of *Vaccinium oxycoccus* or *V. macrocarpon*; commonly used to make cranberry sauce (a traditional accompaniment to turkey) and for the preparation of juice. There is some evidence that cranberry juice is effective in preventing and treating urinary tract infections, by inhibiting the adherence of bacteria to epithelial cells of the urinary tract. An 80-g portion is a *source of vitamin C and copper; provides 3.2g of dietary fibre; supplies 15kcal (60kJ). A 300-mL portion of juice is a rich *source of vitamin C and copper; a good source of iron; supplies 150kcal (630kJ).

crapaud Large edible Caribbean frog, *Leptodactylus fallax*, also known as mountain chicken.

crawfish Crustaceans (without claws) of the family *Palinuridae, Panulirus, Palinurus*, and *Jasus* spp., also called langouste, spiny lobster, rock lobster, sea crayfish. *See* LOBSTER.

crayfish Crustaceans; freshwater crayfish are members of the families *Astacidae, Parasticidae*, and *Austroastacidae*, sea crayfish (*crawfish) of the family *Palinuridae*. *See also* LOBSTER.

CRBP Cellular retinol binding protein; *see* VITAMIN A.

C-reactive protein An *acute phase protein released by the liver in response to acute injury, infection, or other inflammatory stimuli; a marker for acute inflammation and infection. So called because it was originally discovered as a protein that reacted with the C polysaccharide of *Pneumococcus* spp.

cream Fatty part of milk; 4% of ordinary milk, 4.8% of Channel Islands milk. Half cream is similar to 'top of the milk', 12% fat (30-mL portion supplies 45kcal (190kJ)), and cannot be whipped or frozen; single cream,

18% fat (60 kcal, 250 kJ), will not whip and cannot be frozen unless included in a frozen dish; extra thick single cream is also 18% fat, but has been homogenized to a thick spoonable consistency; whipping cream, 34% fat (110 kcal, 460 kJ), will whip to double volume; double cream, 48% fat (135 kcal, 570 kJ), will whip and can be frozen; clotted, Devonshire, and Cornish cream contains 55% fat (150 kcal, 630 kJ). Of this fat, two-thirds is *saturated and 30% mono-unsaturated.

Soured cream is made from single cream; *crème fraîche is soured double cream; 'extra thick double cream' is also 48% fat, but has been homogenized to be spoonable, and will not whip or freeze successfully.

In the USA, light cream is 20–25% fat; heavy cream, 40% fat.

cream, aerosol Cream sterilized and packaged in aerosol canisters with a propellant gas to expel it from the container, giving conveniently available whipped cream. Gelling agents and *stabilizers may also be added.

cream, artificial A non-dairy substitute for *cream, made from vegetable oils, with *stabilizers, *emulsifiers, and sometimes flavourings and colours added.

cream, bitty Cream on the surface of milk appears as particles of fat released from fat globules when the membrane is broken down by lecithinase from *Bacillus cereus*, the spores of which have resisted destruction during *pasteurization.

cream, plastic A term used for a cream containing as much fat as butter (80–83%) but as an emulsion of fat in water, while butter is water in fat. Prepared by intense centrifugal treatment of cream; crumbly, not greasy, in texture; used for preparation of cream cheese and whipped cream.

cream, sleepy Cream that will not churn to butter in the normal time.

cream, synthetic *See* CREAM, ARTIFICIAL.

creamer, non-dairy Milk substitute used in tea and coffee (coffee whitener or creamer) made with glucose, fat, and emulsifying salts. A stable product dry or as liquid. May be made with *casein, in which case it is not technically (or by US law) non-dairy.

creaming Beating together fat and sugar to give a fluffy mixture, for making cakes with a high fat content. The creaming quality of a fat is its ability to take up air during mixing.

cream of tartar Potassium hydrogen tartrate, used with *sodium bicarbonate as tartrate *baking powder because it acts more slowly than *tartaric acid and gives a more prolonged evolution of carbon dioxide. Also used to invert sugar (*see* SUGAR, INVERT) in making boiled sweets and as a *sugar doctor. *See also* TARTARIC ACID.

cream sherry *See* SHERRY.

creatine A derivative of the *amino acids glycine and arginine, important in muscle as a store of phosphate for resynthesis of *ATP during muscle contraction and work. Not a dietary essential, since it is synthesized in the body, but widely sold in supplements to improve athletic performance, with limited evidence of efficacy.

creatinine Formed non-enzymically from *creatine (the anhydride of creatine). Urinary excretion of creatinine is relatively constant from day to day, and reflects mainly the amount of muscle tissue in the body. The amounts of various compounds in urine are often expressed relative to creatinine.

crécy, à la Dish made or garnished with carrots.

creeping sickness *Osteomalacia in livestock due to phosphate deficiency.

crème 1. Term used for cream, custards, and desserts. Crème brûlée is a cream and egg custard with sugar sprinkled on top and caramelized under a hot grill; it is a traditional speciality of Trinity College, Cambridge, and also known as burnt cream or Cambridge cream. Crème caramel is topped with caramel. Crème Chantilly is whipped cream sweetened and flavoured with *vanilla. **2.** Various liqueurs, including crème de bananes (banana); crème de cacao (chocolate); crème de café (coffee); crème de *cassis (blackcurrants); crème de menthe (peppermint); crème de mûres (wild blackberries); crème de myrtilles (wild bilberries); crème de noix (green walnuts and honey); crème de violettes (violet petals).

crème fraîche French; double *cream that has been thickened and slightly soured by lactic fermentation.

cremet Milk curd made in the Dauphinois region of France.

créole The traditional cuisine of Louisiana and the French-speaking Caribbean. *See also* CRIOLLA.

créole, à la Usually a dish served on rice. In the case of savoury dishes, with a garnish or sauce of red peppers and tomatoes; for sweet dishes orange, banana, pineapple, or rum may be included.

créole sauce American; *espagnole sauce with onions, mushrooms, and peppers served with grilled steak.

crêpe French; a thin pancake. Crêpe suzette is made with orange-flavoured batter and served with a sauce flavoured with an orange liqueur.

crépinette French; small sausage-shaped cakes of minced meat wrapped in fat bacon or pig's *caul.

crescioni Italian; fried pastry squares filled with spinach chopped with shallots and raisins.

crespolini Italian; pancakes filled with spinach, cream cheese, and chicken liver, baked in *béchamel sauce.

cress Garden cress or pepper grass is an annual herbaceous plant, *Lepidium sativum*. Seedling leaves can be eaten raw with mustard seed leaves as mustard and cress, or salad rape (*Brassica napus* var. *napus*) and cress. *See also* WATERCRESS.

cress, American (land cress) *Barbarea verna*; the leaves have a peppery flavour. Unlike *watercress it can be grown in soil without running water.

creta praeparata Official British Pharmacopoeia name for prepared chalk, made by washing and drying naturally occurring calcium carbonate. The form in which calcium is added to flour (14oz per 280lb sack, or approximately 3g/kg).

cretinism Underactivity of the *thyroid gland (hypothyroidism) in children, resulting in poor growth, severe mental retardation and deafness. Commonly the result of a dietary deficiency of *iodine; may be congenital if the mother's iodine intake was severely inadequate during pregnancy. Hypothyroidism in adults is myxoedema.

Creutzfeldt–Jakob disease *See* CJD.

crevettes *See* SHRIMPS.

crianza Spanish; ageing (when talking about wines).

crimping 1. Slashing a large fish at intervals before cooking, to make it easier for the heat to penetrate the flesh. **2.** Trimming cucumber or similar foods in such a way that the slices appear to be 'deckled'. **3.** Decorating the double edge of a pie or tart or the edge of shortbread by pinching it at regular intervals with the fingers, giving a fluted effect.

criolla The traditional cuisine of the Spanish-speaking Caribbean and Latin America; derived from French, Spanish, African, and American cookery. *See also* CRÉOLE.

crispbread Name given to a flour and water wafer, originally Swedish and made from rye flour, but may be made from wheat flour. It has a much lower water content than bread, and some brands are richer in protein because of added wheat *gluten. Three pieces of crispbread (30g) provide up to 3g of dietary fibre and supply 100kcal (420kJ).

crisps *See* POTATO CRISPS.

cristal height A measure of leg length taken from the floor to the summit of the iliac crest. As a proportion of height it increases with age in children,

and a reduced rate of increase indicates undernutrition. *See also*
ANTHROPOMETRY.

CRN Council for Responsible Nutrition, representing the dietary
supplement industry.

(((●))) **SEE WEB LINKS**

● The CRN's homepage.

croaker Marine fish, species of the family *Sciaenidae*, also known as drum
or jewfish; also *Argyrosomas hololepidotus* (southern meagre or mulloway
croaker), *A. regius* (meagre croaker).

crocin *See* SAFFRON.

Crohn's disease (regional enteritis) A highly debilitating chronic
inflammation of the *gastro-intestinal tract, most commonly affecting the
distal ileum and colon. A lifelong disease with no cure, it usually affects young
people, with the highest incidence rate in the age group 15–24. Genetic
and immunologic factors seem to play an important role in the occurrence
of the disease. The aetiology is not known; similarities between *Johne's
disease in cattle and Crohn's disease has focused the attention on
Mycobacterium avium subspp. *paratuberculosis* as a putative causative agent.

croissant French; flaky crescent-shaped rolls traditionally served hot for
breakfast, made from a yeast dough with a high butter content. A 50-g
croissant contains 10g of fat of which 30% is saturated; supplies 180kcal
(750kJ). *See also* KIPFEL.

cropadeau Scottish; oatmeal dumpling with haddock liver in the middle.

croque-monsieur French; ham and cheese toasted *sandwich. When
topped with a fried egg it is called croque-madame.

croquette Finely chopped meat, fish, or vegetables, mixed with a rich
sauce or *panada, shaped into balls or small cylinders, coated in egg and
breadcrumbs and fried.

cross-sectional study Epidemiological study involving observation of
exposure (e.g. to food or nutrients) and disease at an individual level. *See also*
ECOLOGICAL STUDY.

croustade Small case of fried bread, pastry, or duchesse potato used
to serve a savoury mixture.

croûte, en Literally 'in a crust'; game, meat, or fish served in a pastry case
or surrounded by slices of bread.

croûtons Small diced or shaped pieces of fried bread used to garnish
soup and salads.

crowberry Small black, relatively tasteless, fruit of the temperate/sub-Arctic evergreen shrub *Empetrum nigrum*.

crowdie Scottish; soft cheese made from buttermilk or soured milk curd, also a dish of buttermilk and oatmeal.

crowdies *See* MILK, FERMENTED.

CRP *See* C-REACTIVE PROTEIN.

Cruciferae Family of plants with flowers with four equal petals; most vegetables in this family belong to the genus *Brassica*.

crudités French; raw vegetables, sliced or cut into small pieces or strips, served with a variety of dressings or dips, as an hors d'œuvre (French *crudité*, 'rawness').

cruller American; deep-fried bun made from baking powder dough. Similar to a *doughnut.

crumb Small particle of bread, cake, or biscuit, as broken off by rubbing.

crumble Flour, fat, and sugar (a rubbed-in plain cake mix) baked as a topping over fruit instead of pastry. For savoury crumble the sugar is omitted and cheese and seasoning are added.

crumb-softeners Derivatives of monoglycerides added to bread as emulsifiers to give a softer crumb and retard staling (*see* RETROGRADATION); also called polysorbates. *See also* FATS, SUPERGLYCINERATED.

crumpet *See* DOUGH CAKES.

crust The crisp outer part of a loaf of bread; also used for the sediment that develops as wines mature.

crustacea Zoological class of hard-shelled marine arthropods (*shellfish), including *crabs, *crayfish, *lobster, *prawns, *scampi, *shrimps.

cryodesiccation *See* FREEZE-DRYING.

cryoprotectant Compounds such as sucrose, sorbitol, starch hydrolysates, and glycerol that protect frozen foods during storage from the loss of quality due to the formation of large ice crystals.

cryptosporidiosis Enteric disease caused by infection with *Cryptosporidium parvum*. Commonly transmitted through ingestion of food or water contaminated with animal faeces. Characterized by severe diarrhoea, abdominal cramps, fever, and headache.

Cryptosporidium spp. Water and potentially food-borne protozoan (coccidian) parasites, causing acute self-limiting gastroenteritis, with influenza-like symptoms (*cryptosporidiosis).

cryptoxanthin Yellow hydroxylated *carotenoid in foods such as yellow maize and the fruit of *physalis, as well as egg yolks and butter. *Vitamin A active.

crystal boiling Chinese; food is heated in a pan of boiling water, then removed from the heat, and cooking is continued by the retained heat.

csipetke Hungarian; dumplings.

CT Computerized tomography; *see* CAT.

CTC machine A device consisting of two contra-rotating toothed rollers that rotate at different speeds and provide a crushing, tearing, and curling action; used in breaking up leaves of tea to form small particles.

cubbeh *See* KIBBEH.

cubeb Grey *pepper (*Piper cubeba*) native to South-East Asia; pungent camphor-like flavour. Also known as Java pepper, tailed cubebs, tailed pepper.

cucumber Fruit of *Cucumis sativus*, a member of the *gourd family, eaten as a salad vegetable; it is 95% water. A 50-g portion provides 0.3 g of dietary fibre and supplies 5 kcal (20 kJ). *See also* GHERKIN. The African horned cucumber is *kiwano.

cucumber tree *See* BILIMBI.

cucurbit A term used for vegetables of the family *Cucurbitaceae*, or *gourds.

CUG Catch-up growth.

cuisson Cooking juices from meat, poultry, or fish.

cuitlacoche *See* HUITLACOCHE.

cullis *See* COULIS.

cultigen A cultivated plant that, because it has been culitivated for many millennia, is not known to have a wild or uncultivated counterpart.

cultivar Horticultural term for a cultivated variety of plant that is distinct and is uniform and stable in its characteristics when propagated; *see also* STRAIN.

Cumberland sauce Sauce made from redcurrant jelly, orange, lemon, and port, served with ham, venison, and lamb.

cumin (cummin) Pungent herb, the crescent-shaped fruit of *Cuminum cyminum* (parsley family); used in curry powder and for flavouring cordials. Black cumin (zireh) is the seed of *Nigella sativa* (*see* KALONJI) and sweet cumin is *anise (*Pimpinella anisum*).

cumquat *See* KUMQUAT.

cup North American and Australian measure for ingredients in cooking; the standard American cup contains 250 mL (8 fl oz).

cupana *See* GUARANA.

cup cake Small individual cake or bun, typically baked in a paper case and topped with icing. Also known as fairy cake.

cupuaçu Fruit of the Amazonian tree *Theobroma grandiflorum*; it contains theacrine (1,3,7,9-tetramethyluric acid) instead of the *caffeine and theobromine found in *cocoa, and can be used to make a caffeine-free chocolate, called cupulate.

cupulate *Caffeine-free *chocolate substitute made using *cupuaçu (*Theobroma grandiflorum*) instead of cocoa (*T. cacao*).

curaçao A *liqueur made from the rind of Seville oranges and brandy or gin; 30% *alcohol, 30% sugar; 300 kcal (1260 kJ)/100 mL.

curculin Sweet-tasting protein from the fruit of the tropical shrub *Curculigo latifolia* (syn. *Molinera latifolia*); it also has flavour modifying activity, which, like *miraculin, causes acids to taste sweet.

curcumin *See* TURMERIC.

curd, fruit Gelled emulsions of sugar, fat or oil, egg, pectin, fruit or fruit juice (commonly lemon).

curdlan A gel-forming polysaccharide (a linear polymer of D-glucose linked $\beta 1 \rightarrow 3$) synthesized by *Agrobacterium* spp.

curds Clotted protein formed when fresh milk is treated with *rennet; the fluid left is *whey.

curing of meat A method of preservation by treating with *salt and *sodium nitrate (and nitrite), which serves to inhibit the growth of pathogenic organisms while salt-tolerant bacteria develop. During the *pickling process the nitrate is converted into nitrite, which combines with the muscle protein, myoglobin, to form the red-coloured nitrosomyoglobin which is characteristic of pickled meat products.

curly kale *See* KALE.

currants Fruit of *Ribes* spp.; white, red, and black. A 100-g portion of *red- or *whitecurrants is a rich *source of vitamin C, and of *blackcurrants an exceptionally rich source; supplies 25 kcal (105 kJ).

currants, dried Made by drying the small seedless black grapes grown in Greece and Australia; usually dried in bunches on the vine or after removal from the vine on supports. The name is derived from 'raisins of Corauntz'

(Corinth). A 25-g portion provides 1.8g of dietary fibre and is a good *source of copper; supplies 65 kcal (275 kJ). *See also* DRIED FRUIT; RAISINS; SULTANAS.

curry Name given by the British (it means 'sauce' in Tamil) to an Indian dish of stewed meat or vegetables. It is served with a pungent sauce whose components and pungency vary. *See also* CURRY POWDER; VINDALOO.

curry plant (curry leaves) An aromatic herb, *Murraya koenigii* (sweet nim), and leaves of the tree *Chalcas koenigii*; both have a curry-like flavour.

curry powder A mixture of turmeric with several spices, including cardamom, cinnamon, cloves, coriander, cumin, and fenugreek, made pungent with ginger, chilli, and pepper. A 10-g portion can contain 7.5–10 mg of iron, but much of this is probably the result of contamination during the milling of the spices.

curuba *See* PASSION FRUIT.

Cushing's syndrome Hypertension, hyperglycaemia and insulin resistance, abdominal obesity, and excessive growth of body and facial hair, due to excessive secretion of *corticosteroids.

cushion The cut of *lamb or *beef nearest the udder.

custard Sweet sauce, traditionally made by cooking milk with eggs; more commonly using custard powder (coloured and flavoured *cornflour) and milk. Confectioner's custard is a thick, sweet sauce based on *cornstarch, used as a filling for cakes and pastries. *See also* CARAMEL CREAM.

custard apple The fruit of tropical trees *Annona* spp. Cherimoya or true custard apple is *A. cherimola*, sugar apple or sweet sop is *A. squamosa*; atemoya is a hybrid of these. Sour sop or guanábana, *A. muricata*, has white fibrous flesh and is less sweet than the others; the fruit may weigh up to 4 kg (8 lb). The bullock's heart (*A. reticulata*) has buff-coloured flesh. Others include ilama (*A. diversifolia*), soncoya (*A. purpurea*), poshte (*A. scleroderma*), and the wild custard apple (*A. senegalensis*).

cutlassfish Marine fish, *Trichiurus* spp.

cutlet *Chop cut from the best end of neck of *lamb, *veal, or *pork.

cutting-and-folding *See* FOLDING-IN.

cutting-in Combining the fat with other ingredients in a mixture by cutting with a knife. *See also* FOLDING-IN.

cuttlefish Marine squid-like cephalopod with calcified internal shells; cuttlefish is *Sepia officinalis*, lesser cuttlefish is *Sepiola rondeleti*, and Ross cuttle is *Rossia macrosoma*.

CVA Cerebrovascular accident. *See* STROKE.

cyamopsis gum *See* GUAR GUM.

cyanocobalamin *See* VITAMIN B_{12}.

cyanogen(et)ic glycosides Organic compounds of cyanide found in a variety of plants (especially *cassava and bitter *almond kernels). Cyanhydrins with one or more sugars. Toxic through liberation of the cyanide when the food is crushed and the glycoside is exposed to degradative enzymes. *See also* AMYGDALIN; PHASEOLUNATIN.

cyclamate A non-nutritive *sweetener, sodium cyclohexyl-sulphamate, thirty times as sweet as sugar, used as the free acid or the calcium salt; it was synthesized in 1937 and introduced commercially in the USA in 1950. Unlike *saccharin, it is stable to heat and can therefore be used in cooking.

cyclitols Cyclic *sugar alcohols such as *inositol, quercitol, and tetritol.

cyclodextrins Enzymically modified starch derivatives (cyclic oligosaccharides of 6–8 glucose units) with a hydrophilic outer surface and a hydrophobic inner cavity, used for encapsulation of flavours and other ingredients in food manufacture, and to form stable oil-in-water emulsions. Can also be used to remove *cholesterol from dairy products and eggs.

cyclosporiasis Infection with the parasitic protozoa *Cyclospora* spp. (especially *C. cayetanensis*), characterized by watery diarrhoea, anorexia, weight loss, bloating, flatulence, abdominal cramps, nausea, vomiting, muscle aches, low-grade fever, and fatigue. Transmitted by ingestion of water or food contaminated with oocysts.

cyder *See* CIDER.

cystathionine Intermediate in the metabolic conversion of *homocysteine to *cysteine. Genetic defects of cystathionase lead to *cystathioninuria.

cystathioninuria A genetic disease affecting the metabolism of the *amino acid *methionine and its conversion to *cysteine, resulting in accumulation of *cystathionine. May result in mental retardation if untreated. Treatment is by feeding a diet low in methionine and supplemented with cysteine, or, in some cases, by administration of high intakes of *vitamin B_6 (about 100–500 times the normal requirement).

cysteine A non-essential *amino acid, but nutritionally important since it spares the essential amino acid *methionine. In addition to its role in protein synthesis, cysteine is important as the precursor of *taurine, in formation of *coenzyme A from the *vitamin *pantothenic acid, and in formation of the tripeptide *glutathione. It is used as a dough 'improver' in baking. *See also* CYSTINE.

cysticercosis Infection by the larval stage of *tapeworms caused by ingestion of their eggs in food and water contaminated by human faeces.

Normally the larval form develops in the animal host, and human beings are infected with the adult form by eating undercooked infected meat.

cystic fibrosis A genetic disease due to a failure of the normal transport of chloride ions across cell membranes. This results in abnormally viscous mucus, affecting especially the lungs and secretion of pancreatic juice, so impairing digestion.

cystine The dimer of *cysteine produced when its sulphydryl group (—SH) is oxidized forming a disulphide (—S—S—) bridge. Disulphide bridges are important in maintaining the structure of proteins, and also in the role of the tripeptide *glutathione as an *antioxidant.

cystinuria A genetic disease in which there is abnormally high excretion of the amino acids *cysteine and cystine, resulting in the formation of kidney stones. Treatment is by feeding a diet low in the sulphur amino acids methionine, cysteine, and cystine.

cytochalasins *Mycotoxins formed by *Aspergillus*, *Helminthosporium*, and *Phomopsis* spp. growing on cereal grains and cereal products.

cytochrome P$_{450}$ A family of *cytochromes which are involved in the *detoxication system of the body (*see* METABOLISM, PHASE I). They act on a wide variety of (potentially toxic) compounds, both endogenous metabolites and foreign compounds (*xenobiotics), rendering them more water-soluble and more readily conjugated for excretion in the urine.

cytochromes *Haem-containing proteins present in all living cells except the strictly *anaerobic bacteria. Some cytochromes react with oxygen directly; others are intermediates in the oxidation of reduced *coenzymes. Unlike *haemoglobin, the iron in the haem of cytochromes undergoes oxidation and reduction.

cytokines A variety of small proteins and glycoproteins that are involved in signalling for cell proliferation and differentiation, inflammation, and regulation of immune responses. Those secreted by lymphocytes are sometimes known as lymphokines, those from monocytes as monokines, and those from adipose tissue as adipokines or adipocytokines.

cytosine One of the *pyrimidine bases of *nucleic acids.

D-, L-, and DL- Prefixes to chemical names for compounds that have a centre of asymmetry in the molecule, and which can therefore have two forms (*isomers).

Most naturally occurring sugars have the D-conformation; apart from a few microbial proteins and some invertebrate peptides, the naturally occurring amino acids involved in protein synthesis have the L-configuration. Chemical synthesis yields a mixture of the D- and L-isomers (the racemic mixture), generally shown as DL-. *See also* R- AND S-.

d- and l- An obsolete way of indicating dextrorotatory and laevorotatory *optical activity, now replaced by (+) and (−).

dab Marine flatfish *Limanda limanda* that occurs in the north-east Atlantic. Yellowtail dab (or yellowtail flounder) is *L. ferruginea*, Pacific sand dab is *Citharichthys sordidus*, yellowfin sole is *L. aspera*.

dabberlocks Edible *seaweed, *Alaria esculenta*.

dadhi *See* MILK, FERMENTED.

dagé Indonesian; fermented *presscake from various oilseeds, legumes, or starch crops, soaked in water and left to undergo bacterial fermentation to form a glutinous mass bound by bacterial polysaccharides.

dahlin *See* INULIN.

daidzein An isoflavone (*see* FLAVONOIDS) that has *phytoestrogen activity. Occurs in foods mainly as the glycoside daidzin.

daidzin *See* DAIDZEIN.

daikon *Radish, large Japanese variety of *Raphanus sativus*. Often pickled in soy sauce, and an ingredient of *kimchi.

daily value Reference amounts of energy, fat, saturated fat, carbohydrate, fibre, sodium, potassium, and cholesterol, as well as protein, vitamins, and minerals, introduced for food labelling in the USA in 1994. The nutrient content of a food must be declared as a percentage of the daily value provided by a standard serving.

daiquiri Correctly a trade name for *rum; commonly used for a mixture of rum and fresh lime juice, or other fruit juice.

dal-chini *See* CASSIA.

DALYs Disability adjusted life years, defined by WHO as the sum of years of potential life lost due to premature mortality and the years of productive life lost due to chronic illness or disability.

damascene Original name for *damson.

damiana Leaf and stem of the shrub *Turnera diffusa* var. *aphrodisiaca* (syn. *T. microphylla*), used as a food flavouring, reputed to have aphrodisiac and antidepressant properties.

damson Small dark purple *plum (*Prunus damascena*); very acid and mainly used to make jam. An 80-g portion provides 2.4 g of dietary fibre and supplies 30 kcal (125 kJ). Introduced into Europe by Crusaders returning from Damascus (early 13th century).

dandelion The leaves of the weed *Taraxacum officinale* may be eaten as a salad or cooked. In France dandelion greens are known as *pissenlit* because of their diuretic action. A 50-g portion of the leaves is a good *source of vitamins C and A (4000 µg carotene); a source of calcium and iron; supplies 25 kcal (105 kJ). The root can be cooked as a vegetable, or may be roasted and used as a substitute for *coffee.

dariole Small narrow mould with sloping sides used to make individual sweets and savouries; originally the name of a small cake.

dark adaptation In the eye, the visual pigment rhodopsin is formed by reaction between *vitamin A aldehyde and the protein opsin, and is bleached by exposure to light, stimulating a nerve impulse (this is the basis of *vision). At an early stage of vitamin A deficiency it takes considerably longer than normal to adapt to seeing in dim light after exposure to bright light, because of the limitation of the amount of rhodopsin that can be reformed. Measuring the time taken to adapt to dim light (the dark adaptation time) thus provides a marker of early vitamin A deficiency. More severe vitamin A deficiency results in *night blindness, and eventually complete blindness.

darne French; thick cut from the middle of a fish.

DART Diet and Reinfarction Trial; intervention trial in the 1980s with diets high in $\omega 3$ polyunsaturated fatty acids (as oily fish or fish oil supplements) in men who had survived a myocardial infarction. The results showed a protective effect of $\omega 3$ polyunsaturated fatty acids.

DART-2 Diet and Angina Randomized Trial; intervention trial in the 1990s to test the hypothesis that diets high in $\omega 3$ polyunsaturated fatty acids (as oily fish or fish oil supplements) would reduce death from cardiac arrhythmias, in men with stable *angina. The results were negative, and there was increased mortality among those taking fish oil supplements.

dartois (d'Artois) Small light pastry, filled and flavoured (either sweet or savoury), served as an hors d'œuvre or dessert.

dasheen *See* TARO.

date Fruit of date palm, *Phoenix dactylifera*, known as far back as 3000 BC. There are three types: 'soft' (about 80% of the dry matter is invert sugars (*see* SUGAR, INVERT)); semi-dry (about 40% of the dry matter is invert sugars and 40% sucrose); and dry (20–40% of the dry matter is invert sugars and 40–60% is sucrose). A 100-g portion of fresh dates (five weighed with stones) is a good *source of vitamin C and supplies 230 kcal (960 kJ); 100 g of dried dates (three weighed with stones) provides 3 g of dietary fibre and supplies 270 kcal (1130 kJ).

Originally from Morocco, the medjool variety was reserved for royalty and dignitaries. In the 1920s, disease threatened the palms in Morocco, and immature trees were given to the USA, where they are now grown commercially.

date, Chinese *See* JUJUBE.

DATEM Diacetyl tartaric esters of mono- and diglycerides used as *emulsifiers to strengthen bread dough and delay staling of the bread.

date marking On packaged foods, 'Best before' is the date up until which the food will remain in optimum condition, i.e. will not be stale. Foods with a shelf life of up to 12 weeks are marked 'best before day, month, year'; foods with a longer shelf life are marked 'best before end of month, year'.

Perishable foods with a shelf life of less than a month may have a 'sell-by' date instead. 'Use by' date is given for foods that are microbiologically highly perishable and could become a danger to health; it is the date up to and including which the food may be safely used if stored properly.

Frozen foods and ice cream carry star markings which correspond to the star marking on freezers and frozen food compartments of refrigerators. Food in a 1-star rated compartment (−4°C, 25°F) will keep for one week; 2-star rated (−11°C, 12°F), 1 month; 3-star rated (−18°C, 0°F), 3 months. Corresponding times for ice cream are 1 day, 1 week, 1 month (after such times they are still fit to eat but the texture changes).

date plum *See* PERSIMMON.

daube, en Braised or stewed.

dauphinois (gratin dauphinois) Dish containing sliced potatoes, baked with milk and cream or cheese.

dawadawa African; fermented dried seeds of the African locust bean *Parkia biglobosa*, usually pressed into balls; various bacteria are involved in the 3–4 day fermentation. Also known as iru.

db/db mouse Genetically obese mouse that is also diabetic; the defect is lack of *leptin receptors.

DBPC Double-blind placebo controlled; in intervention trials, when neither the subjects nor the investigators know the allocation of active treatment or placebo.

DBPCFC Double-blind placebo controlled food challenge, for investigation of food intolerance and allergy; neither the subject nor the investigator knows whether a suspected allergen or a placebo is being tested.

DE 1. *See* DEXTROSE EQUIVALENT VALUE. **2.** Digestible *energy.

deamination Of *amino acids; oxidative or non-oxidative reactions that result in the amino group being released as ammonium, leaving the corresponding keto-acid (oxo-acid) that may be a substrate for *gluconeogenesis or ketogenesis. *See also* TRANSAMINATION.

debranning, abrasive *See* PEARLING.

debrining Removal of much of the salt used in *brining vegetables, to a level that will be acceptable in the final product. Also known as freshening.

decaffeinated *See* CAFFEINE; COFFEE.

decanting Careful pouring of wine from a bottle into a jug or decanter to leave any sediment in the bottle.

decimal reduction time (D value) Term used in sterilizing canned food, etc.; the duration of heat treatment required to reduce the number of microorganisms to one-tenth of the initial value, with the temperature shown as a subscript, e.g. D_{121} is time at 121 °C.

deficiency disease Disease associated with characteristic and identifiable symptoms, signs, or pathological findings, due to insufficient intake, defective absorption or utilization, or excessive metabolism of one or more nutrients. *See also* ANAEMIA; BERIBERI; PELLAGRA; PROTEIN-ENERGY MALNUTRITION; SCURVY.

DEFRA UK Department for Environment, Food and Rural Affairs.

(((⊕))) SEE WEB LINKS
• The DEFRA'S homepage.

defructum Roman; cooking wine that has been reduced to half its volume by boiling.

deglutition The act of swallowing.

degorger Procedure in which vegetables (e.g. aubergine, cucumber) are lightly salted after slicing, then drained, to remove any strong taste.

degumming agents Compounds, including hydrochloric and phosphoric acids, used in the refining of fats and oils to remove mucilaginous matter consisting of gum, resin, proteins.

dehydration Drying, normally used for factory-dried, as distinct from wind-dried, materials. *See also* DRYING.

dehydroascorbic acid Oxidized *vitamin C, which is readily reduced back to the active form in the body, and therefore has vitamin activity.

dehydrocanning A process in which 50% of the water is removed from a food before canning. The advantages are that the texture is retained by the partial dehydration and there is a saving in bulk and weight.

dehydrocholesterol The precursor for the synthesis of *vitamin D in the skin.

dehydrofreezing A process for preservation of fruits and vegetables by evaporation of 50–60% of the water before freezing. The texture and flavour are claimed to be superior to those resulting from either dehydration or freezing alone, and rehydration is more rapid than with dehydrated products.

Delaney amendment (Delaney clause) A provision in the US Food, Drug, and Cosmetic Act (1958) which states that no food additive shall be deemed safe after it is found to induce cancer when ingested by human beings or animals, at any dose level. Such an additive therefore must not be used.

deli North American abbreviation for *delicatessen.

delicatessen Ready-to-eat foods such as cooked meats, salami, pickled and smoked fish, salads, olives, etc. Also used as the name for the shop where such foods are sold. From the German *delikat Essen*, 'fine foods'.

demerara sugar *See* SUGAR.

demersal fish Those fish found living on or near the bottom of the sea, including cod, haddock, whiting, and halibut, also known as white fish. They contain little oil (1–4%).

denaturation A change in the structure of protein by heat, acid, alkali, or other agents which results in loss of solubility and *coagulation. It is normally irreversible. Denatured proteins lose their biological activity (e.g. as *enzymes), but not their nutritional value. Indeed, their digestibility is improved compared with the native structures, which are relatively resistant to enzymic hydrolysis. *See also* COAGULATION.

DENIS Deutsche Nicotinamide Intervention Study; trial of *nicotinamide supplements in people at high risk of developing type I *diabetes mellitus, concluded in 1998 with results showing no benefit of the supplements.

denominación de origen (DO) *See* WINE CLASSIFICATION, SPAIN.

denominazione di origine controllata (DOC) *See* WINE CLASSIFICATION, ITALY.

dental caries *See* CARIES.

dental fluorosis *See* FLUORIDE.

dental plaque *See* PLAQUE, DENTAL.

dent corn *See* MAIZE.

deodorization The removal of an undesirable flavour or odour. Fats are deodorized during refining by bubbling superheated steam through the hot oil under vacuum, when most of the flavoured substances are distilled off.

deoxynivalenol A *trichothecene *mycotoxin produced by *Fusarium* spp. growing on cereals.

deoxyribonucleic acid *See* DNA; NUCLEIC ACIDS.

depectinization The removal of *pectins from fruit juice to produce a clear, thin juice instead of a viscous, cloudy liquid, by the use of enzymes which hydrolyse pectins to smaller, soluble compounds.

Derby English hard cheese, often flavoured with sage.

Derbyshire neck *See* GOITRE.

dermatitis A lesion or inflammation of the skin; many nutritional deficiency diseases include more or less specific skin lesions (e.g. *ariboflavinosis, *kwashiorkor, *pellagra, *scurvy), but most cases of dermatitis are not associated with nutritional deficiency, and do not respond to nutritional supplements.

DES Dietary Energy Supply.

designer foods *See* FOODS, FUNCTIONAL.

desmosines The compounds that form the cross-linkage between chains of the *connective tissue protein *elastin.

desmutagen Compound acting directly on a *mutagen to decrease its mutagenicity.

desnutrin Intracellular *lipase in *adipose tissue, distinct from hormone-sensitive lipase, that makes a significant contribution to both basal fatty acid release from adipose tissue and also in fasting, when its activity increases; it is induced by glucocorticoid hormones. Catalyses hydrolysis of triacylglycerol to diacylglycerol, but has no action on diacylglycerol.

detoxication The metabolism of (potentially) toxic compounds to yield less toxic derivatives which are more soluble in water and can be excreted in the urine or *bile. A wide variety of 'foreign compounds' (i.e. compounds that are not normal metabolites in the body), sometimes referred to as *xenobiotics, and some hormones and other normal body metabolites, are metabolized in the same way. *See also* DIET, DETOX; METABOLISM, PHASE I; METABOLISM, PHASE II.

devilled Food grilled or fried after coating with condiments or breadcrumbs. *See also* BUTTER, DEVILLED.

devils on horseback Bacon wrapped around stoned prunes, skewered with a toothpick and then grilled. *See also* ANGELS ON HORSEBACK.

dewberry A hybrid fruit, a large variety of *blackberry; rather than climbing, the plant trails on the ground.

DEXA Dual Energy X-ray Absorptiometry, the standard method for assessing bone mineral density, and hence the risk or progression of *osteoporosis.

dexfenfluramine *Anorectic drug formerly used in the treatment of *obesity, withdrawn in 1995 because of reports of heart valve damage.

dextran A *polysaccharide composed of linked *fructose units, produced by the action of *Betacoccus arabinosus* and *Leuconostoc* spp. on *sugar. It can cause problems in sugar factories, but is clinically useful as a plasma extender for transfusion.

dextrin A mixture of soluble compounds formed by the partial breakdown of *starch by heat, acid, or enzymes (*amylases). Formed when bread is toasted, and nutritionally equivalent to starch.

dextrin, limit When a branched polysaccharide such as *glycogen or *amylopectin is hydrolysed enzymically, glucose units are removed one at a time until a branch point is reached. The hydrolysis then stops, leaving what is termed a limit dextrin; further hydrolysis requires a different enzyme.

dextronic acid *See* GLUCONIC ACID.

dextrose Alternative name for *glucose. Commercially the term 'glucose' is often used to mean corn syrup (a mixture of glucose with other sugars and *dextrins; *see* SYRUP, CORN) and pure glucose is called dextrose.

dextrose equivalent value (DE) A term used to indicate the degree of hydrolysis of starch into glucose in corn syrup (*see* SYRUP, CORN). It is the percentage of the total solids that have been converted to reducing sugars: the higher the DE, the more sugars and less dextrins are present.

Liquid glucoses are commercially available ranging from 2 DE to 65 DE. A complete acid hydrolysis converts all the starch into glucose but produces bitter degradation products. Glucose syrups above 55 DE are termed 'high conversion' (of starch); of 35–55 DE, regular conversion; below 20 DE the products of hydrolysis are maltins or maltodextrins.

DFD *See* MEAT, DFD

DFE *See* DIETARY FOLATE EQUIVALENTS.

DGO Declared geographical origin; *see* WINE CLASSIFICATION, BULGARIA.

DH UK Department of Health.

(((●))) SEE WEB LINKS
- The DH's homepage.

DHA Depending on context may be dehydro-ascorbic acid (*see* VITAMIN C) or docosahexaenoic acid, a long-chain polyunsaturated *fatty acid (C22:6 ω3); *see* OIL, FISH.

dhal Indian term for various split peas, e.g. the pigeon pea (*Cajanus indicus*) and khesari (*Lathyrus sativus*). Red or massur dhal is the lentil (*Lens esculenta*).

dhanyia *See* CORIANDER.

dhokla Indian; steamed cakes made from *chickpea or other *legume meal that has been soaked in water with buttermilk or curds for several hours, seasoned with ginger and chillies.

dhool The name given to leaves of *tea up to the stage of drying.

dhupa *See* COCOA BUTTER EQUIVALENTS.

diabesity Term coined to describe the development of type II *diabetes mellitus together with *obesity. *See also* METABOLIC SYNDROME.

diabetes There are two distinct conditions: diabetes insipidus and diabetes mellitus. The latter condition is more common, and is often referred to simply as diabetes or sugar diabetes. *Haemochromatosis is known as bronze diabetes.

diabetes insipidus A metabolic disorder characterized by extreme thirst, excessive consumption of liquids, and excessive urination, due to failure of secretion of the antidiuretic hormone.

diabetes mellitus A metabolic disorder involving impaired *glucose homeostasis due to either failure of secretion of the *hormone *insulin (insulin-dependent or type I diabetes) or impaired responses of tissues to insulin (non-insulin-dependent or type II diabetes). If untreated, the blood concentration of glucose rises to abnormally high levels (hyperglycaemia) after a meal and glucose is excreted in the urine (glucosuria). Prolonged hyperglycaemia may damage nerves, blood vessels, and kidneys, and lead to development of cataracts, so effective control of blood glucose levels is important.

Type I diabetes mellitus develops in childhood (juvenile-onset diabetes) and is due to failure to secrete *insulin, and hence is called insulin-dependent diabetes. Treatment is by injection of insulin (originally purified from beef or pig pancreas, now biosynthetic human insulin), together with restriction of the intake of sugars. *Ketoacidosis is a problem in poorly controlled type I diabetes mellitus.

Type II diabetes mellitus generally arises in middle age (maturity-onset diabetes) and is due to resistance of the tissues to insulin action; secretion of insulin by the pancreas may be normal or higher than normal. It is referred to as non-insulin-dependent diabetes and can sometimes be treated by restricting the consumption of sugars and reducing weight, or by the use of oral drugs which stimulate insulin secretion and/or enhance the insulin responsiveness of tissues (sulphonylureas and biguanides). It is also treated by injection of insulin to supplement secretion from the pancreas and overcome the resistance. Impairment of *glucose tolerance similar to that seen in diabetes mellitus sometimes occurs in late pregnancy, when it is known as gestational diabetes. Sometimes pregnancy is the stress that precipitates diabetes, but more commonly the condition resolves when the child is born.

diabetes, renal The excretion of glucose in the urine without undue elevation of the blood glucose concentration. It is due to a reduction of the renal threshold which allows the blood glucose to be excreted. *See also* GLUCOSE TOLERANCE.

diable, à la Highly spiced; *see* DEVILLED.

diacetyl The main flavour and aroma agent in butter, formed during the ripening stage by the organism *Streptococcus lactis cremoris*. It is added to margarine to enhance the flavour.

dialysis The process of separating small solutes from large ones by use of a semipermeable or selectively permeable membrane (*see* MEMBRANE, SEMI-PERMEABLE). *See also* MICROFILTRATION; ULTRAFILTRATION.

diarrhoea Frequent passage of loose watery stools, commonly the result of intestinal infection; more rarely as a result of adverse reaction to foods (*see* FOOD, ADVERSE REACTIONS) or *disaccharide intolerance. Severe diarrhoea in children can lead to dehydration and death; it is treated by feeding a solution of salt and sugar to replace fluid and electrolyte losses.

Osmotic diarrhoea is associated with retention of water in the bowel as a result of an accumulation of unabsorbed water-soluble compounds; especially associated with excessive intake of *sorbitol and *mannitol. Also occurs in *disaccharide intolerance.

diastase *See* AMYLASE.

diastatic activity of flour A measure of the ability of flour to produce maltose from its starch by the action of its own *amylase (diastase). The maltose is needed for yeast fermentation in bread making.

didronel Etidronate disodium (the disodium salt of (1-hydroxyethylidene) diphosphonic acid), used to enhance bone mineralization in women with post-menopausal *osteoporosis.

dieppoise, à la Sea fish garnished with crayfish tails and mussels, served with a white wine sauce.

diet Strictly, a diet is simply the pattern of foods eaten; the normal or habitual intake of food of an individual or population. Commonly used to mean a modified pattern of food consumption for some special purpose, e.g. a slimming, therapeutic, or low-salt diet, and sometimes named for the person who originated it.

dietary fibre *See* FIBRE, DIETARY.

dietary folate equivalents (DFE) Method for calculating *folic acid intake taking into account the lower availability of mixed folates in food compared with synthetic tetrahydrofolate used in food enrichment and supplements. 1 μg DFE = 1 μg food folate or 0.6 μg synthetic folate; total DFE = μg food folate + 1.7 times μg synthetic folate.

dietary guidelines Advice on consumption of foods or food components for which there is a related public health concern, expressed in relation to total diet, often in qualitative terms (more/less/increased/reduced), based on consensus research findings relating diet and health. *See also* EATWELL PLATE; FOOD PYRAMID; NUTRITIONAL GUIDELINES.

dietary pattern analysis Statistical technique, based on *cluster analysis, to analyse food consumption records in order to classify the results into predefined types of diet.

Dietary Reference Intakes (DRI) US term for *Dietary Reference Values. In addition to average requirement and *RDA, they include tolerable upper levels (UL) of intake from supplements.

Dietary Reference Values A set of standards of the amounts of each nutrient needed to maintain good health. People differ in the daily amounts of nutrients they need; for most nutrients the measured average requirement plus 20% (statistically 2 standard deviations) takes care of the needs of nearly everyone and in the UK this is termed *Reference Nutrient Intake, elsewhere known as *Recommended Daily Allowances or Intakes (RDA or RDI), Population Reference Intake (PRI), or Dietary Reference Intake (DRI). This figure is used to calculate the needs of large groups of people in institutional or community planning. Obviously some people require less than the average (up to 20% or 2 standard deviations less). This lower level is termed the Lower Reference Nutrient Intake, LRNI (also known as the Minimum Safe Intake, MSI, or Lower Threshold Intake). This is an intake at or below which it is unlikely that normal health could be maintained. If the diet of an individual indicates an intake of any nutrient at or below LRNI then detailed investigation of his/her nutritional status would be recommended.

For energy intake only a single Dietary Reference Value is used, the average requirement because there is potential harm (from *obesity) from ingesting too much. *See also* ENERGY BALANCE.

dietary supplements Legally defined in USA as products intended to supplement the diet that contain one or more of certain specified ingredients (vitamins, minerals, herbs or other botanicals, amino acids), and so increase intake.

diet, Atkins Weight reducing diet originally proposed in 1972; a ketogenic diet (*see* DIET, KETOGENIC) in which carbohydrate intake is severely limited but fat and protein are permitted in unlimited amounts. It is effective for weight loss, since ketonaemia reduces appetite, and protein appears to reduce appetite, but it runs counter to modern advice on a prudent diet.

diet, Beverley Hills Weight reducing diet based on the unfounded belief that enzymes from certain fruits are required to digest foods, and that undigested food in the *gastro-intestinal tract leads to obesity.

diet, bland A diet that is non-irritating, does not over-stimulate the digestive tract, and is soothing to the intestines; generally avoiding alcohol, strong tea or coffee, pickles, and spices.

diet, blood group Weight reducing diet based on the unfounded belief that blood groups evolved at different times, and the diet prevalent at the time a person's blood group evolved is optimum for health and weight control.

diet, cabbage soup Weight reducing diet that advocates consumption of large amounts of home-made cabbage soup with a very limited range of other foods; likely to be nutritionally inadequate in many respects.

diet, combining A system of eating based on the unfounded concept that carbohydrates and proteins should not be eaten at the same meal. It ignores the fact that almost all carbohydrate-rich foods also contain significant amounts of protein. In any case, in the absence of adequate carbohydrate, protein is oxidized as a metabolic fuel (i.e. to provide energy) and therefore not available for tissue building. Also called food combining or Hay diet.

diet, detox Weight reducing diet based on the unfounded belief that weight gain is the result of accumulation of toxins in the body, and a period of fasting and strict avoidance of such supposed toxins as caffeine and food additives is beneficial.

diet, diabetic For the control of *diabetes mellitus, designed not to cause a rapid increase in blood *glucose. Recommendation in the UK is 50–55% carbohydrates, with limits on sucrose, and 35% fat; in the USA, 55–60% carbohydrates.

diet, duvet Weight reducing regime based on the observation that sleep deprivation leads to increased secretion of *cortisol and *ghrelin (which stimulates appetite) and reduced secretion of *leptin (which reduces appetite). By extrapolation it is assumed that increasing the time spent sleeping will reduce appetite and food intake, and so permit weight loss.

diet, elemental *See* DIET, FORMULA.

diet, elimination For determination of foods causing allergy or intolerance, by eliminating groups of foods from the diet until signs and symptoms cease, then reintroducing individual foods (ideally as a blind test). *See* FOOD, ADVERSE REACTIONS.

dietetics The study or prescription of diets under special circumstances (e.g. metabolic or other illness) and for special physiological needs such as pregnancy, growth, weight reduction. *See also* DIETITIAN.

diet, exclusion *See* DIET, ELIMINATION.

diet, Feingold Exclusion of foods containing synthetic colours, flavours, and preservatives and limitation of intake of fruits and vegetables such as oranges, apricots, peaches, tomatoes, and cucumbers; intended to treat hyperactive children. There is little evidence either that these foods cause hyperactivity or that the exclusion diet is beneficial, although there is some evidence that some synthetic colours may affect behaviour and be a factor in hyperactivity.

diet, formula Composed of simple substances that do not require digestion, are readily absorbed, and leave a minimum residue in the intestine: glucose, amino acids or peptides, mono- and diacylglycerols rather than starch, proteins, and fats.

diet, F-plan Weight reducing diet based on consumption of foods high in dietary fibre, since they are likely to have greater satiety value and low energy content.

diethylpropion *Anorectic drug used in the treatment of *obesity, but not recommended.

diethylstilboestrol First synthetic non-steroidal oestrogen, used at one time for chemical castration of cockerels, banned in the USA and elsewhere in 1959. *See also* CAPON.

diet, Gerson Alternative dietary therapy for cancer based on the unfounded concept of stimulating the body to rid itself of cancer-related toxins. A very low-salt diet based largely on consumption of large amounts of organic fruits and vegetables as juice; coffee enemas are also recommended. There is no evidence that it is effective as a treatment for cancer.

diet, GI Weight reducing diet based on classification of foods by their *glycaemic index, on the basis that low glycaemic foods will have greater satiety value.

diet, Hay *See* DIET, COMBINING.

dietitian (dietician) According to the US Department of Labor, Dictionary of Occupational Titles, one who applies the principles of nutrition to the feeding of individuals and groups; plans menus and special diets; supervises the preparation and serving of meals; and instructs in the principles of nutrition as applied to selection of foods. In the UK the training and state registration of dietitians (i.e. legal permission to practise) is controlled by law. *See also* NUTRITIONIST.

diet, ketogenic A diet poor in carbohydrate (20–30 g) and rich in fat; causes accumulation of *ketone bodies in tissue. *See also* DIET, ATKINS.

diet, liquid Diet consisting of foods that can be served as liquids or strained purées, prescribed in acute inflammation of the *gastro-intestinal tract and for patients unable to consume normal foods, especially after surgery.

diet, macrobiotic A system of eating associated with Zen Buddhism; consists of several stages, finally reaching Diet 7 which is restricted to cereals. Cases of severe malnutrition have been reported on this diet. It involves the Chinese concept of *yin* (female) and *yang* (male) whereby foods, and even different vitamins (indeed, everything in life) are predominantly one or the other and must be balanced.

diet, oligoallergenic Comprised of very few foods or an elemental diet (*see* DIET, ELEMENTAL) used to diagnose whether particular symptoms are the result of allergic response to food.

diet, pH Weight reducing diet based on balancing intake of *acid-forming and base-forming foods, with little scientific basis.

diet, polymeric For *enteral feeding, a liquid diet that contains intact proteins and polysaccharides, as opposed to an elemental diet (*see* DIET, ELEMENTAL), which contains amino acids rather than intact proteins.

diet, 'salt-free' Diets low in *sodium, for the treatment of *hypertension and other conditions. Most of the sodium of the diet is consumed as sodium chloride or *salt, and hence such diets are referred to as salt-restricted or low-salt diets, or sometimes 'salt-free', to emphasize that no salt is added to foods in preparation or at the table. Since foods naturally contain sodium chloride, a truly salt-free diet is not possible. It is the sodium and not the chloride that is important.

Foods low in salt (0–20 mg/100 g) include sugar, flour, fruit, green vegetables, macaroni, and nuts. Medium salt foods (50–100 mg/100 g) include chicken, fish, eggs, meat, and milk. High salt foods (500–2000 mg/100 g) include corned beef, bread, ham, bacon, kippers, sausages, and cheese.

diet, South Beach Weight reducing diet based on high protein and low carbohydrate intake. *See also* DIET, ATKINS.

diet, therapeutic Any diet specially formulated to treat disease or a metabolic disorder.

diet, X-plan Weight reducing diet based on detailed daily menus and a programme of exercise.

diet, zone Weight reducing diet based on the unfounded belief that each meal should comprise a fixed proportion of macronutrients: 40% carbohydrate, 30% fat, and 30% protein.

differential cell count *See* LEUCOCYTES.

digester *See* AUTOCLAVE.

digestibility The proportion of a foodstuff absorbed from the digestive tract into the bloodstream, normally 90–95%. It is measured as the difference between intake and faecal output, with allowance being made for that part of the faeces that is not derived from undigested food residues (shed cells of the intestinal tract, bacteria, residues of digestive juices). Digestibility measured in this way is referred to as 'true digestibility', as distinct from the approximate measure, 'apparent digestibility', which is simply the difference between intake and output.

digestif French term for a *liqueur or *spirit drunk after dinner, supposedly to aid digestion.

digestion The breakdown of a complex compound into its constituent parts, achieved either chemically or enzymically. Most frequently refers to the digestion of food, which means breakdown by digestive enzymes of *proteins to *amino acids, *starch to *glucose, *fats to *glycerol and *fatty acids. These breakdown products are then absorbed into the bloodstream. *See also* GASTRO-INTESTINAL TRACT.

digestive juices The secretions of the *gastro-intestinal tract which are involved in the *digestion of foods: *bile, *gastric secretion, *intestinal juice, *pancreatic juice, *saliva.

digestive tract *See* GASTRO-INTESTINAL TRACT.

diglycerides (diacylglycerols) *Glycerol esterified with two fatty acids; an intermediate in the digestion of *triacylglycerols, and used as *emulsifying agents in food manufacture.

dika nut *See* MANGO, AFRICAN.

dill The aromatic herb *Anethum graveolens*, a member of the parsley family. The dried ripe fruit (dill seeds) are used in pickles, sauces, etc. The leaves are used, fresh, dried, or frozen (dill weed) to flavour fish and other dishes. Dill pepper is a mixture of dill seed, dill weed, and ground black *pepper, used as a condiment.

dimethylpolysiloxane Antifoaming agent used in fats, oils, and other foods. Also called methyl polysilicone or methyl silicone.

dim sum (dim sim) Chinese; steamed dumplings and other delicacies.

diner American; originally a cheap roadside restaurant built to resemble a railway carriage; the first diners were converted from discarded horse-drawn trolleys in 1897, when they were replaced by electric trolleys.

dipeptide A *peptide consisting of two *amino acids.

diphenyl Or biphenyl, used for the treatment of fruit after harvesting to prevent the growth of mould. For making *marmalade, *citrus fruits that have not been treated with diphenyl are available.

dipsesis (dipsosis) Extreme thirst, a craving for abnormal kinds of drinks.

dipsetic Tending to produce thirst.

dipsogen A thirst-provoking agent.

dipsomania A morbid craving for alcoholic drinks.

direct extract *See* MEAT EXTRACT.

disaccharidases Enzymes that hydrolyse *disaccharides to their constituent monosaccharides in the intestinal mucosa: sucrase (also known as invertase) acts on sucrose and isomaltose, lactase on lactose, maltase on maltose, and trehalase on trehalose.

disaccharide Sugars composed of two monosaccharide units; the nutritionally important disaccharides are *sucrose, *lactose, and *maltose. *See* CARBOHYDRATE.

disaccharide intolerance Impaired ability to digest lactose, maltose, or sucrose, due to lack of lactase, maltase, or sucrase in the small intestinal mucosa. The undigested sugars remain in the intestinal contents, and are fermented by bacteria in the large intestine, resulting in painful, explosive, watery *diarrhoea. Treatment is by omitting the offending sugar from the diet.

Lack of all three enzymes is generally caused by intestinal infections, and the enzymes gradually recover after the infection has been cured. Lack of just one of the enzymes, and hence intolerance of just one of the disaccharides, is normally an inherited condition. Sucrose intolerance due to genetic lack of sucrase is common among the Inuit.

Lactose intolerance due to loss of lactase is normal in most ethnic groups after puberty; it is only among people of northern ethnic origin that lactase persists into adult life.

diseases of affluence Chronic non-communicable diseases (*hypertension, *diabetes mellitus, *atherosclerosis, coronary heart disease and other cardiovascular diseases, and *cancer) associated with over-nutrition and obesity. *See also* NUTRITION TRANSITION.

disodium guanylate, disodium inosinate Sodium salts of the *purines, guanylic and inosinic acids, used as *flavour enhancers, frequently together with *monosodium glutamate.

dispersed phase Droplets in an *emulsion.

distillers' dried solubles *See* SPENT WASH.

DIT *See* THERMOGENESIS, DIET-INDUCED.

dittany The herb *Origanum dictamnus*, also known as dittany of Crete. Used as a substitute for *oregano or *marjoram, and the flowers are used to make a herb tea.

diuresis Increased formation and excretion of urine; it occurs in diseases such as *diabetes, and also in response to *diuretics.

diuretics Compounds that increase the production and excretion of urine. They may be either compounds that occur naturally in foods (including *caffeine and *alcohol), or drugs used medically to reduce the volume of body fluid (e.g. in the treatment of *hypertension and *oedema).

diverticular disease Diverticulosis is the presence of pouch-like hernias (diverticula) through the muscle layer of the colon, associated with a low intake of dietary fibre (*see* FIBRE, DIETARY) and high intestinal pressure due to straining during defecation. Faecal matter can be trapped in these diverticula, causing them to become inflamed, causing pain and diarrhoea, the condition of diverticulitis. *See also* GASTRO-INTESTINAL TRACT.

diverticulitis, diverticulosis *See* DIVERTICULAR DISEASE.

djenkolic acid *See* BEAN, DJENKOL.

DNA Deoxyribonucleic acid, the genetic material in the nuclei of all cells. It is a polymer of deoxyribonucleotides; the purine bases adenine and guanine, and the pyrimidine bases thymidine and cytidine, linked to deoxyribose phosphate. The sugar-phosphates form a double-stranded helix, with the bases paired internally. *See also* NUCLEIC ACIDS.

DNA cloning The transfer of a fragment of *DNA containing one or more *genes from an organism into a self-replicating genetic element such as a bacterial plasmid.

DO Denominación de origen; *see* WINE CLASSIFICATION, SPAIN.

doan choy Chinese; brine-pickled cabbage.

DOC Denominazione di origine controllata; *see* WINE CLASSIFICATION, ITALY.

doce Portuguese; sweet wines.

DOCG Denominazione di origine controllata e garantita; *see* WINE CLASSIFICATION, ITALY.

dockage Name given to foreign material in wheat which can be removed readily by a simple cleaning procedure.

docosahexaenoic acid A long-chain polyunsaturated *fatty acid (C22:6 ω3); *see* OIL, FISH.

docosanoids Long-chain polyunsaturated *fatty acids with 22 carbon atoms.

docosapentaenoic acid A long-chain polyunsaturated *fatty acid (C22:5 ω3 or ω6); *see* OIL, FISH.

doenjang Korean; fermented *soya paste, also known as doenzang or tenjan.

dogfish A cartilaginous *fish, *Galeorhinus* spp., *Scilliorinus* spp., *Mustelus* spp., *Squalis acanthias*, and *Galeus melastomas*, small sharks; sometimes called rock salmon, rock eel, flake, huss, or rogg.

doh peeazah (dopiaza) Indian dish; a variant of *korma. The name means 'double onion'.

dolce Italian; sweet wines.

dolma (dolmades, dolmathes) Greek, Turkish; stuffed vegetables, especially vine leaves stuffed with rice and minced meat.

dolomite Calcium magnesium carbonate.

dolphinfish *See* MAHIMAHI.

döner kebab Middle Eastern, Greek, and Turkish (*showarma* in Arabic); slices of lamb, highly flavoured with herbs and spices, wound around a revolving spit, cooked in front of a vertical *charcoal (or sometimes gas) fire. *See also* KEBAB.

dongchimi Korean; sauce prepared from fermented radish root.

dong quai *See* ANGELICA.

doppelkorn *See* KORN.

dormers Victorian; chopped cooked lamb mixed with rice and suet, rolled into sausage shapes, coated in egg and breadcrumbs and fried.

dormouse Squirrel-tailed, or edible dormouse, *Glis glis*; a Roman delicacy, dormice were kept in captivity and fed on acorns and chestnuts; then served stuffed with minced pork and dormouse meat.

dose-response assessment The relationship between the magnitude of exposure to a (potential) toxin and the probability of adverse effects.

dosha (dosa) Indian; pancakes made with rice and lentil flour; the dough is left to undergo bacterial fermentation before cooking.

Double Gloucester English hard *cheese.

double labelled water *See* WATER, DOUBLE LABELLED.

dough Mixture of flour and liquid (water or milk) used to make bread and pastry. May contain yeast or baking powder as leavening agent.

dough cakes A general term to include crumpets, muffins, and pikelets, all made from batter raised with yeast and baked on a hotplate or griddle (hence sometimes known as griddle cakes). Crumpets have sodium bicarbonate added to the batter; muffins are thick and well aerated, less tough than crumpets; pikelets are made from thinned crumpet batter.

doughnut Cake made from fried, sweetened dough leavened with yeast or baking powder; may be filled with jam or cream. The first ring doughnuts were introduced by baker's apprentice Hanson Crockett Gregory in Camden, Maine (1847), by knocking out the undercooked centre of filled doughnuts. The first machine for cutting doughnuts was patented by John Blundell in Thomaston, Maine, 1872.

dough strengtheners Compounds used to modify starch and gluten, to produce a more stable *dough.

Douglas bag An inflatable bag for collecting expired air to measure the consumption of oxygen and production of carbon dioxide, for the measurement of energy expenditure by indirect *calorimetry. *See also* SPIROMETER.

dracunculiasis *See* GUINEA WORM DISEASE.

dragée French; whole nuts, usually almonds, with hard sugar or sugared chocolate coating. Silver dragées are coated with silver leaf.

dragon fruit *See* PITAHAYA.

dragon's eyes *See* LONGAN.

Drambuie Scottish liqueur based on malt whisky, sweetened with heather honey, and flavoured with herbs.

dredging Sprinkling food with flour, sugar, etc. Fish and meat are often dredged with flour before frying, while cakes and biscuits are dredged with sugar as a decoration.

dressing food To prepare food for cooking or serving in such a way that it looks as attractive as possible. Sometimes denotes a special method of preparation, as in dressed *crab. *See also* SALAD DRESSING.

dried solubles, distiller's *See* SPENT WASH.

dripping Unbleached and untreated fat from the fatty tissues or bones of sheep or oxen. Also the rendered fat that drips from meat or poultry as it is roasted.

driselase A mixture of enzymes (*cellulases, xylanases, and laminarinases) produced by *Basidiomycetes* spp., used to degrade plant cell walls.

drisheen Irish; blood pudding; *see* BLACK PUDDING.

drop scones *See* SCONES, DROP.

dropsy *See* OEDEMA.

drug–nutrient interactions Deficiency caused by effects of drugs on the absorption or metabolism of vitamins or minerals. Sometimes this is the mode of action of the drug in treating the disease; in other cases it is an undesirable side-effect.

drumstick The thigh of chicken or other poultry.

drupe Botanical term for a fleshy fruit with a single stone enclosing the seed that does not split along defined lines to liberate the seed, e.g. apricot, cherry, date, mango, olive, peach, plum.

DRV *See* DIETARY REFERENCE VALUES; REFERENCE INTAKES.

dry ice Solid carbon dioxide, which has a temperature of −79°C; used to refrigerate foodstuffs in transit and for carbonation of liquids. It sublimes from the solid to a gas without melting.

drying Method of preserving food by removing most of the water, so as to prevent bacterial and mould growth. Freeze-drying is evaporation of the water from a frozen food, so retaining texture and nutrients. Also called dehydration.

drying agents Hygroscopic compounds used to absorb moisture and maintain a low humidity environment.

drying, freeze Also known as lyophilization. A method of drying in which the material is frozen and subjected to high vacuum. The ice sublimes off as water vapour without melting.

Freeze-dried food is very porous, since it occupies the same volume as the original, and so rehydrates rapidly. There is less loss of flavour and texture than with most other methods of drying. Controlled heat may be applied to the process without melting the frozen material; this is accelerated freeze drying.

drying, osmotic Partial dehydration of fruit by use of a concentrated sugar solution to extract water.

drying, roller The material to be dried is spread over the surface of internally heated rollers and drying is complete within a few seconds. The rollers rotate against a knife that scrapes off the dried film as soon as it forms. There is little damage to nutrients by this method; for example, roller-dried milk is not scorched, but there is more loss of vitamins B_1 and C than in spray drying (*see* DRYING, SPRAY).

drying, spray The material to be dried is sprayed as a fine mist into a hot-air chamber and falls to the bottom as dry powder. The period of heating is very brief and nutritional and functional damage are avoided. Dried powder consists of hollow particles of low density; widely applied to many foods (e.g. milk) and pharmaceuticals.

dry weight basis (dwb) The composition of a wet food based on the mass of dry solids it contains.

dsaoudan *See* EGGS, CHINESE.

DSHEA USA; Dietary Supplement Health and Education Act, 1994.

DSM-IV Diagnostic and Statistical Manual of Mental Disorders, published by the American Psychiatric Association, categorizing psychiatric disorders and diagnostic criteria. Of nutritional interest for the definitions of *eating disorders such as *anorexia nervosa and *bulimia.

DTH Delayed type hypersensitivity; cell-mediated immune responses to allergens. *See* FOOD, ADVERSE REACTIONS.

dual isotopically labelled water *See* WATER, DOUBLE LABELLED.

dubarry, à la A rich cauliflower soup or a cauliflower garnish.

Dublin Bay prawn Scampi or Norway lobster; a shellfish, *Nephrops norvegicus*; *see* LOBSTER.

duck Wild duck or wildfowl; *Anas* spp.; mallard is *A. platyrhynchos*. A 150-g portion is a rich *source of protein, vitamins B_1, B_2, B_{12}, niacin, and copper; a good source of iron and zinc; a source of vitamin B_6; contains 15g of fat, of which one-third is saturated; supplies 200kcal (840kJ).

ductless glands *See* ENDOCRINE GLANDS.

dugléré Method of cooking white fish in white wine and water, adding cream and a velouté sauce.

dukkah Egyptian; a blend of roasted nuts seasoned with spices.

dulce Spanish; sweet wines.

dulce de leche Latin American; confectionery made by condensing milk and sugar to a syrup that is then caramelized by heating and flavoured with vanilla.

dulcin A synthetic material (*p*-phenetylurea or *p*-phenetolcarbamide, discovered in 1883) which is 250 times as sweet as sugar but is not permitted in foods. Also called sucrol and valzin.

dulcitol (dulcite) A six-carbon *sugar alcohol which occurs in some plants and is formed by the reduction of galactose; also known as melampyrin, or galactitol.

dulse Edible purplish-brown *seaweeds, *Rhodymenia palmata* and *Dilsea carnosa*, used in soups and jellies.

dumned Indian term for *steamed. *See also* BHOONA.

dumping syndrome Rapid emptying of the stomach contents into the small intestine; mainly a problem after gastric surgery or removal of the *gall bladder.

dumpling A ball of *dough, usually boiled, but may be baked. Generally served with soups and stews. *See also* DIM SUM.

dun Brown discoloration in salted fish caused by mould growth.

***Dunaliella bardawil* (*D. salina*)** A red marine alga discovered in 1980 in Israel, which is extremely rich in β-carotene, containing 100 times more than most other natural sources.

Dundee cake Rich fruit cake decorated with split almonds.

dunlop Scottish *Cheddar-type cheese.

dunst Very fine *semolina (starch from the endosperm of the wheat grain) approaching the fineness of flour. Also called break middlings (not to be confused with middlings, which is branny *offal).

duodenal ulcer *See* ULCER.

duodenum First part of the small intestine, between the stomach and the jejunum; the major site of *digestion. Pancreatic juice and bile are secreted into the duodenum. So called because it is about twelve fingerbreadths in length. *See also* GASTRO-INTESTINAL TRACT.

duplicate diet method In dietary and nutritional surveys; subjects weigh and put aside a duplicate portion of all the foods they have eaten, for chemical analysis.

durian Fruit of the tree *Durio zibethinus*, grown in Malaysia and Indonesia. Each fruit weighs 2–3kg and has a soft, cream-coloured pulp, with a smell considered disgusting by the uninitiated. A more or less odourless variety has been developed in Thailand by cross-breeding; it remains to be seen whether it will be acceptable to consumers. A 100-g portion is a rich *source of vitamin C; a good source of vitamin B_1; a source of vitamin B_2; supplies 125kcal (500kJ).

durum wheat A hard type of *wheat, *Triticum durum* (most bread wheats are *Triticum vulgare*); mainly used for the production of *semolina to make *pasta.

Dutching *See* COCOA, DUTCH.

duxelles Mince of mushrooms with chopped shallot and herbs, used to flavour stuffing, soups, and sauces.

D value *See* DECIMAL REDUCTION TIME.

dwb *See* DRY WEIGHT BASIS.

dynorphin A *neuropeptide, one of the endogenous opioids; among other actions it stimulates feeding.

dysgeusia Distortion of the sense of taste—a common side-effect of some drugs.

dyspepsia Any pain or discomfort associated with eating. Dyspepsia may be a symptom of gastritis, peptic ulcer, gall-bladder disease, *hiatus hernia, etc.; if there is no structural change in the intestinal tract, it is called 'functional dyspepsia'. Treatment includes a bland diet (*see* DIET, BLAND). *See also* INDIGESTION.

dysphagia Difficulty in swallowing, commonly associated with disorders of the *oesophagus. Inability to swallow is aphagia.

E- *See* E-Numbers.

e On food labels, before the weight or volume, to indicate that the weight or volume of the package may vary slightly, but this is an accurate average.

EAA index Essential amino acid index, an index of *protein quality.

EAR Estimated average requirement; the mean observed requirement of a nutrient to meet the chosen criterion of adequacy in depletion/repletion studies. Used as the basis for setting *reference intakes, at EAR + 2 × SD.

earth almond *See* TIGER NUT.

earth-nut The small edible tuber of the umbellifer *Conopodium denudatum*, or *C. majus*, also called pignut or fairy potato. Also another name for the *peanut.

Easter soup (Mayieritsa) Greek soup traditionally prepared to celebrate the end of the Lenten fast, made from the pluck (i.e. tripe, intestines, heart, and liver) and feet of a lamb.

eating disorders A spectrum of disturbed eating patterns, including *anorexia nervosa, *bulimia nervosa, and *binge-eating disorder, which involve an over-concern about body weight and size. The average prevalence rate for young females is 0.3% for anorexia nervosa and 1% for bulimia nervosa. Some evidence from family and twin studies for a genetic predisposition.

eating, phases of Three phases of control of gastric secretion and motility can be distinguished: *cephalic, *gastric, and *intestinal.

eatwell plate A way of showing a healthy diet graphically, by grouping foods and showing the relative amounts of each group that should be eaten each day, based on *nutritional recommendations, as segments of the plate. Developed in UK by the Food Standards Agency to replace the balanced plate. *See also* FOOD PYRAMID.

Use the eatwell plate to help you get the balance right. It shows how much of what you eat should come from each food group.

Fruit and vegetables

Bread, rice, potatoes, pasta and other starchy foods

Meat, fish, eggs, beans and other non-dairy sources of protein

Foods and drinks high in fat and/or sugar

Milk and dairy foods

Eatwell plate.

eau-de-vie Spirit distilled from fermented grape juice (sometimes other fruit juices); may be flavoured with fruits, etc. *See also* MARC.

eau-de-vie de miel Honey brandy made by distilling mead (which, in turn, is made by fermenting honey).

Eccles cake Pastry filled with dried fruit, melted butter, and sugar. Named originally for the town of Eccles in Greater Manchester.

ECF Extra-cellular fluid.

echinacea Herbal preparations of the North American cone flowers (*Echinacea angustifolia*, *E. purpurea*, *E. pullidu*), a traditional native American remedy for colds and other infections. Marketed as an immunostimulant, with some evidence of efficacy.

éclair Small finger-shaped cake prepared from choux pastry (*see* PASTRY, CHOUX), filled with cream or confectioner's *custard, coated with chocolate or coffee-flavoured icing.

E. coli *See* ESCHERICHIA COLI.

ecological study Epidemiological study involving observation of exposure (e.g. to food or nutrients) and disease at a population level. *See also* CROSS-SECTIONAL STUDY.

écrevisse *See* CRAYFISH.

ectomorph Description given to a tall, thin person, possibly with underdeveloped muscles. *See also* ENDOMORPH; MESOMORPH.

Edam Pale yellow, semi-hard Dutch *cheese usually round in shape with red wax coating (black for well-matured Edam). A 30-g portion is a rich *source of vitamin B_{12}, a source of protein and niacin, contains 8g of fat, 230mg of calcium and 300mg of sodium; supplies 100kcal (415kJ).

eddo *See* TARO.

edema *See* OEDEMA.

edentulous Without teeth.

edetate *See* EDTA.

edgebone Incorrect name for the *aitchbone.

edible portion Used in food composition tables to indicate that the data refer to the part of the food that is usually eaten—e.g. excluding skin or pips of fruit and vegetables, bones in meat and fish.

Edifas Trade name for *cellulose derivatives: Edifas A is methyl ethyl cellulose; Edifas B, sodium carboxymethylcellulose.

EDNOS *Eating disorder not otherwise specified. The subject has an eating disorder that is clinically significant, but does not fulfil the criteria for *anorexia nervosa or *bulimia nervosa.

Edosol Trade name for a low-sodium milk substitute, containing 43mg of sodium/100g, compared with dried milk at 400mg.

EDTA Ethylene diamine tetra-acetic acid, a compound that forms stable chemical complexes with metal ions (i.e. a *chelating agent). Also called Versene, sequestrol, and sequestrene. It can be used both to remove metal ions from a solution (or at least to remove them from activity) and also to add metal ions, for example in plant fertilizers.

eel A long thin fish, *Anguilla* spp.; the European eel is *A. anguilla*, the conger eel is *Conger myriaster*. Eels live in rivers but go to sea to breed; to date, although elvers (young eels) have been caught and raised in tanks, it has not been possible to breed them in captivity. A 100-g portion is a rich *source of protein, niacin, and vitamins A, D, and B_{12}; a good source of niacin and vitamin B_2; a source of vitamins B_1 and B_6; contains 20g of fat and supplies 300kcal (1260kJ).

EFA Essential fatty acids; *see* FATTY ACIDS, ESSENTIAL.

Efamast Trade name for a preparation of *γ-linolenic acid, as a dietary supplement.

EFSA European Food Safety Authority.

((⊕)) SEE WEB LINKS

• The EFSA's homepage.

EGF Epidermal growth factor.

egg In the EU, weight ranges are used for hens' eggs (weighed with shell which is about 10% of the total): very large eggs 73g or over, large 63–73g, medium 53–63g, and small 53g or less. In the USA average weights are used: jumbo 70.0g, extra large 63.8g, large 56.7g, medium 49.6g, small 42.5g, and peewee 35.4g. Ducks' eggs weigh about 85g.

An average portion of two eggs is a rich *source of vitamins D and B_{12}; a good source of protein, niacin, and vitamins A and B_2; a source of zinc; contains 170mg of sodium; 13g of fat, of which 35% is saturated and 50% mono-unsaturated; supplies 175kcal (735kJ). The egg-white is 60% of the whole and the yolk 30%.

egg albumin *See* EGG PROTEINS; EGG-WHITE.

egg nog Hot, sweetened milk with an egg and brandy or sherry mixed in.

egg-plant *See* AUBERGINE.

egg proteins What is generally referred to as egg protein is a mixture of individual proteins, including ovalbumin, ovomucoid, ovoglobulin, conalbumin, vitellin, and vitellenin. *Egg-white contains 10.9% protein, mostly ovalbumin; yolk contains 16% protein, mainly two phosphoproteins, vitellin and vitellenin. *See also* AVIDIN.

eggs, Chinese Known as pidan, houeidan, and dsaoudan, depending on variations in the method of preparation. Prepared by covering fresh duck eggs with a mixture of caustic soda, burnt straw ash, and slaked lime, then storing for several months (they are sometimes referred to as 'hundred-year-old eggs'). The white and yolk coagulate and become discoloured, with partial decomposition of the protein and phospholipids.

eggs flamenca Spanish, Andalusian; dish of eggs baked on a bed of fried potato, onion, peppers, chorizo, etc.

egg, Scotch Hard-boiled eggs cased in seasoned sausage meat and breadcrumbs, fried, and served cold.

egg substitute Name formerly used for golden raising powder, a type of *baking powder.

egg-white The white of an egg is in three layers: an outer layer of thin white, a layer of thick white, richer in ovomucin, and an inner layer of thin white surrounding the yolk. The ratio of thick to thin white varies, depending on the individual hen. A higher proportion of thick white is desirable for frying and poaching, since it helps the egg to coagulate into a small firm mass instead of spreading; thin white produces a larger volume of froth when beaten than does thick. *See also* ALBUMIN INDEX; EGG PROTEINS.

egg-white injury *See* AVIDIN; BIOTIN.

EGRac test *See* ENZYME ACTIVATION ASSAYS; GLUTATHIONE REDUCTASE.

egusi *See* WATERMELON.

EH *See* EQUILIBRIUM HUMIDITY.

eicosanoids Compounds formed in the body from long-chain polyunsaturated *fatty acids (*eicosenoic acids). The lipoxygenase pathway leads to synthesis of leukotrienes, lipoxins, and hydro-fatty acids; the cyclo-oxygenase pathway leads to synthesis of prostaglandins, thromboxanes, and prostacyclin, all of which act as local hormones and are involved in inflammation, *platelet aggregation, and a variety of other functions. *See also* ISOPROSTANES.

eicosapentaenoic acid (EPA) A long-chain polyunsaturated *fatty acid (C20:5 w3); *see* OIL, FISH.

eicosenoic acids Long-chain polyunsaturated *fatty acids; with 20 carbon atoms.

einkorn A type of *wheat, the wild form of which, *Triticum boeoticum*, was probably the ancestor of all cultivated wheats. Still grown in some parts of southern Europe and the Middle East, usually for animal feed. The name means 'one seed', from the single seed found in each spikelet.

eiswein *Wine made from grapes that have frozen on the vine, picked and processed while still frozen, so that the juice is highly concentrated and very sweet. Similar Canadian wines are known as ice wine. *See* WINE CLASSIFICATION, GERMANY.

eiweiss milch *See* PROTEIN MILK.

ekra Romanian Jewish; purée made from salt herring roe, similar to *taramosalata.

elaichi *See* CARDAMOM.

elastase An *endopeptidase secreted by the *pancreas that catalyses hydrolysis of the esters of small neutral amino acids. Secreted as the inactive precursor, pro-elastase, which is activated by *trypsin.

elastin Insoluble elastic protein in *connective tissue, which is not affected by cooking; the cause of tough meat.

elder (elderberry) A common hedgerow bush (*Sambucus nigra*; American elder is *S. canadensis* and grape elder is *S. racemosa*); the flowers are used to flavour cordials, syrups, fruit jellies, and elderflower wine. The fruit is used for making jelly and wine (elderberry wine). Stems and leaves contain alkaloids that cause nausea, vomiting, and diarrhoea. *See also* SAMBUCA.

electrical conductivity of the body *See* BIOELECTRICAL IMPEDANCE; TOBEC.

electrolysis Separation of ions in a solution by use of direct current. *See also* ELECTROLYTES.

electrolytes *Salts that dissociate in solution and will carry an electric current; clinically used to mean the mineral salts of blood plasma and other body fluids, especially sodium and potassium.

electronic heating *See* MICROWAVE COOKING.

electrophoresis Technique for separating *amino acids, *proteins, *DNA, and other compounds on the basis of their size and charge at a given *pH, by determining how far they travel when subjected to an electric field. For proteins, electrophoresis in the presence of the detergent sodium dodecyl sulphate (SDS) permits determination of molecular mass, since all proteins have essentially the same charge when coated with SDS. The support medium may be cellulose, cellulose acetate, or a gel such as starch or polyacrylamide.

electroporation The process of applying a high-intensity electric field to cells in order to permeabilize membranes transiently, to introduce foreign *DNA into the nucleus as a means of creating transgenic plants (*see* GENETICALLY MODIFIED PLANTS).

electropure process A method of *pasteurizing milk by passing low-frequency, alternating current through it.

elements, minor *See* MINERALS, TRACE; MINERALS, ULTRA-TRACE.

ELISA Enzyme-linked immunosorbent assay; extremely sensitive and specific analytical technique using antibodies linked to an enzyme system to amplify sensitivity. It can be used to detect contamination of food with organisms capable of causing *food-borne infection.

elixir Alcoholic extract (tincture) of a naturally occurring substance; originally devised by medieval alchemists (the elixir of life), now used for a variety of medicines, liqueurs, and *bitters.

elongases Enzymes in mitochondria and endoplasmic reticulum that catalyse the synthesis of long-chain fatty acids from palmitate (C16:0) synthesized by fatty acid synthetase, or by elongation of dietary fatty acids.

elver Young *eel, about 5 cm in length.

emaciation Extreme thinness and wasting, caused by disease or undernutrition. *See also* CACHEXIA; PROTEIN-ENERGY MALNUTRITION.

emblic Berry of the South-East Asian malacca tree, *Emblica officinalis*, similar in appearance to the gooseberry. Also known as the Indian gooseberry. An exceptionally rich source of vitamin C: 600 mg per 100 g.

embolism Blockage of a blood vessel caused by a foreign object (embolus) such as a quantity of air or gas, a piece of tissue or tumour, a blood clot (thrombus), or fatty tissue derived from *atheroma, in the circulation.

emetic Substance that causes vomiting.

emincé French; a dish of meat cut into thin slices, covered with sauce, and baked in an earthenware dish.

Emmental Swiss; semi-hard cow's milk cheese; has large round holes formed by gases from bacterial fermentation during ripening. Used in *fondue.

emmer A type of *wheat known to have been used more than 8 000 years ago. Wild emmer is *Triticum dicoccoides* and true emmer is *T. dicoccum*. Nowadays grown mainly for animal feed.

empanadas Spanish (Galician); pies and pasties with a variety of savoury fillings.

emping Indonesian; a flat, crisp, fried wafer biscuit made from *melinjo flour.

emperor Marine fish, *Lethrinus* spp.

EMS *See* EOSINOPHILIA MYALGIA SYNDROME.

emulsification Reduction in droplet size of immiscible liquids to achieve a stable *emulsion. Also known as homogenization.

emulsifying agents Substances that are soluble in both fat and water and enable fat to be uniformly dispersed in water as an *emulsion. Foods that consist of such emulsions include *butter, *margarine, *salad dressings, *mayonnaise, and *ice cream. *Stabilizers maintain emulsions in a stable form. Emulsifying agents are also used in baking to aid the smooth incorporation of fat into the dough and to keep the crumb soft.

   Emulsifying agents used in foods include *agar, *albumin, *alginates, *casein, egg yolk, *glycerol monostearate, *gums, *Irish moss, *lecithin, soaps.

emulsifying salts Sodium citrate, phosphates, and tartrate, used in the manufacture of milk powder, evaporated milk, sterilized cream, and processed cheese.

emulsin A mixture of *enzymes (glycosidases) in bitter *almond which hydrolyse the glucoside *amygdalin to benzaldehyde, glucose, and cyanide.

emulsion An intimate mixture of two immiscible liquids (for example oil and water), one being dispersed in the other in the form of fine droplets. They will stay mixed only as long as they are stirred together, unless an *emulsifying agent is added.

enantiomers Stereoisomers of a compound which are mirror images of each other; *see* D-, L-, AND DL-.

encapsulation Core material, which may be liquid or powder, is encased in an outer shell or case, to protect it, or permit release in response to a given environmental change (e.g. temperature, *pH, etc.). When the encapsulated particles are less than 50 μm in diameter the process is known as microencapsulation.

enchilada Mexican; *tortilla fried in oil, filled with meat, cheese, or vegetables and served with chilli sauce. *See also* TACO; TAMAL.

endemic The usual cases of a particular illness in a community.

ENDIT European Nicotinamide Intervention Trial; trial of *nicotinamide supplements in people at high risk of developing type I *diabetes mellitus, concluded in 2004 with results showing no benefit of the supplements.

endive Curly serrated green leaves of *Cichorium endivia*. Called *chicory in the USA and *chicorée frisée* in France. A 50-g portion is a *source of vitamin A (1000 μg carotene); it supplies 5 kcal (20 kJ), but little vitamin C. There is also broad-leaved Batavian endive which resembles *lettuce.

endocarp *See* PERICARP.

endocrine glands Ductless glands that produce and secrete *hormones, including the *thyroid gland (secreting thyroxine and tri-iodothyronine), *pancreas (*insulin and *glucagon), adrenal glands (*adrenaline, *noradrenaline, *glucocorticoids, *mineralocorticoids), ovary and testes (sex steroids).

Some endocrine glands respond directly to chemical changes in the bloodstream; others are controlled by hormones secreted by the pituitary gland, under the control of the hypothalamus. *See also* AUTOCRINE; JUXTACRINE; PARACRINE.

endocytosis The process by which cells take up materials without it passing through the cell membrane. The membrane folds around material outside the cell, resulting in the formation of a vesicle into which the material is incorporated. This vesicle is then pinched off from the cell surface so that it lies within the cell. *See also* ENDOCYTOSIS, RECEPTOR-MEDIATED; PHAGOCYTOSIS; PINOCYTOSIS.

endocytotis, receptor-mediated Cell surface receptors bind the material to be taken up, and the receptors and ligand are then taken into the cell by *endocytosis; this is the process for uptake of *LDL into liver cells.

endomorph In relation to body build, means short and stocky. *See* ECTOMORPH; MESOMORPH.

endomysium *See* MUSCLE.

endopeptidases *Enzymes that hydrolyse proteins (i.e. proteinases or peptidases), by cleaving *peptide bonds within the protein chain, as opposed to *exopeptidases, which remove amino acids from the end of the chain. The main endopeptidases in *digestion are chymotrypsin, elastase, pepsin, and trypsin.

endoplasmic reticulum, rough Intracellular array of membranes studded with *ribosomes synthesizing proteins that are to be exported from the cell. Contiguous with the *Golgi apparatus where these proteins undergo post-synthetic modification.

endoplasmic reticulum, smooth Intracellular array of membranes containing an electron transport chain and the mixed function oxidases associated with phase I metabolism (*see* METABOLISM, PHASE I) of foreign compounds.

endosperm The inner part of cereal grains; in wheat it comprises about 83% of the grain. Mainly starch, it is the source of *semolina. Contains only about 10% of the vitamin B_1, 35% of the vitamin B_2, 40% of the niacin, and 50% of the vitamin B_6 and pantothenic acid of the whole grain. *See also* FLOUR, EXTRACTION RATE; SEMOLINA.

endotoxins Toxins produced by bacteria as an integral part of the cell, so they cannot be separated by filtration; unlike *exotoxins, they do not usually stimulate antitoxin formation but the antibodies that they induce act directly on the bacteria. They are relatively stable to heat compared with exotoxins.

enema *See* NUTRIENT ENEMATA.

energy The ability to do work. The SI unit of energy is the joule, and nutritionally relevant amounts of energy are kilojoules (kJ, 1000J) and megajoules (MJ, 1000000J). The *calorie is still widely used in nutrition; 1 cal = 4.186J (approximated to 4.2). While it is usual to speak of the calorie or joule content of a food it is more correct to refer to the energy yield.

The total chemical energy in a food, as released by complete combustion (in the bomb *calorimeter) is gross energy. Allowing for the losses of unabsorbed food in the faeces gives digestible energy. Allowing for loss in the urine due to incomplete combustion in the body (e.g. urea from the incomplete combustion of proteins) gives metabolizable energy. Allowing for the loss due to diet-induced thermogenesis (*see* THERMOGENESIS, DIET-INDUCED) gives net energy, i.e. the actual amount available for use in the body.

The following factors are used for energy yields of foods: *protein, 17kJ (4kcal); *fat, 37kJ (9kcal); *carbohydrate, 16kJ (4kcal); *alcohol, 29kJ (7kcal); *sugar alcohols, 10kJ (2.4kcal); organic acids, 13kJ (3kcal).

energy, activation The energy needed to excite electrons to an unstable state in order for a chemical reaction to proceed.

energy balance The difference between intake of energy from foods and expenditure on basal metabolism (*see* BASAL METABOLIC RATE) and physical activity. Positive energy balance leads to increased body tissue, the normal process of growth. In adults positive energy balance leads to creation of reserves of fat, resulting in overweight and *obesity. Negative energy balance leads to utilization of body reserves of fat and protein, resulting in wasting and undernutrition.

energy drinks Beverages containing glucose, vitamins, minerals, herb extracts and caffeine, and sometimes other ingredients, claimed to provide energy and to promote alertness and well-being. Some contain sweeteners instead of glucose.

energy expenditure The total energy cost of maintaining constant conditions in the body, i.e. homeostasis (basal metabolism, BMR; *see* BASAL METABOLIC RATE) plus the energy cost of physical activities. The average total energy expenditure in Western countries is about 1.4 times BMR; a desirable level of physical activity is about 1.7 times BMR.

energy, kinetic Energy due to motion of an object.

energy metabolism The various reactions involved in the oxidation of metabolic fuels (mainly carbohydrates, fats, and proteins), to provide energy (linked to the formation of *ATP (adenosine triphosphate) from ADP (adenosine diphosphate) and phosphate ions).

energy, potential Energy due to the position of an object.

energy requirements Energy requirements are calculated from *basal metabolic rate and physical activity. Average energy requirements for adults are 8 MJ (1900 kcal)/day for women and 10 MJ (2400 kcal) for men, but obviously vary widely with the level of physical activity.

enfleurage A method of extracting essential oils (*see* OILS, ESSENTIAL) from flowers by placing them on glass trays covered with purified *lard or other fat, which eventually becomes saturated with the oil.

Engels' law The concept that as income increases, families spend more on food, although this is a smaller proportion of overall expenditure.

enhancer A region in *DNA that may be up- or downstream of a *gene, which serves to increase the rate at which the gene is transcribed (*see* TRANSCRIPTION).

enocianina Sugar-free grape extract used to colour fruit flavours. Prepared by acid extraction of the skins of black grapes; it is blue in neutral conditions and red in acid.

en papillote French method of cooking in a closed container, a parchment paper or aluminium foil case.

enrichment The addition of nutrients to foods. Although often used interchangeably, the term *fortification is used of legally required additions, and enrichment of the voluntary addition of nutrients above the levels originally present. *See also* FORTIFICATION; NUTRIFICATION; RESTORATION.

enrobing In confectionery manufacture, the process of coating a product with chocolate, or other materials.

ENS *See* ENTERIC NERVOUS SYSTEM.

ensete *See* BANANA, FALSE.

enteral foods *See* FOODS, MEDICAL.

enteric nervous system A complex of neurones within the gut wall (the *myenteric and *submucosal plexuses) that regulates control of gut motility, fluid, and electrolyte transport and control of intestinal blood flow. Together with the sympathetic and parasympathetic nervous systems it forms the autonomic nervous system. Influenced by the autonomic nervous system, but can perform many functions independently.

enteritis Inflammation of the mucosal lining of the small intestine, usually resulting from infection. Regional enteritis is *Crohn's disease.

enterocins *Bacteriocins produced by *Enterococcus* spp.

enterocolitis Inflammation of the mucosal lining of the small and large intestine, usually resulting from infection.

enterocytes The absorptive cells of the intestinal mucosa.

enterogastrone Hormone secreted by the small intestine which inhibits the activity of the stomach. Its secretion is stimulated by fat; hence, fat in the diet inhibits gastric activity.

enteroglucagon A *peptide *hormone secreted by the colon and terminal ileum; acts to delay gastric emptying; now known as glucagon-like peptide (*see* GLP).

enterohepatic circulation Reabsorption from the small intestine of many of the compounds secreted in *bile.

enterokinase Obsolete name for the intestinal *enzyme *enteropeptidase.

enterolith Stone within the intestine; commonly builds up around a *gall stone or swallowed fruit stone.

enteropathy Any disease or disorder of the intestinal tract.

enteropeptidase An enzyme secreted by the small intestinal mucosa which activates trypsinogen (from the *pancreatic juice) to the active proteolytic enzyme *trypsin; sometimes called enterokinase. *See also* PROTEIN DIGESTION.

enterostatin A pentapeptide released from the amino terminal of the precursor protein of pancreatic *colipase during fat ingestion; it selectively suppresses the intake of dietary fat.

enterotoxin Substances toxic to the cells of the intestinal mucosa, normally produced by bacteria.

enteroviruses Viruses that multiply mainly in the intestinal tract.

enthalpy The sum of the internal energy and the product of the pressure and volume of a substance.

entoleter A machine used to disinfest cereals and other foods. The material is fed to the centre of a high-speed rotating disc carrying studs so that it is thrown against the studs; the impact kills insects and destroys their eggs.

entrecôte Steak cut from the middle part of the sirloin of *beef; in France a steak taken from between two ribs.

entrée A dressed savoury dish, served hot or cold, complete in its dish with the sauce. The term is used both for the main part of a meal (especially in France and the USA) and also to describe courses intermediate between hors d'œuvre and main course.

entremeses Spanish; mixed hors d'œuvre dishes served as a prelude to a meal.

entremets French; originally a dish served between courses, now the dessert course. The first recipe for entremets (a boar's head) is attributed to Chiquart Amicco, chef to the Duke of Savoy, in 1420.

entropy A measure of the degree of disorder in a system.

E-numbers Within the EU food *additives may be listed on labels either by name or by their number in the EU list of permitted additives. *See* APPENDIX VIII.

enzyme A *protein that catalyses a metabolic reaction, so increasing its rate. Enzymes are specific for both the compounds acted on (the substrates) and the reaction catalysed. Because of this, enzymes extracted from plants, animals, or micro-organisms, or those produced by *genetic manipulation, are widely used in the chemical, pharmaceutical, and food industries (e.g. *chymosin in cheese making, *maltase in beer production, for synthesis of *vitamin C and *citric acid).

Because they are proteins, enzymes are permanently inactivated by heat, strong acid or alkali, and other conditions which cause *denaturation of proteins.

Many enzymes contain non-protein components which are essential for their function. These are known as prosthetic groups, *coenzymes, or cofactors, and may be metal ions, metal ions in organic combination (e.g. haem in *haemoglobin and *cytochromes), or a variety of organic compounds, many of which are derived from *vitamins. The (inactive) protein without its prosthetic group is known as the apo-enzyme, and the active assembly of protein plus prosthetic group is the holo-enzyme. *See also* ENZYME ACTIVATION ASSAYS.

enzyme activation A number of compounds increase the activity of enzymes; sometimes this is a part of normal metabolic regulation and integration (e.g. the responses to *hormones), and sometimes it is the action of drugs.

enzyme activation assays Used to assess nutritional status with respect to *vitamins B_1, B_2, and B_6. A sample of red blood cells in a test-tube is tested for activity of the relevant *enzyme before and after adding extra vitamin-derived coenzyme; enhancement of the enzyme activity beyond a standard level serves as a biochemical index of a deficiency of the vitamin in question. The enzymes involved are transketolase for vitamin B_1, glutathione reductase for vitamin B_2, and either aspartate or alanine aminotransferase for vitamin B_6.

enzyme induction Synthesis of new enzyme protein in response to some stimulus, a hormone, metabolic intermediate, or other compound (e.g. a drug or food additive).

enzyme inhibition A number of compounds reduce the activity of enzymes; sometimes this is a part of normal metabolic regulation and integration (e.g. the responses to *hormones), and sometimes it is the action of drugs or toxins. Some inhibitors are reversible, others act irreversibly on the enzymes, and therefore have a longer duration of action (the activity of the enzyme remains low until more has been synthesized).

enzyme precursors *See* ZYMOGENS.

enzyme repression Reduction in synthesis of enzyme protein in response to some stimulus such as a hormone or the presence of large amounts of the end-product of its activity.

eosinophilia myalgia syndrome Often lethal blood and muscle disorder reported in 1989 among people using supplements of the *amino acid *tryptophan, as a result of which tryptophan supplements were withdrawn in most countries. Subsequently shown to be associated mainly (or perhaps solely) with a single batch of tryptophan from one manufacturer, but doubts remain about the safety of tryptophan supplements.

EPA Eicosapentaenoic acid; a long-chain polyunsaturated fatty acid (C20:5 ω3). *See* OIL, FISH.

epazote Herb (*Chenopodium ambriosiodes*) used in Mexican cooking and to make a *herb tea. Also known as Mexican tea, wormseed, goosefoot, and Jerusalem oak.

EPIC European Prospective Investigation into Cancer and Nutrition; investigating the relationships between diet, nutritional status, life-style and environmental factors and the incidence of cancer and other chronic diseases. The largest study of diet and health yet undertaken, with more than 520 000 people in ten European countries.

((⊕)) SEE WEB LINKS
• The EPIC's homepage.

epicarp *See* FLAVEDO; PERICARP.

epidemic Sudden outbreak of a disease affecting a large proportion of people.

epidemiology The study of the distribution and causes of diseases in populations.

epidermin A *lantibiotic synthesized by *Staphylococcus epidermidis* that inhibits many Gram-positive bacteria.

epigastric In the upper central abdomen.

epigenetics The study of the processes involved in the development of an organism, including *gene silencing during tissue differentiation. Also the study of heritable changes in gene function that occur without a change in the sequence of *DNA—the way in which environmental factors (including nutrition) affecting a parent can result in changes in the way genes are expressed in the offspring. *See also* CpG ISLANDS; PROGRAMMING.

épigramme French; small cuts of neck or breast of lamb.

epinephrine *See* ADRENALINE.

epistasis Gene–gene interactions, in which a *gene variant will confer susceptibility to a disease only in the presence of a variant of another gene. *See also* SUSCEPTIBILITY ALLELES.

époisses French soft cheese with orange rind; may be spiced or dipped in *marc de Bourgogne.

Epsom salts Magnesium sulphate, originally found in a mineral spring in Epsom, Surrey, England; acts as a laxative (*see* LAXATIVE, OSMOTIC) because the *osmotic pressure of the solution causes it to retain water in the intestine and so increase the bulk and moisture content of the faeces.

equilibrium, dynamic In an adult in *nitrogen balance the total body protein content remains unchanged, but studies with isotopically labelled amino acids reveal that there is continual breakdown of tissue proteins and replacement synthesis. Originally described by Rudolph Schoenheimer in *The Dynamic State of Body Constituents* (1946).

equilibrium humidity The relative humidity of the atmosphere with which the substance under consideration is in equilibrium.

equilibrium, nitrogen *See* NITROGEN BALANCE.

equol A *phytoestrogen formed by intestinal bacterial metabolism of *daidzein.

ercalciol *See* VITAMIN D.

erdbeergeist German spirit distilled from strawberries with added alcohol.

erepsin Name given to a mixture of enzymes contained in *intestinal juice, including aminopeptidases and dipeptidases.

ergocalciferol *See* VITAMIN D.

ergogenic aids Various compounds that (may) improve physical work output and athletic performance: i) products providing metabolic fuels; e.g. *glucose or *oligosaccharides as a source of carbohydrate, *medium-chain triglycerides as a source of fat; ii) products providing coenzymes that might be limiting, such as *creatine, creatine phosphate, *carnitine, and various vitamins; iii) anabolic substances that may enhance performance by changing body composition, such as protein, *hydroxy-methylbutyrate, anabolic *steroids; iv) substances that may enhance recovery, such as fluid, electrolytes, and herbal products; v) erythropoietin (training at high altitude) to stimulate erythropoeisis, and so increase oxygen-carrying capacity of the blood.

ergosterol A *sterol isolated from yeast; when irradiated with ultraviolet light, it is converted to ercalciol (ergocalciferol, vitamin D_2). This is the main industrial source of *vitamin D.

ergot A fungus that grows on grasses and cereal grains; the ergot of medical importance is *Claviceps purpurea*, which grows on *rye. The consumption of infected rye causes the disease known as St Anthony's fire (*ergotism), and can be fatal. The first connection with infected rye (spurred rye, so called because the grain heads of infected rye appear spurred) was recorded by physicians in Marbourg (France) in 1597.

The active principles in ergot are alkaloids (ergotinine, ergotoxine, ergotamine, ergometrine, etc.), which yield lysergic acid on hydrolysis. Its effect is to increase the tone and contraction of smooth muscle, particularly of the pregnant uterus. For this reason ergot has been used in obstetrics.

ergotism Poisoning due to an *ergot infection of *rye which occurs occasionally among people eating rye bread. The last outbreak in the UK was in Manchester in 1925, when there were 200 cases. Symptoms appear when as little as 1% of ergot-infected rye is included in the flour.

eriodictin A *flavonoid (flavonone) found in citrus pith, a constituent of what is sometimes called vitamin P.

erucic acid A mono-unsaturated *fatty acid (C22:1 ω9), found in *rape seed (*Brassica napus*) and mustard seed (*B. junca* and *B. nigra*) oils; it may constitute 30–50% of the oil in some varieties. It causes fatty infiltration of heart muscle in experimental animals. Low erucic acid varieties of rape seed (*canola) have been developed for food use.

eructation The act of bringing up air from the stomach, with a characteristic sound. Also known as belching.

erythorbic acid The D-isomer of *ascorbic acid, also called D-araboascorbic acid and iso-ascorbic acid, with only slight *vitamin C activity, used in foods as an antioxidant.

erythritol Four carbon *sugar alcohol derived from erythrose.

erythroamylose An old name for *amylopectin.

erythrocytes *See* BLOOD CELLS, RED.

erythropoiesis The formation and development of the red *blood cells in the bone marrow.

erythropoietin Peptide *hormone secreted by the kidney that acts on bone marrow to stimulate formation and development of the red *blood cells; it acts by preventing *apoptosis of precursor cells; its secretion is stimulated by hypoxia and *anaemia.

erythrosine BS Red colour permitted in foods in most countries (known as Red number 3 in the USA). Used in preserved cherries, sausages, and meat and fish pastes; it is unstable to light and heat. The disodium or potassium salt of 2,4,5,7-tetraiodofluorescein.

ESADDI Estimated safe and adequate daily dietary intakes of nutrients for which there is insufficient evidence to determine average requirements and *reference intakes.

escabeche Caribbean; fish, poultry, or game cooked in oil and vinegar or cooked and then pickled in oil and vinegar marinade. From the Spanish for pickled. Fish prepared in this way is also known as escovitch or caveached fish.

escalope Thin slice of meat (generally veal or pork), round or oval shaped, cut from the top of the leg or fillet. Also a thin slice of fish.

escargot *See* SNAIL.

escarole *See* ENDIVE.

escolar *See* MACKEREL.

escovitch *See* ESCABECHE.

esculin *See* AESCULIN.

espagnole sauce A thick, brown *roux, diluted with stock made from meat or bones, with onion, carrot, garlic, herbs, tomato pulp, and sherry.

Escherichia coli A species of bacteria including both harmless strains that inhabit the intestines and some types that can cause *food-borne disease. Four strains of *E. coli* are especially pathogenic, causing gastroenteritis: enteropathogenic (EPEC), enterotoxigenic (ETEC), enteroinvasive (EIEC), and enterohaemorrhagic (EHEC). In industrialized countries the main problem is enterohaemorrhagic *E. coli*, which can cause the potentially fatal haemolytic uraemic syndrome. The main sources of infection are raw or undercooked ground meat products and raw milk, and faecal contamination of foods and water.

ESPACI European Society for Paediatric Clinical Immunology.

ESPEN European Society for Parenteral and Enteral Nutrition.
( ) SEE WEB LINKS
• The ESPEN's homepage.

ESPGHAN European Society for Paediatric Gastroenterology, Hepatology and Nutrition.
( ) SEE WEB LINKS
• The ESPGHAN's homepage.

espresso Italian; strong black *coffee made by forcing steam through finely ground coffee.

espumante Portuguese; sparkling wines.

espumoso Spanish; sparkling wines.

ESR Depending on context, may be erythrocyte sedimentation rate or electron spin resonance.

essential amino acid index An index of *protein quality.

essential amino acid pattern The quantities of essential *amino acids considered desirable in the diet.

essential amino acids *See* AMINO ACIDS, ESSENTIAL.

essential fatty acids *See* FATTY ACIDS, ESSENTIAL.

essential nutrient Those nutrients that are required by the body and cannot be synthesized in the body in adequate amounts to meet requirements, so must be provided by the diet: includes the essential *amino acids and *fatty acids, *vitamins, and *minerals. Really a tautology, since nutrients are defined as essential dietary constituents.

esterases *Enzymes that hydrolyse *esters, i.e. cleave the ester linkage to yield free acid and alcohol. Those that hydrolyse the ester linkages of fats are generally known as *lipases, and those that hydrolyse *phospholipids as phospholipases.

esters Compounds formed by condensation between an acid and an alcohol, e.g. ethyl alcohol and acetic acid yield the ester ethyl acetate. *Fats are esters of the alcohol glycerol and long-chain *fatty acids. Many esters are used as synthetic *flavours.

estouffade Meat cooked very slowly in very little liquid; braised or casseroled.

ethane breath test *See* BREATH TEST, ETHANE AND PENTANE.

ethanoic acid *See* ACETIC ACID.

ethanol Systematic name for ethyl *alcohol.

ethanolamine One of the water-soluble bases of *phospholipids, 2-aminoethanol. Used as softening agent for hides, as dispersing agent for agricultural chemicals, and to peel fruits and vegetables.

ethene *See* ETHYLENE.

ethyl alcohol *See* ALCOHOL.

ethyl carbamate *See* URETHANE.

ethylene (ethene) A gas, $CH_2{=}{=}CH_2$, produced by fruit as a hormone to speed ripening of *climacteric fruits. This explains why some fruits ripen faster if they are stored in a plastic bag. It is used commercially in small amounts to speed fruit ripening after harvesting.

ethylene diamine tetra-acetic acid *See* EDTA.

ethyl formate Used as a fumigant against raisin moth, dried fruit beetle, fig moth, etc., and as a flavour; an ingredient of artificial lemon, strawberry, and rum flavours.

ethylmethylcellulose *See* CELLULOSE DERIVATIVES.

ethyl vanillin A synthetic compound, the ethyl analogue of vanillin, the major flavouring component of *vanilla.

EUFIC European Food Information Council.

 SEE WEB LINKS

• The EUFIC's homepage.

eugenol Flavouring obtained from *clove oil and also found in carnation and cinnamon leaves.

eutrophia Normal nutrition.

evaporation, flash A short, rapid application of heat so that a small volume (about 1% of the total) is quickly distilled off, carrying with it the greater part of the volatile components. The flash distillate is collected separately from the later distillate and is added back to the concentrate to restore the flavour; applied to the concentration of products such as fruit juices.

evening primrose An annual herb, *Oenothera biennis*; the oil from the seeds is a rich source of *γ-linolenic acid, which may account for 8% of total *fatty acids. It is used as a dietary supplement and may have beneficial effects in a number of conditions.

ewedu *Corchorus olitorius*; the leaves are used as an alternative to *spinach and as a pot-herb in West Africa. Also known as moroheiya, Jew's mallow, Egyptian mallow, and bush okra.

exchange list List of portions of foods in which energy yield, fat, carbohydrate, and/or protein content are equivalent, so simplifying meal and diet planning for people with special needs.

exergonic Chemical reactions that proceed with the output of energy, usually as heat (then sometimes known as exothermic reactions) or light. The reactions involved in the oxidation of foodstuffs are generally exergonic.

exocarp *See* PERICARP.

exopeptidases Proteolytic enzymes that hydrolyse the peptide bonds of the terminal amino acids of proteins or peptides, as opposed to *endopeptidases, which cleave at sites within the peptide chain. There are two groups: aminopeptidases, which remove the amino acid at the amino terminal of the protein, and carboxypeptidases, which remove the amino acid at the carboxyl terminal.

exothermic *See* EXERGONIC.

exotoxins Toxins produced by bacteria that diffuse out of the cells and stimulate the production of antitoxins (antibodies that neutralize them). They are generally heat-labile and inactivated in about 1 hour at 60°C. Exotoxins include those produced by the organisms responsible for *botulism, tetanus, and diphtheria. *See also* ENDOTOXINS.

expansion rings The concentric rings stamped into the ends of the can to allow bulging during heat processing without straining the seams.

expeller cake *See* PRESSCAKE.

extraction rate *See* FLOUR, EXTRACTION RATE.

extract of malt *See* MALT.

extract of meat *See* MEAT EXTRACT.

extract of yeast *See* YEAST EXTRACT.

extremophiles Micro-organisms that can grow under extreme conditions of heat (*thermophiles and extreme thermophiles, some of which live in hot springs at 100°C), or cold (*psychrophyles), in high concentrations of salt (*halophiles), high pressure, or extremes of acid or alkali.

extrinsic factor *See* ANAEMIA, PERNICIOUS; VITAMIN B$_{12}$.

extruder The die equipment that is used to shape items during *extrusion.

extrusion The process of shaping items by forcing them through a die.

extrusion cooking Food, commonly a cereal product, is heated under pressure, then extruded through fine pores, when the superheated water evaporates rapidly, leaving a textured product.

FAD Flavin adenine dinucleotide, one of the *coenzymes formed from *vitamin B$_2$ (riboflavin).

faeces Body waste, composed of undigested food residues, remains of digestive secretions that have not been reabsorbed, bacteria from the intestinal tract, cells, cell debris and mucus from the intestinal lining, and substances excreted into the intestinal tract (mainly in the *bile). The average amount is about 100 g/day, but varies widely depending on the intake of *dietary fibre.

fagara *See* PEPPER, SZECHWAN.

faggot **1.** Traditional British meatball made from pig *offal and meat. **2.** Bundle of herbs, *bouquet garni.

fair maids Cornish name for *pilchards (thought to be a corruption of the Spanish *fumade*, 'smoked').

fairy cakes *See* CUP CAKE.

fairy potato *See* EARTH-NUT.

faki soupa Greek; *lentil soup.

falafel (felafel) Israeli, Middle Eastern; small deep-fried balls of spiced *chickpea flour, normally served in *pitta bread with salad and a piquant sauce.

FANSA The Food and Nutrition Science Alliance, a partnership of the American Dietetic Association, American Society for Clinical Nutrition, American Society for Nutritional Sciences and Institute of Food Technologists.

fansi *See* BEAN, FRENCH.

FAO Food and Agriculture Organization of the United Nations, founded in 1943, headquarters in Rome. Its goal is to achieve freedom from hunger worldwide. According to its constitution the specific objectives are 'raising the levels of nutrition and standards of living . . . and securing improvements in the efficiency of production and distribution of all food and agricultural products'.

(⊕) SEE WEB LINKS

• The FAO's homepage.

FAOSTAT Statistical Division of the UN Food and Agriculture Organization (*see* FAO).

 SEE WEB LINKS

• The FAOSTAT's homepage.

farce Stuffing, hence forcemeat as a name for meats used as stuffing.

farina General term for starch. More specifically in the UK refers to *potato starch; in the USA is defined as the starch obtained from wheat other than *durum wheat, the starch from which is *semolina.

farinaceous Starchy.

farina dolce Italian; flour made from dried *chestnuts.

farl Scottish; triangular oatmeal cake.

fascioliasis Infection with the *trematodes *Fasciola hepatica* or *F. gigantica* acquired from watercress and other plants grown in infected water, leading to liver and gall bladder disease.

fasolada Greek; bean soup.

fasolia Greek; a variety of dishes prepared with dried beans.

fasting Going without food. The metabolic fasting state begins some 4 hours after a meal, when the digestion and absorption of food is complete and body reserves of fat and *glycogen begin to be mobilized. In more prolonged fasting the blood concentration of *ketone bodies rises, as they are exported from the liver for use by muscle and other tissues as a metabolic fuel.

fat Chemically fats (or lipids) are substances that are insoluble in water but soluble in organic solvents such as ether, chloroform, and benzene, and are actual or potential esters of *fatty acids. The term includes *triacylglycerols (triglycerides), phospholipids, waxes, and sterols.

In more general use the term 'fats' refers to the neutral fats which are triacylglycerols, mixed esters of *fatty acids with *glycerol. In general triacylglycerols that are solid at room temperature are called fats, and those that are liquid are known as oils. *See also* SAPONIFICATION.

fat analogues *See* FAT REPLACERS; FAT SUBSTITUTES.

fat, blood Total blood fat in the fasting state is about 590 mg per 100 mL plasma: 150 mg neutral fats (*triacylglycerols), 160 mg (4 mmol) cholesterol, 200 mg phospholipids. This is mainly in the plasma *lipoproteins. After a meal the total fat increases, as a result of the *chylomicrons containing the recently absorbed dietary fat. *See also* LIPIDS, PLASMA.

fat, brown *See* ADIPOSE TISSUE, BROWN.

fat-extenders *See* FATS, SUPERGLYCINERATED.

fat-free EU regulations restrict use of the term 'fat-free' to foods that contain less than 0.15 g of fat/100 g; in the USA low-fat foods must state the percentage of fat; thus a product described as 95% fat-free contains only 5 g of fat/100 g.

fat free mass In body composition, the mass of tissues excluding fat.

fat hen A common wild plant (*Chenopodium album*); the leaves have a strong scent of chrysanthemum leaves when crushed, and can be used in soup or fried as a vegetable. The name comes from the fact that it was formerly used to feed hens. The seeds can be ground into a flour for preparation of bread, cakes, and gruel; they have a flavour similar to that of *buckwheat. Also known as bacon weed, dirty dick, muck hill, or dung weed (because it commonly grows around dung heaps), goose foot (because of the shape of the leaves), and pig weed.

fat mimetics *See* FAT REPLACERS; FAT SUBSTITUTES.

fat mouse Genetically obese mouse that secretes pro-insulin rather than *insulin, because of a defect in the gene for the pro-insulin converting enzyme, *carboxypeptidase E. The same enzyme is also involved in the post-synthetic modification of other peptide hormone precursors, including pro-opiomelanocortin.

fat, neutral *Fats that are esters of fatty acids with glycerol, *triacylglycerols.

fat replacers Compounds that can provide some or all of the functions of fat in a food, but with a lower energy yield. They may be based on carbohydrate or microgranulated protein, or a blend of both, or fatty acid esters of sucrose that are not digested, but, unlike carbohydrate and protein-based products, are stable at frying temperatures. *See also* FAT SUBSTITUTES.

fat, saturated *Fats containing only or mainly saturated *fatty acids.

fats, high-ratio *See* FATS, SUPERGLYCINERATED.

fats, hydrogenated *See* HYDROGENATION.

fats, non-saponifiable *See* SAPONIFICATION.

fat-soluble vitamins *Vitamins A, D, E, and K; they occur in food dissolved in the fats and are stored in the body to a greater extent than the water-soluble vitamins.

fat spread A general term for bread spreads (yellow fats), including *butter, *margarine, and low-fat spreads. Reduced fat spreads contain not more than 60% fat, and low-fat spreads not more than 40%, compared with 80% fat in butter and margarine. Very low-fat spreads contain less than 20% fat, and some as little as 5%.

fats, saponifiable *See* SAPONIFICATION.

fats, superglycerinated Neutral fats are *triacylglycerols, with three molecules of fatty acid esterified to each molecule of glycerol. Mono- and diacylglycerols (sometimes called mono- and diglycerides) are known as superglycerinated high-ratio fats or fat extenders.

Glyceryl monostearate (GMS) is solid at room temperature, flexible, and non-greasy; it is used as a protective coating for foods, as a plasticizer for softening the crumb of bread, to reduce spattering in frying fats, as an emulsifier and stabilizer. Glyceryl mono-oleate (GMO) is semi-liquid at room temperature.

fat substitutes Compounds that resemble conventional fats and oils, and provide all the food functions of fat, including stability at cooking and frying temperatures, but with a lower energy yield. Some (e.g. sucrose esters of fatty acids) are not absorbed at all, so have zero energy yield. *See also* CAPRENIN; FAT REPLACERS; SALATRIMS.

fats, yellow *See* FAT SPREAD.

fatty acids Organic *acids consisting of a carbon chain with a carboxyl group at carbon-1. The nutritionally important fatty acids have an even number of carbon atoms, commonly between twelve and twenty-two; small amounts of fatty acids with an odd number of carbon atoms also occur.

Saturated fatty acids are those in which every carbon atom carries its full 'quota' of hydrogen atoms, and therefore there are only single bonds between adjacent carbon atoms.

Unsaturated fatty acids have one or more carbon–carbon double bonds in the molecule. These double bonds can take up hydrogen, which is the process of *hydrogenation, forming saturated fatty acids.

Fatty acids with only one double bond are termed mono-unsaturated; *oleic acid is the main one in *fats and oils. Fatty acids with two or more double bonds are polyunsaturated fatty acids, often abbreviated to PUFA.

Unsaturated fatty acids lower levels of *cholesterol in the blood, while saturated fatty acids raise it. To reduce the risk of *heart disease, it is recommended that saturated fatty acid intake should not exceed about 10% of energy.

In general fats from animal sources are high in saturated and relatively low in unsaturated fatty acids; vegetable and fish oils are generally higher in unsaturated and lower in saturated fatty acids.

In addition to their accepted names, fatty acids can be named by a shorthand giving the number of carbon atoms in the molecule (e.g. C18), then a colon and the number of double bonds (e.g. C18:2), followed by the position of the first double bond from the methyl end of the molecule as n- or ω (e.g. C18:2 n-6, or C18:2 ω6).

fatty acids, essential (EFA) Two polyunsaturated *fatty acids cannot be made in the body and are therefore dietary essentials: linoleic (C18:2 ω6) and α-linolenic (C18:3 ω3). Several other fatty acids have some EFA activity in that they cure some, but not all, of the signs of (experimental) deficiency. *Arachidonic, *eicosapentaenoic (EPA), and *docosahexaenoic (DHA) acids are physiologically important, although they are not dietary essentials since they can be formed from linoleic and α-linolenic acids.

The requirement to prevent deficiency is about 1% of total energy intake, equivalent to 260mg/MJ; a desirable intake, and the basis of *reference intakes, is 8–10% of energy intake, about 2–2.6g/MJ. Although all fatty foods contain some essential fatty acids, the richest sources are vegetable and fish oils.

fatty acids, free (FFA) Fatty acids may be liberated from triacylglycerols (triglyceride) either by enzymic hydrolysis (when they are generally known as non-esterified fatty acids, NEFA, or unesterified fatty acids, UFA) or as a result of hydrolytic rancidity of the fat. Determination of FFA is therefore an index of the quality of fats.

Free fatty acids circulate in the bloodstream, bound to albumin. They are released from *adipose tissue, especially in the fasting state, as a fuel for muscle and other tissues. The normal concentration in plasma in the fed state is about 0.5μmol/L, rising to about 2μmol/L in fasting and with exercise.

fatty acids, non-esterified (NEFA unesterified; fatty acids (UFA)) *See* FATTY ACIDS, FREE.

fatty acids, volatile Short-chain fatty acids: acetic, propionic, and butyric acids which, apart from their presence in some foods, are produced by intestinal bacteria by fermentation of undigested starch and dietary fibre. To some extent they can be absorbed and used as a source of energy. Butyric acid formed in the colon may have some anticarcinogenic action.

fat, unsaturated *Fats containing a high proportion of unsaturated *fatty acids.

fat, white *See* ADIPOSE TISSUE.

favism Acute haemolytic *anaemia induced in genetically susceptible people by eating broad beans, *Vicia faba*. The disease is due to deficiency of the *enzyme glucose 6-phosphate dehydrogenase in the red blood cells, which are then susceptible to oxidative damage resulting from the toxins, vicine and convicine, in the beans. The condition affects some 100 million people worldwide, and is commonest in people of Mediterranean and Afro-Caribbean origin.

FBS *See* FOOD BALANCE SHEETS.

FD&C US abbreviation for synthetic colours permitted for use in food, drugs, and cosmetics.

FDA Food and Drug Administration; US government regulatory agency.

(⊕) SEE WEB LINKS
- The FDA's homepage.
- The FDA *Consumer* Magazine's homepage.

FDF Food and Drink Federation, voice of the UK food and drink manufacturing industry.

(⊕) SEE WEB LINKS
- The FDF's homepage.

fecula (fécule) Foods that are almost solely *starch; prepared from roots and stems by grating, e.g. *tapioca, *sago, and *arrowroot; starchy powder from rice, potatoes, etc.

feijoa Fruit of South American tree *Feijoa sellowiana* (*Acca sellowiana*), mainly grown in New Zealand. Feijoa beans are adzuki beans (*see* BEAN, ADZUKI).

felafel *See* FALAFEL.

fenelar Norwegian; leg of mutton dry-brined with salt, saltpetre, and sugar, then in a sweet pickle, smoked and air dried.

fenfluramine *Anorectic drug formerly used in the treatment of *obesity, withdrawn in 1995 because of reports of heart valve damage.

feng kuo Chinese (Cantonese); savoury filling of chopped roast meat or seafood with mushrooms and bamboo shoots, flavoured with oyster sauce and wrapped in dough made from flour, cornflour, and lotus root flour, then fried.

fennel **1.** Aromatic seeds and feathery leaves of the perennial plant, *Foeniculum vulgare*, used to flavour a variety of dishes. **2.** Florence fennel or finnochio, an annual plant, *Foeniculum dulce* (or *F. vulgare* var. *azoricum*); the swollen bases of the leaves have an aniseed flavour, and are eaten raw or cooked; a 60-g portion supplies 10kcal (40kJ).

fen-phen The combination of *fenfluramine and *phentermine, formerly used as an *anorectic drug in the treatment of obesity; withdrawn in 1995 because of reports of heart valve damage.

fenugreek Seeds of the legume *Trigonella feonumgraecum*, eaten as a vegetable; the seeds are used for flavouring. It is traditionally eaten by women in the Orient to help gain weight. Also known as methe.

ferment As a noun, the old name for *enzyme. As a verb, to carry out the process of *fermentation.

fermentation Anaerobic *metabolism. Used generally of alcohol fermentation of sugars, also production of lactic acid, citric acid, etc., by micro-organisms, which may be yeasts, bacteria, or fungi.

fermentation, malolactic Fermentation by *Lactobacillus*, *Leuconostoc*, and *Pediococcus* spp. in which *malic acid is converted to *lactic acid and CO_2, so reducing the acidity, since lactic acid is a weaker acid than malic.

fermentation, panary Yeast fermentation of dough in bread making.

fermentation, secondary In wine making; may be induced by the addition of further sugar and yeast to produce carbon dioxide for sparkling wines, or a malo lactic fermentation using *Lactobacillus* spp. to convert sharp-tasting malic acid to the milder lactic acid; again this produces carbon dioxide, characteristic of pétillant (lightly sparkling) wines. *See also* VINEGAR.

ferritin *See* IRON STORAGE.

ferroportin The transport protein for iron that permits efflux of iron from intestinal mucosal cells into the bloodstream; regulated by *hepcidin in response to the state of body iron reserves.

ferrous gluconate *Iron salt of *gluconic acid, used in iron supplements and as a colouring agent in olives.

ferrum redactum *See* IRON, REDUCED.

feta Greek, general Balkan; semi-hard white *cheese from ewe's or goat's milk; preserved in salt water. A 30-g portion is a rich *source of vitamin B_{12}; a source of protein; contains 6g of fat, of which three-quarters is saturated, 450mg of sodium, and 100mg of calcium; supplies 75kcal (310kJ).

fetal Warfarin syndrome Abnormalities of bone and neurological development in infants born to mothers treated with the *anticoagulant *Warfarin during pregnancy.

fettucini Ribbon-shaped *pasta.

FFA Free fatty acids. *See* FATTY ACIDS, FREE.

FFM *See* FAT FREE MASS.

FFQ *See* FOOD FREQUENCY QUESTIONNAIRE.

fibre, crude The term given to the indigestible part of foods, defined as the residue left after successive extraction under closely specified conditions with petroleum ether, 1.25% sulphuric acid, and 1.25% sodium hydroxide, minus ash. No real relation to dietary fibre (*see* FIBRE, DIETARY).

fibre, dietary Material mostly derived from plant cell walls which is not digested by human digestive enzymes but is partially metabolized by intestinal bacteria to yield volatile fatty acids (*see* FATTY ACIDS, VOLATILE) that can be used as a source of energy. A large proportion consists of *non-starch polysaccharides (NSP); these include soluble fibre that reduces levels of blood cholesterol and increases the viscosity of the intestinal contents, and insoluble fibre (cellulose) that acts as a laxative. Earlier known as roughage or bulk.

fibre, insoluble The part of dietary fibre (or *non-starch polysaccharide) that is not soluble in water, i.e. *cellulose, hemicelluloses, and lignin. These increase the bulk of the intestinal contents.

fibre, soluble The part of the dietary fibre (or *non-starch polysaccharide) that forms a gel in water and hence is soluble, i.e. *pectins and plant *gums. These increase the viscosity of the intestinal contents.

fibrin The protein formed from *fibrinogen which is responsible for the clotting of *blood.

fibrinogen The blood protein that is responsible for clotting. When *prothrombin is activated to thrombin in response to injury, it converts fibrinogen to fibrin, which is deposited as strands that form the clot.

ficain See FICIN.

ficin Proteolytic *enzyme from the *fig, used as a milk-clotting agent. Also known as ficain.

fiddleheads Canadian name for *bracken fronds.

fideuá See FIGUEREDAS.

field egg See AUBERGINE.

fig The fruit of *Ficus carica*; eaten fresh or dried. Figs have mild laxative properties (syrup of figs is a medicinal preparation). A 40-g portion of dried figs (two figs) is a *source of calcium, iron, and copper; provides 3g of dietary fibre; supplies 80kcal (335kJ); and contains 50% sugars. A 100-g portion of fresh figs (two figs) supplies 60kcal (245kJ).

fig, Adam's See PLANTAIN.

fig, berberry (fig, Indian) See PRICKLY PEAR.

figgy pudding Pudding made with raisins; originally dried figs stewed in wine. Figgy duff or figgie hobbin is the Cornish name for a pastry containing raisins.

FIGLU test A test for *folic acid nutritional status, based on excretion of formiminoglutamic acid (FIGLU), a metabolite of the *amino acid *histidine, which is normally metabolized by a folic acid-dependent enzyme.

fig, jelly Fruit of *Ficus pumila* var. *awkeotsang*.

fig, sour Fruit of the South African succulent creeper *Carpobrotus edulis*.

figueredas Spanish (Valenciana); a spiced seafood dish similar to *paella, but served on a bed of pasta rather than rice. This is the Catalan name; in Spanish it is fideuá.

filbert *See* HAZELNUT.

filé powder Dried powdered young leaves of the sassafras tree (*Sassafras albidum*); very aromatic, an essential ingredient of *gumbo.

fillet The lean, tender strip of meat beneath an animal's ribs, especially beef. Now also used to mean a lean cut of veal, lamb, or pork from the top of the hind leg. Filet mignon (French 'dainty fillet') is a small, round cut of beef from the centre of the fillet, similar to *tournedos.

filleting Removing the bones from a piece of meat or fish, to make a *fillet.

filth test Name given to a test originated in the USA for determining the contamination of a food with rodent hairs and insect fragments as an index of the hygienic handling of the food.

filter cake Solid matter retained by *filtration of a liquid.

filtrate The liquid that passes through a filter; *see* FILTRATION.

filtration The separation of solids from liquids by passing the mixture through a bed of porous material (the filter medium), either under gravity and hydrostatic pressure alone or using pressure above, or vacuum below, to force the liquid through the filter bed. Water may be filtered through *charcoal to remove unpleasant flavours and colours; bacterial filters for water have pores fine enough to remove bacteria (but not viruses). *See also* FILTER CAKE; FILTRATE.

financière, à la Meat or poultry in a rich Madeira sauce containing mushrooms and truffles, or with a garnish of cocks' combs, cocks' kidneys, truffles, olives, and mushrooms.

fines herbes Mixture of chopped parsley, tarragon, chives, chervil, marjoram, and sometimes watercress.

finfish A term used to differentiate true fish from other seafoods, such as shellfish, crayfish, and jellyfish.

fingerware Edible *seaweed, *Laminaria digitata*.

fining agents Substances used to clarify liquids by precipitation, e.g. *egg albumin, casein, bentonite, *fuller's earth, *isinglass, *gelatine, etc.

finnan haddock Smoke-cured haddock (named after Findon in Scotland). *See also* ARBROATH SMOKIE.

fino Very dry *sherry.

finocchio See FENNEL.

fior d'Alpi Italian; liqueur flavoured with alpine herbs and flowers; there is a sugar-encrusted twig in each bottle.

fireless cooker See HAYBOX COOKING.

fire point The temperature at which a frying oil will sustain combustion. It ranges between 340 and 360°C for different fats. See also FLASH POINT; SMOKE POINT.

firkin A quarter of a barrel of beer, 9 imperial gallons (40L); also 56lb (25.5kg) of butter.

firmi Indian; rice dessert with almonds and pistachio nuts.

firming agents Fresh fruits contain insoluble *pectins as a firm gel around the fibrous tissues which keeps the fruit firm. Breakdown of cell structure allows conversion of pectin to pectic acid, with loss of firmness. The addition of calcium chloride or carbonate forms a calcium pectate gel which protects the fruit against softening; these are known as firming agents. Alum is sometimes used to firm pickles.

first teeth See TEETH, DECIDUOUS.

fish cakes Chopped or minced fish, mixed with potato, bound with egg and flour (or *matzo meal) and seasoned with onion, pepper, and sometimes herbs, then deep fried. See also GEFILLTE FISH.

fish days Historical; days on which fish, but not meat, could be eaten. Originally decreed by the Church (Fridays, fast days, and throughout Lent); more were decreed in England during the 16th century, both to encourage ship building and the training of mariners, and also because of the shortage of meat, in order to permit an increase in the numbers of cattle. The Vatican rescinded the rule forbidding Catholics to eat meat on Fridays in 1966.

fish, demersal Fish species living on or near the sea bed—the white (non-oily) fish such as cod, haddock, whiting, plaice, and sole. Caught by trawls that are dragged along the bottom of the sea, or by seine nets. Known in USA as ground fish. See also FISH, PELAGIC; FISH, WHITE.

fish, fatty See FISH, OILY.

fish fingers Shaped fish fillets or minced fish, covered with breadcrumbs; approximately 50% fish. Known in USA as fish sticks. Two fish fingers, grilled (55g), are a rich *source of iodine; a source of protein and niacin; contain 5g of fat, of which one-third is saturated and one-third polyunsaturated; and supply 120kcal (500kJ).

fish flour *See* FISH PROTEIN CONCENTRATE.

fish, ground *See* FISH, DEMERSAL.

fish ham Japanese product made from a red fish such as *tuna or marlin, pickled with salt and nitrite, mixed with whale meat and pork fat and stuffed into a large sausage-type casing.

fish meal Surplus fish, waste from filleting (fish-house waste), and fish unsuitable for human consumption are dried and powdered. The resultant meal is a valuable source of protein for animal feed, or, after deodorization, as human food since it contains about 70% protein. That made from white fish is termed white fish meal, distinct from the oily type which is sometimes of very poor quality and is generally used as fertilizer. *See also* FISH PROTEIN CONCENTRATE; FISH SOLUBLES.

fish nuggets Pieces of fish (not minced) formed into small irregular shapes. May be formed from fillets, fillet pieces, or fish blocks; normally breaded. *See also* GOUJON.

fish, oily Anchovies, herring, mackerel, pilchard, salmon, sardine, trout, tuna, and whitebait, containing about 15% fat (varying from 5 to 20% through the year) and containing 10–40 µg vitamin D per 100 g, as distinct from white fish, which contain 1–2% fat and only a trace of vitamin D. *See also* OIL, FISH.

fish paste A spread made from ground fish and cereal. In the UK it legally contains not less than 70% fish.

fish, pelagic Literally 'of or pertaining to the ocean'—fish normally caught at or near the surface of the sea. Mainly the migratory, shoaling, seasonal fish—oily fish such as herring, mackerel, and tunny. *See also* FISH, DEMERSAL; FISH, OILY.

fish protein concentrate Deodorized, decolorized, defatted *fish meal, also known as fish flour. A cheap source of protein for enrichment of foods. Approximately 70% protein.

fish sausage Japanese product made from chopped fish fillet, spiced and flavoured, with added fat and starch, and packed into sausage casing.

fish solubles The aqueous fraction from pressing cooked fish in the manufacture of *fish meal. Contains amino acids, vitamins, and minerals, and is either added to animal feed or mixed back with the fish meal and dried. Also known as stickwater.

fish stick *See* SEAFOOD STICK; also American name for *fish fingers.

fish, stinking *See* MOMONI.

fish tapeworm *See* TAPEWORM.

fish, white Non-oily fish, i.e. 1–2% fat, e.g. cod, dogfish, haddock, halibut, plaice, saithe, skate, sole, and whiting. All are similar in nutrient composition; a 150-g portion, steamed (200g with skin and bones), is an exceptionally rich *source of iodine; a rich source of protein, niacin, and selenium; supplies 120kcal (500kJ).

fistula An abnormal passage from an internal organ to the body surface, or between two organs.

five-spice powder Chinese; a mixture of star *anise, anise pepper, fennel, cloves, and cinnamon, and sometimes also powdered dried orange peel.

flabelliferins *Saponins of β-*sitosterol from the fruit pulp of the palmyrah palm, *Borassus flabellifer*, that have hypocholesterolaemic action.

flageolet Small green variety of haricot bean. *See* BEAN, HARICOT.

flamande, à la Dish served with a garnish of braised vegetables and bacon or small pork sausages.

flambé Brandy or another spirit is poured over the food (particularly crêpes and Christmas pudding) and set alight before serving. Also the process of singeing poultry before cooking.

flame photometry Analytical technique in which a solution is vaporized in a flame, and the absorption of light by the analyte is measured at specific wavelengths.

flan Open fruit tart, on a base of pastry or sponge.

flán Spanish; *see* CARAMEL CREAM.

flapjack **1.** Biscuit made from fat, sugar, rolled oats, and syrup. **2.** A thick pancake.

flash evaporation *See* EVAPORATION, FLASH.

flash pasteurization *See* PASTEURIZATION.

flash point With reference to frying oils, the temperature at which the decomposition products can be ignited, but will not support combustion; range between 290 and 330°C. *See also* FIRE POINT; SMOKE POINT.

flatfish *Fish with a flattened shape, including dab, flounder, halibut, plaice, sole, and turbot.

flatogens Substances that cause gas production, *flatulence, in the intestine, by providing fermentable substrate for intestinal bacteria. Those identified include small *oligosaccharides such as raffinose, stachyose, and verbascose in a variety of beans. *See also* NON-STARCH POLYSACCHARIDES.

flat sours Bacteria such as *Bacillus stearothermophilus* render canned food sour by fermenting carbohydrates to lactic, formic, and acetic acids, without gas production. This means that the ends of the can are not swelled out but remain flat. Economically they are the most important of the *thermophilic spoilage agents; some species can grow slowly at 25 °C and thus spoil products after long storage periods.

flatulence (flatus) Production of gas in the intestine; hydrogen, carbon dioxide, and methane. May be caused by a variety of foods including beans, Brussels sprouts, cabbage, cauliflower, onion, radishes, melon, and avocado, which contain *flatogens.

flavanols, flavanones *See* FLAVONOIDS.

flavedo The coloured outer peel layer of citrus fruits, also called the epicarp or zest. It contains the oil sacs, and hence the aromatic oils, and numerous plastids which are green and contain chlorophyll in the unripe fruit, turning yellow or orange in the ripe fruit, when they contain carotene and xanthophyll.

flavin The group of compounds containing the iso-alloxazine ring structure, as in riboflavin (*vitamin B_2), and hence a general term for riboflavin derivatives and analogues.

flavin adenine dinucleotide (FAD) A *coenzyme in oxidation reactions, derived from *vitamin B_2, phosphate, ribose, and adenine.

flavin mononucleotide (FMN) A *coenzyme in oxidation reactions, correctly riboflavin monophosphate. *See* VITAMIN B_2.

flavonal, flavone *See* FLAVONOIDS.

flavonoids Compounds widely distributed in nature as pigments in flowers, fruit, vegetables, and tree barks. They are glycosides of flavones; the sugar moiety may be either rhamnose or rhamnoglucose, and depending on the different reactive groups in the flavone may be a flavonol, flavanol, flavanone, flavonal, or isoflavone.

Some of the flavonoids have pharmacological actions, but they are not known to be dietary essentials, although claims have been made (they were at one time classified as *vitamin P), and are sometimes called bioflavonoids. They make a contribution to the total *antioxidant intake, and some are *phytoestrogens.

flavonols *See* FLAVONOIDS.

flavoproteins Enzymes that contain the vitamin *riboflavin, or a derivative such as flavin adenine dinucleotide or riboflavin monophosphate, as the *prosthetic group. Mainly involved in oxidation reactions in *metabolism.

flavour *See* TASTE; ORGANOLEPTIC.

flavour enhancer (flavour potentiator) A substance that enhances the flavours of other substances without itself imparting any characteristic flavour of its own, e.g. *monosodium glutamate and ribotide as well as sugar, salt, and vinegar in small quantities.

flavour potentiator *See* FLAVOUR ENHANCER.

flavour profile A method of judging the flavour of foods by examination of a list of the separate factors into which the flavour can be analysed, the so-called character notes.

flavours, biogenetic Flavours naturally present in a food.

flavour scalping The adsorption of food flavours by packaging materials; may result in loss of flavour and taste, or may be used deliberately to remove unwanted flavours during storage. *See also* PACKAGING, ACTIVE.

flavours, synthetic Mostly mixtures of *esters, e.g. banana oil is ethyl butyrate and amyl acetate; apple oil is ethyl butyrate, ethyl valerianate, ethyl salicylate, amyl butyrate, glycerol, chloroform, and alcohol; pineapple oil is ethyl and amyl butyrates, acetaldehyde, chloroform, glycerol, and alcohol.

flavours, thermogenetic Flavours formed by heat treatment during food processing and cooking.

flavour threshold The lowest concentration at which a flavour can be detected.

flax The annual herb *Linum usitatissimum*, grown for the stem fibres (used to make linen) and as an oilseed crop, also called linseed. The oil is rich in the essential *fatty acid *α-linolenic acid, and whole or crushed seeds are added to bread and eaten as a health food.

flea seed *See* PSYLLIUM.

fleishig Jewish term for dishes containing meat, which cannot be served with or before milk dishes. *See also* MILCHIG; PAREVE.

fleuron Small crescent-shaped piece of puff pastry used as a garnish.

flint corn *See* MAIZE.

flip Drink made with beaten egg and milk, with added wine or spirit, and sweetened.

flippers *See* SWELLS.

flitch Side of bacon; half a pig, slit down the back, with the legs and shoulders removed.

floats Caribbean (Trinidad); fried biscuits made with yeast dough. *See also* BAKES.

flocculant A substance that causes suspended particles in a suspension to coalesce into a precipitate.

flocculation The process of removing suspended particles in a suspension by coalescing them into larger particles that will precipitate.

flor de Jamaica *See* ROSELLE.

Florence oil Name given to a high grade of *olive oil.

florentine **1.** Thin biscuits with nuts and dried fruit coated with chocolate. **2.** Garnished with spinach.

flounder Small marine *flatfish, *Platichthys flesus*, also called fluke. Speckled flounder is *Paralichthys woolmani*, arrowtooth flounder is *Atheresthes stomias*, winter flounder is *Pseudopleuronectes americanus*.

flounder, Japanese *See* HALIBUT, BASTARD.

flour Most commonly refers to ground wheat, although also used for other cereals and applied to powdered dried matter such as *fish flour, potato flour, etc. Ground wheat yields wholemeal flour (100% extraction); whiter flours are obtained by separation of the bran and the germ from the starchy endosperm. *See also* BREAD; FLOUR, EXTRACTION RATE.

flour, ageing and bleaching *See* AGEING.

flour, agglomerated A dispersible flour, easily wetted, produced by agglomerating the fine particles in steam to yield particles that are greater than 100 μm in diameter, so the flour is dust-free.

flour, air classified Sieving cannot separate particles smaller than 80 μm, and for production of flour with more precisely defined particle size it is subjected to centrifugation against an air current.

flour enrichment The addition of vitamins and minerals to flour, to contain not less than: in the UK, vitamin B_1, 0.24 mg; niacin, 1.6 mg; iron, 1.65 mg; calcium, 120 mg/100 g; in the USA, vitamin B_1, 0.44–0.56 mg; vitamin B_2, 0.2–0.33 mg; niacin, 3.6–4.4 mg; iron, 2.9–3.7 mg/100 g; folic acid 140 μg/100 g.

flour, enzyme inactivated Flour in which the *enzyme α-amylase has been inactivated by heat to prevent degradation of the starch when it is used as a thickening agent in gravies, soups, etc.

flour, extraction rate The yield of flour obtained from wheat in the milling process. A 100% extraction (or straight-run) is wholemeal flour containing all of the grain; lower extraction rates are the whiter flours from which progressively more of the *bran and *germ (and thus B vitamins and iron) are excluded, down to a figure of 72% extraction, which is normal white flour. Patent flour is of lower extraction rate, 30–50%, and so comprises mostly the *endosperm of the grain. *See also* BREAD.

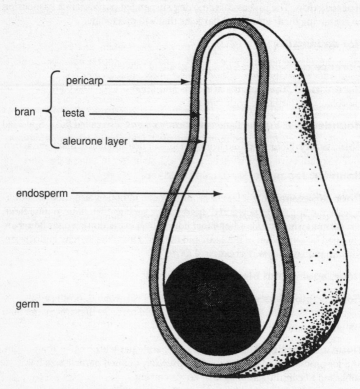

Flour. Cross-section of a grain of wheat

flour, high-ratio Flour of very fine, uniform particle size, treated with chlorine to reduce the *gluten strength. Used for making cakes, since it is possible to add up to 140 parts sugar to 100 parts of this flour, whereas only half this quantity of sugar can be incorporated into ordinary flour. *See* FLOUR STRENGTH.

flour improvers *See* AGEING.

flour, national Name given to the 85% extraction flour when introduced in the UK in February 1941; later called wheatmeal flour, and discontinued in 1956.

flour, patent Flour of 30–50% extraction rate; mainly the endosperm of the grain.

flour, self-raising Wheat flour to which *baking powder has been added to produce carbon dioxide in the presence of water and heat; the dough is thus aerated without fermentation. Usually 'weaker' flours are used (*see* FLOUR STRENGTH). Legally, self-raising flour must contain not less than 0.4% available carbon dioxide.

flour strength A property of the flour proteins enabling the dough to retain gas during fermentation to give a 'bold' loaf. 'Strong' flour is higher in protein, has greater elasticity and resistance to extension, and greater ability to absorb water. A 'weak' flour gives a loaf that lacks volume.

flour, Vienna Especially fine flour used to make *strudel pastry, Vienna bread (*see* BREAD, VIENNA), and cakes.

flour, waxy Flour prepared from varieties of rice and maize that have starch with waxy adhesive properties, and acts as a stabilizer in sauces. *See also* CORNFLOUR.

flour, wheatmeal *See* FLOUR, NATIONAL.

flour, wholemeal Flour made from the entire grain of wheat, i.e. a 100% extraction rate.

fluid balance *See* WATER BALANCE.

fluke Small *flatfish, *Platichthys* spp., also called flounder.

flummery Old English pudding made by boiling down the water from soaked oatmeal until it becomes thick and gelatinous, then mixed with milk, buttermilk, or yoghurt and left to ferment. Similar to *frumenty. Dutch flummery is made with gelatine or isinglass and egg yolk; Spanish flummery with cream, rice flour, and cinnamon.

Fluon *See* PTFE.

fluoridation The addition of *fluoride to drinking water. Drinking water containing about 1 part per million of fluoride protects teeth from decay, and in some areas fluoride is added to drinking water to achieve this level. Naturally, the fluoride content of water ranges between 0.05 and 14ppm. Effect in preventing caries first observed by a dentist, Frederick Motley, in Colorado Springs, 1916.

fluoride The *ion of the element fluorine. Although it occurs in small amounts in plants and animals, and has effects on the formation of dental enamel and bones, it is not considered to be a dietary essential and no deficiency signs are known.

Water containing more than about 12ppm fluoride can lead to chalky white patches on the surface of the teeth, known as mottled enamel. At higher levels there is strong brown mottling of the teeth and inappropriate deposition of fluoride in bones known as fluorosis.

fluorosis Damage to teeth (brown mottling of the enamel) and bones caused by an excessive intake of *fluoride.

flying fish Marine fish, species of the family *Exocoetidae*.

FMN Flavin mononucleotide (correctly riboflavin monophosphate), one of the *coenzymes derived from *vitamin B_2.

FNB The Food and Nutrition Board of the US Institute of Medicine.
((⊕)) SEE WEB LINKS
• The FNB's homepage.

FNIC Food and Nutrition Information Center, located at the National Agricultural Library, part of the US Department of Agriculture.
((⊕)) SEE WEB LINKS
• The FNIC's homepage.

FOAD Fetal origins of adult disease. *See* EPIGENETICS; PROGRAMMING, METABOLIC.

foam cells Lipid-engorged *macrophages that have taken up oxidized *LDL. They infiltrate under the endothelium of blood vessels, undergo necrosis, and deposit lipid as fatty streaks that eventually develop into atherosclerotic plaque. *See also* ATHEROSCLEROSIS.

foccacia *See* BREAD, ITALIAN.

foie gras French for 'fat liver'; the liver of goose or duck that has been specially fed and fattened; may be cooked whole or in smaller pieces.

folacin, folate *See* FOLIC ACID.

folding-in A method of combining a mixture of flour and other ingredients so that it retains its lightness; it is used for mixing meringues, soufflés, and some cakes. Sometimes called cutting and folding. *See also* CUTTING-IN.

folic acid A *vitamin that functions as a carrier of one-carbon units in a variety of metabolic reactions. Essential for the synthesis of purines and pyrimidines (and so for *nucleic acid synthesis and hence cell division); the principal deficiency disease is megaloblastic *anaemia, due to failure of the normal maturation of red *blood cells, with release into the circulation of immature precursor cells. Occurs in foods in various forms, of which probably about half is biologically available. Rich sources include liver, kidney, green leafy vegetables, and yeast.

The *reference intake is 200 µg/day (UK and EU), 400 µg *dietary folate equivalents (USA/Canada). Supplements of 400 µg free folic acid per day, beginning before conception, reduce the incidence of spina bifida and other neural tube defects in babies; it is unlikely that ordinary foods could provide this much folate. High intakes of folate also lower plasma *homocysteine, and may be protective against heart disease. Since 1998 cereal products are, by law, fortified with folic acid in the USA and a number of other countries.

folinic acid The 5-formyl derivative of *folic acid; more stable to oxidation than folic acid itself, and commonly used in pharmaceutical preparations. The synthetic (racemic) compound is known as leucovorin.

follow-up study *See* COHORT STUDY.

fondant Minute sugar crystals in a saturated sugar syrup; used as the creamy filling in chocolates and biscuits and for decorating cakes. Prepared by boiling sugar solution with the addition of glucose syrup (*see* SYRUP, CORN) or an inverting agent (*see* SUGAR, INVERT) and cooling rapidly while stirring.

fondue French or Swiss; cheese melted with wine and herbs, eaten by dipping small squares of bread into the hot mixture. Fondue bourguignonne is small cubes of marinated meat, cooked on a long fork in a vessel of hot oil at the table.

fonduta Italian (Piedmontese); dish made from Fontina cheese and truffles.

fonio A variety of *millet, *Digitaria exilis*, important in West Africa, also known as hungry rice.

food (foodstuffs) Any solid or liquid material consumed by a living organism to supply *energy, and build and replace tissue. Defined by the FAO/WHO *Codex Alimentarius Commission as a substance, whether processed, semi-processed, or raw, which is intended for human consumption and includes drink, chewing gum, and any substance that has been used in the manufacture, preparation, or treatment of food but does not include cosmetics, tobacco, or substances used only as drugs. Defined in EU directives as products intended for human consumption in an unprocessed, processed, or mixed state, with the exception of tobacco products, cosmetics, and pharmaceuticals.

food accounts In dietary and nutritional surveys; the subject is asked to keep a record of the amounts (and/or cost) of all food entering the household, and meals eaten outside the home, over a period of (typically) one week. In some cases an inventory of the food stocks in the home is made at the beginning and end of the study period.

foodaceuticals *See* FOODS, FUNCTIONAL.

food, adverse reactions **1.** Food aversion, unpleasant reactions caused by emotional responses to certain foods rather than to the foods themselves, which are unlikely to occur in blind testing when the foods are disguised. **2.** Food allergy, physiological reactions to specific foods or ingredients due to an immunological response. *Antibodies to the *allergen are formed as a result of previous exposure or sensitization, and cause a variety of symptoms when the food is eaten, including gastro-intestinal disturbances, skin rashes, asthma, and, in severe cases, anaphylactic shock, which may be fatal. **3.** Food intolerance, physiological reactions to specific foods or ingredients which are not due to immunological responses, but may result from the irritant action of spices, pharmacological actions of some naturally occurring compounds (e.g. *caffeine), or an inability to metabolize a component of the food as a result of an enzyme defect.

See also AMINO ACID DISORDERS; DISACCHARIDE INTOLERANCE; GENETIC DISEASE.

food allergy *See* FOOD, ADVERSE REACTIONS.

food balance sheets Data collected by the Statistical Division of the UN Food and Agriculture Organization (*see* FAOSTAT) for individual countries showing the domestic supply of foods (production, imports, exports, changes in stocks), domestic utilization (processing, seed, other uses, waste, and food), and the supply, energy, fat, and protein yield per head of the population.

food-borne disease Infectious or toxic disease caused by agents that enter the body through the consumption of food. The causative agents may be present in food as a result of infection of animals from which food is prepared, or contamination at source or during manufacture, storage, and preparation.

There are three main categories: i) diseases caused by micro-organisms (including parasites) that invade and multiply in the body; ii) diseases caused by toxins produced by micro-organisms growing in the gastro-intestinal tract; iii) diseases caused by the ingestion of food contaminated with poisonous chemicals or containing natural toxins or the toxins produced by micro-organisms in the food. *See also* FOOD POISONING.

food chain The chain between green plants (the primary producers of food energy) through a sequence of organisms in which each eats the one below it in the chain, and is eaten in turn by the one above. Also used for the chain of events from the original source of a foodstuff (from the sea, the soil, or the wild) through all the stages of handling until it reaches the table.

food checklist In dietary and nutritional surveys; subjects are provided with a list of foods, and asked to tick each one that is eaten, with space to add in foods not on the list. Less precise than *household measures method or *weighed inventory method.

food combining *See* DIET, COMBINING.

food composition tables Tables of the chemical composition, energy, and nutrient yield of foods, based on chemical analysis. Although the analyses are performed with great precision, they are, of necessity, only performed on a few samples of each type of food. There is considerable variation, especially in the content of vitamins and minerals, between different samples of the same food, so calculation of nutrient intakes based on use of food composition tables, even when intake has been weighed, can only be considered to be accurate to within about ±10%, at best. First American tables *Chemical Composition of American Food Materials* published by *USDA in 1896; first UK tables *The Chemical Composition of Foods* by R. A. McCance and E. M. Widdowson published in 1940.

food, convenience Processed foods in which a considerable amount of the preparation has already been carried out by the manufacturer, e.g. cooked meats, canned foods, baked foods, breakfast cereals, and frozen meals.

food, designer *See* FOOD, FUNCTIONAL.

food, diabetic Foods that are specially formulated to be suitable for consumption by people with *diabetes mellitus; generally low in carbohydrate (and especially sugar), and frequently containing *sorbitol, *xylulose, or sugar derivatives that are slowly or incompletely absorbed.

food, dietetic *See* FOOD, MEDICAL; PARNUTS.

food, drunken Chinese; meat or fish is highly seasoned and marinated, then steamed or lightly simmered. After draining it is steeped in wine for several days before serving.

food exchange *See* EXCHANGE LIST.

food, exotic Food introduced from a foreign country.

food, fast Fast service foods, a general term used for a limited menu of foods that lend themselves to production-line techniques; suppliers tend to specialize in products such as *hamburgers, *pizzas, chicken, or *sandwiches.

food frequency questionnaire In dietary and nutritional surveys; subjects are asked to indicate how often they eat foods from a list, and the approximate portion size.

food, functional A conventional food (as opposed to a supplement) that is intended to be consumed as part of the normal diet, composed of naturally occurring (as opposed to synthetic) components, perhaps in unnatural concentration or present in foods that would not normally supply them. It has a positive effect on target function(s) beyond simple nutritional value, and may enhance well-being and health or reduce the risk of disease or provide health benefits so as to improve the quality of life. Sometimes known as nutraceuticals, vitafoods, foodaceuticals, phytochemical foods, pharmafoods, and designer foods. *See also* FOSHU; NUTRACEUTICALS; PREBIOTICS; PROBIOTICS.

food, fusion Cuisine using foods and recipes from different countries, especially mixing European and Oriental styles of cooking.

food, genetically modified Produced by *genetic modification of the plant or animal. EU legislation requires that all foods containing genetically modified (GM) protein or DNA, including those in catering outlets, must be so labelled, unless there is less than 0.9% GM material in the food. Products made from GM crops, but highly purified, so that no GM protein or DNA is present, were formerly exempt from labelling, but now must be labelled. Foods manufactured using products of GM organisms (e.g. cheese made using GM *chymosin) and meat, milk, and eggs from animals fed on GM crops need not be labelled as containing GM material.

food, gluten-free Formulated without any wheat or rye protein (although the starch may be used) for people suffering from *coeliac disease. *See also* GLUTEN.

food guides The translation of *nutritional standards and *dietary guidelines in terms of recommendations on daily food intake, forming a framework for selecting the kinds and amounts of foods of various types that, together, provide a nutritionally satisfactory diet. They are based on nutrient standards, composition of foods, food intake patterns, and factors affecting food choice. *See also* EATWELL PLATE; FOOD PYRAMID.

food insecurity The absence of *food security; some sections of the population may not have access to appropriate food for financial or other reasons.

food, instant Dried foods that reconstitute rapidly when water is added, e.g. tea, coffee, milk, soups, precooked cereal products, potatoes, etc. The dried powders may be agglomerated to control particle size and improve solubility (*see* INSTANTIZATION). 'Instant puddings' are formulated with pregelatinized starch and disperse rapidly in cold milk.

food, intermediate moisture These are semi-moist with about 25% (15–50%) moisture but with some of the water bound (and so unavailable to *micro-organisms) by the addition of glycerol, sorbitol, salt, or organic acids, so preventing the growth of micro-organisms.

food intolerance *See* FOOD, ADVERSE REACTIONS.

food intoxication Illness due to ingestion of toxic compounds present in foods as a result of chemical contamination or formation by micro-organisms.

food, medical Defined as foods formulated for consumption or enteral administration under the supervision of a physician and intended for the specific dietary management of diseases or conditions for which there are special nutritional requirements. Also known as dietetic foods. *See also* PARNUTS.

food miles Term used to describe the distances travelled (and amount of aviation fuel used) in the global trade in foods.

food, natural A term widely used but with little meaning and sometimes misleading since all foods come from natural sources. No legal definition seems possible but guidelines suggest the term should be applied only to single foods that have been subjected only to mild processing, i.e. largely by physical methods such as heating, concentrating, freezing, etc., but not chemically or 'severely' processed.

food, novel Foods and ingredients consisting of or containing chemical substances not hitherto used for human consumption, including micro-organisms, fungi, or algae and substances isolated from them, and organisms obtained using genetic modification techniques.

food poisoning May be due to i) contamination with harmful bacteria or other micro-organisms; ii) toxic chemicals; iii) adverse reactions to proteins or other natural constituents of foods (*see* FOOD, ADVERSE REACTIONS); iv) chemical contamination. *See also* *FOOD-BORNE DISEASE.

The commonest bacterial contamination is due to species of *Salmonella*, *Staphylococcus*, *Campylobacter*, *Listeria*, *Bacillus cereus*, and *Clostridium welchii*. Very rarely, food poisoning is due to *Clostridium botulinum*; *see* BOTULISM. Hepatitis A and E viruses are commonly food-borne.

Staphylococcal poisoning causes rapid symptoms (within 2–4 hours): abdominal cramp, nausea, vomiting, and diarrhoea; recovery is normally rapid. Salmonellae produce an *endotoxin that is not destroyed by cooking and causes acute gastroenteritis after 12–24 hours: nausea, vomiting, and diarrhoea may persist for several weeks.

When the cause has not been identified, likely causes are: if onset is in less than 1 hour, probably chemical poisoning; between 1 and 7 hours, probably *Staphylococcus*; between 8 and 14 hours, probably *Clostridium perfringens*; more than 14 hours, some other infectious agents.

food pyramid A way of showing a healthy diet graphically, by grouping foods and showing the amounts of each group that should be eaten each day, based on *nutritional recommendations, as steps in a pyramid. Originally developed in the USA in 1992, and now adopted in many countries, with differences to allow for different national patterns of diet. *See also* EATWELL PLATE.

food science The study of the basic chemical, physical, biochemical, and biophysical properties of foods and their constituents, and of changes that these may undergo during handling, preservation, processing, storage, distribution, and preparation for consumption. Hence the term food scientist.

food security The condition when all people in a country have, at all times, physical and financial access to adequate, safe, and nutritious food to meet their dietary needs and food preferences.

food sensitivity *See* FOOD, ADVERSE REACTIONS.

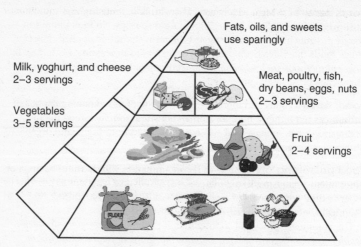

Fats, oils, and sweets use sparingly

Milk, yoghurt, and cheese 2–3 servings

Meat, poultry, fish, dry beans, eggs, nuts 2–3 servings

Vegetables 3–5 servings

Fruit 2–4 servings

Bread, cereal, rice, and pasta 6–11 servings

Food pyramid.

food standard A set of criteria that a food must meet if it is to be suitable for human consumption, such as source, composition, appearance, freshness, permissible additives, and maximum bacterial content.

Food Standards Agency Permanent advisory body to the Department for Environment, Food and Rural Affairs in the UK.

((()) SEE WEB LINKS

• The Food Standard Agency's homepage.

food tables *See* FOOD COMPOSITION TABLES.

food technology The application of science and technology to the treatment, processing, preservation, and distribution of foods. Hence the term food technologist.

foo-foo (fou-fou, fu-fu) Caribbean, West African; small dumplings made by soaking *cassava, boiled green *plantain, or sometimes *yam and allowing it to undergo bacterial fermentation before pounding and boiling.

fool A purée of fruit with cream or custard.

forcemeat A highly seasoned *stuffing made from chopped or minced veal, pork, or sausage meat mixed with onion and a range of herbs (French: *farce*, stuffing).

foremilk *See* COLOSTRUM.

forestière, à la Meat or poultry with a garnish of mushrooms, and ham or bacon.

formiminoglutamic acid *See* FIGLU TEST.

formula feeding *See* FORMULA, INFANT.

formula, hypoallergenic For infants who are intolerant of cow's milk; commonly based on *soya protein or partially hydrolysed cow's milk protein, with many containing *maltodextrins rather than *lactose. *See also* FORMULA, INFANT.

formula, infant Modified milk products or milk substitutes for feeding infants in place of breast-feeding. The nutritional composition is adjusted to approximate to that of breast milk, and is controlled by legal standards. Special formula preparations are available for premature babies and those of very *low birth weight. *See also* FORMULA, HYPOALLERGENIC.

formulation aids Compounds used to produce a desired physical state or texture in food, such as binders, fillers, and plasticizers.

fortification The deliberate addition of specific nutrients to foods as a means of providing the population with an increased level of intake. Generally synonymous with enrichment, supplementation, and restoration; in the USA enrichment is used to mean the addition to foods of nutrients that they do not normally contain, while fortification is the restoration of nutrients lost in processing. *See also* ENRICHMENT; NUTRIFICATION; RESTORATION; WINE, FORTIFIED.

fortune cookies American Chinese; thin folded cookies containing a prediction, served in Chinese restaurants in the USA. Introduced by Los Angeles noodle maker, David Jung, in 1916, apparently derived from the way in which rebels in China traditionally exchanged messages concealed in buns.

FOSHU Japanese term; Foods for Specified Health Use; legally defined in Japan as foods that are expected to have a specific health effect due to relevant constituents, or foods from which allergens have been removed. *See also* FOOD, FUNCTIONAL.

four ale Originally sold at four pence per quart. The four ale bar is the public bar.

four, au Cooked in the oven.

fovantini *See* PASTA.

FPC *See* FISH PROTEIN CONCENTRATE.

fractional test meal A method of examining the secretion of gastric juices; the stomach contents are sampled at intervals via a stomach tube after a test meal of gruel. It is usual to test for total and free acidity, and in addition peptic activity may be measured.

frail A rush basket for raisins, figs, etc.; also a quantity of raisins, usually about 75 lb (34 kg).

frangipane (frangipani) Originally a jasmine perfume which gave its name to an almond cream flavoured with the perfume. Now cake-filling made from eggs, milk, and flour with flavouring, and also a pastry filled with an almond-flavoured mixture, invented by Count Cesare Frangipani in Rome in 1532.

frankfurter A seasoned, smoked beef and pork *sausage (*hot dog). A 100-g portion (two large sausages) is a good *source of protein and niacin; a source of vitamin B_1 and iron; contains 25 g of fat and 1 000 mg of sodium; supplies 270 kcal (1 140 kJ).

frappé 1. Iced, frozen, or chilled. 2. Egg-white and sugar syrup whipped until so aerated that the density reaches 100 g in 200 mL (5 lb per gallon).

free fatty acids (FFA) See FATTY ACIDS, FREE.

free flow agents Alternative name for *anti-caking agents.

free from For a food label or advertising to bear a claim that it is free from fat, saturates, cholesterol, sodium, or alcohol it must contain no more than a specified (low) amount. The precise levels at which such claims are permitted differ from one country to another. In the USA the food so described must contain only a trivial or physiologically insignificant amount of the specified nutrient.

free radicals Highly reactive molecules with an unpaired electron. See ANTIOXIDANT NUTRIENTS.

free range Applied to laying hens kept at no more than one thousand birds to the hectare with free access to open air and grass during daylight.

freeze concentration Concentration of a liquid by freezing out ice, leaving a more concentrated solution; it requires less input of energy, and causes less loss of flavour, than concentration by evaporation. Used in the concentration of fruit juices and *vinegar. See also APPLE JACK.

freezerburn A change in the texture of frozen meat, fish, and poultry during storage due to sublimation of the ice.

freezer temperatures For long-term storage of frozen foods (up to 2–3 months), domestic freezers run at −18 °C (0 °F); in the UK this is a 3-star rated deep freeze. A freezing compartment of a refrigerator (for short-term storage of frozen foods) is between −11 °C (12 °F), 2-star rated, for storage up to 4 weeks; and −4 °C (25 °F), 1-star rated, for storage up to a week. See also DATE MARKING.

A 3-star rated deep freeze with a snowflake symbol is one that is suitable for freezing foods, as opposed to storing ready-frozen food; it has a higher cooling capacity than a simple deep freeze storage cabinet.

freezing In blast freezing the food is frozen by a blast of cold air; small foods may be frozen as a fluidized bed, when it is supported on an upwards blast of cold air. In plate freezing the food is in contact with vertical or horizontal plates of refrigerant-cooled metal. In cryogenic freezing the food is in direct contact with the refrigerant, which is commonly liquid nitrogen or carbon dioxide; the latent heat of sublimation or vaporization comes from the food being treated.

freezing, quick Rapid freezing of food by exposure to a blast of air at a very low temperature. Unlike slow freezing, very small crystals of ice are formed which do not rupture the cells of the food and so the structure is relatively undamaged.

A quick-frozen food is commonly defined as one that has been cooled from a temperature of 0°C to −5°C or lower, in a period of not more than two hours, and then cooled to −18°C.

French dressing *See* SALAD DRESSING.

French fried onions American name for onion rings, fried in batter.

French fries *See* CHIPS.

frenching Breaking up the fibres of meat by cutting, usually diagonally or in a criss-cross pattern.

French paradox The observation that although consumption of saturated *fatty acids in France is relatively high, the incidence of cardiovascular disease is lower than expected.

French toast North American breakfast dish; slices of bread dipped in beaten egg, fried, and served with cinnamon and sugar. Originally called German toast, renamed in 1918. Known in France as *pain perdu* ('lost bread'), a recipe created to use up stale bread.

fresh For food labelling and advertising purposes, the US Food and Drug Administration has defined fresh to mean a food that is raw, has never been frozen or heated, and contains no preservatives. (*Irradiation at low levels is permitted.) 'Fresh frozen' and 'frozen fresh' may be used for foods that are quickly frozen while still fresh, and *blanching before freezing is permitted.

freshening *See* DEBRINING.

friability The hardness of a food and its tendency to crack.

friandises A variety of small sweets, preserved fruits, etc., served as *petits fours or desserts.

fricadelle Minced meat balls.

fricandeau Dish made from the long fillet of *veal, braised or roasted.

fricassée A combination of sautéing and stewing; food is fried briefly with a small amount of fat, then stewed.

frigi-canning A process of preserving food by controlled heating sufficient to destroy the vegetative forms of micro-organisms followed by sealing aseptically and storing at a low temperature, but above freezing point.

frijoles Mexican; dish of boiled fava or lima (butter) beans which have been left to cool, then fried. Also known as refried beans. *See also* BEAN, FRIJOLE.

frisée Alternative name for *endive.

frites *See* CHIPS.

fritter A portion of sweet or savoury food, coated in batter and fried.

fritto misto Italian; small thin pieces of a variety of types of meat, fish, or vegetables, coated with egg and breadcrumbs or batter, and deep fried.

frizzante Italian; lightly sparkling wines, equivalent to French pétillant. *See also* SPUMANTE.

frogs' legs The back and legs of the edible frog, *Rana esculenta*. A 100-g portion is a rich *source of protein; a source of vitamins B_1, B_2, and iron; has a trace of fat; supplies 75 kcal (315 kJ).

fromage à la crème (cœur à la crème) French; sour milk cheese. The curd is drained, mixed with cream, and pressed in heart-shaped moulds.

fromage frais (fromage blanc) French; 'fresh cheese'; soft, unripened cheese, 80% water, made from skimmed or semi-skimmed milk, and which may include added cream; 1–8% fat; a 100-g portion of 8% fat variety is a rich *source of vitamin B_{12}; a good source of vitamin B_2; a source of protein and vitamin A; contains 8 g of fat, 30 mg of sodium, 90 mg of calcium; supplies 115 kcal (470 kJ). *See also* QUARK.

frosting 1. American name for icing on cakes; in the UK icing made from sugar and egg-white (known as American or royal icing). 2. A way of decorating the rim of a glass in which a cold drink is to be served; the edge is coated with whipped egg-white, dipped into caster sugar, and allowed to dry. 3. For a *margarita cocktail the edge of the glass is frosted by dipping it into lemon juice, then salt.

frothing *Dredging the surface of roast joints and poultry with flour before *basting, in order to give an attractive brown finish.

fructans (fructosans) Polysaccharides of *fructose, such as *inulin. Not digested, and hence a part of dietary fibre (*see* FIBRE, DIETARY) or *non-starch polysaccharides. Short-chain fructans have the same sweetness as sucrose, but no energy yield since they are not digested.

fructo-oligosaccharides *See* OLIGOSACCHARIDES.

fructosan *See* FRUCTANS.

fructose Also known as fruit sugar or laevulose. A six-carbon monosaccharide *sugar (hexose) differing from *glucose in having a ketone group (at carbon-2) instead of an aldehyde group (at carbon-1). Found as the free sugar in fruits and honey, and as a constituent of the *disaccharide *sucrose. It is 1.7 times as sweet as sucrose. Commercially prepared by the hydrolysis of the polysaccharide *inulin from the Jerusalem artichoke. *See also* SUGAR, INVERT; SYRUP, HIGH FRUCTOSE.

fruit Botanically, the part of a plant containing seeds; other parts of the plant are vegetables. In general usage, fruits are sweet or eaten sweetened (and hence include rhubarb, which is leaf stalks), while vegetables are savoury or eaten with salt (and hence include tomatoes, which are fruits). *See also* HERB.

fruit acids *See* ACIDS, FRUIT.

fruitarian A person who eats only fruits, nuts, and seeds; an extreme form of *vegetarianism.

fruit cordials (fruit drinks, fruit squash) *See* SOFT DRINKS.

fruit, dried Dried currants, dates, figs, prunes, raisins, and sultanas all have similar analyses; a 100-g portion is a *source of iron and supplies 250 kcal (1050 kJ).

fruit gums *See* GUMDROPS.

fruit juice Legally defined in UK as 100% pure fruit juices made from fresh fruit or fruit concentrates. Only the flesh may be used, not the pith or peel.

fruit leather Extruded mixtures of dried fruit purées and other ingredients (such as sugar, starch, glucose, acid, and pectin), as a snack food.

fruit mince *See* MINCEMEAT.

frumenty An old English pudding made from whole wheat stewed in water for 24 hours until the grains have burst and set in a thick jelly, then boiled with milk. Similar to *flummery.

frying Cooking foods with oil at temperatures well above the boiling point of water. Deep frying, in which a food is completely immersed in oil, reaches a temperature around 185 °C. Nutrient losses are less than in roasting, about 10–20% thiamin, 10–15% riboflavin and nicotinic acid from meat; about 20% thiamin from fish.

frying, dry Frying without the use of fat by using an anti-stick agent of silicone or a vegetable extract.

FSA UK Food Standards Agency, permanent advisory body to the Department for Environment, Food and Rural Affairs. (Also, confusingly, the UK Financial Services Authority which regulates financial services.)

(((●))) SEE WEB LINKS

• The Food Standards Agency's homepage.

fucoidan Complex polysaccharide from brown seaweeds containing fucose, uronic acids, galactose, and xylose.

fudge A sweet in which crystallization of the sugar (graining) is deliberately induced by the addition of *fondant (saturated *syrup containing sugar crystals). *See also* CARAMELS.

fufu West African; starchy paste prepared by pounding steamed or boiled *cassava (or sometimes other root vegetables). Fermented fufu is made from roots that have been soaked in water for several days beforehand.

fuga The Japanese puffer fish, *Fuga* spp., responsible for *tetrodontin poisoning.

fula West African; dumplings made from millet that has been steeped in water overnight, to undergo a lactic acid fermentation, then boiled.

fuller's earth An adsorbent clay, calcium montmorillonite, or bentonite; adsorbs both by physical means and by ion exchange. Used to bleach oils, clarify liquids, and absorb grease.

fumaric acid Unsaturated dicarboxylic acid, used as an acidulant.

fumeol Refined smoke with the bitter principles removed; used for preparing 'liquid' smokes for dipping foods to give them a smoked flavour. *See also* SMOKING.

fumet French; concentrated stock from meat, fish, or vegetables prepared by boiling down to a syrupy consistency, used to give flavour and body to sauces.

fumigants Volatile compounds used for controlling insects or pests.

fumonisins *Mycotoxins produced by *Fusarium moniliforme* and related *Fusarium* spp. The most important substrate is maize. Fumonisin B1 causes animal diseases, including encephalomalacia in horses, pulmonary oedema in pigs, and hepatocarcinoma in rats. There is some evidence that fumonisins in contaminated maize are a factor in human oesophageal cancer.

funchi Caribbean; corn meal pudding.

fungal protein *See* MYCOPROTEIN.

fungi Subdivision of Thallophyta, plants without differentiation into root, stem, and leaf; they cannot photosynthesize, and all are parasites or saprophytes. Microfungi are *moulds, as opposed to larger fungi, which are *mushrooms and toadstools; mycorrhizal fungi form symbiotic associations with tree roots. *Yeasts are sometimes classed with fungi.

Species of moulds such as *Penicillium*, *Aspergillus*, etc., are important causes of food spoilage in the presence of oxygen and relatively high humidity. Those that produce toxins (*mycotoxins) are especially problematical. On the other hand species of *Penicillium* such as *P. cambertii* and *P. roquefortii* are desirable and essential in the ripening of certain *cheeses.

A number of larger fungi (*mushrooms) are cultivated, and other wild species are harvested for their delicate flavour. The mycelium of smaller fungi (including *Graphium*, *Fusarium*, and *Rhizopus* species) are grown commercially on waste carbohydrate as a rich source of protein for food manufacture. *See* MYCOPROTEIN.

furcellaran Danish agar; a sulphated polysaccharide extracted from the red alga, *Furcellaria fastigiata*, structurally similar to *carrageenan; used as a gelling agent.

Fusarium venenatum A filamentous fungus used for production of *mycoprotein, and now used as an expression system for production of enzymes and other products as a result of *genetic modification.

fusel oil A mixture of organic acids, higher alcohols (propyl, butyl, and amyl), aldehydes, and esters, known collectively as *congeners, produced in alcoholic fermentation.

It is present in low concentration in wines and beer, and in high concentration in pot-still spirit. On maturation of the liquor fusel oil changes and imparts the special flavour to the spirit. Many of the symptoms of *hangover can be attributed to fusel oil in alcoholic beverages.

fu-yung Chinese dishes prepared with egg-white and cornflour mixed with minced chicken; commonly applied to a variety of dishes with egg scrambled into the mixture.

F value A unit of measurement used to compare relative sterilizing effects of different procedures; equal to 1 minute at 121.1°C.

gabelle French, historical; salt tax.

gaffelbitar Semi-preserved *herring in which microbial growth is checked by the addition of salt at a concentration of 10–12%, and sometimes *benzoic acid as a preservative.

gage *See* GREENGAGE.

galactans *Polysaccharides composed of *galactose derivatives; a major constituent of *carageenan.

galactitol *See* DULCITOL.

galactolipids Glycolipids in the myelin sheath of nerves that contain galactose and/or N-acetylgalactosamine; also known as cerebrosides.

galactomannans Storage polysaccharides consisting of galactose and mannose, found in bacteria, yeasts, and legumes.

galacto-oligosaccharides *See* OLIGOSACCHARIDES.

galactosaemia Genetic disease; inability to metabolize the sugar *galactose. Unless galactose is excluded from the diet, the infants suffer mental retardation, growth failure, vomiting, and jaundice, with enlargement of liver and spleen and development of cataracts. Special infant foods are prepared entirely free from *lactose, which is the only important source of galactose in the diet.

galactose A six-carbon sugar (a monosaccharide) differing from *glucose only in the orientation of the hydroxyl group on carbon-4. It is about one-third as sweet as sucrose. The main dietary source is the disaccharide *lactose in milk, and it is important in formation of the *galactolipids (cerebrosides) of nerve tissue. *See also* GALACTOSAEMIA.

galangal The fresh or dried rhizome of the tropical Asian herbs *Alpinia galanga* (greater galangal), *A. officinarum* (lesser galangal), or *Kaempferia galangal*; related to ginger, with a pungent peppery flavour, widely used in Thai cooking.

galanin A *neuropeptide that inhibits the secretion of transmitters in the nervous system and hormones in the endocrine system. Central nervous system actions include stimulation of eating, especially fat; galanin antagonists suppress fat intake.

galantine A dish of white meat or poultry, boned, rolled, cooked with herbs, glazed with *aspic jelly, and served cold.

galenicals Crude drugs, infusions, decoctions, and tinctures prepared from medicinal plants.

galette Round, flat cake of flaky pastry, or thin fried potato cakes or pancakes.

galgal The fruit of *Citrus pseudolimon*, cultivated in India for manufacture of pickles.

gallates Salts and esters of gallic acid, found in many plants. Used in making dyes and inks, and medicinally as an astringent. Propyl, octyl, and dodecyl gallates are legally permitted antioxidants in foods.

gall bladder The organ situated in the liver which stores the *bile formed in the liver before its secretion into the small intestine. *See* GASTRO-INTESTINAL TRACT.

gallimaufry Medieval; chicken stew with bacon, mustard, and wine.

gallon A unit of volume. The imperial gallon is 4.546 litres, and the US (Queen Anne) gallon is 3.7853 litres; therefore 1 imperial gallon = 1.2 US gallons.

gallstones (cholelithiasis) Concretions composed of cholesterol, bile pigments, and calcium salts, formed in the bile duct of the *gall-bladder when the bile becomes supersaturated.

GALT Gut-associated lymphoid tissue; the immune system cells associated with the *gastro-intestinal tract, comprising up to 70% of total body immune system tissue.

gamay A *grape variety widely used for *wine making, not one of the classic varieties. The grape of the Beaujolais and Mâcon districts of France, making light, fragrant, red wines that are best drunk young.

game Non-domesticated (i.e. wild) animals and birds shot for sport and eaten. *Rabbit and *pigeon may be shot at any time, but other game species, such as *grouse, *hare, *partridge, *pheasant, *quail, deer (*venison), and wild *duck may not be shot during the close season, to protect breeding stocks. Game birds are generally raised on farms to provide sport, rather than being hunted in the wild, and increasingly game species are farmed and killed in conventional humane ways to provide food. Traditionally, game is hung for several days to soften the meat, whereupon it develops a strong flavour.

game chips *See* POTATO CHIPS.

gammelost Norwegian; dark brown cheese with mould growth on the rind that is pressed into the paste while it is ripening.

gammon Hind legs of pig, cured while still part of the carcass. Ham is the same part of the pig but is cured after removal from the carcass. *See also* BACON; PORK.

garam masala A mixture of aromatic spices widely used in Indian cooking; contains powdered black pepper, cumin, cinnamon, cloves, mace, cardamom seeds, and sometimes also coriander and/or bay leaf.

garbanzo *See* CHICKPEA.

garbellers 15th century; people appointed by the Grocers' Company of London to inspect spices and other groceries and destroy adulterated products.

garbias *See* GARBURE.

garbure Southern French; thick soup or vegetable purée. Spanish equivalent is garbias.

garfish Marine fish, *Belone belone*.

garhi yakhni *See* YAKHNI.

gari **1.** Fermented *cassava meal. Cassava is grated, soaked in water, and left to undergo bacterial fermentation for 2–5 days in permeable sacks so that liquid drains out; the resulting solid mass is sieved and lightly toasted or fried (garified). **2.** Japanese; pickled *ginger.

Garibaldi biscuit Square or rectangular biscuit with a layer of currants inside (popularly known as squashed-fly biscuit).

garlic The bulb of *Allium sativum* with a pungent odour when crushed, widely used to flavour foods. There is some evidence that garlic has a beneficial effect in lowering blood *cholesterol. Elephant garlic is *Allium ampeloprasum*, a large bulb (up to 500g) with a mild garlic flavour.

garlic mustard A common wild plant of hedgerows and woodland, *Alliaria petiolata*; the leaves have a garlic-like flavour and can be used in salads or cooked as a vegetable.

garnish Small pieces of vegetables, herbs, croûtons, pastry, etc., used to decorate a dish before serving.

garrafeira Portuguese; aged, strong table wines.

Gas-6 Growth arrest-specific gene 6. The gene product contains γ-*carboxyglutamate, and hence requires *vitamin K for its synthesis; it is important in the regulation of growth and development. Impairment of its synthesis in women treated with *Warfarin during pregnancy leads to the neurological abnormalities of the *fetal Warfarin syndrome.

gastrectomy Surgical removal of all or part of the stomach.

gastric acid *See* GASTRIC SECRETION.

gastric inhibitory peptide *See* GIP.

gastric phase of eating Increased *gastric secretion in response to stretching of mechanoreceptors caused by food entering the stomach.

gastric secretion Gastric juice contains the *enzymes *chymosin (in infants) and lipase, the inactive precursor of pepsin (pepsinogen), *intrinsic factor, mucin, and hydrochloric acid. The acid is secreted by the parietal cells at a strength of 0.16mol/L (0.5–0.6% acid); the same cells also secrete intrinsic factor, and failure of acid secretion (*achlorhydria) is associated with a failure to absorb *vitamin B_{12} because of lack of intrinsic factor (*see* ANAEMIA, PERNICIOUS) and reduced absorption of iron. Gastric secretion declines with increasing age, as a result of gastric *atrophy.
  Pepsinogen is secreted by the chief cells of the gastric mucosa, and is activated to pepsin by either gastric acid or the action of existing pepsin; it is a proteolytic enzyme. The only function of chymosin is to coagulate milk; the lipase hydrolyses a proportion of dietary fat.

gastric ulcer *See* ULCER.

gastrin Polypeptide *hormone secreted by the stomach in response to food (especially meat) which stimulates *gastric and pancreatic secretion. Also secreted by the G-cells of the *pancreas.

gastrinoma *Gastrin-secreting tumour of the G-cells of the *pancreas. *See also* ZOLLINGER–ELLISON SYNDROME.

gastrin-releasing peptide A *neuropeptide secreted by the vagus (10th cranial) nerve that stimulates the secretion of gastrin by the G-cells of the gastric mucosa.

gastritis Inflammation of the mucosal lining of the stomach; may result from infection or excessive alcohol consumption. Atrophic gastritis is the progressive loss of gastric secretion with increasing age.

gastro enteritis Inflammation of the mucosal lining of the stomach and/or small or large intestine, normally resulting from infection.

gastro enterology The study and treatment of diseases of the *gastro-intestinal tract.

gastroferrin Glycoprotein secreted by the *oxyntic cells of the gastric mucosa that binds *iron in the stomach, so enhancing iron absorption by preventing the formation of insoluble Fe^{2+} salts in the duodenum and jejunum.

gastro-intestinal tract The whole of the digestive tract, from the mouth to the anus. Average length 4.5 m (15 feet).

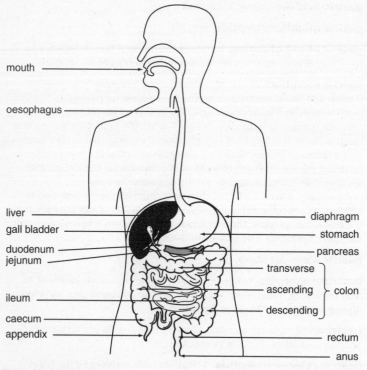

mouth

oesophagus

liver

gall bladder

duodenum

jejunum

ileum

caecum

appendix

diaphragm

stomach

pancreas

transverse

ascending

descending

colon

rectum

anus

Gastro-intestinal tract.

gastroplasty Surgical alteration of the shape and capacity of the stomach, without removing any part. Has been used as a treatment for severe *obesity.

gastrostomy feeding Feeding a liquid diet directly into the stomach through a tube that has been surgically introduced through the abdominal wall. *See also* NASOGASTRIC TUBE; NUTRITION, ENTERAL.

gâteau Elaborate cake with sponge, biscuit, or pastry base, topped with fruit, jelly, and cream. Black Forest gâteau is a chocolate sponge with whipped cream and cherries, decorated with chocolate curlicues.

gaufre *See* WAFFLE.

gaufrette French; wafer.

gavage The process of feeding liquids by tube directly into the stomach.

gazpacho Spanish; uncooked vegetable soup made by blending green pepper, cucumber, onions, and tomatoes, with breadcrumbs, olive oil, vinegar, and garlic; served ice-cold with a garnish of chopped vegetables.

Gc globulin The plasma *vitamin D binding protein, also known as the group-specific component or transcalciferin. There is considerable *polymorphism in human populations, and it has been widely used in studies of population genetics and forensic medicine.

GC-MS Gas chromatography linked to a mass spectrometer as the detection system.

gean Scottish name for the fruit of *Prunus avium avium*; also known as wild cherry, sweet cherry, and mazzard.

gefillte fish (gefilte, gefültte) Literally, German for stuffed fish. The dish is of Russian or Polish origin where it is commonly referred to as Jewish fish. The fish is served whole with the filleted portion chopped and stuffed back between the skin and the backbone. More frequently today, the fish is simply chopped and made into balls, which are either fried or boiled. In the UK it has been legally referred to as 'fish cutlets in fish sauce' rather than *fish cake.

geist German name for liqueur made by macerating soft fruit in alcohol, then distilling.

gel A sol or colloidal suspension that has set to a jelly.

gelatine A soluble protein prepared from *collagen, bones, or skins or scraps from skins of animals by boiling with water or by acid or alkaline extraction. Used for sugar confectionery, in canned meats, for table jellies, and in pharmaceutical capsules. Gelatine from fish (especially the swim bladder) is *isinglass. As a protein it is of poor nutritional value, since it lacks *tryptophan, and has an unusual amino acid composition: 14% hydroxyproline, 16% proline, and 26% glycine.

gelatine, Chinese *See* AGAR.

gelatine sugar *See* GLYCINE.

gelatinization Formation of a water-retentive gel by expansion of *starch granules when heated in moist conditions.

gelation The formation of the pectin gel that gives fruit preserves and jams their texture; dependent on the pectin, sugar, acid, and water content of the fruit.

gel electrophoresis *See* ELECTROPHORESIS.

gellan gum Extracellular *polysaccharide produced by *Sphingomonas paucimobilis* (formerly *Pseudomonas elodea*); a polymer of tetrasaccharide units consisting of acyl-glucose, glucose, rhamnose, and glucuronic acid. Used as a gelling agent and thickener in foods.

gene construct The exogenous *DNA integrated into the host genome in the process of producing a *transgenic organism, including the promoter and control regions as well as the DNA sequence coding for the protein.

gene, marker A readily detectable gene (e.g. conferring antibiotic or herbicide resistance) transferred into a transgenic organism together with the gene of interest, to permit ready identification of those cells in which the gene transfer has been achieved. Unlike a reporter gene (*see* GENE, REPORTER) it confers a survival advantage on the transfected cells when they are grown in the presence of the antibiotic or herbicide.

gene probe Sequences of DNA labelled with radioactive isotopes, fluorescent dyes, or enzymes that bind selectively to specific genes, allowing identification or isolation.

gene, reporter A readily detectable gene (e.g. that for β-*glucuronidase, firefly *luciferase, or *green fluorescent protein) transferred into a transgenic organism together with the gene of interest, to permit ready identification of those cells in which the gene transfer has been achieved. Unlike a marker gene (*see* GENE, MARKER) it does not confer any advantage on the transfected cells under laboratory conditions, but leads to the expression of a readily measured enzyme.

generic descriptor The name used to cover the different chemical forms of a *vitamin that have the same biological activity. *See also* VITAMERS.

generoso Portuguese, Spanish; fortified wines.

genetically modified plants Two methods are used to transfer foreign *DNA into plant cells: i) the gene can be incorporated into the genome of a pathogenic bacterium (*Agrobacterium* spp.); ii) direct gene transfer methods either by hydrolysing the cellulose cell wall enzymically, followed by stimulation of DNA uptake into the resulting protoplasts by use of polyethylene glycol or electric pulses, or by shooting DNA-coated particles of heavy metal into tissues (the technique of particle bombardment or biolistic transformation).

genetic disease Also known as inborn error of metabolism. Disease due to a single defective gene, with a characteristic pattern of inheritance in families. Many affect the ability to metabolize individual *amino acids or *carbohydrates and can be treated by dietary restriction. *See also* AMINO ACID DISORDERS; DISACCHARIDE INTOLERANCE.

genetic engineering Overall term for procedures that result in a directed alteration of the genotype of an organism.

genetic modification A change in the genes in a living organism, as occurs in nature, and which has been used for many years in selective breeding, or, more quickly and specifically, in the laboratory (*genetic engineering). *See also* FOOD, GENETICALLY MODIFIED.

geneva *See* GIN.

genistein An isoflavone (*see* FLAVONOIDS) that has *phytoestrogen activity. Occurs in foods mainly as the glycoside genistin.

genistin *See* GENISTEIN.

genoa cake A rich, dark, fruit cake containing glacé cherries and decorated with almonds or Brazil nuts.

genoese Whisked sponge mixture of eggs, sugar, flour, and soft creamed butter. Victoria sponge is a type of genoese.

genome The complete sequence of *genes in an organism, hence the science of genomics.

genomics, nutritional General term to include both *nutrigenetics and *nutrigenomics.

genotype The genetic makeup of an organism; *see also* PHENOTYPE.

gentiobiose A disaccharide consisting of two molecules of glucose joined $1,6\text{-}\beta$.

Gerber test An analytical test for the fat (*cream) in milk.

German pound cake Similar to *genoa cake, but containing less fruit and no almonds.

German toast *See* FRENCH TOAST.

germ, wheat The embryo or sprouting portion of *wheat, comprising about 2.5% of the seed. Contains 64% of the vitamin B_1, 26% of the vitamin B_2, 21% of the vitamin B_6, and most of the fat of the wheat grain. It is discarded, with the bran, when the grain is milled to white *flour. *See* FLOUR, EXTRACTION RATE.

geuze (gueuze) *See* BEER.

gewürztraminer A *grape variety widely used for *wine making, not one of the classic varieties; the wines have a characteristic spicy flavour and aroma.

GFP *See* GREEN FLUORESCENT PROTEIN.

GH Growth hormone; *see* SOMATOTROPHIN.

ghania Freshwater fish, a member of the *carp family, *Labeo gonius*.

ghatti gum *See* GUM, GHATTI.

ghee *See* BUTTER, CLARIFIED.

gherkin The true or West Indian gherkin is a small *cucumber, *Cucumis anguira*, used mainly for pickling. Immature fruits of the common cucumber, *C. sativus*, are also called gherkins when they are pickled.

GHIH Growth hormone inhibiting hormone; *see* SOMATOSTATIN.

ghrelin A peptide *hormone secreted by cells in the gastro-intestinal tract that both stimulates the secretion of growth hormone and regulates feeding behaviour and energy balance by acting on the hypothalamus. Secretion is increased in the fasting state and under conditions of negative energy balance, and decreased under conditions of positive energy balance. Secretion is increased in *anorexia and is low in the fasting state in *obesity.

ghrt *See* BUTTER, CLARIFIED.

GI *See* GLYCAEMIC INDEX.

giardiasis Intestinal inflammation and *diarrhoea caused by infection with the protozoan parasite *Giardia lamblia* (syn. *G. intestinalis*), as a result of faecal contamination of food and water. The infectious phase is a resistant oocyst that is activated on exposure to gastric acidity and intestinal alkalinity, leading to formation of trophozoites that attach to the apical surfaces of enterocytes and multiply. Detachment from enterocytes causes trophozoites to encyst; the cysts are excreted in faeces. Usually self-limiting, but chronic infection can lead to loss of intestinal *lactase and other disaccharidases.

giberellins Plant growth substances derived from giberellic acid, originally found in the fungus *Gibberella fujikuroi* growing on rice. About thirty giberellins are known; they cause stem extension and allow mutant dwarf forms of plants to revert to normal size, induce flower formation, and break bud dormancy. They are used to accelerate the germination of barley for *malting.

gibier French; wild animals that are hunted for food; *game.

giblets The edible part of the entrails of a bird; gizzard, liver, heart, and neck.

gigot French; leg of lamb or mutton. In Ireland, gigot chops are neck chops used for stewing.

gill Obsolete British measure of liquid, 5 or 10 fl oz (¼ or ½ pint), varying regionally.

gin Alcoholic drink made by distilling fermented cereal, flavoured mainly with juniper berries together with coriander seeds, angelica, cinnamon, orange and lemon peel, and sometimes other botanicals. Distillate is diluted to 40% *alcohol by volume, 220 kcal (925 kJ) per 100 mL. The name is derived from the French *genièvre* (juniper); originally known as geneva, Schiedam, or hollands, since it is Dutch in origin.

There are two types of English gin: Plymouth gin, with a fuller flavour, and London gin. Plymouth gin has a protected designation, and legally may be distilled only in Plymouth (Devon); it is made by adding the botanicals to the still, while for London gin the botanical extracts are added to the distilled liquor. Dutch and German gins are more strongly flavoured than English or American; steinhäger and schinkenhäger are distilled from a mash of wheat, barley, and juniper berries; wacholder is made from neutral spirit flavoured with juniper. Dutch gin may be *jonge* (young) or *oude* (aged, matured).

Pink gin is gin mixed with *Angostura bitters.

gingelly (gingili) *See* SESAME.

ginger The rhizome of *Zingiber officinale* (syn. *Amomum zingiber*) used as a spice. The first oriental spice to be grown in the New World; Jamaican ginger first reached Europe in 1585. Preserved ginger is made from young fleshy rhizomes boiled with sugar and either packed in syrup or crystallized. Japanese pickled ginger (gari) is made from paper-thin slices of rhizome pickled in vinegar.

ginger ale Carbonated beverage flavoured with *ginger and other flavourings.

ginger beer Alcoholic beverage made by fermenting sugar solution flavoured with *ginger.

gingerbread Cake or biscuits flavoured with ginger and treacle, often baked in the shape of an animal or person, and glazed.

ginger paralysis *See* JAMAICA GINGER PARALYSIS.

gingivitis Inflammation, swelling, and bleeding of the gums; may be due to *scurvy, but most commonly the result of poor dental hygiene. *See also* PERIODONTITIS.

gingko The maidenhair tree, *Gingko biloba*. The seeds are edible when roasted but may be toxic when raw. Extracts from the leaves are used as a herbal remedy; they contain potentially active *flavonoids and *terpenes, but there is limited evidence of efficacy.

gin-nan *Food poisoning associated with excessive consumption of (uncooked) *gingko seeds.

ginseng Herbal products from the roots of three species; Korean or Chinese ginseng is *Panax ginseng*, Siberian is *Eleutherococcus senticosus*, American is *P. quinquefolius*. Reported to have an immunostimulant action, to increase work capacity, and act as an *adaptogen, with limited evidence of efficacy.

GIP Glucose-dependent insulinotropic peptide, secreted by the duodenal mucosa. It was originally thought to act as inhibitor of *gastric acid secretion and named gastric inhibitory peptide. Like *GLP-1 it stimulates *insulin secretion before glucose has been absorbed, so that there is a higher insulin response to oral than to intravenous glucose. *See also* INCRETINS.

gipping (of fish) Partial evisceration to remove intestines but not pyloric caeca which contains enzymes responsible for the characteristic flavour of *herring when it is subsequently salted.

girolle French name for the chanterelle, an edible wild *mushroom, *Cantharellus cibarius*.

giros *See* KEBAB.

GISSI-prevenzione trial Gruppo Italiano per la Sperimentazione della Streptochinasi nell'Infarto Miocardico; intervention trial in the 1980s with supplements of long-chain ω3 polyunsaturated fatty acids and/or vitamin E in people who had survived a myocardial infarction.

GI tract *See* GASTRO-INTESTINAL TRACT.

gizzard Muscular, thick-walled stomach in birds; its function is to grind food, typically with swallowed grit and small stones.

gjetost Norwegian; sweet, semi-caramelized hard cheese made from whey. Normally goat's milk; mysost is similar, made from cow's milk.

GL *See* GLYCAEMIC LOAD.

glacé **1.** Iced or frozen. **2.** Having a smooth glossy surface or glaze.

Glasgow magistrate *see* HERRING, RED Alternative name for red herring (*s*).

glaze Glossy surface on sweet or savoury food.

glessie *See* TOFFEE.

gliadin A group of cereal proteins that are soluble in 65–75% alcohol. Now more correctly known as prolamins. *See also* COELIAC DISEASE; GLUTEN.

globins *Proteins that are rich in the *amino acid *histidine (and hence basic), relatively deficient in *isoleucine, and contain average amounts of *arginine and *tryptophan. Often found as the protein part of conjugated proteins such as haemoglobin.

globulins Globular (as opposed to fibrous) *proteins that are relatively insoluble in water, but soluble in dilute salt solutions. They occur in blood (serum globulins, including immunoglobulins), milk (lactoglobulins), and some plants.

glossitis Inflammation of the tongue; may be one of the signs of *riboflavin deficiency.

Gloucester cheese Originally there were Single and Double Gloucester versions with minor differences; the commonest now is Double Gloucester.

GLP-1 Glucagon-like peptide-1, a peptide *hormone secreted by cells of the distal ileum in response to food intake; formed by post-synthetic modification of proglucagon, and formerly known as enteroglucagon. Like *GIP it stimulates *insulin secretion before glucose has been absorbed, so that there is a higher insulin response to oral than to intravenous glucose. *See also* INCRETINS.

glucagon A *hormone secreted by the α-islet cells of the *pancreas which causes an increase in blood glucose by increasing the breakdown of liver *glycogen and stimulating the synthesis of *glucose from *amino acids (*gluconeogenesis).

glucan Soluble undigested complex polysaccharide of glucose; found especially in oats, barley, and rye. *See also* FIBRE, SOLUBLE; NON-STARCH POLYSACCHARIDES.

glucaric acid Alternative name for saccharic acid, the dicarboxylic acid derived from *glucose.

glucide (gluside) Name occasionally used for *saccharin.

glucitol Obsolete name for sorbitol, one of the *sugar alcohols or *glycitols.

glucocorticoids The *steroid *hormones secreted by the adrenal cortex which regulate carbohydrate metabolism.

glucokinase An *isoenzyme of *hexokinase that is specific for glucose, and has a high K_m (*see* MICHAELIS EQUATION); found only in liver and β-islet cells of the *pancreas. *See also* MODY.

glucomannan A polysaccharide consisting of *glucose and *mannose.

gluconeogenesis The metabolic pathways involved in the synthesis of *glucose from non-carbohydrate precursors such as glycerol, lactate, and amino acids.

gluconic acid The acid formed by oxidation of the hydroxyl group on carbon-1 of glucose to a carboxylic acid group. Also termed dextronic acid, maltonic acid, and glycogenic acid.

glucono-δ-lactone (glucono-delta-lactone) A derivative (the lactone) of *gluconic acid; slowly liberates acid at a controlled rate; used in chemically leavened (aerated) *bread to liberate carbon dioxide from bicarbonate.

glucosaccharic acid *See* SACCHARIC ACID.

glucosamine The amino derivative of *glucose, a constituent of a variety of complex *polysaccharides. A component of cartilage in joints; glucosamine sulphate has been used in treatment of osteoarthritis with some evidence of efficacy.

glucosan A general term for polysaccharides of *glucose, such as *starch, *cellulose, and *glycogen.

glucose A six-carbon monosaccharide sugar (hexose), $C_6H_{12}O_6$, occurring free in plant and animal tissues and formed by the hydrolysis of *starch and *glycogen. Also known as dextrose, grape sugar, and blood sugar.

The major dietary carbohydrates are starches, which are polymers of glucose and disaccharides; sucrose (glucose-fructose); lactose (glucose-galactose); maltose and isomaltose, which are dimers of glucose.

It is used in the manufacture of confectionery, since its mixture with *fructose prevents sucrose from crystallizing (*see* SWEETS, BOILED); it is 74% as sweet as sucrose.

glucose, confectioners' Glucose syrups (*see* SYRUP, CORN) are known as glucose in confectionery making (*glucose is referred to as dextrose).

glucose metabolism Process through which glucose is oxidized to carbon dioxide and water as a metabolic fuel (i.e. to provide energy). The overall reaction is: $C_6H_{12}O_6 + 6O_2 \rightarrow 6CO_2 + 6H_2O$, occurring in a series of stages. The oxidation of glucose to carbon dioxide and water yields 16.4 kJ (3.9 kcal)/g; 2.88 MJ (686 kcal)/mol.

The first series of reactions does not require oxygen and is referred to as (anaerobic) glycolysis or glucose fermentation, yielding two molecules of the three-carbon compound pyruvic acid. Under anaerobic conditions this can be reduced to *lactic acid.

Pyruvic acid is normally oxidized to acetyl CoA, which is then oxidized to carbon dioxide and water in a series of reactions known as the *citric acid cycle. Both glycolysis and the citric acid cycle are linked to the formation of *ATP from ADP and phosphate, as a metabolically usable energy source.

glucose oxidase *Enzyme that oxidizes glucose to gluconic acid, with the formation of hydrogen peroxide. Used for specific quantitative determination of glucose, including urinary glucose excreted in *diabetes, and also to remove traces of glucose from foodstuffs (e.g. from dried egg to prevent the *Maillard reaction during storage). Originally isolated from the mould *Penicillium notatum* and called notatin.

glucose 6-phosphate dehydrogenase deficiency *See* FAVISM.

glucose syrups *See* DEXTROSE EQUIVALENT VALUE; SYRUP, CORN.

glucose tolerance The ability of the body to deal with a relatively large dose of glucose is used to diagnose *diabetes mellitus. The fasting subject ingests 75g of glucose (or 1g/kg body weight) and the concentration of blood glucose is measured at intervals. In normal subjects the fasting glucose concentration is between 4.5 and 5.5mmol/L, and rises to about 7.5mmol/L, returning to the starting level within 1–1½ hours. In diabetics, the blood glucose concentration rises considerably higher and takes longer to return to the baseline value. The graph of the results forms a glucose-tolerance curve.

glucose tolerance factor *See* CHROMIUM.

glucosides Complexes of substances with glucose. The general name for such complexes with other sugars is glycosides.

glucosinolates Substances occurring widely in plants of the genus *Brassica* (e.g. *broccoli, *Brussels sprouts, *cabbage); broken down by the *enzyme myrosinase to yield, among other products, the mustard oils which are responsible for the pungent flavour (especially in mustard and horseradish). Some glucosinolates interfere with the metabolism of *iodine by the *thyroid gland, and hence are *goitrogens. There is evidence that the various glucosinolates in vegetables may have useful anti-cancer activity, since they increase the rate at which a variety of potentially toxic and carcinogenic compounds are conjugated and excreted. *See also* METABOLISM, PHASE I; METABOLISM, PHASE II.

glucostatic mechanism of appetite control Control of appetite, hunger, and satiety by receptors in the hypothalamus that are sensitive to arterio-venous differences in blood glucose concentration.

glucosuria (glycosuria) Appearance of *glucose in the urine, as in *diabetes mellitus and after the administration of drugs that lower the renal threshold.

glucuronic acid The acid derived from glucose by the oxidation of the hydroxyl group on carbon-6. Many substances, including hormones and potentially toxic ingested substances, are excreted as conjugates with glucuronic acid, known as *glucuronides. It is present in various complex *polysaccharides.

glucuronides A variety of compounds are metabolized by conjugation with *glucuronic acid to yield water-soluble derivatives for excretion from the body. *See also* METABOLISM, PHASE II.

glühwein Austrian, German; spiced hot wine punch, generally fortified by the addition of rum.

GLUT The family of glucose transport proteins that permit passive (carrier-mediated) uptake of glucose into cells—i.e. not accumulation against a concentration gradient. *See also* SGLT; TRANSPORT, ACTIVE; TRANSPORT, PASSIVE.

glutamate Salts of *glutamic acid.

glutamic acid A non-essential *amino acid; it is acidic since it has two carboxylic acid groups; its amide is glutamine. *See also* MONOSODIUM GLUTAMATE.

glutamine A non-essential amino acid, the amide of *glutamic acid.

glutathione A tripeptide (γ-glutamyl-cysteinyl-glycine), important in maintenance of intracellular redox state and antioxidant protection. The reduced form is GSH; the sulphydryl group of the cysteine residue is oxidized to form a disulphide bridge, and the oxidized peptide is abbreviated to GSSG.

glutathione peroxidase *Selenium-containing *enzyme that protects tissues from oxidative damage by removing peroxides resulting from free radical action, linked to oxidation of *glutathione; part of the body's *antioxidant protection.

glutathione reductase *Enzyme in red *blood cells for which flavin adenine dinucleotide (derived from *vitamin B_2) is the cofactor. Activation of this enzyme *in vitro* by added cofactor provides a means of assessing vitamin B_2 nutritional status, sometimes known as the erythrocyte glutathione reductase activation coefficient (EGRac) test. *See also* ENZYME ACTIVATION ASSAYS.

glutelins Proteins insoluble in water and neutral salt solutions but soluble in dilute acids and alkalis.

gluten The protein complex in wheat, and to a lesser extent rye, which gives dough the viscid property that holds gas when it rises. There is none in oats, barley, or maize. It is a mixture of two proteins, gliadin and glutelin. Allergy to, or intolerance of, the *gliadin fraction of gluten is *coeliac disease.

In the undamaged state with extensible properties it is termed vital gluten; when overheated, these properties are lost and the product, devitalized gluten, is used for protein enrichment of foods. *See also* FOOD, GLUTEN-FREE.

gluten-sensitive enteropathy *See* COELIAC DISEASE.

glutose A six-carbon sugar (hexose) with a keto group on carbon-3; it is not metabolized and non-fermentable.

glycaemic index The ability of a carbohydrate to increase blood glucose, compared with the same amount of glucose: the increase in blood glucose over 2 hours after ingesting 50g of available carbohydrate, expressed as a percentage of that after 50g of glucose or a reference carbohydrate food such as bread or potato. *See also* GLYCAEMIC LOAD; INSULINAEMIC INDEX.

glycaemic load The product of multiplying the amount of carbohydrate in a food by its *glycaemic index.

glycation Any non-enzymic reaction between glucose or another reducing sugar and amino groups in proteins, resulting in formation of a glycoprotein. Glycation of proteins is the basis of many of the adverse effects of poor glycaemic control in *diabetes.

glycerides Esters of *glycerol with *fatty acids. Since glycerol has three hydroxyl groups, it can be esterified with three molecules of fatty acid to form a triacylglycerol (sometimes known as a *triglyceride), the main type of *fat in the diet and body, sometimes known as simple fats or neutral fats. Mono- and diacylglycerols have respectively one and two fatty acids esterified to glycerol, with the remaining hydroxyl group(s) free.

glycerides, partial *See* FAT, SUPERGLYCERINATED.

glycerine (glycerin) *See* GLYCEROL.

glycerol A trihydric alcohol, 1,2,3-propane triol ($CH_2OH-CHOH-CH_2OH$), also known as glycerine. Simple or neutral *fats are esters of glycerol with three molecules of *fatty acid, i.e. triacylglycerols, sometimes known as triglycerides. *See also* GLYCERIDES.

Glycerol is a colourless, odourless, viscous liquid, sweet to taste; it is made from fats by alkaline hydrolysis (*saponification). Used as a solvent for flavours, as a humectant to keep foods moist, and in cake batters to improve texture and slow staling.

glycerose A three-carbon sugar, derived from *glycerol.

glyceryl lactostearate Also known as lactostearin. Formed by glycerolysis of hydrogenated soya bean oil followed by esterification with lactic acid, which results in a mixture of mono- and diacylglycerols and their lactic mono-esters. Used as an emulsifier in shortenings.

glyceryl monostearate *See* FAT, SUPERGLYCERINATED.

glycine A non-essential *amino acid, the simplest of the amino acids, amino-acetic acid, CH_2NH_2COOH. It has a sweet taste (70% of the sweetness of sucrose) and is sometimes mixed with *saccharin as a sweetening agent. Known at one time as collagen sugar.

glycinin Globulin protein in soya bean.

glycitein An isoflavone (*see* FLAVONOIDS) that has *phytoestrogen activity.
Occurs in foods mainly as the glycoside glycitin.

glycitin *See* GLYCITEIN.

glycitols *See* SUGAR ALCOHOLS. Glycitol was used at one time as an
alternative name for *sorbitol.

glycocholic acid One of the *bile acids.

glycogen The storage carbohydrate in liver and muscle, a branched
polymer of *glucose units. It has a similar structure to the amylopectin form
of *starch, but is more highly branched. In an adult there are about 250g of
glycogen in the muscles and 100g in the liver in the fed state.

Since glycogen is rapidly broken down to glucose after an animal is killed,
meat and animal liver do not contain glycogen.

glycogenesis The synthesis of glycogen from glucose in liver and muscle
after a meal, stimulated by the hormone *insulin.

glycogenic acid *See* GLUCONIC ACID.

glycogenolysis The breakdown of *glycogen to *glucose for use as a
metabolic fuel and to maintain the normal blood concentration of glucose
in the fasting state. Stimulated by the hormones *glucagon and *adrenaline.

glycogen storage diseases A group of rare *genetic diseases
characterized by excessive accumulation of *glycogen in liver and/or
muscles and, in some forms, profound *hypoglycaemia in the fasting state.
Treatment is by feeding small frequent meals, rich in carbohydrate.

glycolipids Fatty acids linked by amide bonds to the amino group of
*sphingosine, with covalently bound sugars and *amino sugars; found in
cell membranes, especially in the nervous system, where they act as
receptors and cell surface recognition compounds.

glycolysis The first sequence of reactions in *glucose metabolism, leading
to the formation of two molecules of pyruvic acid from each glucose molecule.

glycoproteins Proteins esterified to one or more oligosaccharides; those
at cell surfaces are important as cell recognition compounds. *See also*
MUCOPROTEINS.

glycosaminoglycans Unbranched polysaccharides composed of
repeating disaccharide units, of an *amino sugar and *glucuronic acid. Most
are esterified to proteins to form proteoglycans.

glycosides Compounds of a sugar attached to another molecule. When
glucose is the sugar, they are called glucosides. A wide variety occur in plants.

glycosuria *See* GLUCOSURIA.

glycyrrhizin Triterpenoid glycoside extracted from *liquorice root *Glycyrrhiza glabra*; 50–100 times as sweet as sucrose but with liquorice flavour. Used to flavour tobacco and pharmaceutical preparations, and as a foaming agent in some non-alcoholic beverages.

GM foods *See* FOOD, GENETICALLY MODIFIED.

GMP *See* GOOD MANUFACTURING PRACTICE.

GMM Genetically modified micro-organism.

GMO Genetically modified organism.

GMS Glyceryl monostearate; *see* FATS, SUPERGLYCERINATED.

gnathostomiasis Rare disease caused by infection with *Gnathostoma spinigerum*, transmitted by consuming raw or undercooked contaminated fish, shellfish, or meat, or drinking contaminated water.

gnocchi Italian; square, round, or other shaped *pasta used to garnish soups or served as a savoury dish with cheese sauce. May also be made from potato flour (potato gnocchi).

goat Ruminant, *Capra* spp.; young is kid. A 100-g serving is a source of Se; a good source of Cu, Fe, Zn, niacin; a rich source of vitamin B_2, B_{12}.

goatfish *See* MULLET.

gobhi bund *See* CABBAGE.

gobhi chote bund *See* BRUSSELS SPROUTS.

gobhi phool *See* CAULIFLOWER.

gobo *See* BURDOCK.

gob stopper Large, spherical, hard sugar sweet (2–4 cm in diameter), usually flavoured with mint and containing a caraway seed in the centre. So called because it fills the mouth for a long time while it slowly dissolves.

gochujang Korean; hot pepper soya bean sauce.

godulbaegi *Ixeris sonchifolia*, also known as Korean lettuce.

gofio Spanish (Canary Islands); flour milled from toasted wheat grains.

goflo Spanish (Canary Islands); bread made from powdered *bracken rhizomes and barley meal or oats.

goitre Enlargement of the *thyroid gland, seen as a swelling in the neck, commonly due to deficiency of *iodine in the diet or to the presence of *goitrogens in foods. In such cases there is commonly underproduction of the *thyroid hormones, i.e. hypothyroid goitre. Euthyroid goitre is a condition in which the enlargement of the gland is sufficient to compensate for a modest deficiency of iodine, permitting normal production of thyroid hormones.

In infancy, iodine deficiency can also lead to severe mental retardation, goitrous cretinism. Supplementation with iodine often prevents the condition, hence the use of iodized salt. Goitre may also result from non-nutritional causes, including excessive stimulation of the thyroid gland, in which case there is overproduction of the thyroid hormones, i.e. hyperthyroid goitre.

goitrogens Substances found in foods (especially *Brassica* spp. but including also groundnuts, cassava, and soya bean) which interfere with the synthesis of *thyroid hormones (*glucosinolates) or the uptake of iodide into the *thyroid gland (thiocyanates), and hence can cause *goitre, especially when the dietary intake of *iodine is marginal.

goji berry Fruit of the deciduous Himalayan shrub *Lycium barbarum*, also known as wolfberry (which includes both *L. barbarum* and *L. chinense*).

golden berry *See* Cape gooseberry.

goldwasser German 'gold water'; an aniseed- and caraway- or cumin-flavoured liqueur containing minute specks of gold leaf.

Golgi apparatus An intracellular organelle in which proteins for export from the cell undergo post-synthetic modification and packaging into vesicles that bud off from the Golgi, migrate to the cell surface, and fuse with the cell membrane for secretion. *Lysosomes are also budded off from the Golgi.

Gomez classification One of the earliest systems for classifying *protein-energy malnutrition in children, based on percentage of expected weight for age: over 90% is normal, 76–90% is mild (first degree) malnutrition, 61–75% is moderate (second degree) malnutrition, and less than 60% is severe (third degree) malnutrition. *See also* Wellcome classification; Waterlow classification.

gonyautoxins Paralytic shellfish toxins (sulphonated derivatives of saxitoxin and neosaxitoxin), produced by *Gonyaulax* spp. and other dinoflagellates causing *red tide. *See also* shellfish poisoning.

goober, goober pea Southern US name for *peanut.

Good Manufacturing Practice (GMP) A set of standards for the food and drink industry aimed at ensuring that products are consistently manufactured to a quality appropriate to their intended use, first published in 1987.

goose Domesticated waterfowl, *Anser anser*. A 150-g portion is a rich *source of protein, iron, vitamins B_2, B_6, B_{12}, and niacin; a good source of vitamin B_1, copper, and zinc; contains more than 30 g of fat, of which one-third is saturated; supplies 470 kcal (1970 kJ).

gooseberry Fruit of the shrub, *Ribes uva-crispa* (syn. *R. grossularia*). The British *National Fruit Collection has 150 varieties. An 80-g portion is a rich *source of vitamin C; provides 2.4 g of dietary fibre; supplies 12 kcal (50 kJ).

A variety of unrelated fruits are also known as gooseberries. Ceylon gooseberry is *Dovyalis hebecarpa*, also known as kitembilla, Chinese gooseberry is *kiwi, Indian gooseberry is *emblic, otaheite or star gooseberry is *Phyllanthus acidus*.

gorny dubnya Russian; bitter liqueur flavoured with ginger, angelica, and cloves.

gossypol Yellow toxic pigment found in some varieties of cottonseed. When included in chicken feed, it causes discoloration of the yolk, but has not been found to be toxic to human beings, and has been investigated as a possible male contraceptive agent.

Gouda Dutch semi-hard *cheese with random holes formed by gases during ripening. A 30-g portion is a rich *source of vitamin B_{12}; a source of protein, niacin, and vitamin A; contains 9 g of fat; supplies 110 kcal (460 kJ).

gougère French; savoury *choux pastry containing cheese.

goujon Small, deep-fried pieces of *fish. The name is derived from gudgeon, a small freshwater fish. Now also used for small pieces of chicken breast.

goulash (gulyas) Hungarian; literally 'cowherd'; beef (or other meat) stewed with potatoes, tomatoes, onions, peppers, and paprika. Distinct from Austrian *gulasch.

gourd Vegetables of the family *Cucurbitaceae*, including calabash or bottle gourd (*Lagenaria vulgaris*), ash gourd (*Benincasa hispida*), snake gourd (*Trichosanthes anguina*, *T. cucumerina*), cucumber (*Cucumis sativus*), vegetable marrow (*Cucurbita pepo*), pumpkin (*Cucurbita moschata*), squash (*Cucurbita maxima*), coocha or chayote (*Sechium edule*), cantaloup melon (*Cucumis melo*), water melon (*Citrullus vulgaris*), wax gourd or hairy melon (*Benincasa hispida*); hedged gourd is *kiwano. All contain more than 90% water and have little food value apart from vitamin C at 10 mg per 100 g. In addition, yellow pumpkin contains 900 µg carotene per 100 g. Melons are sometimes grown for their seeds, which contain 20–40% oil and 20% protein.

gourd, bitter Fruit of the tropical climbing plant *Momordica charantia*. The bitter taste can be minimized by salt-water treatment, and by selecting young fruits; the young shoots are also eaten. Also known as balsam pear.

gout Painful disease caused by accumulation of crystals of *uric acid in the synovial fluid of joints; may be due to excessive synthesis and metabolism of *purines, which are metabolized to uric acid, or to impaired excretion of uric acid. Traditionally associated with a rich diet, although there is little evidence for dietary factors in causing the condition. May be exacerbated by alcohol.

goûter French; light afternoon meal, traditionally at the end of the school day.

G-proteins Guanine nucleotide binding proteins that are activated in response to binding of a *hormone or other ligand to a membrane receptor; when activated the bound GDP is displaced by GTP, and the α-subunit activates another enzyme that produces an intracellular *second messenger. The G-protein has GTPase activity and slowly inactivates itself, so terminating the response.

Gracilaria Genus of red algae, widely cultivated as a source of agar, now also cultivated to feed farmed *abalone.

graddan Hebrides, historical; cereal grains dehusked by holding ears of corn over flames until the husk is burnt, but before the grain is charred.

grading Assessment of the overall quality of a food by a number of criteria (e.g. size, colour, flavour, texture, laboratory analysis).

graining Crystallization of refined sugar when boiled. Prevented by adding glucose or cream of tartar as *sugar doctors.

grains of paradise *See* PEPPER, MELEGUETA.

Gram-negative, Gram-positive A method of classifying bacteria depending on whether or not they retain crystal-violet dye (Gram stain) after staining and decolorizing with alcohol. Named after the Danish botanist H. C. J. Gram (1853–1938).

grams, Indian Various small dried peas (*legumes), e.g. green gram (*Phaseolus aureus*), black gram or urd bean (*Phaseolus mungo*), red gram (*Cajanus indicus*), Bengal gram or *chickpea (*Cicer aretinum*).

grana Hard dry grating cheeses such as *parmesan.

granadilla *See* PASSION FRUIT.

Grand Marnier Trade name of an orange-flavoured liqueur.

grand premier cru *See* WINE CLASSIFICATION, LUXEMBOURG.

granita Italian; water-ice or *sorbet; *see also* SHERBET.

granulometry Technique for measuring the size distribution of particles or granules.

granvas Spanish; sparkling wines made by the tank method.

grape Fruit of varieties of *Vitis vinifera*. One of the oldest cultivated plants (recorded in ancient Egypt in 4000 BC). Can be grouped as dessert grapes, *wine grapes, and varieties that are used for drying to produce raisins, currants, and sultanas (*see* FRUIT, DRIED). Of the many varieties of grape that are grown for *wine making, nine are considered 'classic varieties': cabernet sauvignon, chardonnay, chenin blanc, merlot, pinot noir, riesling, sauvignon blanc, sémillon, syrah. A 100-g portion is a *source of copper; provides 0.5g of dietary fibre; supplies 60kcal (245kJ). North American muscadine grape is *V. rotundifolia*, and slip skin grape is *V. labrusca*.

grapefruit Fruit of *Citrus paradisi*; thought to have arisen as a sport (mutation) of the *pomelo or shaddock (*Citrus grandis*), a coarser *citrus fruit, or as a hybrid between pomelo and sweet orange. It contains 35–40mg vitamin C per 100g. The pith contains *naringin, which is very bitter. Named by the botanist John Lunan in *Hortus Jamaicanensis* (1814) because the fruits grow in 'grape-like' clusters. The ruby grapefruit, with red flesh, was discovered as a sport in Texas in 1929.

grape, muscadine Fruit of *Vitis rotundifolia* with a characteristic musky flavour, astringent and lacking in sweetness.

grape sugar *See* GLUCOSE.

grappa *See* MARC.

GRAS Generally regarded as safe. Designation given to food additives when further evidence was required before the substance could be classified more precisely (US usage).

gras, au Cooked and dressed with rich gravy or sauce.

grass tetany *Magnesium deficiency in cattle.

gratin Also known as gratiné or au gratin, the French term for the thin brown crust formed on top of foods that have been covered with butter and breadcrumbs or cheese, then heated under the grill or in the oven, for example gratin dauphinois.

grattons French; crispy remains of melted fatty tissues of poultry or pork. German equivalent is grieben.

gravadlax (gravlaks, gravlax) Scandinavian; pickled or marinated raw salmon with salt, sugar, and dill.

gravity, final (FG) The density or specific gravity of *beer after fermentation; the difference between original gravity (*see* GRAVITY, ORIGINAL) and final gravity is the amount of sugar that has been fermented.

gravity, original (OG) The density or *specific gravity of *wort before fermentation; an approximate measure of the fermentable sugar, and hence the final strength of the *beer.

gravy Sauce made from the juices and extractives which run out from meat during cooking, normally thickened.

gravy browning Caramelized sugar and starch used to thicken and colour gravy and sauces; may be powder or liquid.

gravy granules Seasoned and coloured granules of modified *starch with a savoury flavour, used to make gravy; they form a gel on addition of boiling water.

Gray (Gy) The SI unit of ionizing radiation (= 100 rad), equivalent to 1 J/kg.

green fluorescent protein (GFP) A protein from the jellyfish *Aequorea victoria* that emits green fluorescence when excited by UV light. The GFP gene is widely used as a reporter gene (*see* GENE, REPORTER) in genetic modification of organisms.

greengage Green variety of *plum introduced into England in the early 18th century by Sir William Gage. A 200-g portion (four raw gages weighed without stones) is a *source of iron and vitamin C; contains 500 mg of potassium and 4–5 g of dietary fibre; supplies 100 kcal (420 kJ).

greenling Marine fish, *Ophiodon elongates*.

green revolution The considerable increase in crop yields worldwide in the 1960s and 1970s as a result of higher yielding cultivars and increased use of fertilizers, pesticides, and irrigation.

greens *See* COLLARD; SPRING GREENS.

green S Food *colour, also known as Wool green S and Brilliant acid green BS.

green sickness Seventeenth-century name for iron deficiency *anaemia, especially in young women, and sometimes described as one of the signs of 'love melancholy'.

grenache A *grape variety widely used for *wine making, not one of the classic varieties.

grenadin French; small slice of fillet of veal, *larded and braised.

grenadine French; syrup made from *pomegranate juice, used as a beverage and to flavour beer.

griddle Also girdle; iron plate used for baking scones, etc., on top of stove.

grieben German; *see* GRATTONS.

griebenschmaltz German; dripping containing the crispy remnant of the fatty tissue of the animal (grieben). *See also* GRATTONS.

grill To cook by radiant heat; some of the fat is lost. *Barbecues cook by grilling.

grillade à l'ardoise Andorran method of cooking on a red-hot roof slate heated over a wood fire (French: *ardoise*, slate).

grilse Young *salmon that has returned to fresh water after one year at sea.

grind To reduce hard foods such as nuts and coffee beans to small particles using a food mill or grinder.

griskin *Chine of pork; also used for a thin, poor piece of loin.

grissini Italian finger rolls or breadsticks, 15–45 cm (6–18 in) long, normally crisp and dry.

grist Cereal for grinding.

g

gristle The *connective tissue of the meat, consisting mainly of the insoluble proteins *collagen and *elastin. Usually inedible and accounts for the toughness of some cuts of meat. Prolonged slow cooking converts collagen to *gelatine, but has no effect on elastin.

grits, corn *See* HOMINY.

groats Oats from which the husk has been entirely removed; Embden groats are crushed. Used to make gruel and porridge.

grog British naval drink; sugared rum mixed with hot water. Named after Admiral Vernon (early 18th century) whose nickname 'Old Grog' came from his grosgrain (heavy corded silk) coat.

ground cherry *See* CAPE GOOSEBERRY.

ground fish *See* FISH, DEMERSAL.

ground meat American term for minced meat.

groundnut *See* PEANUT.

groundnut, American Seeds of the native North American legume *Apios americana*, which also produces edible tubers. Tubers can be dried and ground into a powder which is mixed with flour.

groundnut, bambarra Seeds of the African annual herb *Voandseia subterranean*, also known as the jugo bean, Madagascar peanut, or earth pea. It resembles the true groundnut (*see* PEANUT), but the seeds are low in oil. They are hard and require soaking or pounding before cooking.

groundnut, Hausa *Legume grown in West Africa, *Kerslingiella geocarpa*; 20% protein, 60% fat.

ground tomato (ground cherry) *See* CAPE GOOSEBERRY.

grouper Marine fish, *Myctoperca* spp. and *Epinephelus* spp.

group-specific component *See* GC GLOBULIN.

grouse *Game bird, *Lagopus lagopus*. Shooting period in the UK is 12 August to 10 December; eaten fresh or after being hung for 2–4 days to develop flavour. The whole bird weighs about 700g; a 150-g portion is an extremely rich *source of iron and vitamin B_2; a rich source of protein, niacin, and vitamin B_1; contains about 8g of fat, of which one-fifth is saturated; supplies 250kcal (1050kJ).

growth hormone *See* SOMATOTROPHIN.

gruel Thin porridge made from oatmeal, barley, or other cereal.

Gruyère Swiss hard cheese, used in *fondue.

GSH, GSSG *See* GLUTATHIONE.

GTF Glucose tolerance factor; *see* CHROMIUM; GLUCOSE TOLERANCE.

guacamole Mexican; sauce made from very ripe *avocado, mashed with garlic, lemon juice, and chilli.

guanábana *See* CUSTARD APPLE.

guanine One of the *purines.

guarana Ground and roasted seeds of the Amazonian climbing shrub, *Paullina cupana* (*P. sorbilis*). It contains caffeine; used as an ingredient of drinks (known as cupana in Brazil and tai in USA), chewing gum, a powder to be sprinkled on food, and capsules and tablets. Claimed to have weight-reducing properties, but with little evidence of efficacy.

guar gum Cyamopsis *gum; from the cluster bean, *Cyamopsis tetragonoloba*; a water-soluble galactomannan; used in 'slimming' preparations, since it is not digested by digestive enzymes, and experimentally in the treatment of *diabetes, since it slows the absorption of nutrients, and so prevents a rapid rise in *blood sugar after a meal.

guava Fruit of the Central and South American tropical shrub *Psidium guajava*, eaten raw or preserved as guava jelly. Strawberry guava is *Psidium littorale* (syn. *P. cattleianum*), Costa Rican guava is *P. friedrichsthalianum*, and Guinea guava or guisaro is *P. guineense*.

guggulsterone *Steroid isolated from the sap of the Indian tree *Commiphora mukul* that has a hypocholesterolaemic action. It is an antagonist of the bile acid receptor that responds to bile acids by reducing their synthesis, and so acts to increase cholesterol clearance by bile acid synthesis. A lipid extract from the sap is known as gugulipid.

gugulipid *See* GUGGULSTERONE.

guideline daily amounts (GDA) In food labelling, targets for energy, fat (and saturated fat), carbohydrate (and sugars and fibre), based on *reference intakes, and salt, based on prudent upper levels of intake.

guinea corn *See* SORGHUM.

guinea fowl Game bird, *Numida meleagris*, not seasonal, and now widely farmed. Nutritionally similar to *chicken.

guinea pepper *See* PEPPER, MELEGUETA.

guinea worm disease Dracunculiasis, infestation with the parasitic nematode *Dracunculus medinensis* (guinea worm), acquired from drinking water containing *Cyclops* spp., microcrustaceans that carry the infective larvae. Infection begins with the liberation of larvae in the stomach where they mature and reproduce. Fertilized female worms then migrate to subcutaneous tissues, where they form an ulcer, accompanied by intense pain, fever, nausea, and vomiting.

guisaro *See* GUAVA.

gulab jaman Indian dessert; deep-fried balls of ground almond and flour dough, served in syrup.

gulasch Austrian; cubes of meat or poultry fried with onions, then simmered with paprika, tomato, and caraway seed. Distinct from Hungarian *goulash or gulyas.

gullar *See* FIG.

gulsha A *catfish, *Mystus bleekeri*.

gulyas *See* GOULASH.

gum Complex carbohydrates that can disperse in water to form a viscous mucilaginous mass. Used in food processing to stabilize emulsions (such as salad dressings and processed cheese), as a thickening agent, and in sugar confectionery.

The substances may be extracted from seeds (*guar gum, locust (*carob), quince, *psyllium), plant sap or exudates (gum arabic, karaya or sterculia, tragacanth, ghatti, bassora or hog gum, shiraz, mesquite, anguo), and seaweeds (*agar, *kelp, *alginate, *Irish moss), or they may be made from starch or *cellulose. Most (apart from dextrins) are not digested and have no food value, although they contribute to the intake of *non-starch polysaccharides. *See also* FIBRE, SOLUBLE.

gum arabic (gum acacia) Exudate from the stems of *Acacia* spp.; the best product comes from *A. senegal*. Used as thickening agent, as stabilizer, often in combination with other gums, in gum drops and soft jelly gums, and to prevent crystallization in sugar confectionery. Formerly used as the adhesive on postage stamps.

gumbo American (*Creole); soup or stew made from okra, onions, celery, and pepper, flavoured with filé powder (powdered dried *sassafras leaves), and containing chicken, meat, fish, or shellfish. Also a name for *okra.

gum, British Partly hydrolysed starch, *dextrin.

gum, chewing *See* CHEWING GUM.

gum dragon *See* GUM TRAGACANTH.

gum drops (fruit gums) *Sugar confectionery based on *sucrose and *glucose with *gum arabic (hard gums) or a mixture of *gelatine and gum arabic (soft gums).

gum, ghatti Low viscosity gum; polysaccharide stem exudate from *Anogeissus latifolia*, consisting of arabinose, galactose, mannose, xylose, and glucuronic acid. Also known as Indian gum.

gum, guaiac Alcohol-soluble gum, the resin from *Guajacum officinale* or *G. sanctum*. Composed of α- and β-guaiaconic acids with guaiacic acid and vanillin. Used as an *antioxidant in *chewing gum.

gum, Indian *See* GUM, GHATTI.

gum, karaya From trees of the genus *Sterculia*, used as a stabilizer; sometimes used as a laxative. Also called sterculia gum.

gum kondagogu Exudate from the Indian tree *Cochlospermum gossypium*, used as a substitute for *gum tragacanth.

gum, larch A *polysaccharide of galactose and arabinose from the western larch tree (*Larix occidentalis*); a potential substitute for *gum arabic, since it is readily dispersed in water.

gum talha Similar to *gum arabic, exudate from *Acacia seyal* and *A. sieberana*. Used as emulsifier, stabilizer, and thickener.

gum tragacanth Obtained from the trees of *Astralagus* spp., used as a stabilizer; also known as gum dragon.

gur Mixture of sugar crystals and syrup, brown and toffee-like, made by evaporation of juice of sugar cane; also called jaggery.

gurdani Indian; confectionery made from deep-fried Bengal gram meal coated with syrup produced by boiling sugar cane (*gur or *jaggery).

gurnard Marine fish, species of the family *Triglida* and *Peristedion cataphractum*.

gury Russian (Georgian); whole raw white cabbage soaked in brine with beetroot and red peppers.

gut *See* GASTRO-INTESTINAL TRACT.

gutting Removal of the internal organs of fish before cooking.

Guthrie test Test for a number of *genetic diseases (especially *phenylketonuria) based on measuring the concentrations of *amino acids in a small sample of blood taken by pricking the heel of a child a few days after birth, by biological assay using mutated bacteria.

gut sweetbread *See* PANCREAS.

GYE Guinness Yeast Extract; *see* YEAST EXTRACT.

gyle *Alcohol solution formed in the first stage of *vinegar production, 6–9% alcohol. Subsequent fermentation with *Acetobacter* spp. converts the alcohol to *acetic acid.

haché Minced or chopped.

hachis (hachis) Minced or chopped mixture of meat and herbs. Hachis parmentier is similar to cottage pie.

haddock Marine fish, *Melanogrammus aeglefinus*.

haem (heme) The iron-containing pigment (a tetrapyrrole) which forms the oxygen-binding site of *haemoglobin and *myoglobin. It is also part of a variety of other proteins, collectively known as haem proteins, including the *cytochromes.

haemagglutinins (hemagglutinins) *See* LECTINS.

haematemesis (hematemesis) Vomiting bright red blood, due to bleeding in the upper *gastro-intestinal tract.

haematin (hematin) Formed by the oxidation of *haem; the iron is oxidized from the ferrous (Fe^{2+}) to the ferric (Fe^{3+}) state.

haematinic (hematinic) General term for those nutrients, including *iron, *folic acid, and *vitamin B_{12}, required for the formation and development of blood cells in bone marrow (the process of haematopoiesis), deficiency of which may result in *anaemia.

haemin (hemin) The hydrochloride of *haematin, derived from *haemoglobin. The crystals are readily recognizable under the microscope and are used as a test for blood.

haemochromatosis (hemochromatosis) Iron overload; excessive absorption and storage of iron in the body, commonly the result of a genetic defect, leading to tissue damage (including *diabetes) and bronze coloration of the skin. Sometimes called bronze diabetes. *See also* IRON STORAGE; SIDEROSIS.

haemoglobin (hemoglobin) The red *haem-containing protein in red *blood cells which is responsible for the transport of oxygen and carbon dioxide in the bloodstream. Because haem contains *iron, there is a deficiency of haemoglobin and impaired oxygen transport to tissues in iron deficiency *anaemia.

haemoglobin A$_{1c}$ Glycated haemoglobin; *see* HAEMOGLOBIN, GLYCATED.

haemoglobin, glycated (glycolsylated haemoglobin) Haemoglobin linked via lysine to *glucose. The reaction occurs non-enzymically, and is increased when blood concentrations of glucose are persistently higher than normal. Measurement of glycated haemoglobin is used as an index of the control of *diabetes mellitus over the preceding 2–3 months. Normally 3–6% of haemoglobin is glycated; it may rise to 20% in poorly controlled diabetes.

haemoglobinometer (hemoglobinometer) Instrument to measure the amount of haemoglobin in blood by colorimetry.

haemojuvelin Cell surface protein in liver that senses body *iron reserves and controls the synthesis of *hepcidin; mutations are associated with juvenile *haemochromatosis.

haemolysis The breaking open or premature destruction of red blood cells in the circulation. *See also* ANAEMIA, HAEMOLYTIC.

haemorrhagic disease of the newborn (hemorrhagic disease of the newborn) Name formerly given to excessive bleeding due to *vitamin K deficiency, now known as vitamin K deficiency bleeding in infancy; in most countries infants are given vitamin K shortly after birth to prevent this rare but potentially fatal condition.

haemorrhoids (hemorrhoids) Also known as piles; masses or clumps (cushions) of tissue within the anal canal that contain blood vessels and their surrounding, supporting tissue made up of muscle and connective tissue. Caused or exacerbated by a low-fibre diet and consequent straining to defecate. *See also* DIETARY FIBRE.

haemosiderin (hemosiderin) *See* IRON STORAGE.

haggis Scottish; sheep's heart, liver, and lungs cooked and chopped with suet, onions, oatmeal, and seasoning, traditionally stuffed into the stomach of a sheep. Said to have originated with the Romans when they were campaigning in Scotland; when they broke camp in an emergency, the food was wrapped in the sheep's stomach. A similar Norman-French dish was afronchemoyle. A 150-g portion is an exceptionally rich *source of iron; a rich source of protein; a good source of vitamins B_1, B_2, niacin, calcium, and copper; a source of zinc; contains about 33 g of fat, of which half is saturated; supplies 450 kcal (1900 kJ).

hair analysis Measurement of various minerals in hair has been proposed as an index of nutritional status, but interpretation of the results is confounded by adsorption of minerals on to the hair from shampoo, etc.

hake Marine fish, *Merluccius* spp. and *Urophycis* spp., that occur in Atlantic and Pacific oceans. European hake is *M. merluccius*, Atlantic hake is *M. hubbsi*, Pacific hake are *M. productus*, *M. gayi gayi* and *M. gayi peruanus*, red hake is *U. chuss*, white hake is *U. tenuis*, cape hake is *M. capensis* or *M. paradoxus*. Blue hake is *hoki.

hakka muggies Shetland; seasoned cod liver and oatmeal boiled in the stomach (muggie) of a fish. *See also* HAGGIS.

halal Food conforming to the Islamic (Muslim) dietary laws. Meat from permitted animals (in general grazing animals with cloven hooves, and thus excluding pig meat) and birds (excluding birds of prey). The animals are killed under religious supervision by cutting the throat to allow removal of all blood from the carcass, without prior stunning. Food that is not halal is haram.

halawa *See* HALVAH.

halbsüss (halbtrocken) *See* WINE SWEETNESS.

haldi *See* TURMERIC.

half-life **1.** The time taken for half the *protein or tissue in question to be replaced. Proteins are continuously degraded and replaced even in the mature adult, and the half-life is used as a quantitative measure of this dynamic equilibrium. The values of half-life of different proteins range from a few minutes or hours for *enzymes that control the rate of metabolic pathways, to almost a year for structural proteins such as collagen. The average half-life of human liver and serum proteins is 10 days, and of the total body protein, 80 days. **2.** Of radioactive isotopes, the time in which half the original material undergoes radioactive decay.

halibut Marine fish, *Hippoglossus hippoglossus* and *H. stenolepis*. Greenland, black, or mock halibut is *Reinhardtius hippoglossoides*.

halibut, bastard Marine flatfish from the western Pacific Ocean, *Paralicthys olivaceus*. Also known as hirame and Japanese flounder.

halibut liver oil The oil from the liver of the *halibut, one of the richest natural sources of vitamins A and D; contains 50 mg of vitamin A and 80 µg of vitamin D per gram.

halophiles (halophilic bacteria) Bacteria and other micro-organisms able to grow in high concentrations of salt. The growth of coliform bacteria is inhibited at 8–9% salt, *Clostridia* at 7–10%, food-poisoning staphylococci at 15–20%, and *Penicillium* at 20%. Film-forming *yeasts can grow in 24% brine.

halvah (halva, halwa, halawa, chalva) **1.** A sweetmeat made from sesame seeds with glucose or sugar; it contains 25% fat. **2.** Indian desserts of various types, made from carrot, pumpkin, or banana, sweetened and flavoured.

halverine Name sometimes given to low-fat *spreads with less than the statutory amount of fat in a *margarine.

ham The whole hind leg of the pig, removed from the carcass and cured. Hams cured or smoked in different ways have different flavours; some have protected geographical designation and sometimes the process is secret. A 100-g portion is a rich *source of protein, niacin, and vitamin B_1; a good source of copper; a source of vitamin B_2, iron, zinc, and selenium; contains 5 g of fat, of which 40% is saturated; supplies 120 kcal (500 kJ). *See also* BACON; GAMMON.

hamanatto Fermented soy paste or sauce, made by fermenting whole soybeans with *Aspergillus oryzae*.

Haman's ears Jewish; biscuits made from very thin pieces of egg dough, deep fried.

Haman taschen Traditional Jewish cakes for the festival of Purim; pastry made from *kuchen dough filled with poppy seed and honey, chopped stewed prunes, or cream cheese.

hamburger Or Hamburg steak, also known as beefburger. A flat cake made from ground (minced) *beef, seasoned with salt, pepper, and herbs, and bound with egg and flour. Commercial beefburgers are usually 80–100% meat, but must by law (in the UK) contain 52% lean meat, of which 80% must be beef. Cereal, cereal fibre, or bean fibre may be added as filler or 'meat extender'.

   A 100-g portion (4 oz raw weight) is a rich *source of protein, vitamin B_{12}, niacin, copper, and iron; a good source of zinc; a source of vitamins B_2 and B_6; contains 900 mg of sodium and 17 g of fat, of which half is saturated and half mono-unsaturated; supplies 260 kcal (1100 kJ).

ham, green Ham that has been cured but not smoked.

hamin *See* CHOLENT.

hamma *See* KISHK.

ham, parma (prosciutto di Parma, prosciutto crudo) Italian; smoked, raw ham served in very thin slices. Protected by a designation of geographical origin.

hangover Headache and feeling of malaise resulting from excessive consumption of *alcoholic beverages. The severity differs with different beverages, and is due to both the toxic effects of alcohol and the presence of higher alcohols and esters (collectively known as *congeners or *fusel oil), the substances that give different beverages their distinctive flavours.

Hansa can An all-aluminium can (developed in Germany) with easily opened ends.

happoshu Japanese; beer-like alcoholic beverage with a low malt content, typically <25%. Lower-priced in Japan than beer because taxes are based on the malt content.

haptocorrin *See* TRANSCOBALAMIN.

haram Food forbidden by Islamic law (the opposite of *halal).

harasume Japanese; transparent noodles made from mung bean paste.

hardening of oils *See* HYDROGENATION.

hard sauce Butter and sugar, flavoured with brandy or rum, served with rich puddings.

hare Game animal, similar to *rabbit but larger; caught wild but not farmed commercially. *Lepus europaeus* is the common hare, but some twenty *Lepus* species occur in Europe. A 150-g portion is an extremely rich *source of iron (15 mg); a rich source of protein; contains 12 g of fat; supplies 300 kcal (1260 kJ).

hare's lettuce *See* SOW THISTLE.

haricot French for beans. Haricot de mouton is a stew made with chunks of mutton and beans.

harissa North African; pungent condiment containing dried red chillies, *coriander and *cumin seeds, and garlic.

harrief *See* SCHUG.

Hartnup disease A genetic disease affecting the absorption and tissue uptake of the amino acid *tryptophan, with considerable loss in the urine. Characterized by development of *pellagra, and treated by administration of supplements of *niacin.

Harvard standard Tables of height and weight for age used as reference values for the assessment of growth and nutritional status in children, based on data collected in the USA in the 1930s. Now largely replaced by the *NCHS (US National Center for Health Statistics) standards.

HarvestPlus International research initiative coordinated by the International Center for Tropical Agriculture and the International Food Policy Research Institute to develop micronutrient-rich dietary staples (initially *beans, *cassava, *maize, *rice, sweet potatoes (*see* POTATO, SWEET), and *wheat) by conventional plant breeding techniques.

(⊕) SEE WEB LINKS

• HarvestPlus's homepage.

hash Dish of cooked meat reheated in highly flavoured sauce. In the USA canned corned beef (*see* BEEF, CORNED) is known as corned beef hash.

hash browns American; cooked potatoes, chopped, formed into small cakes, and fried.

haslet (harslet) Old English country dish made from pig's offal (heart, liver, lungs, and sweetbreads) cooked in small pieces with seasoning and flour. Also known as pig's fry.

hasty pudding English, 16th century; made from flour, milk, butter, and spices, which, since they were usually readily available, could be quickly made into a pudding for unexpected visitors. Made in the USA with maize (corn) flour instead of wheat flour.

hâtelet *See* ATTELET.

Haugh unit A measure of the quality (and freshness) of eggs, based on the height of the thick albumin surrounding the yolk and the weight of the egg shell. *See also* ALBUMIN INDEX.

haunch Hindquarters of deer; *see* VENISON.

havarti Danish cheese, similar to *tilsit.

haybox cooking The food is cooked for only a short time, then placed in a well-lagged container, the haybox, where it remains hot for many hours, so cooking continues without further use of fuel. Also known as the fireless cooker.

hazard A biological, chemical, or physical agent that is reasonably likely to cause illness or injury if it is not controlled.

hazard characterization Of food, the qualitative and quantitative evaluation of the nature of the adverse effects associated with biological, chemical, and physical agents that may be present.

haze Term in brewing to indicate cloudiness of *beer. Chill haze appears at 0°C and disappears at 20°C; permanent haze remains at 20°C but there is no fundamental difference. It is caused by *gums derived from the barley, leucoanthocyanins from the *malt and *hops, and glucose, pentoses, and amino acids.

hazelnut Fruit of the tree *Corylus avellana*; cultivated varieties include Barcelona nut, cob nut, and filbert (*C. maxima*); the British *National Fruit Collection has almost 50 varieties. A 50-g portion (fifty nuts) is a rich *source of copper and vitamin E; a source of protein, niacin, vitamins B_1 and B_2, calcium, zinc, and iron; contains 32g of fat (most of which is mono-unsaturated); provides 5g of dietary fibre; supplies 325kcal (1300kJ).

hazelnut, Chilean Fruit of the tree *Gevuina avellana*, also known as Chile nut, gevuina nut, guevin nut, and neufen nut.

HCG Human chorionic gonadotrophin.

HDL High density *lipoprotein, secreted as an 'empty' apoprotein by the liver; it takes up surplus *cholesterol from peripheral tissues for transfer to the liver, either directly or by transfer to *IDL, forming *LDL.

headcheese Mock *brawn.

headspace The space between the surface of a food and the underside of the lid in a container.

health foods Foods and supplements promoted as being beneficial to health, although there is often little or no evidence to support the claims. They include vegetable foods and wholegrain cereals (for which there is evidence of health benefits); food processed without chemical additives; food grown on *organic compost; supplements such as bees' royal jelly, *lecithin, *seaweed, herbs, etc.; and various pills and potions.

healthy US legislation permits a claim of 'healthy' for a food that is *low in fat and saturated fat, and contains no more than 480 mg of sodium and 60 mg of cholesterol per serving.

heart Usually from ox, lamb, pig, or sheep; a 150-g portion is a rich *source of protein, niacin, iron, and vitamins B_1 and B_2; also, unusually for a meat product, a good source of vitamin C; contains about 9 g of fat, of which half is saturated; supplies 270 kcal (1130 kJ).

heartburn A burning sensation in the chest usually caused by reflux (regurgitation) of acid digestive juices from the stomach into the oesophagus. A common form of *indigestion, treated by *antacids.

heath hen Game bird, *Tympanuchus cupido cupido*, native to New England.

heating, ohmic Method of sterilization involving direct discharge of electrical currents in a liquid food slurry; used especially for particulate-containing products such as soups.

heat of combustion *Energy released by complete combustion, as for example, in the bomb *calorimeter. Values can be used to predict energy physiologically available from foods only if an allowance is made for material not completely oxidized in the body.

heat, specific Heat capacity of a substance per unit mass. The amount of energy required to raise the temperature of unit mass of an object by a unit increase in temperature.

hedonic scale Term used in tasting panels where the judges indicate the extent of their like or dislike for the food.

heel-prick test *See* GUTHRIE TEST.

Hegsted score Method of expressing the lipid content of a diet, calculated as 2.16 × % energy from saturated fat −1.65 × % energy from polyunsaturated fat −0.0677 × mg cholesterol. *See also* Keys score.

Helicobacter pylori Pathogenic bacterium that colonizes the gastric mucosa, is a major cause of duodenal and gastric ulcers, and is implicated in the aetiology of gastric cancer.

hemicelluloses A constituent of *non-starch polysaccharide; miscellaneous acidic and neutral oligosaccharides found in plant cell walls together with cellulose and lignin, that can be extracted with dilute alkali. Composed of polyuronic acids combined with xylose, glucose, mannose, and arabinose. Most *gums and mucilages are hemicelluloses.

hemoglobin American spelling of *haemoglobin; similarly, hematin = haematin, heme = haem, hemosiderin = haemosiderin.

hemp seed Fruits of *Cannabis sativa*, eaten toasted in China, and as a condiment in Japan; the oil is added to salad dressings and dips, but is not suitable for cooking. The seed contains only negligible amounts of narcotic cannabinoids.

hepatitis Inflammatory liver disease, characterized by jaundice, abdominal pain, and anorexia. May be due to bacterial or viral infection, alcohol abuse, or various toxins. Treatment is usually conservative, with a very low fat diet (secretion of *bile is impaired) and complete abstinence from alcohol.

Hepatitis A and E are spread by faecal contamination of air, food, or water; infection with hepatitis B, C, and D is by contact with blood or other body fluids from infected people. Even after recovery, people may continue to be carriers of the virus, especially for hepatitis B and C. Liver cancer and cirrhosis are more common among people who have suffered from hepatitis B or C.

hepatomegaly Enlargement of the liver as a result of congestion (e.g. in heart failure), inflammation, or fatty infiltration (as in *kwashiorkor).

hepcidin A peptide *hormone synthesized in the liver when body *iron reserves are high. It inhibits intestinal absorption of iron by binding to *ferroportin and inducing its degradation, so preventing the efflux of iron from mucosal cells into the bloodstream. Also induced in inflammation in response to interleukin-6 (IL-6) and TNF-α (*see* TUMOUR NECROSIS FACTOR-α). *See also* HAEMOJUVELIN.

herb Any soft-stemmed, aromatic plant used fresh or dried to flavour and garnish dishes, and sometimes for medicinal effects. Not clearly distinguished from *spices, except that herbs are usually the leaves or the whole of the plant while spices are only part of the plant, commonly the seeds, or sometimes the roots or rhizomes.

A *pot herb is any plant with stalks and leaves that can be boiled as a vegetable or used in soups and stews (in larger amounts than herbs used for flavouring).

herbes de Provence A traditional blend of aromatic herbs from the hills of southern France. Typically contains *bay leaf, *thyme, *fennel, *rosemary, *chervil, *oregano, summer *savory, *tarragon, *mint, and *marjoram.

herb tea (tisane) An infusion made from any kind of herb, fruit, or flower. Camomile, lime blossom, and fennel seeds are commonly used. Medicinal or health claims are sometimes made, largely on traditional rather than scientific grounds.

herring Oily *fish, *Clupea harengus*; young herrings are sild. Sprat is *Clupea sprattus*; young are brislings. Pilchard is *Clupea pilchardus*; young are sardines. Kippers, bloaters, and red herrings are salted and smoked herrings; bucklings are hot-smoked herrings. *Gaffelbitar is preserved herring. A 150-g portion (weighed with bones), grilled, is an exceptionally rich *source of vitamins D, B_{12}, and selenium; a rich source of protein, niacin, and vitamin B_6; a source of vitamins B_1, B_2, iodine, and iron; contains 200 mg of sodium, about 13–28 g of fat, varying with the season, of which one-third is *saturated and half is mono-unsaturated; supplies 200–360 kcal (800–1500 kJ).

herring, Bismarck Pickled and spiced whole *herring.

herring, Hansa Salted *herring, dating from 13th century, prepared by the fishermen of the Hanseatic League, the ports of the Baltic and north German rivers, after the fish had been landed, as opposed to fish salted at sea.

herring, liquefied *Herring reduced to liquid state by enzyme action at slightly acid *pH; used as protein concentrate for animal feed.

herring, red *Herrings that have been well salted and smoked for about ten days. Bloaters are salted less and smoked for a shorter time; *kippers lightly salted and smoked overnight. Also called Yarmouth bloaters.

herring, soused Young herring caught in spring, lightly salted, and stored in barrels for a short time to allow fermentation to occur. They are called maatjesharing in Dutch and matjes in German.

hesperidin A *flavonoid found in the pith of unripe citrus fruits; a complex of glucose and rhamnose with the flavonone hesperin.

Hess test A test for capillary fragility in *scurvy. A slight pressure is applied to the arm for 5 minutes and a shower of petechiae (small blood spots) appear on the skin below the area of application.

heterofermentative Of micro-organisms, producing more than one main metabolic product. *See also* HOMOFERMENTATIVE.

heterogeusia Altered perception of taste; may be associated with *zinc deficiency or a side-effect of medication.

heteropolysaccharide *Polysaccharide containing more than one type of *monosaccharide.

heterosides *See* HOLOSIDES.

heterotrophes *See* AUTOTROPHES.

heterozygous In genetics, when an individual carries two different *alleles of a gene, and is therefore a heterozygote. *See also* HOMOZYGOUS.

hexamethylene tetramine Preservative (fungicide), E239. Also known as hexamine.

hexamic acid Trade name for cyclohexyl sulphamic acid, the free acid of *cyclamate, a synthetic sweetener about 27 times as sweet as sugar.

hexamine *See* HEXAMETHYLENE TETRAMINE.

hexokinase The enzyme that catalyses the formation of glucose 6-phosphate from glucose, and also acts on a number of other *hexoses. *See also* GLUCOKINASE.

hexose monophosphate shunt *See* GLUCOSE METABOLISM.

hexoses Six-carbon (monosaccharide) *sugars such as *glucose or *fructose.

hexuronic acid The acid derived from a hexose *sugar by oxidation of the hydroxyl group on carbon-6. The hexuronic acid derived from glucose is glucuronic acid.

HFA Height for age.

HFCS High-fructose corn syrup. *See* SYRUP, HIGH FRUCTOSE.

HF heating High-frequency heating. *See* MICROWAVE COOKING.

hGH Human growth hormone; *see* SOMATOTROPHIN.

HHP High hydrostatic pressure, a method for *pasteurization of fruit juices by applying pressures of 400–600 MPa to disrupt bacteria; there is less loss of nutrients and less change in flavour and colour than with heat treatment.

hiatus hernia (hiatal hernia) Protrusion of a part of the stomach upwards through the diaphragm. The condition occurs in about 40% of the population, most people suffering no ill-effects; in a small number of people there is reflux of stomach contents into the oesophagus, causing *heartburn. *See also* GASTRO-INTESTINAL TRACT.

hickory nut North American *walnut, *Carya* spp.; the best known is the *pecan nut.

high-density lipoprotein *See* HDL.

higher in EU legislation states that for a food label or advertising to bear a claim that it is higher in a nutrient it must contain at least 25% more of the claimed nutrient than a similar food for which no claim is made. *See also* HIGH IN.

high-frequency heating *See* MICROWAVE COOKING.

high in EU legislation states that for a food label or advertising to bear a claim that it is high in a nutrient it must contain 50% more of the claimed nutrient than a similar product for which no claim is made. Claims may also be made for foods containing more than 12g of protein, 6g of dietary fibre (*see* FIBRE, DIETARY), or more than 30% of the labelling Reference Amount of a vitamin or mineral/100 g. US legislation permits a claim of 'high in' for foods containing more than 20% of the Daily Value for a particular nutrient in a serving. *See also* HIGHER IN.

high-performance liquid chromatography Also known as high-pressure liquid chromatography, and generally abbreviated to hplc. An extremely sensitive analytical technique, typically able to separate and measure nanograms or smaller amounts of compounds in samples of 10–100 μl.

high-ratio fats (shortenings) *See* FAT, SUPERGLYCERINATED.

high-ratio flour *See* FLOUR, HIGH-RATIO.

high-temperature short-time treatment (HTST) *See* STERILIZATION, HTST.

hilsa (hilsah) Marine herring-like fish, *Tenualosa ilisha*, from the northern Indian Ocean. Migrates into river systems during part of its life-cycle.

himbeergeist German spirit distilled from raspberries with added alcohol.

hindle wakes Very old English method of cooking chicken, stuffed with fruit and spices, including prunes. Possibly a corruption of *hen de la wake*, a feast of 14th-century Flemish introduction.

hirame *See* HALIBUT, BASTARD.

Hirschsprung's disease *See* MEGACOLON.

histamine The amine formed by decarboxylation of the amino acid *histidine in the body, also found in small amounts in cheeses, beer, chocolate, sauerkraut, and wines. Excessive release of histamine from mast cells is responsible for many of the symptoms of allergic reactions. It also stimulates secretion of *gastric acid, and administration of histamine provides a test for *achlorhydria.

histidinaemia Genetic disease due to a defect in the metabolism of the *amino acid *histidine. If untreated it leads to mental retardation and nervous system abnormalities. Treatment is by feeding a diet very low in histidine.

histidine An essential *amino acid with a basic side-chain.

histones Proteins rich in arginine and lysine, soluble in water but not in dilute ammonia. They occur mainly in the cell nucleus and are concerned with the regulation of *DNA.

hiyu Japanese name for Chinese spinach (*Amaranthus gangeticus*), also known as bhaji and *callaloo.

HMG CoA reductase inhibitors Drugs which inhibit the enzyme hydroxymethylglutaryl CoA (HMG CoA) reductase, the controlling enzyme of *cholesterol synthesis, used in the treatment of *hypercholesterolaemia.

hochoshi Japanese; cutting specialists, groups of people with their own secret methods for cutting fish, meat, and vegetables. During the 12th century, ceremonial cutting of food became a spectacle for Japanese nobility.

hock **1.** Generic term for white wines from the Rhine region, known in the USA as Rhine wines; traditionally bottled in brown glass, to distinguish from Moselle wines (in green glass). **2.** The knuckle of *pork; also used in the USA for foreleg pork shank.

hodge podge Victorian; stew made from left-over cooked meat with vegetables.

hogget One-year-old sheep. *See* LAMB.

hogshead A traditional UK measure of volume or size of barrel: for beer or cider it contains 54 gallons (243 L); for wine it contains 52½ gallons (236 L).

hoisin sauce Chinese; spicy vegetable-based brownish-red sauce.

hoki Marine fish, *Macruronus novaezealandiae*; New Zealand's most abundant commercial fish species. Also known as whiptail, blue hake, or blue grenadier. Chilean hoki is *M. magellanicus*.

holishkes Middle-European, Jewish; cabbage leaves stuffed with rice, minced meat, and sultanas. Also known as parakes or galuptzi.

hollandaise sauce Rich *sauce made from egg yolks, butter, and lemon.

hollands *See* GIN.

holocellulose Mixture of *cellulose and *hemicellulose in wood, the fibrous residue that remains after the extractives, lignin, and ash-forming elements have been removed.

holoenzyme An *enzyme protein together with its *coenzyme or *prosthetic group. *See also* ENZYME ACTIVATION ASSAYS.

holosides Complexes of sugars that yield only sugars on hydrolysis. As distinct from heterosides which yield other substances as well as sugars on hydrolysis, e.g. tannins, anthocyanins, nucleosides.

homard *See* LOBSTER.

homeostasis The maintenance of a stable internal environment in the body.

hominy Prepared *maize kernels, also known as samp. Lye hominy has the pericarp and germ removed by soaking in caustic soda. Pearled hominy is degermed hulled maize. Corn grits are ground hominy. *See also* POLENTA.

homocysteine An amino acid formed as an intermediate in the metabolism of *methionine, and in the formation of *cysteine from methionine; it is demethylated methionine. Does not occur in foods to any significant extent, and is not generally considered to be of nutritional importance. High blood concentrations of homocysteine (occurring as a result of poor *folic acid, *vitamin B$_6$, and B$_{12}$ status) have been implicated in the development of *atherosclerosis, heart disease, and stroke. *See also* HOMOCYSTINURIA.

homocystinuria A *genetic disease affecting the metabolism of the *amino acid *methionine and its conversion to cysteine, characterized by excretion of *homocysteine and its derivatives. May result in mental retardation and early death from *atherosclerosis and coronary thrombosis if untreated, as well as fractures of bones and dislocation of the lens of the eye. Treatment (which must be continued throughout life) is either by feeding a diet low in methionine and supplemented with cysteine or, in some cases, by administration of high intakes of *vitamin B$_6$ (about 100–500 times the normal requirement).

homofermentative Of micro-organisms, producing only one main metabolic product. *See also* HETEROFERMENTATIVE.

homogenization Emulsions usually consist of a suspension of globules of varying size. Homogenization reduces these globules to a smaller and more uniform size. In homogenized milk the smaller globules adsorb more of the protein, which acts as a stabilizer, and the cream does not rise to the top.

homogenizer, ultrasonic High-speed vibrator (above a frequency of 20 kHz, hence ultrasonic) used to cream soups, disperse dried milk, disperse essential oils (*see* OILS, ESSENTIAL) in soft drinks, stabilize tomato purée, prepare peanut butter, etc. *See also* HOMOGENIZATION.

homozygous In genetics, when both *alleles of a gene are the same, and the individual is therefore a homozygote. *See also* HETEROZYGOTE.

honey Syrupy liquid made by bees (the honey bee is *Apis mellifera*) from the nectar of flowers (which is essentially *sucrose). The flavour and colour depend upon the flowers from which the nectar was obtained and the composition also varies with the source. Average composition: water 18% (12–26%), invert sugar, i.e. glucose and fructose, 74% (69–75%), sucrose 1.9% (0–4%), ash 0.18% (0.1–0.8%), organic acids 0.1–0.4%. If the ratio of fructose to glucose is high, there is a tendency for the honey to crystallize.

Comb honey is honey stored by bees in cells of freshly built, broodless combs and sold in the comb; drained honey is drained or centrifuged from decapped combs.

honey berry Variety of *raspberry.

honeydew A variety of *melon.

honeydew honey During periods of prolonged drought, bees may supplement their nectar supplies with honeydew, the sweet fluid excreted on leaves by leaf-sucking insects. The resultant *honey is dark, with an unpleasant taste.

honeyware *See* BADDERLOCKS.

Hongroise, à la Dish cooked in a cream sauce seasoned with paprika; the term is synonymous with à l'Autrichienne.

hontarako Japanese; salted and dried cod roe.

hop The dried female flowers of perennial deciduous vine *Humulus lupulus* contain bitter resins and essential oils (*see* OILS, ESSENTIAL) and are added to *beer both to preserve it and to enhance the flavour. Shoots with male flowers can be eaten as a vegetable.

HOPE Heart Outcomes Prevention Evaluation study; intervention trial in the 1990s of the *ACE inhibitor ramipril and vitamin E in patients at high risk for cardiovascular events. The results showed a beneficial effect of ramipril, but not of vitamin E.

hopper Indian; steamed batter cake made from rice flour mixed with coconut water and allowed to undergo lactic acid fermentation overnight.

horchata de chufas Spanish; aqueous extract of *tiger nut (*Cyperus esculentus*) used as a drink.

hordein A protein in barley; one of the prolamines.

hordenin Alkaloid found in germinated barley, sorghum, and millet which can cause *hypertension and respiratory inhibition.

hormone A compound produced in the body in *endocrine glands, and released into the bloodstream, where it act as a chemical messenger to affect other tissues and organs. *See also* AUTOCRINE; ENDOCRINE; JUXTACRINE; PARACRINE.

hormones, anabolic Natural or synthetic *hormones that stimulate growth and the development of muscle tissue. *See also* SOMATOTROPHIN, BOVINE.

hormones, sex Male hormones, or androgens, include testosterone, dihydrotestosterone, and androsterone; female hormones include progesterone and the *oestrogens (oestradiol and oestrone). Chemically, all are *steroids, derived from *cholesterol.

horned melon *See* KIWANO.

hors d'œuvre Small savoury dishes served as an appetizer either as the first course of a meal or before the meal with cocktails or an apéritif. It is French for 'outside the main work' of the meal.

horse *Equus caballus*; a 150-g portion is an exceptionally rich *source of iron; a rich source of protein and niacin; a source of vitamins B_1 and B_2; contains about 5g of fat, of which one-third is *saturated; supplies 175kcal (735kJ).

horseradish The root of the perennial herb *Armoracia rusticana* (syn. *Cochlearia armoracia, A. lapathifolia*). Its pungency is caused by volatile oils (*see* GLUCOSINOLATES). Used as a condiment, usually as a creamed sauce, or grated and mixed with beetroot (*chrane). Japanese horseradish is *Wasabia japonica*; *see* WASABI.

horseradish tree *See* MORINGA.

horse's neck A long drink based on ginger ale with ice, *bitters, and a spirit.

Hortvet freezing test Test for the adulteration of milk with water by measuring the freezing point; milk normally freezes between −0.53 to −0.55°C; if diluted with water it will freeze above −0.53°C.

hot breads American term for *waffles and *pancakes.

hotch-potch Thick soup or stew of meat and vegetables.

hot cross bun Spiced yeast bun traditionally eaten in the UK at Easter; the top is decorated with a cross of dough.

hot dog *Frankfurter sausage in a long bread roll. Reputedly named after a cartoon drawn by Tad Dorgan of Chicago in 1906 showed a dachshund dog inside a frankfurter bun.

hotpot Baked *stew or casserole of meat or fish, topped with sliced potatoes.

hot sauce A tomato sauce with pungent flavour due to *cayenne.

Hot Springs Conference International Conference held in 1943 at which the Food and Agriculture Organization (*see* FAO) of the United Nations originated.

hot-water crust Pastry made by melting lard into boiling water and pouring the mixture on to the flour, then kneading it into a dough.

houeidan *See* EGGS, CHINESE.

household measures (household record method) In dietary and nutritional surveys; subjects keep a record of all foods eaten, using household measures (cups, spoons, etc.) rather than weight, as in the *weighed inventory method.

Hovis Trade name for a mixture of brown flour and wheatgerm; from Latin *hominis vis*, 'strength of man'; originally, in the 1880s, called Smith's Old Patent Germ Bread. Now a trade name for white, brown, and wholemeal breads.

Howard mould count Standardized microscopical technique for measuring mould contamination.

howtowdie Scottish; boiled chicken with poached egg and spinach.

hplc *See* HIGH-PERFORMANCE LIQUID CHROMATOGRAPHY.

HSH Hydrogenated starch hydrolysates. *See* SYRUP, HYDROGENATED.

hsiao mai Chinese; fish-filled wraplings or *wuntun.

5HT *See* 5-HYDROXYTRYPTAMINE.

HTST *See* STERILIZATION, HTST.

huckleberry Wild North American berry, the fruit of *Gaylussacia baccata* and other species (named after the French chemist Gay-Lussac, 1778–1850). Similar to *blueberry but has larger seeds; used in tarts, pies, and preserves.

huevos a la flamenca *See* EGGS FLAMENCA.

huff paste Northern British name for pastry made from suet, flour, and water, used to enclose meat, fish, or poultry while baking.

huitlacoche Edible parasitic fungus *Ustilago maydis* that infects ears of *maize, causing kernels to swell and darken. Also known as corn smut, cuitlacoche, maize mushroom, and Mexican maize truffle. *See also* SMUT.

hull *See* HUSK.

humble pie *See* UMBLES.

humbug Hard boiled *sweet, normally peppermint-flavoured, cushion-shaped.

humectants Substances such as *glycerol, *sorbitol, invert sugar (*see* SUGAR, INVERT), and *honey that prevent loss of moisture from foods, especially flour confectionery; they also prevent sugar crystallizing and the growth of ice crystals in frozen foods.

humidity The moistness of air. Weight of water per unit weight of air is absolute or specific humidity. Saturation humidity is the absolute humidity of air that is saturated with water vapour at a given temperature. Relative humidity is the degree of saturation: the ratio of water vapour pressure in the atmosphere to water vapour pressure that would be exerted by pure water at the same temperature.

hummus (houmous) Middle Eastern; a purée of *chickpeas and *tahini with garlic, oil, and lemon juice. A 100-g portion is a *source of protein, niacin, vitamin B_1, iron, and zinc; provides 2.5g of dietary fibre; contains 13g of fat; supplies 190kcal (760kJ).

humulones Bitter aromatic acids in *hops, used to flavour and preserve *beer.

hurricane A New Orleans cocktail based on rum, passion fruit juice, and lime juice, in equal measures.

hurum Indian; puffed *rice prepared by parboiling and flaking waxy rice, adding fat and expanding in heated sand.

hush puppies Southern USA; fried, seasoned, batter cakes, served especially with fish.

husk (hull) The outer cellulose covering of seeds and grains. In wheat it is loosely attached and removed during threshing; in rice it is firmly attached. High in fibre content and of limited use as animal feed. *See also* PEARLING.

HVP Hydrolysed vegetable protein, used as a flavour enhancer.

hydrocolloids Water-soluble *gums; may be *non-starch polysaccharides, *gelatine, or *caseinate.

hydrocooling Vegetables are washed in cold water, then subjected to vacuum while still wet. The evaporation of the water chills the vegetables for transport. The term is also applied to vegetables washed in ice-water without vacuum treatment.

hydrodyne process Method of tenderizing meat in which it is subjected to supersonic shock waves generated under water by a small explosive charge to shatter the fibres without affecting its other properties; faster than other methods.

hydrogenation Conversion of liquid oils to semi-hard fats by the addition of hydrogen to the unsaturated double bonds; used for margarines and shortenings intended for bakery products. Invented by English chemist William Norman, 1901. *See* FATTY ACIDS, UNSATURATED.

hydrogen breath test *See* BREATH TEST, HYDROGEN.

hydrogen-ion concentration A measure of the acidity or alkalinity of a solution by the concentration of hydrogen (H^+) ions present, usually expressed as *pH.

hydrogen peroxide (H_2O_2) Readily loses active oxygen, the effective sterilizing agent, forming water. Anti-microbial agent; can be used at 0.1% to preserve milk (Buddeized milk), but destroys vitamin C, methionine, and tryptophan. Not permitted in the UK.

hydrogen swells *See* SWELLS.

hydrolysis The reaction of cleaving a bond by addition of water, as, e.g., in digestion of *proteins (proteolysis), *triacylglycerols (lipolysis), and *polysaccharides. *See also* SAPONIFICATION.

hydromel Reputedly the most popular beverage of the ancient world, prepared by mixing honey with water, sometimes flavoured with herbs and spices, and leaving it in the sun to ferment.

hydrophilic A solute that will dissolve in water and other polar solvents, as opposed to *hydrophobic.

hydrophobic A solute that will dissolve in non-polar solvents, but not in water, as opposed to *hydrophilic.

hydroponics The cultivation of plants without soil in a solution of inorganic salts.

hydroxyapatite The calcium phosphate complex which is the main mineral of bones, $Ca_{10}(PO_4)_6(OH)_2$.

hydroxybenzoic acid esters *See* PARABENS.

β-hydroxybutyrate One of the *ketone bodies formed in fasting.

hydroxycholecalciferol *See* VITAMIN D.

hydroxylysine Amino acid in *connective tissue proteins (collagen and *elastin) and a small number of other proteins; incorporated into the protein as *lysine and then hydroxylated in a vitamin-C-dependent reaction.

hydroxy-methylbutyrate (HMB) A metabolite of *leucine that is believed to regulate protein metabolism. It has been suggested that HMB supplements decrease protein catabolism, thereby creating a net anabolic effect, but there are few studies of efficacy or safety.

hydroxyproline Amino acid in *connective tissue proteins (*collagen and *elastin) and a small number of other proteins; incorporated into the protein as *proline and then hydroxylated in a vitamin-C-dependent reaction. Peptides of hydroxyproline are excreted in the urine and the output is increased when collagen turnover is high, as in rapid growth or resorption of tissue. Measurement of hydroxyproline in meat products permits estimation of the connective tissue content of the product. *See also* GRISTLE.

hydroxyproline index Urinary excretion of *hydroxyproline is reduced in children suffering *protein-energy malnutrition. The index is the ratio of urinary hydroxyproline to creatinine per kg of body weight, and is low in malnourished children.

5-hydroxytryptamine (5HT) Also called serotonin. A neurotransmitter amine synthesized from the *amino acid *tryptophan, also formed in blood platelets; it acts as a vasoconstrictor. Found in *plantains and some other foods, but metabolized in the intestinal mucosa.

hygrometer Instrument for measuring *humidity and *water activity. Also known as a psychrometer.

hygroscopic Readily absorbing water, as when table salt becomes damp. Materials such as calcium chloride and *silica gel absorb water so readily that they are used as drying agents.

hygroscopic foods Foods in which the partial pressure of water vapour varies with the moisture content, so that they take up moisture from the atmosphere.

hyper- Prefix meaning above the normal range, or abnormally high.

hyperalimentation Provision of unusually large amounts of energy, either intravenously (*see* NUTRITION, PARENTERAL) or by *nasogastric or gastrostomy tube (*see* NUTRITION, ENTERAL).

hyperammonaemia High blood ammonia concentration, especially after protein intake, leading to coma, convulsions, and possibly death. May be due to a variety of genetic diseases affecting amino acid metabolism (*see* AMINO ACID DISORDERS). Treatment is normally by severe restriction of protein intake. Also occurs in liver failure. *See also* LACTULOSE.

hypercalcaemia, idiopathic Elevated plasma concentrations of calcium believed to be due to hypersensitivity of some children to *vitamin D toxicity. There is excessive absorption of calcium, with loss of appetite, vomiting, constipation, flabby muscles, and deposition of calcium in the soft tissues and kidneys. It can be fatal in infants.

hyperchlorhydria Excess secretion of hydrochloric acid in the stomach due to secretion of a greater volume of *gastric juice rather than to a higher concentration.

hypercholesterolaemia Abnormally high concentrations of *cholesterol in the blood. Generally considered to be a sign of high risk for *atherosclerosis and *ischaemic heart disease. Treatment is by restriction of fat (especially *saturated fat) and cholesterol intake and a high intake of non-starch polysaccharides, which increase the excretion of cholesterol and its metabolites (the *bile salts) in the faeces. Drugs (*statins and other *HMG CoA reductase inhibitors) may be given to inhibit the synthesis of cholesterol in the body, and in severe cases, *ion-exchange resins may be fed, to increase the excretion of bile salts.

Familial hypercholesterolaemia is a genetic disease in which affected individuals have extremely high blood concentrations of cholesterol, frequently dying from ischaemic heart disease in early adulthood; treatment is as for other forms of hypercholesterolaemia, but more rigorous. *See also* LIPIDS, PLASMA.

hyperfiltration *See* OSMOSIS, REVERSE.

hyperglycaemia High blood sugar; elevated plasma concentration of *glucose, caused by a failure of the normal hormonal mechanisms of blood glucose control. *See also* DIABETES MELLITUS; GLUCOSE TOLERANCE.

hypericum *See* ST JOHN'S WORT.

hyperinsulinaemia Excessive secretion of *insulin, either as a result of an *insulinoma (insulin-secreting tumour of β-islet cells of the *pancreas), or due to hyperglycaemia resulting from insulin resistance.

hyperkalaemia Excessively high blood concentration of *potassium.

hyperkinetic syndrome (hyperkinesis) Mental disorder of children, characterized by excessive activity and impaired attention and learning ability. Has been attributed (with some evidence) to adverse reactions to food *additives, and especially synthetic colours.

hyperlipidaemia (hyperlipoproteinaemia) A variety of conditions in which there are increased concentrations of *lipids in plasma: *phospholipids, *triacylglycerols, free and esterified *cholesterol, or *unesterified fatty acids. Familial hyperlipidaemias are due to genetic diseases; less severe hyperlipidaemia is commonly seen in people in affluent developed countries, associated with increased risk of *atherosclerosis and *ischaemic heart disease. *See also* HYPERCHOLESTEROLAEMIA; LIPIDS, PLASMA.

hyperlipoproteinaemia *See* HYPERLIPIDAEMIA.

hyperoxaluria Genetic disease leading to excessive formation of *oxalic acid, which forms kidney stones. Treatment includes a diet low in those fruits and vegetables that are sources of oxalic acid and in some cases supplements of *vitamin B_6 some 50–100 times greater than reference intakes.

hyperphagia Over-eating; an abnormally increased appetite for, and consumption of, food.

hyperphosphataemia Excessively high blood concentration of *phosphate.

hyperplasia Growth of tissue by increase in the number of cells. *See also* HYPERTROPHY; NEOPLASIA.

hypersalivation Excessive flow of *saliva.

hypersensitivity, delayed An *adverse reaction to food, occurring several hours after ingestion, caused by cell-mediated immune responses (activated lymphocytes) as opposed to immunoglobulin-mediated responses, which occur rapidly.

hypertension High *blood pressure; a risk factor for ischaemic disease, stroke, and kidney disease. May be due to increased sensitivity to *salt (correctly sensitivity to *sodium), and treated by restriction of salt intake, together with drugs; increased intake of fruits and vegetables (as a safe source of potassium) is recommended. *See also* DIET, SALT-FREE.

hyperthyroidism *See* THYROTOXICOSIS.

hypertonic A solution more concentrated than the body fluids; *see* ISOTONIC.

hypertrophy Growth of tissue by increase in the size of cells with no increase in the number of cells. *See also* HYPERPLASIA; NEOPLASIA.

hypervitaminosis Toxicity due to excessively high intakes of vitamins. A problem with *vitamins A, D, B_6, and *niacin, at levels of intake from supplements considerably higher than might be obtained from foods, although hypervitaminosis A and D may result from (enriched) foods. *See also* HYPERCALCAEMIA, IDEOPATHIC.

hypo- Prefix meaning below the normal range, or abnormally low.

hypocalcaemia Low blood *calcium, leading to vomiting and uncontrollable twitching of muscles if severe; may be due to underactivity of the parathyroid gland, kidney failure, or *vitamin D deficiency.

hypochlorhydria Partial deficiency of hydrochloric acid secretion in the *gastric juice. *See also* ACHLORHYDRIA; ANAEMIA, PERNICIOUS.

hypocretins *See* OREXINS.

hypogeusia Diminished sense of taste. An early sign of marginal zinc deficiency, and potentially useful as an index of zinc status.

hypoglycaemia Abnormally low concentration of plasma glucose; may result in loss of consciousness, hypoglycaemic coma.

hypoglycaemic agents Drugs used to lower blood glucose concentrations in *diabetes mellitus.

hypokalaemia Abnormally low plasma *potassium.

hypophosphataemia Abnormally low blood concentration of *phosphate.

hypoplasia Impaired or incomplete development of an organ or tissue. *See also* APLASIA.

hypoproteinaemia Abnormally low plasma protein concentration.

hyposite Little-used word, from the Greek, for low-energy food.

hypothermia Low body temperature (normal is around 37°C). Occurs among elderly people far more readily than in younger adults, often with fatal results. Also used in connection with deliberate reduction of body temperature to 28°C to permit heart and brain surgery.

hypothyroidism Underactivity of the thyroid gland, leading to reduced secretion of *thyroid hormones and a reduction in *basal metabolic rate. Commonly associated with *goitre due to *iodine deficiency. In hypothyroid adults there is a characteristic moon-faced appearance, lethargy, and mental apathy. In infants, hypothyroidism can lead to severe mental retardation, *cretinism. *See also* THYROTOXICOSIS.

hypotonia Floppiness, decreased tone of skeletal muscles. Muscles contract very slowly in response to a stimulus and cannot maintain a contraction for as long as a normal.

hypotonic A solution more dilute than the body fluids; *see* ISOTONIC.

hypovitaminosis *Vitamin deficiency.

hypoxanthine A *purine, an intermediate in the metabolism of *adenine and *guanine to *uric acid.

hyssop Pungent aromatic herb, *Hyssopus officinialis*, used in salads, soups, and in making liqueurs.

I

IARC International Agency for Research on Cancer, part of *WHO; its mission is to coordinate and conduct research on the causes of human cancer, the mechanisms of carcinogenesis, and to develop scientific strategies for cancer control.

 SEE WEB LINKS

• The IARC's homepage.

IASO International Association for the Study of Obesity.

SEE WEB LINKS

• The IASO's homepage.

iatrogenic A condition caused by medical intervention or drug treatment; iatrogenic nutrient deficiency is due to *drug–nutrient interactions.

Iberian moss *See* CARRAGEENAN.

IBS Irritable bowel syndrome; abdominal pain and bloating, with either constipation or diarrhoea. The cause is unknown; there are no abnormalities on radiological or endoscopic examination, and no evidence of intestinal pathogens.

ICD International Statistical Classification of Diseases and Related Health Problems, published by *WHO, providing a standard classification of diseases to permit international comparability in health and disease statistics.

ice cream A frozen confection made from fat, milk solids, and sugar. Some countries permit the use of non-milk fat and term the product ice cream, while if milk fat is used, it is termed dairy ice cream.

According to UK regulations, it must contain not less than 5% fat and 7% other milk solids; according to US regulations, 10% milk fat and 20% other milk solids. Stabilizers such as carboxy methylcellulose, *gums, and alginates are included, and emulsifiers such as polysorbate and monoglycerides. Mono- and diglycerides bind the looser globules of water and are added in 'non-drip' ice cream.

ice cream, Philadelphia Made from scalded cream, with no added thickening agents.

ice, eutectic The solid formed when a mixture of 76.7% water and 23.3% salt (by weight) is frozen. It melts at −21 °C. It has about three times the refrigerant effect of solid carbon dioxide (*dry ice), and is especially useful for icing fish at sea.

icefish Marine fish, *Dissostichus mawsoni* and *D. eleginoides*, also known as toothfish.

Iceland moss A lichen, *Cetraria islandica*, that can be boiled to make a jelly.

ice lolly (ice lollipop) A frozen ice cream or water-ice on a stick; known in the USA as a *popsicle.

ice wine *See* EISWEIN.

ICF Intracellular fluid.

ichthyosarcotoxins Toxins in fish.

icing *See* FROSTING; SUGAR, ICING.

icterus *See* JAUNDICE.

IDA *Iron deficiency *anaemia.

IDD *Iodine deficiency disease; *see* GOITRE.

IDDM Insulin-dependent *diabetes mellitus.

idi (idli) Indian, Sri Lankan; steamed bread made from rice and legume flour. The dough is left to undergo bacterial fermentation overnight; the main organisms are *Leuconostoc mesenteroides* and *Streptococcus faecalis*.

idiopathic Of unknown aetiology.

idiosyncracy Unusual and unexpected sensitivity or reaction to a drug or food.

IDL Intermediate density *lipoprotein, formed in the circulation by tissue removal of *triacylglycerol and *cholesterol from *VLDL, and transfer of apoproteins C-I and C-II to *HDL. *See also* LDL.

IFN-γ *See* INTERFERON-γ.

IGF *See* INSULIN-LIKE GROWTH FACTORS.

IGT Impaired *glucose tolerance.

IHD *See* ISCHAEMIC HEART DISEASE.

IL-1, IL-2, IL-4 Interleukins 1, 2, and 4; *cytokines involved in cell-mediated immune responses.

ilamae *See* CUSTARD APPLE.

ileitis Inflammation of the ileum. *See* GASTRO-INTESTINAL TRACT.

ileostomy Surgical formation of an opening of the ileum on the abdominal wall, performed to treat severe ulcerative *colitis; *see* GASTRO-INTESTINAL TRACT.

ileum Last portion of the small intestine, between the jejunum and the colon (large intestine); *see* GASTRO-INTESTINAL TRACT.

ileus Functional obstruction of the small intestine as a result of loss of peristalsis, commonly following surgery.

illipé butter *See* BUTTER, VEGETABLE.

ILSI International Life Sciences Institute, a non-profit foundation that seeks to improve the well-being of the general public through the advancement of science. Its goal is to further the understanding of scientific issues relating to nutrition, food safety, toxicology, risk assessment, and the environment by bringing together scientists from academia, government, and industry.

(⊕) SEE WEB LINKS

• The ILSI's homepage.

imam bayildi Turkish, Greek; dish of *aubergines baked with olive oil, onions, tomatoes, and garlic; may be served hot or cold. There are two versions of the origin of the name, which means the 'imam (or priest) fainted': either he swooned in ecstasy when he tasted the dish or he fainted from fright at the cost of the large amount of olive oil used to prepare it.

imli Indian; sauce made from *tamarind.

immune system Series of defence mechanisms of the body. There are two major parts: humoral, mediated through antibodies secreted into the circulation (*immunoglobulins); and cell-mediated. *Lymphocytes produce antibodies against, and bind to, the antigens of foreign cells, leading to death of the invading organisms; other white blood cells are phagocytic and engulf the invading organisms.

immunoassay A variety of analytical techniques with very high specificity and sensitivity using antibodies raised against the analyte, coupled with an enzyme, fluorescent dye, or radioactive material as a detection system. *See also* ELISA; FLUORESCENCE IMMUNOASSAY; RADIOIMMUNOASSAY.

immunoglobulins *See* ANTIBODIES.

immunomagnetic separation Technique for rapid isolation of food-borne pathogens using magnetic microspheres coated with antibodies.

immunonutrition (immune-enhancing diets) The use of enteral feeding formulas (*see* NUTRITION, ENTERAL) in severe trauma and following surgery, enriched with nutrients such as arginine, ω3 fatty acids, glutamine, nucleotides, β-carotene, and branched-chain amino acids that may enhance immune system function.

IMP Inosine monophosphate, one of the *purine nucleotides.

impériale, à l' Dishes with a rich garnish of foie gras, truffles, cocks' combs, and kidneys.

imperial rolls See SPRING ROLLS.

improvers, flour See AGEING.

IMS See IMMUNOMAGNETIC SEPARATION.

INACG International Nutritional Anemia Consultative Group of the International Life Sciences Institute (ILSI). Now superseded by the Micronutrient forum.

(())) SEE WEB LINKS

• The Micronutrient forum's homepage.

inanition Exhaustion and wasting due to complete lack or non-assimilation of food; a state of starvation.

inborn errors of metabolism See GENETIC DISEASE.

Incaparina A number of protein-rich dietary supplements developed by the Institute of Nutrition of Central America and Panama (INCAP), based on cottonseed flour, or soya and vegetables, with various nutrient supplements.

incidence The number of new cases of a disease in the population in a specified period of time (usually one year), commonly expressed per 100000 of the population per year. See also PREVALENCE.

incretins *Hormones that increase the amount of *insulin secreted in response to *glucose; they reduce *glucagon secretion and delay gastric emptying. They may also have actions to improve insulin sensitivity, and they may increase the formation of β-islet cells of the *pancreas. See also GIP; GLP-1; OREXINS; PANCREAS.

index of nutritional quality (INQ) An attempt to provide an overall figure for the nutrient content of a food or a diet. It is the ratio of the percentage of the *reference intake of each nutrient to the percentage of the average requirement for energy provided by the food.

indicação de proveniencia regulamentada (IPR) See WINE CLASSIFICATION, PORTUGAL.

indigestion Discomfort and distension of the stomach after a meal, also known as dyspepsia, including *heartburn. Persistent indigestion may be a symptom of a digestive disorder such as *hiatus hernia or peptic *ulcer.

indigo carmine Blue food colour, derivative of indigotin, which comes from tropical leguminous plants, *Indigofera* spp.

induction (of enzymes) New synthesis of an *enzyme in response to a *hormone or other stimulus that increases *transcription (and hence expression) of the gene for that enzyme. *See also* REPRESSION.

induction period The lag period during which a fat or oil shows stability to oxidation because of its content of *antioxidants, natural or added, which are oxidized preferentially. After this there is a sudden and large consumption of oxygen and the fat becomes rancid.

infant formula *See* FORMULA, INFANT.

infarction Death of an area of tissue because its blood supply has been stopped.

INFOODS International Network of Food Data Systems, created to develop standards and guidelines for collection of food composition data, and standardized terminology and nomenclature.

((())) SEE WEB LINKS
• The INFOODS homepage.

infuse To extract the flavour from herbs, spices, etc., by steeping them in a liquid, usually by pouring boiling liquid over them, covering them and leaving them to stand without further cooking or heating, as in making tea. The result is an infusion.

infusion *See* INFUSE.

ingredient Any substance used in the manufacture or preparation of a foodstuff and still present in the finished product, even if in an altered form. Contaminants and adulterants are not considered to be ingredients.

injera Ethiopean; flat bread made from *teff flour fermented for 30–72 hours with a starter from a previous batch.

inorganic Materials of *mineral, as distinct from animal or vegetable, origin. Apart from carbonates and cyanides, inorganic chemicals are those that contain no carbon. *See also* ORGANIC.

inositol A carbohydrate derivative, a constituent of *phospholipids (phosphatidyl inositol) involved in membrane structure and as part of the signalling mechanism for some *hormones that act at the cell surface. It is an essential nutrient for micro-organisms and some animals, although there is no evidence that it is a dietary essential for human beings. Obsolete names are inosite and meat sugar. *See also* PHYTATE.

INQ *See* INDEX OF NUTRITIONAL QUALITY.

in silico Experiments conducted by computer simulation. *See also* IN VITRO; IN VIVO.

instantization Processing of dried foods so as to facilitate reconstitution of the final product, e.g. by agglomerating of particles. *See also* FOOD, INSTANT.

insulin *Hormone secreted by the β-islet cells of the *pancreas which controls *carbohydrate metabolism. *Diabetes mellitus is the result of an inadequate supply of insulin or impairment of its function. Since insulin is a protein it would be digested if taken by mouth so must be injected. *See also* DIET, DIABETIC; GLUCOSE TOLERANCE.

insulinaemic index The rise in blood *insulin elicited by a test dose (usually 50 g) of a carbohydrate food compared with that after an equivalent dose of glucose. *See also* GLYCAEMIC INDEX.

insulin-like growth factors (IGF) Peptide hormones (*autocrine or *paracrine agents) that have a structure similar to that of pro-insulin. Many of their actions resemble the mitotic actions of *insulin; their synthesis and secretion are stimulated by growth hormone (*see* SOMATOTROPHIN), and they are responsible for the growth-promoting actions of growth hormone.

insulinoma *Insulin-secreting tumour of the β-islet cells of the *pancreas.

insulin resistance Resistance of target tissues to the actions of *insulin, leading to hyperinsulinaemia and hyperglycaemia, mainly associated with abdominal *adipose tissue. Only the metabolic actions of insulin are affected; the slower actions mediated via *MAP kinases are unaffected, so there is an exaggerated mitotic response to insulin, causing increased proliferation of vascular smooth muscle, leading to *atherosclerosis and *hypertension. *See also* METABOLIC SYNDROME.

interesterification A process to modify the properties of a fat for food manufacturing purposes, by interchanging fatty acids between molecules of triacylglycerol. *Lipases catalyse the exchange of fatty acids at carbons 1 and 3 of glycerol, leaving the fatty acid at carbon-2 unaffected. *See also* TRANSESTERIFICATION.

interferon-γ A *cytokine that increases antigen-presenting activity; it also depletes tissue *tryptophan by induction of indoleamine dioxygenase, and so contributes to the impaired protein synthesis seen in *cachexia.

international units (iu) Used as a measure of relative potency or biological activity of substances, such as vitamins, before techniques were available to measure them by weight or molarity. Still sometimes used (3.33 iu *vitamin A = 1 µg; 40 iu *vitamin D = 1 µg; 1 iu *vitamin E = 1 mg).

intervention study Comparison of an outcome (e.g. morbidity or mortality) between two groups of people deliberately subjected to different dietary or drug regimes.

intestinal flora Bacteria and other micro-organisms that are normally present in the *gastro-intestinal tract.

intestinal juice Also called succus entericus. Digestive juice secreted by the intestinal glands lining the small intestine. It contains a variety of *enzymes, including *enteropeptidase, the enzyme that converts trypsinogen to active *trypsin, *aminopeptidase, *nucleases, and *nucleotidases. *See also* GASTRO-INTESTINAL TRACT.

intestinal phase of eating Inhibition of gastric secretion and motility in response to the presence of food in the duodenum, so as to permit duodenal contents to be digested before more material enters from the stomach.

intestine The *gastro-intestinal tract; more specifically the part after the stomach, i.e. the small intestine (duodenum, jejunum, and ileum) where the greater part of digestion and absorption take place, and the large intestine.

intolerance (of foods) *See* FOOD, ADVERSE REACTIONS.

intrinsic factor A protein secreted in the gastric juice which is required for the absorption of *vitamin B_{12}; impaired secretion results in pernicious *anaemia.

inulin Soluble but undigested polymer of *fructose found particularly in Jerusalem *artichoke, and, to a lesser extent, other root vegetables. Included with *non-starch polysaccharides (*dietary fibre). Also called dahlin and alant starch.

inversion Applied to *sucrose, meaning hydrolysis to glucose and fructose; *see* SUGAR, INVERT.

invertase Enzyme that hydrolyses *sucrose to glucose and fructose (*see* SUGAR, INVERT); also called sucrase and saccharase.

in vitro Literally 'in glass'; used to indicate an observation made experimentally in the test-tube, as distinct from in a living organism. *See* IN VIVO.

in vivo In the living state; experimental observations in living organisms, as distinct from *in vitro.

iodide A salt of the mineral *iodine.

iodine An essential mineral, a *trace element; the reference intake is about 140 µg per day. Iodine is required for synthesis of the *thyroid hormones, which are iodo-tyrosine derivatives, and iodine deficiency leads to *goitre.

Iodine is plentifully supplied by seafoods and by vegetables grown in soil containing iodide. In areas where the soil is deficient in iodide, locally grown vegetables are also deficient, and hence goitre occurs in defined geographical regions, especially inland upland areas over thin limestone soil. Where deficiency is a problem, salt may be iodized to increase iodide intake (*see* SALT, IODIZED).

iodine number (iodine value) Carbon–carbon double bonds in unsaturated *fatty acids react with iodine; this provides a means of determining the degree of unsaturation by measuring the amount of iodine (in grams) that reacts with 100g of oil or fat.

iodine, protein-bound The *thyroid hormones, tri-iodothyronine and thyroxine, are transported in the bloodstream bound to proteins; measurement of protein-bound iodine, as opposed to total plasma iodine, was used as an index of thyroid gland activity before more specific methods of measuring the hormones were developed.

IoM Institute of Medicine of the US National Academies.

(🌐) SEE WEB LINKS
- The IoM's homepage.

ion An atom or molecule that has lost or gained one or more electrons, and thus has an electric charge. Positively charged ions are known as cations, because they migrate towards the cathode (negative pole) in solution, while negatively charged ions migrate towards the positive pole (anode) and hence are known as anions. *See also* ELECTROLYTES.

ion-exchange resin An organic compound that will bind ions under some conditions and release them under others. The best-known example is in water-softening, where calcium ions are removed from the water by binding to the resin, displacing sodium ions. The resin is then regenerated by washing with a concentrated solution of salt, when the sodium ions displace the calcium ions. Ion-exchange resins are used for purification of chemicals, metal recovery, and a variety of analytical techniques.

ionization The process whereby the positive and negative *ions of a *salt separate when dissolved in water. The degree of ionization of an *acid or *alkali determines its strength (*see* pH).

ionizing radiation Electromagnetic radiation that ionizes the air or water through which it passes, e.g. X-rays and γ-rays. Used for the sterilization of food, etc., by *irradiation.

IOTF International Obesity Task Force of the International Association for the Study of Obesity.

(🌐) SEE WEB LINKS
- The IOTF's homepage.
- The IASO's homepage.

IPR Indicação de proveniencia regulamentada; *see* WINE CLASSIFICATION, PORTUGAL.

Irish cream Liqueur prepared from Irish whiskey blended with other spirits and cream, sweetened, and sometimes flavoured with coffee or chocolate.

Irish moss A red *seaweed, *Chondrus crispus*; source of the polysaccharide *carrageenan.

iron An essential *mineral. The average adult contains 4–5g of iron, of which 60–70% is present in the blood as haem in *haemoglobin, and the remainder present in *myoglobin in muscles, a variety of enzymes, and tissue stores. Iron is stored in the liver as ferritin, in other tissues as haemosiderin, and as the blood transport protein transferrin.

   Absorption of iron is aided by *vitamin C taken at the same time as iron-containing foods, and impaired by calcium, phosphate, and *phytate. Iron content of foods per 100g: liver 6–14mg, cereals up to 9mg, nuts 1–5mg, eggs 2–3mg, meat 2–4mg. Iron is added to flour so that it contains not less than 1.65mg per 100g. Fortified cereals provide 35% of the iron of British diets. Prolonged deficiency gives rise to *anaemia.

iron balance Losses in faeces are 0.3–0.5mg per day, in sweat and skin cells 0.5mg, traces in hair and urine, total loss 0.5–1.5mg per day. Blood loss leads to a considerable loss of iron. The average diet contains 10–15mg, of which 0.5–1.5mg is absorbed. The haem iron of meat and fish is considerably better absorbed than the inorganic iron of vegetable foods. Reference intakes are 8.7mg for adult men and 14.8mg for women; women who have heavy menstrual blood losses may not be able to obtain enough from food, and supplements are necessary.

iron chink Machine designed in 1903 by US inventor E. A. Smith to behead, split, and gut salmon in a continuous operation; so called because it replaced Chinese labour in west coast canneries.

iron overload *See* HAEMOCHROMATOSIS; SIDEROSIS.

iron ration Heat resistant high-energy *chocolate ration enriched with vitamins and minerals devised for the US Army by Capt. Paul Logan and first produced by Hershey Chocolate in 1937, as the Logan Bar Ration D (for daily). Heat resistant because it did not contain *cocoa butter.

iron, reduced Metallic iron in finely divided form, produced by reduction of iron oxide. The form in which iron is sometimes added to foods, such as bread. Also known by its Latin name *ferrum redactum*.

iron storage Ferritin is the iron storage protein in the intestinal mucosa, liver, spleen, and bone marrow. It is a ferric hydroxide-phosphate-protein complex containing 23% iron. Haemosiderin is a long-term storage form of iron in tissues; colloidal iron hydroxide combined with protein and phosphate, probably formed by agglomeration of *ferritin, the short-term storage form. Abnormally high levels of haemosiderin occur in *siderosis. *See also* HAEMOCHROMATOSIS.

iron transport Iron is transported in blood plasma in combination with proteins, as transferrin or siderophilin.

irradiation A method of sterilizing and disinfesting foods using *ionizing radiation (X-rays or γ-rays) to kill micro-organisms and insects. Also used to inhibit sprouting of potatoes. *See also* MICROWAVE COOKING; RADAPPERTIZATION; RADICIDATION; RADURIZATION; ULTRAVIOLET RADIATION.

IRRI International Rice Research Institute, Los Baños, Philippines.

((())) SEE WEB LINKS

• The IRRI's homepage.

irritable bowel syndrome Also known as spastic colon or mucous colitis. Abnormally increased motility of the large and small intestines, leading to pain and alternating diarrhoea and constipation; often precipitated by emotional stress.

iru *See* DAWADAWA

ischaemia Inadequate blood supply to a tissue.

ischaemic heart disease (coronary heart disease) Group of syndromes arising from failure of the coronary arteries to supply sufficient blood to heart muscles; associated with *atherosclerosis of coronary arteries. *See also* ANGINA.

ishiru Japanese; fermented fish sauces made from squid livers (ika-ishiru) or sardine (iwashiishiru).

isinglass *Gelatine prepared from the swim bladder of fish (especially sturgeon). Used commercially to clear wine and beer, and sometimes in jellies and ice cream. Japanese isinglass is *agar.

islets of Langerhans The *endocrine parts of the *pancreas; *glucagon is secreted by the α-cells and *insulin by the β-cells.

ISO International Organization for Standardization, a nongovernmental organization based in Geneva, established in 1947 with the mission of developing a common set of manufacturing, trade, and communications standards to facilitate international trade. The short name 'ISO' was taken from the Greek isos, meaning equal, because the organization's mission is to create equal or uniform standards.

ISO 9000 Quality Standard The international standard for the management of quality, widely used in the food industry, catering, and food distribution, but developed originally for the engineering industry. ISO 9001 covers the specification for design, manufacture, and installation; ISO 9002 the specification for manufacture and installation; ISO 9003 the specification for final inspection and test.

isoacids Obsolete term for isomers of unsaturated fatty acids (including *trans*-isomers) formed during *hydrogenation of oils.

isoascorbic acid *See* ERYTHORBIC ACID.

isoenzymes *Enzymes that have the same catalytic activity, but differ in their structures, properties, and/or tissue or subcellular distribution. Sometimes called isozymes.

isoflavones *See* FLAVONOIDS.

isoleucine An essential *amino acid, rarely limiting in food; one of the branched-chain amino acids.

isomalt A bulk sweetener (*see* SWEETENERS), about half as sweet as sucrose, consisting of a mixture of two disaccharides, glucosyl-glucitol and glucosyl-mannitol. It is about 50% metabolized, yielding 9 kJ (2.4 kcal)/gram. It is thought to be less laxative than *sorbitol or *mannitol, and does not encourage tooth decay, so is used in tooth-friendly sweets (*see* SWEETS, TOOTH-FRIENDLY). It absorbs little water, so products are less sticky than those made with sucrose and have a longer shelf-life.

isomalto-oligosaccharides *See* OLIGOSACCHARIDES.

isomaltose A disaccharide of glucose, differing from *maltose in that the two glucose units are linked $\alpha 1$–6 rather than $\alpha 1$–4; unlike maltose it is not fermentable. Also known as brachyose.

Isomerose Trade name for high-fructose corn syrup (*see* SYRUP, HIGH FRUCTOSE): 70–72% solids; 42% fructose, 55% glucose, 3% polysaccharides.

isomers Molecules containing the same atoms but differently arranged, so that the chemical and biochemical properties differ: i) in positional isomers the functional groups are on different carbon atoms; e.g. leucine and isoleucine; ii) D- and L-isomerism refers to the spatial arrangement of four different chemical groups on the same carbon atom (stereo-isomerism or optical isomerism). *R*- and *S*-isomerism is the same, but determined by a set of systematic chemical rules. *See* D-, L-, AND DL-. iii) *Cis*- and *trans*-isomerism refers to the arrangement of groups adjacent to a carbon–carbon double bond; in the *cis*-isomer the groups are on the same side of the double bond, while in the *trans*-isomer they are on opposite sides.

isoniazid A drug (iso-nicotinic acid hydrazide) used in chemotherapy of tuberculosis. It has anti-*vitamin B_6 activity, and can lead to the development of *pellagra as a result of impaired metabolism of *tryptophan for *NAD synthesis.

isopropyl citrate Ester of isoprophyl alcohol and citrate, used to *chelate metal ions that might otherwise cause *rancidity in oils.

isoprostanes A family of *eicosanoids formed *in vivo* non-enzymically by radical action on arachidonic acid in phospholipids; some are biologically active, and measurement provides a sensitive marker of lipid peroxidation and oxidative stress.

isosyrups *See* SYRUP, HIGH FRUCTOSE.

isothiocyanates A wide variety of compounds containing an —N==C==S group, found especially in cruciferous vegetables; they inhibit enzymes of phase I metabolism and activate those of phase II (*see* METABOLISM, PHASE I; METABOLISM, PHASE II), so reducing the formation, and increasing the clearance, of potential *carcinogens. They also inhibit the proliferation of tumour cells, by inducing *apoptosis and arresting cell cycle progression.

isotonic Solutions with the same *osmotic pressure; often used of a solution with the same osmotic pressure as body fluids. Hypertonic and hypotonic refer to solutions that are more and less concentrated, respectively.

isotopes Forms of elements with the same chemical properties, differing in atomic mass because of differing numbers of neutrons in the nucleus. Thus, hydrogen has three isotopes, of atomic masses 1, 2, and 3, generally written as ^{1}H, ^{2}H (deuterium), and ^{3}H (tritium). ^{1}H is the most abundant isotope of hydrogen; ^{2}H is stable, while ^{3}H is radioactive.

Radioactive isotopes are unstable, and decay to stable elements, emitting radiation in the process. This may be α-radiation, β-radiation (electrons), γ-radiation, or X-rays, depending on the isotope. The time taken for half the radioactivity to decay is the *half-life of the isotope, and can vary from a fraction of a second, through several days to years (e.g. the half-life of ^{3}H is 12.5 years, that of ^{14}C is 5200 years).

Stable isotopes can be detected only by their different atomic mass. Since they emit no radiation, they are safe for use in labelled compounds given to human beings. Examples of stable isotopes commonly used in nutrition research include ^{2}H, ^{13}C, ^{15}N, and ^{18}O.

See also WATER, DOUBLE LABELLED.

isozymes *See* ISOENZYMES.

ispaghula Polysaccharide *gum derived from the seed husks of *Plantago ovata*. Used as a thickening agent in foods and as a *laxative. *See also* PSYLLIUM.

itai-itai disease *See* CADMIUM.

italienne, à l' Dishes made partly or wholly of pasta, often with cheese and tomato.

iu *See* INTERNATIONAL UNITS.

IUFoST International Union of Food Science and Technology.
 SEE WEB LINKS
- The IUFoST's homepage.

IUGR Intra-uterine growth retardation, as a result of insufficient transfer of oxygen and nutrients across the placenta.

IUNS International Union of Nutritional Sciences.
 SEE WEB LINKS
- The IUNS's homepage.

IVACG International Vitamin A Consultative Group of the International Life Sciences Institute (ILSI). Now superseded by the Micronutrient forum.
 SEE WEB LINKS
- The Micronutrient forum's homepage.

izaño Edible tubers of the Andean plant *Tropaeolum tuberosum*.

Izarra Trade name of a herb-flavoured liqueur based on *armagnac, made in the Basque region of France; similar to *Chartreuse.

jaboticaba Fruit of the tree *Myrciaria cauliflora* with purple astringent skin and sweet white pulp; the fruits grow straight from the trunk.

jack fruit *See* JAK FRUIT.

JACNE Joint Advisory Committee on Nutrition Education. A UK working party that put the 1983 *NACNE nutritional guidelines into popular language. *See* DIETARY GUIDELINES; NUTRITIONAL RECOMMENDATIONS.

jaggery **1.** Coarse, dark sugar made from the sap of the coconut palm. **2.** Raw sugar-cane juice, used in India as sweetening agent; also known as gur.

jaguar gum Alternative name for *guar gum.

jaiphal Indian name for *nutmeg.

jake paralysis *See* JAMAICA GINGER PARALYSIS.

jak fruit (jack fruit) Large fruit, up to 30 kg, from tropical trees, *Artocarpus* spp., related to *breadfruit. Both pulp and seeds are eaten. A 100-g portion is a *source of vitamin C; supplies 70 kcal (295 kJ).

jalapeño *See* PEPPER.

jalebi Indian sweet; deep-fried spirals of dough served with syrup.

jam A conserve of fruit boiled to a pulp with sugar; sets to a *pectin jelly on cooling. (Known in the USA as jelly.) Standard jam, with certain exceptions, contains a minimum of 35 g of fruit per 100 g; extra jam, with certain exceptions, contains 45 g.

Jamaica ginger paralysis Polyneuritis caused by poisoning from an extract of jake, a variety of *ginger grown in Jamaica which contains triorthocresyl phosphate.

Jamaican pepper *See* ALLSPICE.

jambalaya Southern USA; rice with pork, chicken, and/or shellfish, simmered with celery, peppers, and tomatoes.

jamba oil Oil from the seeds of *rocket.

jambolan Fruit of the South-East Asian tree *Syzygium cumini*, also known as Java plum.

jambos, jambu *See* APPLE, ROSE.

jamón serrano Spanish; dry cured mountain *ham.

Japanese isinglass *See* AGAR.

jardinière, à la Dish prepared or served with a variety of vegetables.

jarmuz Polish; quartered white cabbage, stewed in stock, mixed with soured cream, and garnished with braised chestnuts.

jaundice Yellow colouration of the skin and whites of the eyes as a result of high blood concentrations of *bilirubin, also known as icterus. Hepatic jaundice is the result of liver disease leading to impaired conjugation of bilirubin for excretion in the *bile; free bilirubin circulates in the blood. Obstructive jaundice is the result of blockage of the bile duct (as a result of *gall stones, liver disease, or pancreatic cancer) or *cholestasis; conjugated bilirubin circulates. Haemolytic jaundice is the result of *haemolysis in excess of the capacity of the liver to conjugate the bilirubin formed; again free bilirubin circulates.

javatri Indian name for *nutmeg.

jejuno-ileostomy Surgical procedure in which the terminal *jejunum or proximal *ileum is removed or bypassed. Has been used as a treatment for severe *obesity. *See* GASTRO-INTESTINAL TRACT.

jejunostomy feeding *See* ENTERAL NUTRITION.

jejunum Part of the small intestine, between the duodenum and the ileum; *see* GASTRO-INTESTINAL TRACT.

jello North American name for table *jelly.

jelly 1. Clear jam made from strained fruit juice by boiling with sugar. Also used in this sense in North America to mean any jam. 2. Table jelly is a dessert made from gelatine, sweetened and flavoured; known in North America as jello. 3. *See also* ASPIC.

jellyfish seaweed South-East Asian; strips of dried and salted jellyfish.

jelly roll *See* SWISS ROLL.

jelutong latex The latex of the jelutong tree (*Dyera costulata*) grown in Malaysia and Indonesia, used as a partial replacement for *chicle in the manufacture of *chewing gum.

jeotgal Korean; sauce made from salted and fermented seafood.

jerky, jerked beef South American dried meat. *See* BILTONG; CHARQUI.

Jerusalem oak *See* EPAZOTE.

Jesuit's bark Cinchona bark; *see* QUININE.

jésus French, Swiss; sausage made from pig's liver.

jicama Tropical vine, *Pachyrhizus erosus*; the edible root (up to 2m long) contains *inulin, and is eaten both raw and cooked. The remainder of the plant is toxic, and the seeds contain rotenone, which is an uncoupler of mitochondrial oxidative phosphorylation. *See also* UNCOUPLING PROTEINS.

jigger Measuring cup used by bar staff for spirits, etc., when the bottles do not have a dispenser fitted.

jobfish Marine fish, *Aphareus* spp., *Aprion* spp., and *Pristimoides* spp. Also known as snapper.

Job's tears See ADLAY.

Jodbasedow *See* THYROTOXICOSIS.

john dory A marine fish, *Zeus faber*, also called dory and St Peter's fish.

Johne's disease See MYCOBACTERIUM AVIUM.

Jojoba Seeds of the shrub *Simmondsia chinensis* (*S. californica*) have long been used as food by native Americans, and roasted and ground to prepare beverages. The oil is a liquid wax of long-chain *fatty acids (eicosenoic and decosenoic (erucic) acids) esterified with long-chain alcohols (eicosanol and docosanol). Of interest in cosmetics as a replacement for sperm whale oil but also has food applications, e.g. as a coating agent for *dried fruit.

jonathan Calcined, ground oat chaff used as adulterant for maize and other cereals (mid 19th century).

jonge Young Dutch *gin.

joule The SI (Système Internationale) unit of *energy; used to express energy content of foods and energy expenditure; 4.2 kilojoules (kJ) is equivalent to 1 kilocalorie (kcal). Named after James Prescott Joule (1818–1889), British physicist, who determined the equivalence of heat and energy, and the mechanical equivalent of heat.

jóvenes Spanish; young wines.

jowar Indian name for *sorghum (*Sorghum vulgare*), also known as great millet, kaffir corn, guinea corn.

Judas goat Sheep cannot readily be driven to slaughter but will follow a goat. A Judas goat is used to lead the sheep to the killing pens.

jugged Food (especially hare) cooked in earthenware pot or jug.

jug-jug Caribbean (Barbadian); minced meat and pigeon peas cooked with *millet, served as an accompaniment to ham or roast chicken.

jujube 1. Sweet made from gum and sugar. **2.** Fruit of the South Asian shrub *Ziziphus mauritania* or *Z. jujuba*, an important fruit crop in India; reddish-brown, up to 2 cm in diameter, with a single stone; a 100-g portion is a good *source of vitamin C. Also known as Chinese date.

julep *Whiskey or brandy flavoured with mint and served over ice. Originally developed as a protective against malaria (Old White Springs, Virginia, 1809) and made using brandy; later whiskey was used; the name derives from the Arabic *julab*, for rosewater.

julienne 1. Vegetables cut into thin, match-like strips. **2.** A clear vegetable soup.

jumbals English, 17th century; biscuits made from caraway-flavoured dough, twisted into knots or plaits before baking.

jumble Small rich biscuit flavoured with lemon or almond, formed into a letter S, or into tiny, rock-like heaps.

juneberry *See* SERVICE BERRY.

juniper The ripened berries of the bush *Juniperis communis*, used as a flavouring in *gin, and, together with other herbs, in stuffing or sauces, especially for *game.

junket Dessert made from milk by treating with *rennet to coagulate the protein.

jus, au Dish served with the natural juices or gravy.

juxtacrine A compound secreted by a cell that acts on an adjacent cell; neurotransmitters are juxtacrine agents. *See also* AUTOCRINE; ENDOCRINE GLANDS; HORMONE; PARACRINE.

kabinett German and Austrian *wine classification, used for high-quality wines. Monastic wine producers used to set aside their best wine in a special cupboard or small room (the *kabinett*).

kabuní Albanian; rice sautéed in butter and stock with raisins, served with chicken or meat.

Kahlúa Mexican; trade name of a coffee-flavoured liqueur.

kahweol Diterpene in coffee oil, potentially anticarcinogenic by enhancement of phase II metabolism of foreign compounds (*see* METABOLISM, PHASE II), but unlike *cafestol, probably not associated with *hypercholesterolaemia and hypertriglyceridaemia. Released into the beverage only when coffee is boiled for a prolonged period of time.

kaju katli *See* BARFI.

kakali Freshwater fish, *Xenentodon cancila*.

kakavia Greek; fish soup with tomatoes, vegetables, and garlic, the origin of *bouillabaisse. The name comes from the earthenware pot in which fishermen cooked their fish in the middle of the boat.

kakdi Indian name for *cucumber.

kaki *See* PERSIMMON.

kalakand Indian; sweetened dairy product made by evaporating acidified buffalo milk.

kale Scottish name for any type of *cabbage; in England it means specifically open-headed varieties of cabbage with curly leaves, also known as curly kale or borecole. Distinct from sea kale or Swiss chard (*see* CHARD, SWISS).

kale, Scotch Thick broth or soup containing shredded cabbage.

kalia Polish; chicken broth flavoured with juice from pickled cucumbers and garnished with diced chicken, celery root, parsley root, and carrots.

kalibous Freshwater fish, a member of the *carp family, *Labeo calbasu*.

kalonji Indian; seeds of the wild black onion *Nigella indica*, syn. *N. sativa*, used as a spice. Also known as black cumin, black caraway, black seed, damascena, devil-in-the-bush, fennel flower, melanthion, nigella, nutmeg flower, roman coriander, wild onion seed, and zireh.

kalteszal Polish; soup made from egg yolk, sugar, cinnamon, and beer, served cold.

kamaboko Japanese; fish paste made from puréed white fish, sometimes with added starch; a variety of *surimi.

kamishbrot *See* MANDELBROT.

kamut Variety of durum *wheat (*Triticum durum*). The flour is sold in health food shops and is claimed to be higher in protein, and to cause fewer allergic reactions, than ordinary wheat.

kanga-kopuwai New Zealand (Maori); maize gruel prepared by allowing whole maize cobs to ferment under water for 3 months, then removing the kernels, grinding into a paste and boiling.

kangkong *See* SPINACH, WATER.

kañiwa Grain from the frost- and drought-tolerant Andean herb *Chenopodium pallidicaule*, related to *quinoa.

kanjang (kanjan) Korean; soy sauce made by fermentation of soybean paste (meju).

kanji Indian; beverage made from parboiled black carrots with salt, ground mustard seeds, and chilli powder, left to ferment in the sun, resulting in a sour and spiced flavour.

kaoliang A drink made from the Chinese *sorghum, *Sorghum nervosum*; also used for the grain itself.

karahi Conical metal vessel used to cook *balti.

karasumi Japanese; preserved roe of grey mullet or tuna.

karat Variety of *banana grown in Micronesia that is an especially rich source of β-carotene.

kari-kari Filipino; a brightly coloured vegetable-and-oxtail stew coloured with *annato.

kari phulia Indian name for *curry plant.

karkade Egyptian; sour drink made from *roselle.

Kashin–Beck disease Joint disorder, endemic in parts of China, caused by deficiency of *selenium. *See also* KESHAN DISEASE.

kasha *See* BUCKWHEAT.

kasnudln Austrian; type of ravioli, egg flour dough with sweet or savoury filling.

kasseler German; cured and smoked pork loin.

kataifi Greek; pastry in thin strands; the dough is squeezed through a perforated disc on to a hot metal plate, on which it is dried in long strands. Also the name for rolls made from these pastry strands, filled with chopped nuts and sugar, baked, and served drenched with syrup.

katemfe *See* THAUMATIN.

Kathepsins *See* CATHEPSINS.

katsuobushi Eastern Asian, Indian; tuna dried and fermented with the mould *Aspergillus repens*; may also be smoked. Used together with *kelp to make broths and soups.

kava Polynesian; a non-alcoholic stimulant beverage made from the roots of *Piper methysticum*; there is some evidence that herbal products (kava kava) are effective in treatment of anxiety, but excessive consumption can cause unconsciousness.

kawal Sudanese; balls of paste from the leaves of the legume *Cassia obtusifolia*, fermented for 12–15 days in a sealed earthenware vessel (zeer) then sun-dried. Used in soups and stews.

kcal Abbreviation for kilocalorie (1000 *calories), sometimes shown as Cal.

kebab Turkish for roast meat. Shishkebab is small pieces of mutton rubbed with salt, pepper, etc., and roasted on a skewer (*shish* in Turkish) sometimes interspaced with vegetables. Shashlik is a Georgian version.
   *Döner kebab is a Turkish speciality consisting of marinated mutton or lamb packed into a cylindrical mass and grilled on a vertical rotating spit (*giros* in Greek, *shawarma* in Arabic).

kebobs Indian; slices of mutton or poultry dipped in egg and cooked on a skewer.

kecap Indonesian; soy sauce prepared by double fermentation of black soybeans (*see* SOYBEAN, BLACK); a solid state fermentation is followed by a brine fermentation.

kedgeree Indian; dish of rice and pulses. Modified to English (Victorian) breakfast dish of flaked fish with egg and rice.

kefalotyri Greek hard cheese; the curds are cut and heated before being pressed into moulds.

kefir *See* MILK, FERMENTED.

kefiran An exopolysaccharide produced by *Lactobacillus kefiranofaciens*, found in *kefir grains. Potentially useful as a food additive because of its gelation properties.

kefir grains Used in the culture of milk during manufacture of kefir (*see* MILK, FERMENTED). A mass of microbial polysaccharide, containing *Streptococcus* spp., *Leuconostoc* spp., mesophilic and thermophilic *Lactobacillus* spp., and yeasts.

keftethes Greek; minced meat rissoles.

kei-apple Fruit of the African shrub *Dovyalis caffra*, also known as wild apricot.

keliweli (kellywelly) Ghanaian; spiced deep-fried banana or plantain.

kelor *See* MORINGA.

kelp Large brown *seaweed, *Laminaria* spp. Occasionally used as food or food ingredient but mostly the ash is used as a source of alkali and *iodine. Sometimes claimed as a health food with unspecified properties. 55% of the dry weight is laminarin, a non-starch polysaccharide.

kenima Indian, Nepali; fried soybean cake; the beans are soaked in water and allowed to undergo lactic acid bacterial fermentation before cooking.

kenkey Ghanaian; maize dumplings, wrapped in leaves or maize cob sheaths and steamed. The dough is left to undergo lactic acid bacterial fermentation; a portion is then boiled to produce *aflata, which is mixed with the remainder before cooking. Madidi is similar.

Kelvin scale *See* TEMPERATURE, ABSOLUTE.

kenaf seeds Seeds of *Hibiscus cannabinus*, used as a source of edible oils.

kephalins (cephalins) *Phospholipids containing ethanolamine, hence *phosphatidylethanolamines. Found especially in brain and nerve tissue.

keratin The insoluble protein of hair, horn, hoofs, feathers, and nails. Not hydrolysed by digestive enzymes, and therefore nutritionally useless. Used as fertilizer, since it is slowly broken down by soil bacteria. Steamed feather meal is used to some extent as a supplement for ruminants.

keratinization Process by which epithelial cells become horny due to deposition of *keratin; may occur excessively and inappropriately in *vitamin A deficiency.

keratomalacia Progressive softening and ulceration of the cornea, due to *vitamin A deficiency. Blindness is usually inevitable unless the deficiency is corrected at an early stage.

kermes A red colourant, kermesic acid, derived from the insect *Kermes ilicis* found on several species of oak, particularly *Quercus coccifera*. *See also* COCHINEAL.

kermesic acid *See* COCHINEAL; KERMES.

kesari dhal A legume, *Lathyris sativus*; *see also* LATHYRISM.

Keshan disease Cardiomyopathy associated with *selenium deficiency, affecting especially women and children in areas of China where soil selenium is very low. The cause is almost certainly cocksackie virus, which becomes more virulent under conditions of selenium (and possibly also *vitamin E) deficiency. *See also* KASHIN–BECK DISEASE.

keshy yena (keshi yena) Caribbean (Curaçao); hollowed out Dutch cheese filled with meat, rice, and currants, then baked. The name derives from the Spanish *queso relleno*, stuffed cheese.

keski Freshwater fish, *Corica soborna*.

Kesp Trade name for a textured vegetable protein product made by spinning.

kestose Fructo-oligosaccharide of 2 fructose residues and 1 glucose residue.

ketchup (catsup, catchup) From the Chinese koechap or kitsiap, originally meaning brine of pickled fish. Now used for spicy sauce or condiment made with juice of fruit or vegetables, vinegar, and spices. Tomato ketchup is a common *sauce; first known recipe published in Canada by James Mease in 1812.

ketembilla Fruit of the Sri Lankan shrub *Dovyalis hebecarpa*, also known as Ceylon gooseberry.

ketoacidosis High concentrations of *ketone bodies in the blood, causing metabolic *acidosis because acetoacetate and β-hydroxybutyrate are acids. Especially a problem in type I *diabetes mellitus.

ketogenic amino acids *See* AMINO ACIDS, KETOGENIC.

ketonaemia *See* KETOACIDOSIS.

ketone A chemical compound containing a carbonyl group (C==O), with two alkyl groups attached to the same carbon; the simplest ketone is *acetone (dimethylketone, $(CH_3)_2$—C==O).

ketone bodies Acetoacetate, β-hydroxybutyrate, and acetone; acetoacetate and acetone are chemically *ketones; although β-hydroxybutyrate is not, it is included in the term ketone bodies because of its metabolic relationship with acetoacetate.

In the fasting state (from about 4 hours after a meal), fatty acids are mobilized from adipose tissue as a metabolic fuel. Most tissues have only a limited capacity for fatty acid oxidation; however, the liver can oxidize more than is required for its own needs. Acetoacetate and β-hydroxybutyrate are formed from fatty acids in the liver, and are transported in the bloodstream for use as metabolic fuels by other tissues. Acetoacetate is unstable and breaks down to *acetone, which is poorly metabolized, and is excreted in the urine and on the breath.

ketonuria Excretion of *ketone bodies in the urine.

ketose Sugars containing a ketone group, which are therefore not chemically reducing sugars (e.g. fructose), as opposed to *aldose sugars.

ketosis High concentrations of *ketone bodies in the blood.

Keys score Method of expressing the lipid content of a diet, calculated as $1.35 \times (2 \times \%$ energy from saturated fat – % energy from polyunsaturated fat) + $1.5 \times \sqrt{(\text{mg cholesterol}/1000\text{kcal})}$. *See also* HEGSTED SCORE.

khalisha Freshwater fish, *Colisa fascitus*.

kheer (sheer) Indian creamed-rice dessert.

khira *See* CUCUMBER.

khoa Indian; heat-concentrated milk product, usually prepared from buffalo milk, used to prepare sweets such as *barfi, peda, and *gulabjaman.

khoya *See* MAWA.

khurchan Indian; concentrated milk product made by simmering whole milk and adding sugar.

khush-khash *See* ORANGE, BITTER.

kibbeh (cubbeh) Lebanese, Middle Eastern; wheat dumplings with a variety of fillings; may be boiled in soup or fried.

kibble To grind or chop coarsely.

kichals Middle-European (especially Jewish); spherical biscuits made from beaten egg, caster sugar, and self-raising flour.

kid Young goat (*Capra aegragus*) usually under 3 months old; similar to *lamb, but with a stronger flavour.

kidney Usually from lamb, ox, or pig; a 150-g portion is a rich *source of protein, niacin, iron, zinc, copper, selenium, vitamins A, B_1, B_2, B_{12}, and folate; a good source of vitamin B_6 and, unusually for a meat product, vitamin C; a source of iodine; contains about 9g of fat, of which one-third is saturated; supplies 150kcal (630kJ).

kidney failure *See* RENAL FAILURE.

kielbasa Polish; garlicky well-seasoned pork and beef sausage; may be smoked.

kieves Irish name for *mash tuns.

kilderkin Cask for beer (18 gallons = 80.1 L) and ale (16 gallons = 71.2 L).

kilka Brackish- and freshwater fish *Clupeonella cultriventris*, found in the Black Sea and Caspian Sea; also in lakes in Turkey and Bulgaria. Also known as Black Sea sprat.

kilo As a prefix for units of measurement, one thousand times (i.e. 10^3); symbol k.

kimchi Korean; dish based on fermented cabbage with garlic, red peppers, and pimientos, often with the addition of fish and other foods.

kinases *Enzymes that catalyse the phosphorylation of substrates by transfer of phosphate from *ATP (or sometimes *GTP). *See also* PROTEIN KINASES.

kinema Indian; cooked soybeans fermented with *Bacillus subtilis*.

king, à la Dish served in a rich cream sauce (often flavoured with sherry) and including mushrooms and green peppers.

kingklip Marine fish, *Genypterus capensis*.

kinky hair syndrome *See* MENKES SYNDROME.

kipfel (kipfl) Austrian; crescent shaped roll created to celebrate the lifting of the siege of Vienna (1683). Reputedly the precursor of the *croissant, believed to have been introduced into France by Marie Antoinette.

kipper *Herring that has been lightly salted and smoked, by a process invented by John Woodger, a fish curer of Seahouses, Northumberland, in 1843. A 150-g portion of flesh (about 300 g including bones and skin) is an exceptionally rich *source of vitamins B_{12} and D; a rich source of protein, niacin, and iodine; a source of vitamin B_2, iron, and calcium; contains 1500 mg of sodium and 18 g of fat, of which about 20% is saturated and 60% mono-unsaturated; supplies 300 kcal (1260 kJ).

kir *See* CASSIS.

kirsch (kirschwasser) Brandy or *eau-de-vie distilled from fermented cherries, including the crushed stones, giving a pungent flavour; not sweet.

kisel Russian, Baltic; cold dessert made from red fruit juice thickened with cornflour or arrowroot. Polish kisiel is similar.

kishk North African, Middle Eastern, Eastern Asian; yoghurt or fermented milk mixed with parboiled or crushed wheat or flour and left to ferment for 2–3 days, then shaped into small balls and dried. Used in soups. Also known as tarhana (Greece and Turkey).

kisra Sudanese; thin flat bread made from sorghum. The batter is mixed with a starter from a previous batch and left to undergo lactic acid fermentation overnight, then poured on to a heated plate to bake for about one minute.

kitron Greek liqueur prepared by distillation of brandy with lemon leaves; sweetened.

kitul *See* TODDY PALM.

kiwano Fruit of *Cucumis metuliferus*, originally from arid regions of southern Africa, now grown commercially in Australia and New Zealand, but with a limited market because of its bland flavour. Also known as melano, African horned cucumber, jelly melon, hedged gourd, horned melon, English tomato.

kiwi Fruit of *Actinidia sinensis* (syn. *A. deliciosa*), originally a native of China and also known as Chinese gooseberry; commercial growing began in New Zealand in 1906. A 60-g portion (one fruit) is a rich *source of vitamin C; supplies 25 kcal (105 kJ).

Kjeldahl determination Widely used method of determining total nitrogen in a substance by digesting with sulphuric acid and a catalyst; the nitrogen is reduced to ammonia which is then measured. In foodstuffs most of the nitrogen is *protein, and the term crude protein is the total 'Kjeldahl nitrogen' multiplied by a factor of 6.25 (since most proteins contain 16% nitrogen). Invented in 1883 by Johan Gustav Christoffer Thorsager Kjeldahl (1849–1900), Danish chemist.

kleftiko Greek; clay oven. Also a joint of lamb baked in a clay oven. Originally a method of cooking meat in the embers of a fire in a pit in the ground.

kleik Polish; gruel made from barley and bouillon.

klipfish Salted and dried cod, mainly produced in Norway. The fish is boned, stored in salt for a month, washed, and dried slowly. It is known as bacalao in South America and Spain, bacalhau in Portugal.

kluski Polish; light dumplings or strips of noodles, used to garnish soups.

kneading Working dough by stretching and folding until it achieves the required consistency.

kneidl *See* KNÖDELN.

knickerbocker glory Dessert made from layers of jelly of different colours, ice cream, and fruit, topped with whipped cream and served in a tall glass (a sundae glass).

knock out Term used for experimental animal or micro-organism in which a *gene has been specifically deleted in order to determine the function of the gene product (enzyme or other protein).

knödeln (kneidl) German; dumplings made from flour or *matzo meal; served like pasta or in soup. Nockerln are smaller; butternockerln are made with butter; lebernockerln contain finely chopped fried liver.

KO *See* KNOCK OUT.

kocho Ethiopian; baked product made from ensete (*see* BANANA, FALSE) after a slow lactic acid fermentation lasting for several months.

kochwurst German; sausages made from precooked ingredients, including liver, brawn, and blood.

koi Freshwater fish, *Anabas testudineus*.

kofta Indian; spiced meat balls. Kofta may also be moulded over sweet-sour plums, minced dried apricots, and herbs or eggs (these last are known as nargizi or narcissus).

kohlrabi Swollen stem of *Brassica oleracea* var. *gongylodes* (turnip-rooted cabbage, kale turnip (USA)); there are green and purple varieties. A 50-g portion is a rich *source of vitamin C and supplies 10 kcal (40 kJ).

koilonychia Development of (brittle) concave finger nails, commonly associated with *iron deficiency anaemia.

koji Japanese; koji mould (*Aspergillus oryzae*) grown on roasted cereal to provide a starter for fermentation to produce *natto and *mirin. *See also* ASPERGILLUS; TAKADIASTASE.

koko West and Central African; sour cereal porridge made from maize, millet, or sorghum that has been soaked and left to undergo lactic acid bacterial fermentation for 24 hours, then boiled. Also known as uji.

kokoh In the Zen *macrobiotic diet this is a mixture of ground seeds and cereals fed to young infants; it is deficient in a number of nutrients and can result in growth retardation unless supplemented.

kokoretsi Highly seasoned Greek *sausage made from lamb offal (heart, liver, kidneys, sweetbread) with the intestine wound around the coarsely chopped meat, skewered and grilled slowly.

kokum (kokam) Fruit of the tropical tree, *Garcinia indica*, used especially in curries, chutneys, and pickles for its sour astringent flavour. Fat from kokum seeds is used as a cocoa butter extender (*see* COCOA BUTTER EQUIVALENTS). Also known as cocum, or Goa butter.

kolatchen Eastern European; sour cream biscuit made with flour, butter, sour cream, and yeast, served warm.

kolbasa Russian; garlicky well-seasoned pork and beef sausage; may be smoked.

komatsuna Varieties of *turnip (*Brassica campestris* or *B. rapa*) grown as leafy vegetables. Also known as Japanese mustard spinach.

kombu Japanese; dried *seaweed, *Laminaria japonica* (*see also* KELP).

konjac *Gum derived from tubers of *Amorphophallus konjac*; eaten in Japan as a firm jelly.

konnyaku Chinese, Japanese; flour made from tubers of the devil's tongue plant *Amorphophallus rivieri*.

korma Indian; meat or vegetables braised with water, stock, yoghurt, or cream.

korn German; spirit prepared by distillation of fermented maize, sometimes flavoured with juniper. Generally has a relatively low alcohol content; doppelkorn is 38% alcohol.

Korsakoff's psychosis Failure of recent memory, although events from the past are recalled, with confabulation; associated with *vitamin B_1 deficiency, especially in alcoholics. *See also* BERIBERI; WERNICKE–KORSAKOFF SYNDROME.

kosher The selection and preparation of foods in accordance with traditional Jewish ritual and dietary laws. Foods that are not kosher are traife.

   The only kosher flesh foods are from animals that chew the cud and have cloven hoofs, such as cattle, sheep, goats, and deer; the hindquarters must not be eaten. The only fish permitted are those with fins and scales; birds of prey and scavengers are not kosher. Moreover, the animals must be slaughtered according to ritual, without stunning, before the meat can be considered kosher. *See also* PASSOVER.

koubo *See* PITAYA.

koulouria Greek; sweet bread usually baked in a ring, flavoured with sesame seeds.

koumiss *See* MILK, FERMENTED.

kourabiethes Greek; shortbread traditionally baked for Christmas and New Year.

kpokpoi West African; small (2–3mm) steamed balls of fermented maize or yam flour; similar to *couscous (which is not fermented).

kraftbrühe Austrian; soup made from minced beef, carrot, onion, leek, and Hamburg parsley root, cooked in consommé.

krapiva Russian; nettle soup.

kräuterbutter German; butter mixed with chopped herbs.

kreatopita Greek pie made with three kinds of meat (usually lamb, goat or kid, and chicken), together with cheese, onions, tomatoes, and raisins, with a pastry top.

Krebs's cycle *See* CITRIC ACID CYCLE.

kreplach Jewish; *pasta envelopes filled with minced meat (similar to *ravioli), cooked in, and served with, soup.

krill Various species of planktonic crustaceans but is mostly the shrimp *Euphausia superba*. This is the main food of whales, and some penguins and other seabirds; occurs in shoals in the Antarctic, containing up to $12 kg/m^3$. Collected in limited quantities for use as human food: a 100-g portion is a rich *source of protein and niacin; a good source of calcium; a source of iron; supplies 100 kcal (420 kJ).

kromeski Russian, Polish; minced poultry, game, or meat, bound to a stiff paste with sauce, wrapped in bacon, coated in batter, and fried.

krupnik Polish, Jewish; barley and mushroom soup.

krupuk Indonesian; cracker made from fish or seafood mixed with rice or sago flour, dried then deep fried.

kryptoxanthin *See* CRYPTOXANTHIN.

kuban *See* MILK, FERMENTED.

kuchen dough Pastry dough, containing egg, margarine, and yeast.

kudzu *See* KUZU.

kugelhopf German, Alsatian; cake made from yeast dough in the shape of an inverted flower pot, with a hole through the centre which is usually filled with raisins and currants.

kula *See* BANANAS.

kulfi Indian; ice cream containing rice flour or sesame seed and ground almonds.

kumara New Zealand name for sweet potato. *See* POTATO, SWEET.

kumiss *See* MILK, FERMENTED.

kümmel German; liqueur flavoured with caraway seeds, fennel, and orris root; 40% alcohol.

kumquat A *citrus fruit, *Fortunella* spp.; widely distributed in S. China and now cultivated elsewhere; small, ovoid, with acid pulp and sweet, edible skin. A 50-g portion is a rich *source of vitamin C and supplies 30 kcal (125 kJ).

kuru (trembling disease) Progressive degeneration of brain cells, historically associated with cannibalism in Papua New Guinea, and believed to be caused by a *prion. More or less eradicated since ritual cannibalism was abolished.

kurut North African, Middle Eastern, Eastern Asian; hard dried balls of fermented milk or milk curds.

kusaya Japanese; slow-dried fish dipped in a dilute brine before drying; has a characteristic strong aroma and taste.

kushuk Iraqi; parboiled wheat and turnip allowed to undergo lactic acid bacterial fermentation for 4–10 days; liquid used as soup and the solid eaten as porridge or mixed with vegetables. Also an alternative name for *kishk.

kusum Seeds from the Indian tree *Schleichera trijuga* (syn. *S. oleosa*); the edible oil is rich in arachidic acid.

kuzu (kudzu) Tubers of the kuzu vine *Pueraria thunbergiana*, a legume; the starch is used as a thickening agent in Chinese and Japanese cuisine.

kvass (kwass) Russian and Eastern European; beer, normally home-brewed from rye, buckwheat, or wheat, with malt and yeast, often flavoured with mint; 2–4% *alcohol by volume, 1–5% carbohydrate, 60–150 kcal (250–630 kJ) per 300 mL.

kwashiorkor *See* PROTEIN-ENERGY MALNUTRITION.

k

L- *See* D-, L-, AND DL-.

labelled substances To follow the metabolic fate of foodstuffs, etc., in the body, they can be labelled by introduction of an unusual chemical substituent or with a stable or radioactive *isotope, so that the products can readily be identified.

labelling *See* NUTRITIONAL LABELLING.

laberdan *Cod salted and packed in barrels immediately it is landed at port, rather than later at a factory.

labneh (labaneh) Middle Eastern; strained concentrated yoghurt.

labni Cream cheese made from yoghurt.

lac A red colourant (a complex mixture of anthraquinones) obtained from the insect *Laccifera lacca* (syn. *Coccus lacca*) found on the trees *Schleichera oleosa*, *Ziziphus mauritiana*, and *Butea monosperma*, which grow in India and Malaysia. The lac insects are also the source of shellac.

laccase *Enzyme in bacteria, potato, and mushrooms that catalyses oxidation of polyphenols to quinones.

lachuch Yemeni, Middle Eastern; leavened *pitta made with fermented sourdough.

lacon Spanish; dry cured pork foreleg made by a process similar to that for dry cured *ham.

lacquer With reference to canned foods, a layer of gum and gum resin coated on to tinplate or steel and hardened with heat. The layer of lacquer protects the metal from attack by acid fruit juices.

lactalbumin One of the proteins of milk (casein 3%, lactalbumin 0.5%, lactoglobulin 0.25%). Not precipitated from acid solution as is *casein; hence, *whey contains lactalbumin and lactoglobulin, which are precipitated by heat and can be used to make whey cheese.

lactase The enzyme that hydrolyses *lactose to glucose and galactose in the brush border of intestinal mucosal cells. *See also* DISACCHARIDE INTOLERANCE.

lactates Salts of *lactic acid.

lactation The process of synthesizing and secreting milk from the breasts.
   Lactating women have slightly increased energy and protein requirements compared with those who are not breast-feeding (although considerable reserves of fat are laid down in pregnancy to cope with the stress of lactation), and high requirements for iron and calcium. These increased needs are reflected in the increased *reference intakes for lactating women.

lactein bread *See* BREAD, LACTEIN.

lactic acid The acid produced by the anaerobic fermentation of carbohydrates. Originally discovered in sour milk, it is responsible for the flavour of fermented milk (*see* MILK, FERMENTED) and for the precipitation of the *casein curd in cottage *cheese. Also produced by fermentation in silage, *pickles, *sauerkraut, cocoa, and tobacco (its value here is in suppressing the growth of unwanted organisms), and as the product of *glucose metabolism in muscle under conditions of maximum exertion.
   Used as an acidulant (as well as citric and tartaric acids) in sugar confectionery, soft drinks, pickles, and sauces.

lactic acid bacteria A heterogeneous group of *Gram-positive bacteria that ferment carbohydrates to lactic acid as the main end-product. *Homofermentative organisms convert fermentable carbohydrates almost quantitatively to lactic acid; *heterofermentative organisms also produce acetic acid, ethanol, and CO_2.

lactic acid, buffered A mixture of *lactic acid and sodium lactate used in sugar confectionery to provide an acid taste without *inversion of the sugar, which occurs at lower *pH.

lactic acidosis High blood concentrations of *lactic acid. May be a result of vigorous exercise, when muscle metabolizes anaerobically, or may arise as a result of a variety of metabolic disorders. Deficiency of *vitamin B_1 leads to high blood concentrations of both lactate and *pyruvate, especially after moderate exercise, because pyruvate dehydrogenase is a thiamin-dependent enzyme.

lacticin A *bacteriocin produced by *Lactococcus lactis* that inhibits the growth of a variety of *Gram-positive bacteria, including pathogens such as *Listeria monocytogenes*, *Clostridium* spp., *Staphylococcus* spp., and *Streptococcus* spp. It is used either as an ingredient or through the action of a bacteriocin-producing *starter culture.

lactitol (lactit) *Sugar alcohol derived from *lactulose. Not digested by digestive enzymes but fermented by intestinal bacteria to short-chain fatty acids, some of which are absorbed; it yields about 2kcal/g and hence has a potential use as a low-calorie bulk sweetener; also retards crystallization and improves moisture retention in foods. Also known as lactositol, lactobiosit.

***Lactobacillus casei* factor** *See* FOLIC ACID.

***Lactobacillus* spp.** *Lactic acid bacteria, many of which are used in food fermentation, including milk, meat, and plant products. There are three main groups, reflecting the ability to ferment various hexoses, pentoses, and disaccharides to lactic acid or lactic acid and other metabolites. Some species are also used as *probiotic micro-organisms.

lactobionic acid Formed by oxidation of the aldehyde group in the *glucose moiety of *lactose. Potentially useful as an *acidulant and to chelate minerals to enhance their absorption.

lactobiose *See* LACTOSE.

lactobiosit *See* LACTITOL.

Lactococcus lactis *Homofermentative *lactic acid bacteria used in manufacture of dairy products.

lactoferrin Iron-binding protein in milk (one of the *whey proteins) that acts to minimize bacterial growth by depriving them of available *iron. *See also* LACTALBUMIN.

lactoflavin Obsolete name for riboflavin isolated from milk. *See* VITAMIN B_2.

lactogen A drug or other substance that increases the production and secretion of milk.

lactoglobulin *See* LACTALBUMIN.

lactometer Floating device used to measure the specific gravity of milk (1.027–1.035).

Lac-tone Trade name; protein-rich baby food (26% protein) made in India from peanut flour, skimmed milk powder, wheat flour, and barley flour, with added vitamins and calcium.

lacto-ovo-vegetarian One whose diet excludes meat and fish but permits milk and eggs.

lactoperoxidase Enzyme in milk, a peroxidase, that has antibacterial action; measurement of peroxidase activity is a test for the efficacy of *pasteurization.

lactose The *carbohydrate of milk, sometimes called milk sugar. A *disaccharide of *glucose and *galactose. Used pharmaceutically as a tablet filler and as a medium for growth of micro-organisms. The fermentation of lactose to *lactic acid by bacteria is responsible for the souring of milk. Ordinary lactose is α-lactose, which is 16% as sweet as sucrose; if crystallized above 93°C, it is converted to the β-form which is more soluble and sweeter.

lactose intolerance *See* DISACCHARIDE INTOLERANCE.

lacto-serum Grandiloquent word for *whey.

lactositol *See* LACTITOL.

lactostearin *See* GLYCERYL LACTOSTEARATE.

lactosucrose A *prebiotic *oligosaccharide, galactosylsucrose, manufactured from sucrose and lactose in a reaction catalysed by β-fructofuranosidase. Used as a sweetener in foods and beverages.

lactovegetarian *See* VEGETARIANS.

lactulose A *disaccharide of galactose and fructose which does not occur naturally but is formed in heated or stored milk by isomerization of *lactose. About half as sweet as sucrose. Not hydrolysed by human digestive enzymes but fermented by intestinal bacteria to form *lactic and *pyruvic acids. Thought to promote the growth of *Lactobacillus bifidus* and so added to some infant formulae; in large amounts it is a *laxative, and can be used to acidify the intestinal contents to treat *hyperammonaemia. *See also* LACTITOL.

ladies' fingers *See* OKRA; also a short kind of banana.

ladyfish Marine fish, *Elopidae* spp.

laetrile Name given to an extract of apricot kernels. Claimed as a cancer cure, although there is no supporting evidence, and sometimes called vitamin B_{17}, although there is no evidence that it is a dietary essential or has any metabolic function. *See also* AMYGDALIN.

laevorotatory *See* OPTICAL ACTIVITY.

laevulose *See* FRUCTOSE.

lafun West and East African; flour made from yam, cassava, or plantain that has been soaked in water and allowed to undergo lactic acid bacterial fermentation for 2–5 days, then sun-dried and pounded into flour.

lager *See* BEER.

la kama Moroccan spice mixture: cinnamon, black peppercorns, ginger, turmeric, and nutmeg.

lakerda (lakertha) Greek; pickled raw fish (usually *tuna or swordfish).

laksa A perennial herb, *Persicaria odorato*, also known as Vietnamese mint or coriander, widely used in South-East Asian cuisine.

lamb Meat from sheep (*Ovis aries*) younger than 12–14 months. A 150-g portion is a rich *source of protein, niacin, iron, zinc, copper, and vitamin B_{12}; a good source of vitamins B_1, B_2, and B_6; different cuts contain up to 30g of fat, of which half is saturated; supplies 400–600kcal (1700–2500kJ). *See also* MUTTON.

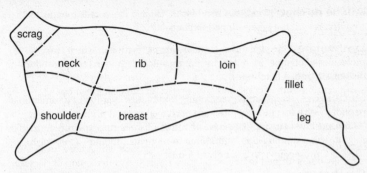

Lamb. Cuts of lamb

lambang oil *See* CANDLENUT.

lambanog Filipino; distilled spirit made from fermented nectar of coconut palm flowers. Also known as coconut vodka.

lambic *See* BEER.

lambrusco Italian; *wine with low alcohol content, lightly sparkling or *frizzante, made from the lambrusco variety of grape.

lamb's lettuce (corn salad) A hardy annual plant, *Valerianella locusta* or *V. olitoria*, used in salads in winter and early spring. A 50-g portion is a rich *source of vitamins A (as carotene) and C; supplies 5 kcal (20 kJ).

lamb's wool Old English drink made by pouring hot ale over pulped roasted apples and adding sugar and spices.

laminarin A non-starch polysaccharide from kelp (*Laminaria* spp.); a short polymer of glucose linked $\beta(1-3)$ with $\beta(1-6)$ branch points.

lampern *See* LAMPREY.

lamprey Cartilaginous fish resembling eels; sea lamprey is *Petromyzon marinus*, river lamprey or lampern is *Lampetra fluviatilis*.

Lancashire English hard cheese with a crumbly texture.

landrace Variety of plant or animal, highly adapted to local conditions, often associated with traditional agriculture.

landwein *See* WINE CLASSIFICATION, GERMANY.

langouste *Shellfish, *Palinurus vulgaris*; *see* LOBSTER.

langsat Fruit of the Malaysian shrub *Lansium domesticum*. White flesh is juicy and aromatic. Usually eaten fresh, but can also be used in cooking.

langue de chat Thin, flat, crisp biscuit, shaped like a cat's tongue, sometimes with the edges dipped in chocolate.

lanthionine Thio-dialanine, an analogue of *cystine in which two molecules of alanine are linked by a monosulphide bridge (as opposed to the disulphide bridge in cystine).

lantibiotics *Lanthionine-containing *antibiotics, a group of antimicrobial peptides (*see* BACTERIOCINS) that are produced by, and primarily act on, *Gram-positive bacteria. They have an intramolecular ring structure formed by the thio-ether amino acids lanthionine or methyllanthionine. One, *nisin, is used as a preservative in a variety of foods.

lao-chao South-East Asian; sweet slightly alcoholic glutinous rice. Boiled rice is inoculated with a starter (*ragi), which introduces various *amylase-producing moulds, including *Rhizopus* spp., and fermented for 2–3 days.

lapskaus Norwegian; boiled salted meat.

lard Rendered fat from pig carcasses (sheep and cattle are also used). The best quality is from the fat surrounding the kidneys; neutral lard is the highest quality, prepared by agitating the minced fat with water at a temperature below 50°C; kidney fat provides No. 1 quality; back fat No. 2 quality.

Leaf lard is made from the residue of kidney and back fat after the preparation of neutral lard by heating with water above 100°C in an autoclave. Prime Steam Lard is fat from any part of the carcass, rendered in the autoclave.

Lard used to be stored in pig's bladder, hence the expression 'bladder of lard' for a grossly obese person.

lard compounds Blends of animal fats, such as oleostearin or *premier jus, with vegetable oils, to produce products similar to lard in consistency and texture. *See also* LARD SUBSTITUTES.

lardine *See* MARGARINE.

larding Method of adding fat to lean meat so that it does not dry out during long slow cooking. Narrow strips of bacon fat (lardons) are threaded into the surface of the meat with a special 'larding needle' before cooking. *See also* BARDING.

lardons *See* LARDING.

lard substitutes Vegetable shortenings made from mixtures of partially *hydrogenated vegetable oils that have the consistency of *lard. *See also* LARD COMPOUNDS.

lardy cake West of England; made from bread dough, lard, sugar, and dried fruit.

largebaim Freshwater fish, *Mastacembelus armatus*.

lasagne Sheets of *pasta; lasagne verdi is flavoured with spinach. Wide ribbons are lasagnette.

lasoda fruit of the Indian tree *Cordia myxa*, used unripe to make pickles.

lassi Indian; beverage made from yoghurt or buttermilk, mixed with water.

late blowing *See* BLOWING.

lathyrism Bone and nerve damage associated with high intakes of *Lathyrus sativus* (kesari dhal, chickling pea, chickling vetch). The crop is often grown in dry districts in Asia and North Africa together with wheat. Normally little is eaten, but when there is a drought and the wheat crop is poor, the dhal predominates and is eaten as a major food.

latkes Jewish; pancakes made from grated potatoes.

latte Very milky white *coffee.

laung *See* CLOVES.

lauric acid A medium-chain saturated *fatty acid (C12:0) in butter, coconut oil, and palm oil.

laver Edible *seaweed. Laver bread is made from *Porphyra* spp., by boiling in salted water and mincing to a gelatinous mass. It is made into a cake with oatmeal or fried. Locally known in South Wales as bara lawr.

lax Scandinavian name for salmon; *see also* GRAVADLAX; LOX.

laxarinic acid *See* MALTOL.

laxative (aperient) A substance that enhances the expulsion of food residues from the body, so treating *constipation. Strong laxatives are called purgative or cathartic.

laxative, bulk Non-starch polysaccharides and cellulose retain water and add bulk to the contents of the intestine.

laxative, emollient Non-absorbable compounds that coat and lubricate faeces, e.g. liquid paraffin and didactyl sodium sulphosuccinate.

laxative, osmotic Poorly absorbed solutes that remain in the intestinal lumen and so create an osmotic gradient into the intestinal lumen, increasing water influx, e.g. magnesium sulphate (*Epsom salts) and hydroxide. Unabsorbed carbohydrates such as *lactulose and *sugar alcohols are substrates for bacterial fermentation and also act as osmotic laxatives. *See also* DISACCHARIDE INTOLERANCE.

laxative, secretory Compounds that cause increased fluid and electrolyte secretion into the intestinal lumen, including castor oil (the active ingredient is ricinoleic acid) and a variety of anthroquinone derivatives, including cascara, aloe, senna, and fig syrup (naturally occurring), and phenolphthalein, bisacodyl, and danthron (synthetic compounds). They can also cause abdominal cramps as a result of excessive stimulation of smooth muscle.

lazybed Narrow strip of land, about 500–800m in length, used traditionally in the Andes for growing potatoes, and adopted in Ireland about 1640; one lazybed will provide enough potatoes for a family for a year.

LCAT Lecithin cholesterol acyl transferase, the *enzyme that catalyses esterification of *cholesterol by transfer of fatty acids from *lecithin. *See also* ACAT.

LC-MS Liquid chromatography linked to a mass spectrometer as the detection system.

LD$_{50}$ An index of toxicity (lethal dose 50%), the amount of the substance that kills 50% of the test population of experimental animals when administered as a single dose.

LDL Low density *lipoprotein, formed in the circulation from *IDL by uptake of *cholesterol (as cholesteryl esters) from *HDL. Normally cleared by the liver by receptor-mediated *endocytosis, but oxidized LDL is not recognized by the liver receptor, and is taken up by *macrophages, which become *foam cells.

leaching The process of extracting soluble compounds from a food with water or another solvent; may be deliberate (as, e.g., in water extraction of sugar from beet, or solvent extraction of oil from oilseeds), or accidental, when vitamins and minerals leach into cooking water and are lost.

lead A mineral of no nutritional interest, since it is not known to have any function in the body. It is toxic and its effects are cumulative. May be present in food from traces naturally present in the soil or as contamination; from shellfish that have absorbed it from seawater; from lead glazes on cooking vessels; and in drinking water where lead pipes are used. Traces are excreted in the urine.

lean body mass Measure of body composition excluding fat, i.e. cells, extracellular fluid, and skeleton.

Leatherhead Food International The former British Food Manufacturing Industries Research Association.

(⊕) SEE WEB LINKS

• Leatherhead Food International's homepage.

leathers, fruit Fruit purées dried in air in thin layers, 4–5mm thick, then built up into thicker preparations.

leaven *Yeast, or a piece of dough kept to ferment the next batch.

leavening Baked goods may be leavened mechanically by air incorporated in dough mixing, or by steam produced in baking; chemically using a *baking powder (sodium, potassium, or ammonium bicarbonate together with an acid); or biologically by *yeast *fermentation.

leben (laban) Middle Eastern and North African; fermented milk similar to *yoghurt; the *starter culture includes yeast, so it contains some alcohol.

lebernockerln *See* KNÖDELN.

lebkuchen German, Swiss; gingerbread, often baked in carved moulds, traditionally eaten at Christmas.

lecithin Phosphatidyl choline, a *phospholipid containing *choline. Commercial lecithin, prepared from soya bean, peanut, and maize, is a mixture of phospholipids in which phosphatidyl choline predominates. Used in food processing as an *emulsifier, e.g. in salad dressing, processed cheese, and chocolate, and as an anti-spattering agent in frying oils. Is plentiful in the diet and not a dietary essential.

leckerli Swiss; biscuits made with honey, almonds, candied peel, cloves, nutmeg, and ginger.

lectins Proteins from *legumes and other sources which bind to the carbohydrates found at cell surfaces. They therefore cause red blood cells to agglutinate *in vitro*, hence the old names haemagglutinins and phytoagglutinins.

Raw or undercooked beans of some varieties of *Phaseolus vulgaris* (red kidney beans) cause vomiting and diarrhoea within two hours of consumption due to the high level of lectins, but they are rapidly inactivated by boiling.

leek A member of the onion family that has been known as a food for over 4000 years in the Middle East. The lower part is usually blanched by planting in trenches or earthing up, and eaten along with the upper long green leaves. The wild leek is *Allium ampeloprasum*, the cultivated leek is *A. porrum*; great headed leek or levant garlic is *A. porrum* var. *holmense*. A 125-g portion is a rich *source of vitamin C; a good source of folate; a source of iron; provides 3.1g of dietary fibre; supplies 30kcal (125kJ).

leerfish Marine fish, *Lichia amia*.

legumes Members of the family *Leguminosae* consumed as dry mature seeds (grain legumes or pulses) or as immature green seeds in the pod. On soaking and boiling, the dried seeds double in weight, so a 100-g cooked portion is approximately 50g as a dried product.

Legumes include the groundnut, *Arachis hypogaea*, and soya bean, *Glycine max*, grown for their oil and protein, the yam bean *Pachyrrhizus erosus*, and African yam bean *Sphenostylis stenocarpa*, grown for their edible tubers as well as seeds. *See also* BEANS.

legumin Globulin protein in legumes.

Leicester English hard cheese coloured with *annatto.

lekach Jewish; sponge cake made with ginger and honey.

lemon Sour yellow fruit of *Citrus limon*. A 100-g portion of fruit, or 100ml of juice, is a rich *source of vitamin C; supplies 7kcal (28kJ).

lemonade Originally a beverage made from lemon juice with water and sugar; now also a wide variety of carbonated beverages.

lemon balm *See* BALM.

lemon curd Cooked mixture of sugar, butter, eggs, and lemons. Legally (UK regulations) must contain 4% fat, 0.33% citric acid, 1% dried egg or equivalent, 0.125% oil of lemon or 0.25% oil of orange, and not less than 65% soluble solids.

lemon grass A tropical grass, *Cymbopogon citratrus* (syn. *Andropogon schoenanthus*), with lemon-like odour, widely used in South-East Asian cuisine. Also known as camel's hay, citronella, geranium grass, cochin grass, and the dry powder as sereh.

lemon oil The peel oil of the lemon, 0.15–0.3% of the weight of the fruit.

lemon verbena South American woody shrub, *Lippia citriodora* (syn. *Aloysia triphylla*); the fresh or dried leaves are used to flavour drinks and salads.

lentils *Legumes; dried seeds of many varieties of *Lens esculenta*, they may be green, yellow, or orange-red. When ground, they are frequently used to thicken soup. A 120-g portion is a rich *source of copper and selenium; a good source of iron; a source of protein, vitamin B_6, folate, and zinc; contains 0.6g of fat, of which 20% is saturated; provides 4.8g of dietary fibre; supplies 125kcal (520kJ).

leptin *Hormone secreted by adipose tissue that acts to regulate long-term *appetite and energy expenditure by signalling the state of body fat reserves. Lack of leptin secretion is an extremely rare cause of *obesity; most obese people secrete higher than normal amounts of leptin, but are less sensitive to its actions.

lettuce Leaves of the plant *Lactuca sativa*; many varieties are grown commercially. A poor source of nutrients; an 80-g portion supplies 10kcal (40kJ).

lettuce, Korean *Ixeris sonchifolia*, also known as Godulbaegi.

lettuce, miner's *See* PURSLANE.

leucine An essential *amino acid; rarely limiting in foods; one of the branched-chain amino acids.

leucocytes White blood cells, normally 5000–9000/mm^3; includes polymorphonuclear neutrophils, lymphocytes, monocytes, polymorphonuclear eosinophils, and polymorphonuclear basophils. A 'white cell count' determines the total; a 'differential cell count' estimates the numbers of each type. Fever, haemorrhage, and violent exercise cause an increase (leucocytosis); starvation and debilitating conditions a decrease (leucopenia).

leucocytosis Increase in the number of *leucocytes in the blood.

***Leuconostoc* spp.** *Heterofermentative *lactic acid bacteria used in the fermentation of vegetables (e.g. cabbage and cucumbers), where they initiate lactic acid fermentation. *L. mesenteroides* subspp. *cremoris* is used in dairy *starter cultures because it produces *diacetyl, which has a buttery flavour. *L. mesenteroides* subspp. *mesenteroides* produces *dextrans and *levans that are used industrially.

leucopenia Decrease in the number of *leucocytes in the blood.

leucosin One of the water-soluble proteins of wheat flour.

leucovorin The synthetic (*racemic) 5-formyl derivative of *folic acid; more stable to oxidation than folic acid itself, and commonly used in pharmaceutical preparations. Also known as folinic acid.

leukotrienes *Eicosanoids synthesized by the lipoxygenase pathway.

levans Polymers of *fructose (the principal one is *inulin) that occur in tubers and some grasses.

leveret A young *hare.

levitin One of the proteins of egg yolk; about one-fifth of the total, the remainder being vitellin. Rich in sulphur, it accounts for half of the sulphur in the yolk.

Leyden Dutch semi-hard cheese containing caraway and cumin seeds.

Leyden hutspot Dutch; *hotpot made from (stale) beef and root vegetables, traditionally served on 3 October, together with white bread and herrings, to celebrate the relief of the siege of Leyden (1574).

liberty cabbage American name coined for *sauerkraut in 1918.

liberty fries American name coined for French fries (*chips) in 2003.

licorice *See* LIQUORICE.

licoroso Portuguese; fortified sweet wines.

lieben German and Austrian classification for semi-sweet wines; *see* WINE SWEETNESS.

Lieberkühn, crypts of Glands lining the small intestine which secrete the intestinal juice.

light (lite) As applied to foods usually indicates: i) a lower content of fat compared with the standard product (e.g. *breadspreads, sausages); ii) sodium chloride substitutes lower in *sodium (*see* SALT, LIGHT); iii) low-alcohol *beer or *wine. US legislation restricts the term 'light' to modified foods that contain one-third less energy or half the fat of a reference unmodified food, or to indicate that the sodium content of a low-fat, low-calorie food has been reduced by half. *See also* FAT-FREE; FREE FROM; LOW IN; REDUCED.

lights Butchers' term for the lungs of an animal.

lignans Naturally occurring compounds in various foods that have both oestrogenic and antioestrogenic activity (*phytoestrogens); may provide some protection against breast and uterine cancer, and useful as menopausal hormone replacement therapy.

lignin (lignocellulose) Indigestible part of the cell wall of plants (a polymer of aromatic alcohols). It is included in measurement of *dietary fibre, but not of *non-starch polysaccharide.

lignocellulose Complex of *lignin and *cellulose in the cell walls of plants.

Lillet French; trade name of a light *vermouth made from red or white Bordeaux wines in which fruit peel and herbs are steeped; aged in oak casks.

lima beans US term for flat, kidney-shaped bean; smaller ones are butter limas, called butter beans in the UK (*see* BEANS, BUTTER), and larger are potato limas.

Limburger Originally Belgian; strongly flavoured soft cheese.

limbé *See* MANGOSTEEN.

lime The fruit of *Citrus aurantifolia*, cultivated almost solely in the tropics, since it is less hardy than other *citrus fruits. Used to prevent *scurvy in the British Navy (replacing, at the time, lemon juice) and so giving rise to the nickname of 'Limeys' for British sailors and for British people in general. Contains about 10–20mg vitamin C per 100g fruit or fresh juice.

lime berry Fruit of the South-East Asian shrub *Triphasia trifolia* (syn. *T. aurantiola*).

lime, kaffir The leaves of *Citrus histrix*, used in Thai cuisine.

limequat A citrus fruit, a hybrid between the West Indian *lime and the *kumquat.

lime, sweet Fruit of *Citrus limettioides* or *C. lumia*. Sometimes confused with the sweet lemon (*C. limetta*).

limiting amino acid *See* AMINO ACID, LIMITING.

limoncello Italian *liqueur made by soaking zest of lemon peel in alcohol and adding sugar.

limonoids Triterpene derivatives (limonin and isolimonin) found as aglycones in citrus seeds, peel oil, and albedo, and as glucosides in juice; responsible for delayed bitterness of the fruit. There is some evidence that they may be protective against cancer.

limosis Abnormal hunger or excessive desire for food.

limpet A *shellfish, *Patella vulgata*.

lin *See* TENCH.

linamarin *Cyanogenic glucoside found in *cassava (manioc) which may be a cause of neuropathies in areas where cassava is a major food; the cyanide is removed in traditional processing by grating and exposing to air.

ling Marine fish, *Molva* spp., widely distributed in the Atlantic Ocean. Ling cod is a Pacific fish, *Ophiodon elongatus;* rock ling is *Genypterus tigerinus*; and blue ling is *M. dyptergia*.

lingonberry Fruit of the small evergreen shrub *Vaccinium vitis-idaea*; contains high levels of *benzoic acid. Also known as cowberry or lingberry.

linguiça Portuguese; pork sausage seasoned with garlic, cinnamon, and cumin, cured in brine.

linguini *See* PASTA.

linie aquavit Norwegian *aquavit aged in oak casks that are shipped to Australia and back before bottling, thus crossing the equator (*linie*) twice.

linkage analysis A technique for identifying genes that may be involved in the pathophysiology of complex diseases involving interactions between genotype and diet and/or other environmental factors, by examining the segregation of variant *DNA loci (marker alleles) in affected pairs of family members. Marker alleles that are shared more often than would be expected by chance suggest that there is a linkage between the marker and the disease of interest. *See also* LOD SCORE.

linoleic acid An essential polyunsaturated *fatty acid (C18:2 ω6), predominant in most edible vegetable oils.

linoleic acid, conjugated Isomers of *linoleic acid in which two or more of the double bonds are conjugated (i.e. alternating with single bonds) rather than separated by a methylene bridge. They occur naturally in small amounts in ruminant (and hence also dairy) fats and have *anticarcinogenic and *cholesterol lowering activity in experimental animals.

α-linolenic acid An essential polyunsaturated *fatty acid (C18:3 ω3).

γ-linolenic acid A non-essential polyunsaturated *fatty acid (C18:3 ω6) which has some pharmacological actions. Found in oils from the seeds of evening primrose, borage, and blackcurrant.

linseed *See* FLAX.

Linzer torte Austrian; flan made with eggs, ground almonds, and mixed peel, with a covering of jam and a lattice of pastry on top.

liothyronine Alternative name for the *thyroid hormone tri-iodothyronine.

lipaemia Increase in blood lipids, as occurs normally after a meal.

lipase *Enzyme that hydrolyses fats (triacylglycerols) to glycerol and fatty acids. Most lipases have low specificity and will act on any triacylglycerol or long-chain ester. Present in the *pancreatic juice, liver, and *adipose tissue, and in many seeds and grains. Sometimes responsible for the development of rancidity in stored foods. Lipases have been used in baking to permit *in situ* formation of mono- and diacylglycerol as emulsifiers.

lipase, hormone-sensitive The main *lipase of *adipose tissue; its activity is stimulated by *adrenaline, and suppressed by *insulin. *See also* DESNUTRIN.

lipase, lipoprotein An extra-cellular enzyme that hydrolyses *triacylglycerol in *chylomicrons and *VLDL, permitting tissues to take up fatty acids for metabolism or storage as triacylglycerol. Its synthesis is induced (*see* INDUCTION) by *insulin.

lipectomy Surgical removal of subcutaneous fat.

lipidema Condition in which fat deposits accumulate in the lower extremities, from hips to ankles, with tenderness of the affected parts.

lipids (lipides, lipins) A general term for fats and oils (*triacylglycerols), waxes, *phospholipids, steroids, and terpenes. Their common property is insolubility in water and solubility in hydrocarbons, chloroform, and alcohols.

lipids, non-saponified The water-insoluble material remaining in a fat or oil after *saponification; mainly *sterols, higher alcohols, hydrocarbons, and pigments.

lipids, plasma *Triacylglycerols, free and esterified *cholesterol and *phospholipids, present in lipoproteins in *blood plasma. *See* CHYLOMICRONS; HDL; IDL; LDL; VLDL.

lipins *See* LIPIDS.

lipochromes Plant pigments soluble in fats and organic solvents, such as chlorophyll, carotenoids.

lipodystrophy Abnormal pattern of subcutaneous fat deposits.

lipofuscin A group of pigments that accumulate in several body tissues, particularly the myocardium, and are associated with the ageing process.

lipogenesis Synthesis of fatty acids and triacylglycerol.

lipoic acid A coenzyme (together with *vitamin B_1) in the metabolism of *pyruvate and in the citric acid cycle. Although it is an essential growth factor for various micro-organisms, there is no evidence that it is a human dietary requirement.

lipolysis The *hydrolysis of triacylglycerol to glycerol and fatty acids. *See* LIPASE.

lipoproteins Complexes of protein and lipids; *see* CHYLOMICRONS; HDL; IDL; LDL; LIPIDS, PLASMA; VLDL.

lipostatic mechanism of appetite control Control of appetite, hunger, and satiety (and energy expenditure) in response to *leptin secreted from adipose tissue, which signals the state of body fat reserves.

liposuction Procedure for removal of subcutaneous adipose tissue in obese people using a suction device.

lipotropes (lipotrophic factors) Compounds such as *choline, *betaine, and *methionine that act as methyl donors; deficiency may result in fatty infiltration of the liver.

lipovitellenin A lipoprotein complex in egg comprising about one-sixth of the solids of the yolk.

lipoxin *See* EICOSANOIDS.

liptauer Hungarian; cheese spread made from sheep's and cow's milk.

liqueurs Distilled, flavoured, and sweetened alcoholic liquors, usually 20–40% alcohol, 20–30% sugar.

liquorice Used in confectionery and to flavour medicines; liquorice root and extract are obtained from the plant *Glycyrrhiza glabra*; stick liquorice is the evaporated extract of the root. The plant has been grown in the Pontefract district of Yorkshire since the 16th century; hence the name Pontefract cakes for the liquorice sugar confectionery. *See also* GLYCYRRHIZIN.

liquoroso Italian; high-strength, often fortified, wines.

Listeria A genus of bacteria commonly found in soil of which the commonest is *Listeria monocytogenes*. They can cause *food-borne disease (listeriosis). Symptoms are flu-like, with high fever and dizziness. Pregnant women, babies, and the elderly are especially at risk. A *psychrotrophic organism that can grow at refrigeration temperature. The main sources of infection are raw milk, soft cheeses, raw vegetables, and some meat products.

listeriosis *See* LISTERIA.

litchi *See* LYCHEE.

lite *See* LIGHT.

lithium Metal not known to have any physiological function, although it occurs in food and water; lithium salts are used in the treatment of manic-depressive illness.

liver Usually from calf, pig, ox, lamb, or poultry; a 150-g portion (fried or stewed) is an exceptionally rich *source of iron and vitamins A, D, B_2, B_6, and B_{12}; a rich source of protein, zinc, copper, selenium, niacin, and vitamin B_1; also, unusually for meat, a good source of vitamin C; contains 10g of fat, of which one-third is *saturated; supplies 300–380kcal (1250–1600kJ).

The vitamin A content of liver is high enough for it to pose a possible hazard to unborn children, and pregnant women have been advised not to eat liver. (*See* VITAMIN A TOXICITY.) Fish liver is a particularly rich source of vitamins A and D, and fish liver oils (especially cod and halibut) are used as sources of these vitamins as nutritional supplements.

liver sausage *Sausage made from liver. A 150-g portion is an exceptionally rich *source of iron, vitamin A, protein, vitamin B_2, and niacin; a rich source of vitamin B_1; contains 40g of fat, of which 40% is saturated; supplies 450kcal (1900kJ).

livetin A water-soluble protein in egg yolk.

LRNI Lower Reference Nutrient Intake; *see* REFERENCE INTAKES.

lobio Russian (Georgian); bean salad.

lobscouse Sailor's stew of meat and vegetables, classically thickened with ship's biscuit.

lobster A crustacean, *Homerus* spp. Slipper lobster is species of the family *Scyllaridae*, squat lobster is species of the family *Galatheidae*, Indian ocean or whip lobster is *Puerulus* spp. A 100-g portion (meat from half a dressed lobster) is a rich *source of protein, niacin, vitamin B_{12}, and copper; a source of zinc, vitamin B_1, niacin, folate, and calcium; contains 370mg of sodium and 3.5g of fat; supplies 130kcal (550kJ).

lobster, rock (spiny lobster) *See* CRAWFISH.

lockshen (lokshen) Thin noodles, vermicelli; *see* PASTA.

locksoy Chinese; fine-drawn rice macaronil; *see* PASTA.

locoweed *Astralagus* and *Oxytropus* spp., common in arid areas of the western USA. Toxic to cattle, causing locoism: neurological damage, abortion, and birth defects. Apparently caused by the *alkaloid swainsonine, which is also found in mouldy hay.

locust bean *See* CAROB; PETAI.

locust bean, African Seeds of *Parkia filicoidea* or *P. biglobosa*, fermented to produce *dawadawa. The yellow flesh surrounding the seeds is also eaten, either raw or cooked.

LOD score In genetics; the $\log_{10}$ of the likelihood ratios for linkage versus non-linkage between a gene and a disease, in *linkage analysis. For complex diseases involving interactions between genes and diet and/or other environmental factors, a LOD score >3.3 is considered to be evidence of significant linkage.

loempias Dutch, Indonesian; *see* SPRING ROLLS.

LOFFOEX Low fibre, fat-limited exclusion diet. *See* DIET, EXCLUSION.

Logan Bar Ration D *See* IRON RATION.

loganberry Cross between European raspberry and Californian blackberry, *Rubus ursinus* var. *loganobaccus*, named after James Harvey Logan, California judge, 1881. An 80-g portion is a rich *source of vitamin C; a source of copper; provides 4.8g of dietary fibre; and supplies 15kcal (60kJ).

lo han kuo Chinese name for *Momordica grosvenori*. *See* MOGROSIDE.

loin The back portion of animals; *see* PORK; LAMB.

lollipop Boiled sweet or toffee on a small wooden stick. Ice lollipop (ice lolly, popsicle in USA) is water-ice on a stick.

London broil American name for steak, broiled or grilled and sliced thinly against the grain.

longan Fruit of Chinese trees *Dimocarpus longan*, *Euphoria longan*, and *Nephelium longana*, similar to *lychee. Also known as dragon's eyes.

longaniza *See* SOBRESADA.

lonzo Corsican; boned fillet of pork, steeped in wine and herbs, then air dried, thinly sliced, and eaten raw.

loofah Young fruit of the curcubits *Luffa acutangula* and *L. cilindrica* is edible, but becomes too bitter as it matures.

loonzein Rice from which the husk has been removed; also known as brown rice, hulled rice, and cargo rice.

loquat The small pear-shaped fruit of the tree *Eriobotrya japonica*, a member of the apple family, also known as Japanese medlar. A 100-g portion supplies 50 kcal (210 kJ) but only a trace of vitamin C.

lotus The sacred lotus of India and China, *Nelumbium nuciferum* syn. *Nelumbo nucifera*, a water plant whose rhizomes and seeds are eaten. A 100-g portion of the rhizome is a rich *source of vitamin C, and supplies 50 kcal (210 kJ).

loukoum *See* TURKISH DELIGHT.

lovage Herb of the carrot family, *Levisticum officinale*, with a strong scent of celery. The stems can be candied like *angelica or used as a vegetable, and the leaves and stems are used in soup. The seeds can also be used as a seasoning, with a flavour like dill or fennel seed. Scottish lovage is *Ligusticum scoticum*.

love apple Old name for *tomato.

low birth weight Infants born weighing significantly less than normal are considered to be premature; their chances of survival and normal development are considerably improved if they are fed special formula preparations to meet their needs, rather than being breast-fed or fed normal *infant formula. The normal range of weight at birth is between 2.5 and 4.5 kg.

low in EU legislation states that for a food label or advertising to bear a claim that it is low in fat, saturates, cholesterol, sodium, or alcohol, it must provide less than half the amount of the specified nutrient of a reference product for which no claim is made. US legislation sets precise (low) levels at which such claims may be made.

lox American (originally Yiddish) name for smoked salmon; *see also* LAX.

lozenges Shapes stamped out of a mixture of icing sugar, glucose syrup, and gum arabic or gelatine with flavourings, then hardened at 32–43 °C.

LPL Lipoprotein lipase; *see* LIPASE, LIPOPROTEIN.

LRAT lecithin retinol acyltransferase.

LTLT *See* PASTEURIZATION, LTLT.

lucerne The perennial herb, *Medicago sativa*; mainly a forage crop, but the sprouted seeds are eaten. Also known as alfalfa.

luciferase An enzyme that emits light linked to the hydrolysis of ATP to ADP and phosphate; widely used for assay of ATP and as a *reporter gene in genetic engineering.

luganeghe Italian; pork sausages that are not twisted into links.

luminacoids Japanese term, introduced 2003, to include all *oligosaccharides, *sugar alcohols, resistant *starch, indigestible *dextrins, resistant proteins, and other compounds of plant or animal origin that may undergo (bacterial) metabolism in the intestinal lumen; a wider definition than either dietary fibre (*see* FIBRE, DIETARY) or *non-starch polysaccharide.

lumpfish Marine fish, *Cyclopterus lumpus*, also known as lumpsucker. The eggs are salted, pressed, and coloured as Danish or German *caviare.

lumpsucker *See* LUMPFISH.

lunch (luncheon) The midday meal (but in northern England the main meal was traditionally eaten at midday and is known as dinner).

luncheon meat Precooked, canned meat, usually pork. A 150-g portion is a rich *source of protein and niacin; a good source of iron; a source of vitamins B_1 and B_2; contains 40 g of fat, of which 40% is saturated; supplies 450 kcal (1900 kJ).

lupeose *See* STACHYOSE.

lupins Legumes, *Lupinus* spp. The ordinary garden lupin contains toxic quinolidizine *alkaloids and tastes bitter; varieties selected for animal feed and grain crop are low in alkaloids and known as sweet lupins; they are rich in protein and fat, have been part of Middle Eastern cuisine since ancient times, and are grown as an oilseed crop.

lutefisk (lutfisk) Norwegian, Swedish; dried salted cod preserved in potash lye (potassium hydroxide).

lutein A hydroxylated *carotenoid (*see* XANTHOPHYLLS); not *vitamin A active, but may be an important *antioxidant nutrient. Together with *zeaxanthin accumulates in the retina, and is considered to be protective against damage by UV and blue light.

lutfisk *See* LUTEFISK.

luting Strip of pastry placed round a dish to seal on the lid or pastry cover, used when preparing potted game, etc., in covered dishes.

luxus konsumption *See* THERMOGENESIS, DIET-INDUCED.

lychee (litchi) The fruit of the Chinese tree *Litchi chinensis*, the size of a small plum, with a hard case and translucent, white, jelly-like sweet flesh surrounding the seed. A 100-g portion is a rich *source of vitamin C, and supplies 70 kcal (290 kJ). *See also* RAMBUTAN.

lycopene Red *carotenoid pigment found in tomato, pink grapefruit, and palm oil. Not *vitamin A active, but an *antioxidant; also used as a food colour.

lye-peeling A method of removing skins from vegetables by immersion in hot caustic soda (sodium hydroxide) solution (lye) followed by tumbling in a wash to remove the skin and chemicals.

lymph The fluid between blood and the tissues in which oxygen and nutrients are transported to the tissues, and waste products back to the blood.

Dietary fat is absorbed into the lacteals (lymphatic vessels of the intestinal villi) as *chylomicrons which are formed in the intestinal mucosa, and enters the bloodstream through the thoracic duct. After a fatty meal the lymph is rich in emulsified fat and is called chyle.

lymphatics Vessels through which the *lymph flows, draining from the tissues and entering the bloodstream at the thoracic duct.

lymphocytes *See* LEUCOCYTES.

lymphokines *Cytokines secreted by lymphocytes.

lyonnaise, à la Dish with fried shredded onion as a major ingredient.

lyophilic A solute that has a high affinity for the solvent medium. When the solvent is water the term *hydrophilic is used. *See also* LYOPHOBIC.

lyophilization *See* DRYING, FREEZE.

lyophobic A solute that has little or no affinity for the solvent medium. When the solvent is water the term *hydrophobic is used. *See also* LYOPHILIC.

lysergic acid The toxin of *ergot.

lysine An essential *amino acid of special nutritional importance, since it is the limiting amino acid (*see* AMINO ACID, LIMITING) in many cereals. Can be synthesized on a commercial scale, and when added to bread, rice, or cereal-based animal feeds, it improves the nutritional value of the protein.

Not all of the lysine in proteins is biologically *available, since some is linked through its side-chain amino group, either to sugars (*see* MAILLARD REACTION), or to other amino acids. These linkages are not hydrolysed by digestive enzymes, and so the lysine cannot be absorbed. Available lysine is that proportion of the protein-bound lysine in which the side-chain amino group is free, so that it can be absorbed after digestion of the protein.

lysolecithin *Lecithin from which the fatty acid at carbon-2 has been removed.

lysosomes Intracellular organelles that contain a variety of proteolytic and other catabolic enzymes; important in catabolism of many intracellular proteins, *mitochondria, and engulfed organisms (*see* ENDOCYTOSIS). On cell death the lysosomes lyse and release their enzymes to catabolize the cell contents.

lysozyme An enzyme that hydrolyses some of the high molecular weight carbohydrates of bacterial cell walls, and so lyses bacteria. Widely distributed (e.g. in tears and *saliva); egg-white is especially rich.

MA Modified atmosphere. *See* STORAGE, MODIFIED GAS.

maasa West African; shallow fried cakes made from millet or sorghum dough that has been allowed to undergo lactic acid bacterial fermentation for a short time.

maatjes Dutch; cured *herring made from young female herrings.

macadamia nut Fruit of the Australian evergreen tree *Macadamia ternifolia* syn. *M. integrifolia*. A 60-g portion (thirty-six nuts) is a good *source of vitamin B_1; a source of protein, niacin, and iron; contains 45 g of fat, of which 15% is *saturated and 80% mono-unsaturated; supplies 450 kcal (1 900 kJ).

macaroni *See* PASTA.

macaroon Cake made from ground almonds or coconut, sugar, and egg-white, baked on *rice paper. Originated in Italy, where it is known as amaretti.

macassar gum *See* AGAR.

maccaroncelli *See* PASTA.

mace The aril (the bright red, lacy covering) of the seed shell of *nutmeg (*Myristica fragrans*). The mace is removed from the shell and its broken parts are known as blades.

macedoine Mixture of fruits or vegetables, diced, or cut into small even-shaped pieces.

macerases A group of *enzymes (usually extracted from *Aspergillus* spp.) used to break down *pectin in fruits to facilitate maximum extraction of the juice.

mackerel An oily fish, *Scomber* spp. Atlantic mackerel is *S. scombrus*, Pacific mackerel (also known as chub mackerel) is *S. japonicus*. Indian mackerel is *Rastrelliger* spp., snake mackerel or escolar is species of the family *Gempylida*, king mackerel (or kingfish) is *Scomberomorus cavalla*, sierra mackerel (or Pacific sierra) is *Scomberomorus sierra*. A 150-g portion is a rich *source of protein, vitamins D, B_2, B_6, B_{12}, niacin, copper, iodine, and selenium; a source of vitamin B_1 and iron; contains 24 g of fat, of which 20% is saturated; supplies 330 kcal (1 390 kJ).

mackerel, horse (jack mackerel) Marine fish, also known as scad; *Trachurus* spp., *Decapterus* spp., *Hemicaranx* spp., and *Seriola* spp. Atlantic horse mackerel is *T. trachurus*, Pacific horse mackerel is *T. japonicus* and *D. macarellus*, yellowtail or amberjack is *Seriola lalandi*.

macon Mutton, salted and smoked to resemble *bacon.

maconochie A canned meat stew used in the First World War; made by Maconochie Brothers.

macrobiotic diet See DIET, MACROBIOTIC.

macrocytes Large immature precursors of red *blood cells found in the circulation in pernicious *anaemia and in *folic acid deficiency, due to impairment of the normal maturation of red cells; hence macrocytic anaemia.

macromolecules Large polymeric molecules: *proteins, *polysaccharides, and *nucleic acids.

macronutrients Those *nutrients required in large amounts: *carbohydrates, *lipids, and *protein.

macrophages White blood cells that engulf foreign material, especially micro-organisms. *See also* FOAM CELL.

mad cow disease Bovine spongiform encephalopathy; *see* BSE.

Madeira cake Rich cake containing no dried fruit, flavoured with lemon, and traditionally decorated with strips of candied *citron peel.

Madeira nuts See WALNUTS.

Madeira wines Fortified wines (*see* WINE, FORTIFIED) from the island of Madeira; the first vines, imported from Sicily, were planted in 1420 by Prince Henry the Navigator: sercial (dry); verdelho (semi-dry); bual (semi-sweet); malmsey (sweet).

madeleine French; small fancy sponge cake baked in a *dariole mould (or sometimes a scallop-shaped mould). English version is victoria sponge mixture topped with jam and coconut.

madidi See KENKEY.

Madras curry Pungent *curry sauce with a large amount of chilli, but less than *vindaloo.

madrasi masala South Indian; a blend of dry and wet spices; the dry spices are roasted and ground before adding garlic, ginger, and vinegar to make a paste, which is then cooked in oil to develop the flavours before being stored.

Madrid stew *Olla podrida* or rotten pot; Spanish (Castilian) stew containing chickpeas, chicken, beef on the bone, smoked bacon, tocino (salted pork fat), *chorizo, *morcilla, *onion, *cabbage, *carrots, *turnips, and *garlic.

madrilène, à la Dish flavoured with tomato.

MAFF Former UK Ministry of Agriculture, Fisheries and Food, now replaced by *DEFRA.

magenta tongue One of the signs of *vitamin B_2 deficiency.

magma Mixture of sugar syrup and sugar crystals produced during sugar refining.

magnesium An essential mineral; present in all human tissues, especially bone. Involved in the metabolism of *ATP. Present in chlorophyll and so in all green plant foods, and therefore generally plentiful in the diet. Deficiency in human beings leads to disturbances of muscle and nervous system; in cattle, to *grass tetany. Magnesium-deficient plants are yellow (or chlorosed).

magnum Large wine bottle, 1.5L (double old British bottle, called 'reputed quart').

magur A *catfish, *Clarias batrachus*.

maheu African; sour non-alcoholic beverage made from maize or millet by lactic acid fermentation.

mahimahi Marine fish, *Coryphaena hippunus*, widely distributed in tropical and sub tropical waters and produced commercially by *aquaculture. Also known as dolphinfish.

mahleb Spice prepared from black cherry kernels, Syrian in origin, widely used in Greek baked goods.

maidenhair tree *See* GINGKO.

maids of honour Small tartlets filled with almond-flavoured custard; said to have originated in the court of Henry VIII, where they were made by Anne Boleyn when she was lady-in-waiting to Catherine of Aragon.

maigre, au Dish without meat and therefore traditionally suitable for Lent or a fast day.

Maillard reaction Non-enzymic reaction between *lysine in proteins and sugars, on heating or during prolonged storage. It may be important in development of flavour and colour, but leads to reduced *availability of the lysine.

maître d'hôtel 1. Simply prepared dishes garnished with butter creamed with parsley and lemon juice (maître d'hôtel butter); literally 'in the style of the head waiter'. **2.** Especially in the USA, the head waiter. Also shortened to maître d'.

maize Grain of *Zea mays*, also called Indian corn and (in the USA) simply corn. Staple food in many countries, made into *tortillas in Latin America, into *polenta in Italy, and flaked as cornflakes as a breakfast cereal; various preparations in the southern states of the USA are known as hominy, samp, and cerealine.

Two varieties of major commercial importance are flint corn (*Z. mays* var. *indurata*), which is very hard, and dent corn (*Z. mays* var. *dentata*); there is also sweet corn (*Z. mays* var. *saccharata*), and a variety that expands on heating (*Z. mays* var. *everta*; *see* POPCORN). The starch prepared from *Z. mays* var. *dentata* is cornflour; the ground maize is maize meal. There is a white variety; the usual yellow colour is partly due to the *carotenoid *cryptoxanthin.

Because of its low content of the amino acid *tryptophan (and available *niacin), diets based largely on maize are associated with the development of *pellagra. Quality protein maize (QPM) is derived from the Opaque II strain, gives a 10% higher yield than conventional maize, with 70–80% more tryptophan and lysine.

A 60-g portion of sweetcorn kernels is a *source of vitamin C; contains 1.2g of fat, of which 10% is saturated; provides 2.4g of dietary fibre; supplies 75kcal (315kJ).

maize, flaked Partly gelatinized maize used for animal feed. The grain is cracked to small pieces, moistened, cooked, and flaked between rollers.

maize flour Highly refined and very finely ground maize meal from which all bran and germ have been removed. *See also* CORNFLOUR.

maize oil *See* CORN OIL.

maize rice Finely cut *maize with bran and germ partly removed, also called mealie rice.

maize starch, waxy *Starch obtained from varieties of *maize consisting wholly or largely (99%) of *amylopectin, compared with ordinary maize starch with 26% *amylose and 74% amylopectin. The paste is semi-translucent, cohesive, and does not form a gel. *See also* CORNFLOUR; STARCH, WAXY.

makhani Indian; buttered rice prepared by steaming with butter and aromatic spices.

malabsorption syndrome Defect of absorption of one or more nutrients; signs include *diarrhoea, *steatorrhoea, abdominal distension, weight loss, and specific signs of nutrient deficiency.

malai Indian; cream prepared by boiling milk, leaving it to cool, and then skimming off the clotted cream.

malanga See TANNIA.

malaxation In olive oil extraction, the process of churning the paste from milled olives to allow oil droplets to coalesce into larger drops that can be separated by centrifugation. Oil yield is proportional to the time and temperature employed, but oxidation increases with both.

malic acid Organic acid occurring in many fruits, particularly in apples, tomatoes, and plums. Used as a food additive to increase acidity.

mallow, Jew's (Egyptian mallow) See EWEDU.

malmsey See MADEIRA WINES.

malnutrition Disturbance of form or function arising from deficiency or excess of one or more nutrients. See also CACHEXIA; OBESITY; PROTEIN-ENERGY MALNUTRITION; VITAMIN TOXICITY.

malondialdehyde A highly reactive aldehyde produced as a result of lipid oxidation, used as a measure of lipid oxidative *rancidity.

malpighia See CHERRY, WEST INDIAN.

malt (malt extract) Mixture of starch breakdown products containing mainly *maltose (malt sugar), prepared from barley or wheat.
　　The grain is allowed to sprout, when the *enzyme diastase (*amylase) develops and hydrolyses the starch to *maltose. The mixture is then extracted with hot water. Malt extract may remain as a concentrated solution or be evaporated to dryness.

maltase *Enzyme that catalyses the hydrolysis of *maltose to yield two molecules of glucose; present in the brush border of the intestinal mucosal cells.

malted barley See MALT.

malt flour Germinated barley or wheat, in dried form. As well as dextrins, glucose, proteins, and salts derived from the cereal, it is rich in *amylase (diastase) and is added to wheat flour of low *diastatic activity for bread making; used as an ingredient of 'malt' loaf.

malting See BEER.

maltins See MALTODEXTRINS.

maltitol A *sugar alcohol produced by hydrogenation of maltose. Slowly hydrolysed in the intestinal tract to *glucose and *sorbitol, providing 4 kcal (16 kJ)/gram; sweeter than maltose, and 90% as sweet as sucrose (E965).

maltobiose See MALTOSE.

maltodextrins Small *oligosaccharides of glucose produced by partial hydrolysis of *starch, also known as maltins. *See also* DEXTROSE EQUIVALENT VALUE.

maltohexaose Oligosaccharide of six maltose residues linked via α-1,4-glycosidic bonds, formed by *hydrolysis of *starch. Only 0.1 times as sweet as sucrose, but has a higher viscosity; used as a *bulking agent.

maltol Also called laxarinic acid, palatone, veltol (3-hydroxy-2-methyl-γ-pyrone). Found in the bark of young larch trees, pine needles, chicory, and roasted malt; synthesized for use as a fragrant, caramel-like flavour for addition to foods; imparts a 'freshly baked' flavour to bread and cakes.

maltonic acid *See* GLUCONIC ACID.

malto-oligosaccharides Alternative name for MALTODEXTRINS.

maltose Malt sugar, or maltobiose, a *disaccharide of two glucose units linked α1–4. Hydrolysed by *maltase. Does not occur in foods (unless specifically added as *malt) but formed during the digestion of starch. It is one-third as sweet as sucrose. First used to sweeten foods by the Chinese in the 7th century.

maltose figure *See* DIASTATIC ACTIVITY.

maltose intolerance *See* DISACCHARIDE INTOLERANCE.

maltotetraose Oligosaccharide of four maltose residues linked via α-1,4-glycosidic bonds, formed by *hydrolysis of *starch. Only 0.2 times as sweet as sucrose.

maltotriose Oligosaccharide of three maltose residues linked via α-1,4-glycosidic bonds, formed by *hydrolysis of *starch. Only 0.3 times as sweet as sucrose.

malt sugar *See* MALTOSE.

malt whisky *See* WHISKY.

malvasia A *grape variety widely used for *wine making, not one of the classic varieties.

mamey (mammee) The fruit of the Central American evergreen tree *Mammea americana*. African mammee apple is *M. africana*, Indian mammee apple is *M. suriga*. Sometimes called mammee apple. The mamey sapote (*see* SAPOTE) is unrelated.

manche French; cutlet bone. Manchette is the paper frill used to decorate the bone.

manchego Spanish; sheep's milk hard cheese.

mandarin Loose-skinned *citrus fruit, *Citrus reticulata* or *C. nobilio*. Varieties include satsumas and tangerines (although all three names are used indiscriminately) with various hybrids including tangelo, tangor, temple, clementine.

mandelbrot Middle-European (especially Jewish); sponge cake with almonds. Also known as kamishbrot.

mandeln (mandlen) Middle-European (especially Jewish); small pieces of dough shaped like almonds, baked and added to soup before serving.

mandolin Vegetable slicer.

mandoo Korean; dumplings stuffed with a spicy mixture of vegetables or meat.

manganese An essential trace mineral which functions as the *prosthetic group in a number of *enzymes. Dietary deficiency has not been reported in human beings; in experimental animals manganese deficiency leads to impaired synthesis of *mucopolysaccharides. Requirements are not known; US/Canadian *adequate intake is 2.3 mg for men and 1.8 for women.

mangelwurzel (mangoldwurzel) A root vegetable used as cattle feed, *Beta vulgaris* var. *rapa*.

mange-tout Immature pods and embryo seeds of *Pisum sativum* var. *macrocarpum* (syn. *macrocarpon*) eaten whole; also known as sugar pea or snap pea. The name is sometimes used for immature French beans, *Phaseolus vulgaris*. A 100-g portion is a rich *source of vitamin C; a source of vitamins A (as carotene), B_1, and B_2; supplies 25 kcal (105 kJ).

mango Fruit of the tropical tree *Mangifera indica*, originally of Indo-Burmese origin and now grown widely throughout the tropics. The fruit is ovoid, 3–5 in (7.5–12 cm) in diameter, with orange-coloured sweet aromatic flesh surrounding a large central stone. A 150-g portion (one quarter slice) is a rich *source of vitamins C and A (as carotene); a source of copper; supplies 75 kcal (320 kJ).

mango, African Fruit of two trees, *Irvingia gabonensis* (wild or African mango) or *I. barteri* (Gabon chocolate tree), which resemble the cultivated *mango, but are botanically unrelated. The pounded kernels of the seeds (known as dika nuts) are used as a thickener for soups and stews, may be used to make dika bread, and are a source of oil.

mangosteen Fruit of the evergreen tree, *Garcinia mangostana*, the size of an orange with thick purple rind and sweet white pulp in segments. A 100-g portion supplies 75 kcal (320 kJ); little vitamin C. African mangosteen or limbé is *G. livingstonei*.

manihot starch *See* CASSAVA.

manioc *See* CASSAVA.

manketti Fruit of the southern African summer-deciduous tree *Schinziophyton rautenenii*; mainly wild harvested, little cultivated. Both the oily nut and the fruit flesh are eaten and have been a staple food of indigenous people for centuries. Also known as mongogo.

manna Dried exudate from the manna-ash tamarisk tree (*Fraxinus ornus*). Abundant in Sicily and used as a mild laxative for children; it consists of 40–60% *mannitol, 10–16% mannotetrose, 6–16% mannotriose, plus glucose, mucilage, and fraxin. This is thought to be the food eaten by the Israelites in the wilderness (Exod. 16: 15).

Madagascan manna is from *Melampyrum nemorosum*, and is rich in *dulcitol.

manna bread A cake-like product made from crushed, sprouted wheat without yeast; said to be a recipe of the Essenes who lived by the Dead Sea around the beginning of the Christian era.

mannans *Polysaccharides (a constituent of *hemicellulose) containing a high proportion of *mannose. Those that also contain glucose or galactose residues are known as glucomannans and galactomannans, respectively. The galactomannans of *guar and *carob are used as thickeners.

manna sugar (mannite) *See* MANNITOL.

mannitol Mannite or manna sugar, a six-carbon *sugar alcohol found in beets, pumpkin, mushrooms, onions; 50–60% as sweet as sucrose. Extracted commercially from seaweed (*Laminaria* spp.) or made from the sugar *mannose (E421).

mannosans *Polysaccharides containing *mannose.

mannose A 6-carbon (hexose) sugar found in small amounts in legumes, *manna, and some gums. Also called seminose and carubinose.

mannotetrose *See* STACHYOSE.

manometer Instrument for measuring the pressure of liquids or gases.

manzanilla *See* SHERRY.

MAP kinases Mitogen-activated protein *kinases—a family of enzymes that catalyse phosphorylation of target enzymes in response to hormones including insulin and insulin-like growth factor.

maple syrup urine disease A rare genetic disease affecting the metabolism of the *amino acids leucine, isoleucine, and valine leading to accumulation of high concentrations of these three amino acids and the immediate products of their metabolism in the plasma and urine. The urine has a characteristic smell like that of maple syrup (*see* SYRUP, MAPLE).

maraschino **1.** Sweetened spirit prepared by distillation of fermented maraschino cherries (both the juice and the crushed kernels). **2.** Cherries preserved in real or imitation maraschino liqueur, used to decorate cocktails, ice cream, or fruit salad.

marasmic kwashiorkor *See* PROTEIN-ENERGY MALNUTRITION.

marasmus *See* PROTEIN-ENERGY MALNUTRITION.

marbling Streaks of fat between muscle fibres in meat; one of the factors used to assess the quality of meat.

marc **1.** French; spirit distilled from the fermented residue of grape skins, stalks, and seeds after the grapes have been pressed for wine making. The same as grappa (Italy), bagaciera (Portugal), and aguardiente (Spain). Often a harsh raw spirit, drunk young, although some varieties (especially marc de Bourgogne) are matured and smooth. **2.** Insoluble residue after extraction of soluble material from sugar beet (*see* BEET, SUGAR); mainly *non-starch polysaccharides, used as cattle feed.

marengo Chicken or veal sautéed in oil, and cooked in a sauce of white wine, tomatoes, mushroom, and garlic; said to have been invented in 1800 by Napoleon's chef after the battle of Marengo in Italy.

marigold Pot or common marigold (*Calendula officinalis*); petals are used as flavouring and colouring, sometimes as a substitute for *saffron.

margarine (butterine, lardine, oleomargarine) Emulsion of about 80% vegetable, animal, and/or marine fats and 20% water, originally as a substitute for butter. Usually contains emulsifiers, anti-spattering agents, colours, vitamins A and D (sometimes E), and preservatives. Ordinary margarines contain roughly equal parts of saturated, mono-unsaturated, and polyunsaturated *fatty acids; special soft varieties are rich in *polyunsaturates. The energy yield is the same as that of *butter.

A 40-g portion (a medium thickness spread on four slices of bread) is a rich *source of vitamins A and D; contains 32g of fat (the percentage of saturated fat depends on the oils used in manufacture); supplies 290kcal (1220kJ). A single caterer's pat is 10g; contains 8g of fat; supplies 72kcal (300kJ).

Low-fat spreads are made with 20–60% fat and correspondingly higher contents of air and water and less energy. A 40-g portion of low-fat spread contains 16g of fat (of which typically 27% is saturated); supplies 145kcal (610kJ). A single caterer's pat is 10g; contains 4g of fat; supplies 35kcal (150kJ).

margarine, kosher Made only from vegetable fats, since ordinary margarine can include animal fats that may not be *kosher. It is fortified with carotene (which is derived from vegetable sources) as the source of vitamin A, instead of retinol (which may be obtained from non-kosher sources).

margarita Mexican cocktail based on *tequila with lime or lemon juice; traditionally served in glasses frosted with salt around the rim.

margherita The basic *pizza: cheese and tomato.

mariculture *Aquaculture in saline environments.

marinade Mixture of oil with wine, lemon juice, or vinegar and herbs in which meat or fish is soaked before cooking, both to give flavour and to make it more tender. Hence to marinate.

marination, cold As a means of preservation, raw fish is immersed in a 'finishing bath' of *vinegar (5–10% acetic acid) and salt (10–15%) for about a week, then after washing and draining it is immersed in a cold (0–2°C) marinade containing vinegar (1–2% acetic acid) and 2–4% salt, flavoured with various spices and sometimes with the addition of sugar, for up to three months.

marination, hot As a means of preservation, pre-salted fish is cooked in a 'blanching bath' of 2–4% vinegar and 6–8% salt. After cooling, the pieces of fish are placed in a marinade containing 2% acetic acid, 3% salt, and between 4 and 5% *gelatine.

marine biotoxins Toxins in shellfish and marine fish, either produced naturally or accumulated by the fish from their diet (includes *ciguatera and paralytic *shellfish poisoning).

marine oils *See* OIL, FISH.

marinière French; literally 'in the seaman's style'; fish or seafood dishes cooked in white wine and garnished. The most common example is moules marinières (mussels).

marjoram Dried leaves of a number of aromatic plants of different species, used as seasoning for poultry, meats, and cheese dishes; perennial *Origanum majorana*, annual sweet marjoram *Majorana hortensis*; Spanish wild marjoram is *Thymus mastichina*; wild marjoram is *oregano.

marlin Marine fish, *Makaira* spp.

marmalade Defined by EU Directive as *jam made from citrus peel; what was called ginger marmalade is now known as ginger preserve. The name comes from the Portuguese *marmalada*, the quince, which was used to make preserves. Used in German for jam or preserves in general.

marmite **1.** The original form of *pressure cooker used by Papin in 1681; it was an iron pot with a sealing lid. **2.** Cookery term for a stock, or the pot in which stock is prepared.

marque nationale *See* WINE CLASSIFICATION, LUXEMBOURG.

marquise French; chocolate mousse.

marron glacé *Chestnuts preserved in syrup; semi-crystallized.

marrow Varieties of the *gourd *Cucurbita pepo*. Grouped with courgettes, squashes, and pumpkins; 95% water. A 100-g portion provides 1 g of dietary fibre, with only traces of nutrients and only 9 kcal (36 kJ). Courgettes and zucchini are varieties that have been developed for cutting when small. *See also* BONE MARROW.

marsala Sicilian; fortified white wine (*see* WINE, FORTIFIED).

marshmallow Soft sweetmeat made from an aerated mixture of gelatine or egg albumin with sugar or starch syrup. *Nougat is harder, containing less water, and usually incorporating dried fruit and nuts. Originally made using the root of the marshmallow plant (*Althaea officinalis*), which provides a mucilaginous substance as well as starch and sugar.

Martini Trade name for a brand of *vermouth; now also the name for a cocktail based on *gin and vermouth). A sweet martini is made with Italian (sweet) vermouth; a dry martini with French (dry) vermouth; the proportion of gin may vary from 50 to 90%. A vodka martini (vodkatini) contains vodka rather than gin.

marula Fruit of the southern African tree *Sclerocarya caffra* (syn. *S. birrea* subsp. *caffra*). Mainly wild-harvested. A rich *source of vitamin C.

Marumillon 50 Trade name for mixture of the sweet glycosides extracted from stevia leaves. *See also* STEVIOSIDE; REBAUDOSIDE.

Maryland Dish with a butter and cream sauce, often containing wine. Chicken Maryland is deep fried and has a garnish of sweetcorn fritters, fried bananas, and fruit fritters.

marzipan Ground *almonds mixed with powdered sugar, bound with egg, used to decorate cakes and make *petits fours.

masala dosha *See* DOSHA.

mascarpone Italian; soft cream *cheese from Lombardy, usually eaten as a dessert flavoured with fruit; also used in *tiramisù.

mashing In the brewing of *beer, the process in which the malted barley (*see* MALT) is heated with water, to extract the soluble sugars and to continue enzymic reactions started during malting.

mashlum *See* MASLIN.

mash tun Vessel used for *mashing.

mashua *See* ULLUCO.

mask To cover or coat a cooked meat dish with savoury jelly, glaze, or sauce; also to coat the inside of a mould with jelly.

maslin (mashlum) 1. Old term, still used in Scotland, for mixed crop of beans and oats used as cattle food. 2. In Yorkshire and the north of England, a mixed crop of 2–3 parts of wheat and 1 part of rye, used for bread making. 3. **(mesclin, miscellin)** Medieval English; bread made from mixed wheat and rye.

Mason jar Screw-topped glass jar for home bottling; patented 1858 by John Mason of New York.

massecuite The mixture of sugar crystals and syrup (mother liquor) obtained during the crystallization stage of sugar refining.

mast *See* MILK, FERMENTED.

mastic (mastic gum) Resin from the evergreen shrub *Pistacia lenticus* and related species, with a flavour similar to liquorice, used in Greek and Balkan cookery.

mastication Chewing, grinding, and tearing foods with the teeth while it is mixed with saliva.

mastika Greek sweet, milky-white liqueur flavoured with *anise and *mastic.

matai Chinese water *chestnut.

maté (yerba maté) Infusion of the dried leaves of the South American tree *Ilex paraguayensis*, also known as Paraguay or Brazilian tea. Contains caffeine and tannin.

matelote A rich, well-seasoned fish stew made with wine (French for 'sailors' dish').

matoké Steamed green *banana or *plantain.

matsutake Edible wild fungus, *Tricholoma matsutake*, widely collected in Japan and exported canned or dried; *see* MUSHROOMS.

matzo (motza) Jewish; unleavened bread made as thin, flat, round, or square water biscuits, and eaten during *Passover in place of leavened bread. Matzo brei is matzo soaked, mixed with beaten egg, and fried; akin to *French toast.

maw Fourth stomach of the ruminant.

mawa Indian; condensed milk made by heating and stirring continuously until it thickens; used to make desserts and sweetmeats. Also known as khoya.

mawe West African; sourdough or porridge made from dehulled maize meal that has undergone fermentation for 1–3 days.

mawseed *See* POPPY SEED.

MaxEPA Trade name for a standardized mixture of long-chain marine *fatty acids, eicosapentaenoic (EPA, C20:5 ω3) and docosahexaenoic (DHA, C22:6 ω3) acids.

may fish Name given to *shad by 17th-century Dutch colonists in New Amsterdam (New York) because the fish swarm up river in May to spawn. Considered at the time to be a fish for poor people, and mostly dried and smoked for use in stews.

Mayieritsa *See* EASTER SOUP.

mayonnaise A *salad dressing, reputedly invented by the Duke of Richelieu in 1757, and originally named *mahonnaise* to celebrate the French victory at Mahon.

maysin Coagulable globulin protein of maize.

mazindol *Anorectic drug used in the treatment of *obesity, but not recommended.

mazun *See* MILK, FERMENTED.

mazurki Russian; baked sweetmeat made from chopped raisins, almonds, walnuts, figs, prunes, candied fruit, flour, and eggs.

mazzard *See* GEAN.

mbeu *See* OLIVE, AFRICAN.

McGovern committee USA; Senate Select Committee on Nutrition and Human Needs; published *Dietary Goals for the United States*, first draft 1977, final version 1980, based on the proposition that people should eat less of harmful foods rather than more of foods that are good for them. The basis of most current guidelines on healthy eating. *See* DIETARY GUIDELINES; NUTRITIONAL RECOMMENDATIONS.

MCT Medium-chain triacylglycerol.

mcv Mean cell (or corpuscular) volume; used especially of red *blood cells. *See also* ANAEMIA.

MDM Mechanically deboned meat; *see* MEAT, MECHANICALLY RECOVERED.

mead A traditional wine made by fermentation of honey, sometimes flavoured with herbs and spices. One of the oldest alcoholic drinks.

meadowfoam Annual flowering plant, native to North America, *Limnanthes alba*; the seed oil is a rich source of C20:1, C22:1, and C22:2 fatty acids, and can be used as a substitute for whale oil or *jojoba oil.

mealie(s) *See* MAIZE. Mealie rice is *maize rice.

mealie pudding *See* SKIRLIE.

meat Generally refers to the muscle tissue of animals or birds, other parts being termed *offal, organ meat, or variety meat. 150-g portions of meat of all types are rich *sources of protein and niacin; most are rich sources of vitamin B_2 and iron; sources or good sources of vitamin B_1.

*Venison, *horse meat, *goose, and *game birds are exceptionally rich in iron; *pork is exceptionally rich in vitamin B_1. The fat content and proportions of *fatty acids differ considerably between individual carcasses, species, and cuts of meat.

See also BEEF; LAMB; VEAL; PORK; RABBIT; HARE; GOAT; HORSE; VENISON; DUCK; CHICKEN; GOOSE; PARTRIDGE; TURKEY; PHEASANT; GROUSE; QUAIL; PIGEON; HEART; KIDNEY; LIVER; OXTAIL; SWEETBREAD; TONGUE; TRIPE.

meat bar Dehydrated cooked meat and fat; a modern form of *pemmican; 50% protein and 40% fat; provides 560 kcal (2350 kJ)/100 g.

meat, bushmeat Various game animals, including especially primates; commercial (as opposed to subsistence) hunting is a cause for concern on both environmental grounds and also because of health hazards associated with an illegal and unregulated trade.

meat conditioning After an animal has been slaughtered, muscle *glycogen is metabolized to *lactic acid, which tends to improve the texture and keeping qualities of the meat. Meat that has been left until these changes have occurred is 'conditioned'. Electrical stimulation of muscles is sometimes used to hasten the development of *rigor mortis, and shorten the time required for conditioning the meat. *See also* MEAT, DFD.

meat, curing Pickling with the aid of sodium chloride (*salt), sodium nitrate (saltpetre), and some sodium nitrite, which permits the growth of only salt-tolerant bacteria and inhibits the growth of *Clostridium botulinum*. The nitrite is the effective preserving agent and the nitrate is converted into nitrite during the process. The red colour of cured meat is due to the formation of nitrosomyoglobin from the myoglobin of muscle.

meat, DFD Stands for 'dark, firm, dry'; the condition of meat when the *pH remains high through lack of *glycogen (which would form *lactic acid). It poses a microbiological hazard. *See also* MEAT CONDITIONING; RIGOR MORTIS.

meat extender Vegetable proteins (commonly textured soya protein) added to meat products to replace part of the meat.

meat extract The water-soluble part of meat that is mainly responsible for its flavour. Commercially it is made during the manufacture of corned beef (*see* BEEF, CORNED); chopped meat is immersed in boiling water, when the water-soluble extractives are partially leached out, then concentrated. Rich in vitamins B$_1$, B$_{12}$, niacin, and potassium. A powerful oral stimulant of *gastric acid secretion.

meat factor Factor used to calculate the fat-free meat content of sausages and meat products by measuring *nitrogen.

meat, mechanically recovered Residual meat recovered from bones that have already been trimmed by knife. Also known as mechanically deboned meat and (in USA) mechanically separated meat. It consists of the meat and fat that were on the bone, comminuted by forcing through perforated filters, as well as some bone fragments.

meat, reformed An artefact having the appearance of a cut slice or portion of meat, formed by 'tumbling' chopped meat, with or without the addition of finely comminuted meat, the soluble proteins of which bind the small pieces together.

meat speciation Identification of species of animal from which the meat originated.

meat sugar Obsolete name for *inositol.

meat, variety American name for *offal.

meaux mustard *See* MUSTARD.

meconium The green material that fills the *gastro-intestinal tract of the fetus and forms the first bowel movement of the newborn. Meconium *ileus is obstruction of the small intestine of a neonate by impaction of meconium, commonly in *cystic fibrosis.

medium-chain triacylglycerols *Triacylglycerols containing medium-chain (C:6–12) *fatty acids, used in treatment of *malabsorption; they are absorbed more rapidly than conventional fats, and the products of their digestion are transported to the liver, rather than in *chylomicrons. They have been promoted as *ergogenic aids because of their rapid absorption. Few studies have reported beneficial effects for athletic performance, and a number have reported poor tolerance and gastro-intestinal symptoms.

medlar The fruit of the small tree *Mespilus germanica* (also *M. canescens* in North America). Can be eaten fresh from the tree in Mediterranean areas but in colder climates, as in Britain, does not become palatable until it is half rotten (bletted). Japanese medlar is the *loquat.

megacolon Abnormal enlargement of the colon (*see* GASTRO-INTESTINAL TRACT), rarely as a result of lack of the *myenteric plexus (when it is known as Hirschsprung's disease); toxic megacolon occurs in ulcerative *colitis; may also occur with infection with trypanasomes (Chagas's disease).

megaloblasts Abnormally large, nucleated, red blood cell precursors, as seen in *vitamin B$_{12}$ and *folic acid deficiency (*see* ANAEMIA, MEGALOBLASTIC; ANAEMIA, PERNICIOUS).

megavitamin therapy Treatment of diseases with very high doses of vitamins, many times the *reference intakes; little or no evidence for its efficacy; *vitamins A, *D, and *B$_6$ are known to be toxic at high levels of intake.

megrim Marine flatfish, the British smooth sole or scaldfish, *Lepidorhombus* spp.

meio seco Portuguese; medium dry wines.

Meissner's plexus *See* SUBMUCOSAL PLEXUS.

mejing *See* MONOSODIUM GLUTAMATE.

meju Paste made from fermented *soya beans.

mekabu Japanese; the flowering sprout of the lobe leaf *seaweed (wakame) *Undaria pinnatifida*.

melampyrin *See* DULCITOL.

melangeur Mixing vessel consisting of rollers on a rotating horizontal bed. Used to mix substances of pasty consistency (hence melangeuring).

melangolo Italian name for the bitter *orange.

melanin Brown pigment formed when phenolic compounds in cut fruit and vegetables are exposed to air and oxidized; also the brown and black pigments of skin and hair.

melano *See* KIWANO.

melanocortin Peptide *hormone that regulates *melanin synthesis in skin and hair, and also feeding behaviour through receptors in the hypothalamus. The agouti gene product antagonizes melanocortin receptors, leading to obesity and insulin resistance in mutant mice (*see* AGOUTI MOUSE).

melanoidins The final products of the *Maillard reaction.

melba Peach poached in vanilla syrup, set in vanilla ice cream with a purée of raspberries. Created by Escoffier, 1892, in honour of the Australian soprano Dame Nellie Melba.

melba sauce Sweet sauce made from raspberries.

melba toast Originally a split slice of toasted bread, retoasted; now a thin slice of bread dried in the oven to a golden-brown colour. *See also* ZWIEBACK.

melena Black tarry faeces, containing digested blood, the result of bleeding in the upper gastro-intestinal tract.

melezitose Trisaccharide composed of two glucose and one fructose; hydrolysed to glucose plus the disaccharide turanose.

melibiose *Disaccharide of *glucose and *galactose.

melilot Sweet clover, a wild plant (*Melilotus officinalis*) which commonly grows in fields and on waste ground, especially on sandy soil; used as forage. The dried leaves have a sweet hay-like aroma.

melinjo The leaves, flowers, and seeds of the South-East Asian tree *Gnetum gnemon* are all edible; the seeds are used to make a flour used in Indonesia to make *emping.

melissopalynology Analysis of pollens present in honey, in order to determine its botanical and geographical origin.

melitose (melitriose) *See* RAFFINOSE.

melitzanosalata Greek; purée of *aubergine with onion, garlic, and olive oil, served cold as a dip.

mellorine USA; *ice cream made from non-butter fat.

melokhia *See* MELOUKHIA.

melon *Gourds, sweet fruit of *Cucurmis melo*. A 200-g portion is a rich *source of vitamin C (melons with orange or yellow flesh are a rich source of carotene); a source of vitamin B_6; provides 2 g of dietary fibre; supplies 45 kcal (190 kJ). The water melon is *Citrullis vulgaris*, jelly or horned melon is *kiwano.

melon, bitter *Momordica charantia*, also known as foo qua, balsam pear, and bitter gourd.

melon, hairy *See* MELON, WAX.

melon pear *See* PEPINO.

melon, wax (winter melon) A gourd, fruit of *Benincasa hispida*; varieties with a hairy skin are known as hairy melon.

melopita Greek; honey and cheese cake.

meloukhia The leaves of *Corchorus oliotorus*, used as a *pot herb, in soups (Middle East), as a substitute for *spinach (India), or as a salad (in the Caribbean). Sometimes used as a source of jute, but *C. capsularis* is the more important source of fibre. Also known as Jew's mallow.

melting point The temperature at which a compound melts to a liquid. Often characteristic of a particular chemical and used as a means of identification. Particularly valuable as an index of purity, because impurities lower the melting point.

melts *See* SPLEEN.

membrane, semi-permeable (selectively permeable membrane) One that allows the passage of small molecules but not large ones: e.g. pig's bladder is permeable to water but not salt; collodion is permeable to salt but not protein molecules. Used for *dialysis. *See also* MICROFILTRATION; ULTRAFILTRATION.

menadione (menaphthone, menaphtholdiacetate) Synthetic compounds with *vitamin K activity; vitamin K_3, sometimes known as menaquinone-0.

menaquinones Bacterial metabolites with *vitamin K activity; vitamin K_2.

menarche The initiation of menstruation in adolescent girls, normally occurring between the ages of 11 and 15. The age at menarche has become younger in Western countries, possibly associated with a better general standard of nutrition, and is later in less-developed countries.

menatetrenone Menaquinone-4, the vitamer of *vitamin K_2 with 4 isoprene units in the side-chain.

menhaden Oily marine fish, *Brevoortia patronus*, *B. tyrannus*, from Gulf of Mexico and Atlantic seaboard of the USA, a rich source of fish oils (*see* OIL, FISH).

meni Freshwater fish, *Nandus nandus*.

Menkes syndrome Functional *copper deficiency due to a genetic defect of the transport protein required for intestinal absorption of copper and its uptake into tissues. The most obvious feature is sparse, kinky underpigmented hair, as a result of impaired cross-linking of *keratin by formation of disulphide bridges, and impaired formation of melanin; hence sometimes called steely or kinky hair syndrome. Synthesis of collagen and elastin is impaired, resulting in fragile bones and commonly death as a result of rupture of the aorta at an early age. The condition is X-linked, so only males are affected.

menu Commonly used to mean the list of foods and dishes served by a restaurant, but correctly a set meal (with options) or dish of the day, as opposed to à la *carte.

MEOS Microsomal ethanol oxidizing system, a *cytochrome. Provides an alternative pathway to alcohol dehydrogenase for the metabolism of *alcohol; the enzyme is induced by heavy consumption of alcohol.

mercury A toxic metal with no known physiological function. Organic mercury compounds (e.g. methyl mercury) are especially toxic, and can accumulate to potentially hazardous levels in large fish such as tuna.

merguez North African; spiced sausage made from goat or mutton, flavoured with *harissa.

meringue Confection made from whisked egg-white and sugar, baked slowly in a cool oven; flavouring may be added, and the meringues may be filled with cream, ice cream, or fruit.

merlot One of the nine 'classic' *grape varieties used for *wine making; important in some of the great fragrant, rich, red wines; widely grown throughout the world.

merrythought *See* WISHBONE.

mersin Turkish; orange-flavoured liqueur.

mescal *See* TEQUILA.

mesocarp The fleshy middle layer of the pericarp of stone fruit (*drupes), between the *exocarp and the *endocarp; usually the part of the fruit that is eaten, sometimes called the sarcocarp. *See also* ALBEDO.

meso-inositol *See* INOSITOL.

mesomorph Description given to a well-covered individual with well-developed muscles. *See also* ECTOMORPH; ENDOMORPH.

mesophiles Micro-organisms that grow best at temperatures between 25 and 40°C; usually will not grow below 5°C.

MET *See* METABOLIC EQUIVALENT.

metabolic equivalent (MET) Unit of measurement of heat production by the body; $1\,MET = 50\,kcal/hour/m^2$ body surface area.

metabolic rate Rate of utilization of *energy. *See* BASAL METABOLIC RATE.

metabolic syndrome Abdominal *obesity with *insulin resistance, *hypertension, elevated plasma triacylglycerol, and low *HDL. Sometimes known as prediabetes (*see* DIABETES MELLITUS), and formerly called syndrome X. Commonly progresses to type II diabetes mellitus when the capacity of the β-islet cells of the *pancreas to secrete insulin in response to persistent hyperglycaemia is exhausted.

metabolism The processes of interconversion of chemical compounds in the body. Anabolism is the formation of larger and more complex compounds, commonly linked to the utilization of metabolic energy. Catabolism is the process of breaking down larger molecules to smaller ones, commonly oxidation reactions linked to release of energy. There is approximately a 30%

variation in the underlying metabolic rate (*basal metabolic rate) between different individuals, determined in part by the activity of the *thyroid gland. *See also* ENERGY.

metabolism, first pass Many drugs that are taken by mouth are absorbed into the hepatic portal vein and undergo metabolism in the liver; this may reduce the amount of active drug that enters the peripheral circulation very considerably, so that parenteral administration is necessary.

metabolism, inborn errors of *See* GENETIC DISEASE.

metabolism, phase I The first phase of metabolism of foreign compounds (xenobiotics), involving metabolic activation. Generally regarded as detoxication reactions, but may in fact convert inactive precursors into metabolically active compounds, and involved in activation of precursors to carcinogens.

metabolism, phase II The second phase of the metabolism of foreign compounds, in which the activated derivatives formed in phase I metabolism are conjugated with amino acids, *glucuronic acid or *glutathione, to yield water-soluble derivatives that are excreted in urine or bile.

metabolite Any intermediate in a metabolic pathway.

metabolome *See* METABOLOMICS.

metabolomics Measurement of all the small molecules (metabolites) present in the organism, which represent interactions of the genome, transcriptome, and proteome with the environment.

metabonomics An extension of *metabolomics to study the metabolic changes in response to drugs, environmental changes, and disease.

metacercaria The mature infectious stage of parasitic trematodes.

metalloproteins Proteins containing a metal. For example, *haemoglobin, *cytochromes, peroxidase, ferritin, and siderophilin all contain iron; many enzymes contain copper, manganese, or zinc as a prosthetic group.

metallothionein A family of small (M_r 6–7000) *cysteine-rich proteins that bind *zinc, *copper, and a number of toxic metals.

methaemoglobin Oxidized *haemoglobin (unlike oxyhaemoglobin, in which oxygen is bound, without oxidizing the iron) which cannot transport oxygen to the tissues. Present in small quantities in normal blood, increased after certain drugs and after smoking; found rarely as a congenital abnormality (methaemoglobinaemia).

It can be formed in the blood of babies after consumption of the small amounts of nitrate found naturally in vegetables and some drinking water, since the lack of acidity in the stomach permits reduction of nitrate to nitrite.

methaglen (metheglin) A traditional British wine made from honey (and thus a form of *mead) to which herbs are added before fermentation. Originally for medicinal purposes.

methe *See* FENUGREEK.

methionine An essential *amino acid; one of the three containing sulphur; cystine and *cysteine are the other two. Cystine and cysteine are not essential, but can be made only from methionine, and therefore the requirement for methionine is lower if there is an adequate intake of cyst(e)ine.

méthode champenoise Sparkling *wines made by a second fermentation in the bottle, as for *champagne, but not produced in the Champagne region of north-eastern France.

methotrexate A *folic acid antagonist used in cancer chemotherapy.

methyl alcohol (methanol, wood alcohol) The first member of the *alcohol series, CH_3—OH. It is highly toxic and leads to mental disturbance, blindness, and death when consumed over a period. It is added to industrial alcohol and methylated spirits, to 'denature' the ethyl alcohol and render it undrinkable. *See* ALCOHOL, DENATURED.

methylated spirits *See* ALCOHOL, DENATURED.

methyl cellulose *See* CELLULOSE.

methylene blue dye-reduction test *See* MILK, DYE REDUCTION TEST OF.

3-methyl-histidine Derivative of the amino acid, *histidine, found mainly in the contractile proteins of muscle (myosin and actin). Useful, among other purposes, as an index of the lean meat content of prepared foods, since it is not present in collagen or other added materials.

methylisoborneol (MIB) Microbial metabolite that can cause earthy or musty off-flavour in freshwater fish.

metmyoglobin *See* NITROSOMYOGLOBIN.

metodo classico Italian; sparkling wines made by the *méthode champenoise.

mettwurst German; fermented smoked dried sausage or salami made from minced, cured pork, and beef.

meunière Fish dredged with flour, fried in butter, and served with this butter and chopped parsley; literally, 'in the style of the miller's wife'.

mezzethakia (orektika) Greek; appetizers or hors d'œuvre; sometimes abbreviated to mezes or mezze.

micelles Small droplets of partially hydrolysed lipids, 4–6nm in diameter, emulsified by *bile salts. Fatty acids and monoacylglycerol are absorbed in the duodenum and upper jejunum, cholesterol and other lipid-soluble nutrients throughout the small intestine, and the bile salts in the distal ileum. In milk, 95% of the *casein is in micelles ~150nm in diameter.

Michaelis equation A description of the hyperbolic dependence of the rate of an enzyme-catalysed reaction on the concentration of substrate. The rate of reaction $v = V_{max}/(1 + (K_m/[S]))$, where V_{max} is the maximum velocity of the reaction, K_m the Michaelis constant, and $[S]$ the concentration of substrate. Correctly the Michaelis–Menten equation, since it was published jointly by Michaelis and Menten. K_m can be considered to be the concentration of substrate at which the enzyme achieves half V_{max}.

Michaelis–Menten kinetics Enzymes that show a hyperbolic dependence on the rate of reaction on the concentration of substrate are said to show Michaelis–Menten kinetics, as opposed to allosteric enzymes that show a sigmoid dependence on the rate of reaction on the concentration of substrate. *See also* MICHAELIS EQUATION.

micro Prefix for units of measurement, one millionth part (i.e. 10^{-6}); symbol μ (or sometimes mc).

micro-aerophiles Micro-organisms that can grow in low concentrations of oxygen and so lead to spoilage of foodstuffs unless all oxygen is excluded.

microbiological assay Method of measuring compounds such as vitamins and amino acids, using *micro-organisms. The principle is that the organism is inoculated into a medium containing all the growth factors needed except the one being measured; the rate of growth is proportional to the amount of this nutrient added in the test substance.

microbiota Micro-organisms that are normally associated with a particular tissue or organ; in nutrition this is usually taken to mean the intestinal microflora.

microcapsules *See* ENCAPSULATION.

microencapsulation *See* ENCAPSULATION.

microfiltration Filtration under pressure through a membrane of small pore size (0.1–10μm; larger pores than for *ultrafiltration). Used for clarification of beverages and to sterilize liquids by filtering out micro-organisms.

microgram One-thousandth part of a milligram, and hence 1 millionth part of a gram; symbol μg (occasionally mcg, and the obsolete symbol γ is sometimes used).

micrometre (micron) One-thousandth of a millimetre, and hence one millionth of a metre; symbol μm.

micronization Extremely rapid heating with infra-red radiation produced by heating propane on a ceramic tile or with nichrome wire elements. Suggested as an alternative to steam heating or toasting where the shorter heating time is less damaging to the foodstuff.

micronutrients Those *nutrients required in small amounts: *vitamins and minerals (*see* MINERAL SALTS; MINERALS, TRACE; MINERALS, ULTRA-TRACE).

micro-organisms Bacteria, yeasts, and moulds; can cause food spoilage, and disease (pathogens); used to process and preserve food by *fermentation and have been used as foodstuffs (single cell protein and mycoprotein). *See also* FOOD-BORNE DISEASE; FOOD POISONING.

microwave cooking Rapid heating by passing high frequency waves from a magnetron through the food or liquid to be heated. Water absorbs the microwaves very well, so food with a high water content cooks more rapidly; fat absorbs the energy more slowly, so foods consisting of mixtures of fat and water cook unevenly. The cooking time is short and microwaves do not cause browning, so the food may not develop flavours associated with longer cooking times. First commercial microwave cooker was introduced by Raytheon Co., Waltham, Massachussetts, in 1947.

microwave susceptor A metal film in packaging of foods for *microwave cooking that rapidly reaches a high temperature, allowing the food to cook quickly, and promoting browning reactions.

middlings *See* WHEATFEED.

Midori Japanese; trade name of a pale-green liqueur made from melons, now manufactured in Mexico.

mid-upper-arm circumference (MUAC) A rapid way of assessing nutritional status, especially applicable to children. *See also* ANTHROPOMETRY.

mie goreng Indonesian; fried wheat-flour noodles with chicken, prawns, etc., topped with strips of omelette.

mien (mi) Chinese; noodles made from wheat and ground dried beans, introduced during the Han dynasty (1st century) using techniques imported from the West.

migaki-nishin Japanese; mixture of dried fish fillets and *abalone.

mignardise Small, dainty dishes.

mignon Small or dainty; hence filet mignon is small portions of beef fillet.

mignonette 1. Coarsely ground white pepper. 2. *See* NOUET.

migration In food packaging, the release of compounds from the packaging material into the food; some diffusible compounds remaining from manufacture of plastics may taint the food or present health hazards.

miki South-East Asian; noodles made from wheat flour, eggs, and soda ash.

mikiyuk Alaskan Inuit; partially dried whale meat, allowed to undergo bacterial fermentation for several months or years.

milanaise, à la Dish garnished with spaghetti, tomato sauce, and ham or tongue. Also food dipped in egg and a mixture of breadcrumbs and cheese, then fried.

milchig Jewish term for dishes containing milk or milk products, which cannot be served with or after meat dishes. *See also* FLEISHIG; PAREVE.

milfoil (yarrow) A common wild plant, *Achillea millefolium*, with finely divided leaves that can be used in salads or chopped to replace chervil or parsley as a garnish.

milk The secretion of the mammary gland of mammals. A 300-mL portion of cow's milk is a rich *source of vitamins B_2, B_{12}, calcium, and iodine; a source of protein, vitamin A, and vitamin B_1; full cream milk contains 11.4g of fat of which 63% is saturated; supplies 200kcal (840kJ); skimmed milk contains 0.3g of fat; supplies 100kcal (420kJ); Channel Islands milk contains 14.4g of fat of which 68% is saturated; supplies 230kcal (970kJ).

Ordinary milk contains 3.9% fat; Channel Islands milk, 5.1%; sheep's milk, 6.0%; buffalo milk, 7.5%; human milk contains 4.1% fat.

A 280-mL portion of goat's milk is a rich source of vitamin B_{12} and calcium; a good source of vitamin B_2; a source of protein, vitamin A, zinc, and copper; contains 13.5g of fat of which 51% is saturated; supplies 215kcal (900kJ).

milk, accredited Term not used after October 1954. Referred to milk untreated by heat, from cows examined at specific intervals for freedom from disease.

milk, acidophilus Resembles *yoghurt but is more astringent in taste and cultured only with *Lactobacillus acidophilus*; claimed to enhance the growth of beneficial bacteria in the intestine.

milk, alcohol stability test of For sourness of milk; milk that contains an acceptable level of lactic acid will not flocculate when shaken with double its volume of alcohol.

milk-alkali syndrome Weakness and lethargy caused by prolonged adherence to a diet rich in milk, i.e. more than about 1L (2 pints) daily, and alkalis.

milk, aniseed Dutch (*anijs melk*); hot sweet milk drink flavoured with *aniseed, traditionally drunk when ice skating.

milk baby Infant with iron deficiency *anaemia caused by excessive ingestion of milk and delayed or inadequate addition of iron-rich foods to the diet.

milk, citrated Milk to which sodium citrate has been added to combine with the calcium and inhibit the curdling of *caseinogen which would normally occur in the stomach. Claimed, with little evidence, to be of value in feeding infants and invalids.

milk, clabbered Unpasteurized milk that has soured naturally, becoming thick and curdy. Clabber cheese is curd or cottage cheese.

milk, clot on boiling test of For sourness of milk, since milk that contains more than about 0.1% lactic acid will not form a clot on boiling.

milk crumb In chocolate manufacture, a mix prepared from cocoa beans, milk, and sugar. More expensive than using milk powder, but the product has a better texture, and a caramelized flavour from *Maillard reaction products.

milk, dried Milk that has been evaporated to dryness, usually by spray- or roller-drying. May be whole (full-cream) milk (26% fat), three-quarter cream (not less than 20% fat), half-cream (not less than 14% fat), quarter-cream (not less than 8% fat), or skimmed milk (1% fat). *See also* MILK, INSTANT.

milk, dye-reduction test of When either of the dyes methylene blue or resazurin is added to milk, the bacteria present take up oxygen and change the colour of the dye; methylene blue loses its colour; resazurin changes from blue-purple to pink. The speed of the change indicates the bacterial content. Pasteurized milk (*see* PASTEURIZATION) must not reduce dye in less than half an hour.

milk, evaporated (condensed milk) Full-fat, skimmed, or partly skimmed milk, sweetened or unsweetened, that has been concentrated by partial evaporation.

milk, feed flavours in Tainting of milk by volatile compounds in the animals' feedstuff; in severe cases the milk may need to be vacuum processed before it can be used.

milk, fermented In various countries, milk is fermented with a mixture of bacteria (and sometimes yeasts) when the lactose is converted to lactic acid and in some cases to alcohol. The acidity (and alcohol) prevent the growth of potentially hazardous micro-organisms, and the fermentation thus acts to preserve the milk for a time.

These fermented milks include busa (Turkestan), cieddu (Italy), dadhi (India), kefir (Balkans), kumiss (Steppes), laban Zabadi (Egypt), mazun (Armenia), taette (N. Europe), skyr (Iceland), masl (Iran), crowdies (Scotland), kuban, and yoghurt.

milk, filled Milk from which the natural fat has been removed and replaced with fat from another source. The reason may be economic, if the butter fat can be replaced by a cheaper one, or, more recently, to replace a fat rich in saturated *fatty acids with a vegetable oil with a lower content of saturated fatty acids.

milkfish Marine fish *Chanos chanos*, widely distributed in Indian and Pacific oceans.

milk, freezing-point test of A test for the adulteration of milk with water. Milk normally freezes between −0.53 and −0.56°C; when it has been adulterated the freezing point rises nearer to that of water. A freezing point above −0.53°C is indicative of adulteration.

milk, homogenized Mechanical treatment (*homogenization) that breaks up the fat globules in milk; the smaller globules adsorb more of the protein, which acts as a stabilizer, and the cream does not rise to the top.

milk, humanized Cow's milk that has had its composition modified to resemble human milk, for infant feeding. The main change is a reduction in protein content, achieved by dilution with carbohydrate and restoration of the fat content.

milk, instant Dried milk that mixes readily with water, first introduced by the Carnation Company in 1954, following development of a process for crystallizing lactose.

milk, irradiated Milk that has been subjected to ultraviolet light, when the 7-dehydrocholesterol naturally present is converted into *vitamin D.

milk, lactose-hydrolysed Milk in which the *lactose has been hydrolysed to glucose and galactose by treatment with the enzyme *lactase, intended for infants who are lactase-deficient (lactose intolerant). *See also* DISACCHARIDE INTOLERANCE.

milk, long A Scandinavian soured milk which is viscous because of 'ropiness' caused by bacteria. *See* ROPE.

milk, malted A preparation of milk and the liquid separated from a mash of barley malt and wheat flour, evaporated to dryness.

milk, methylene blue test of *See* MILK, DYE REDUCTION TEST OF.

milk of magnesia Magnesium hydroxide solution used as an *antacid and *laxative.

milk, pasteurized *See* PASTEURIZATION.

milk, ropy *See* MILK, LONG; ROPE.

milk shake Beverage made from milk whisked with fruit syrup and ice cream.

milk, sorcerers' *See* MILK, WITCHES'.

milk-stone Deposit of calcium and magnesium phosphates, protein, etc., produced when milk is heated to temperatures above 60°C.

milk, sweetened (condensed milk) Evaporated to less than one-third volume with sugar added as a preservative; may be full cream or skimmed. First patented in the USA and the UK by Borden in 1856.

milk teeth *See* TEETH, DECIDUOUS.

milk thistle An annual or biennial thistle, *Silybum marianum* (syn. *Carduus marianus*); the flower receptacle can be eaten like globe *artichoke. Traditionally used for treatment of inflammatory liver disease and cirrhosis with some evidence of efficacy, but by injection rather than eaten.

milk, toned Dried, skimmed milk added to a high-fat milk such as buffalo milk, to reduce the fat content but maintain the total solids.

milk, tuberculin tested (TT) Historical; milk from herd that has been attested free from bovine tuberculosis.

milk, UHT Milk sterilized for a very short time (2 seconds) at ultra-high temperature (137°C).

milk weed *See* SOW THISTLE.

milk, witches' Secretion of the mammary gland of the newborn of both sexes; due to the presence of the *hormone prolactin from the mother's blood. Also known as sorcerers' milk.

mille-feuille Cake made of layers of puff pastry split and filled with cream and jam, and iced on top; also puff pastry savoury (literally, 'a thousand leaves').

millerator Wheat-cleaning machine consisting of two sieves, the upper one retaining particles larger than wheat grains, the lower one rejecting particles smaller than wheat.

miller's offal *See* WHEATFEED.

millet Cereal of a number of species of *Gramineae*, smaller than wheat and rice, and high in fibre content. Common millet (*Panicum* and *Selaria* spp.), also known as China, Italian, Indian, French hog, proso, panicled, and broom corn millet, grows very rapidly, 2–2½ months from sowing to harvest. Protein 10%, fat 2.5%, carbohydrate 73%.

Red, finger, South Indian millet, coracan, or ragi is *Eleusine coracana*. Protein 6%, fat 1.5%, carbohydrate 75%.

Bulrush millet, pearl millet, bajoa, or Kaffir manna corn is *Pennisetum typhoideum*, *P. americanum* or *P. glaucum*; the staple food in poor parts of India. Protein 11%, fat 5%, carbohydrate 69%.

Other species are foxtail millet (*Setaria italica*); hungry rice or fonio (*Digitaria exilis* or *D. iburua*), jajeo millet (*Acroceras amplectens*), Japanese millet (*Echinochloa frumentica*), Kodo or haraka millet (*Paspalum scrobiculatum*), and teff (*Eragrostis tef*, *E. abyssinica*). *See also* SORGHUM.

milli Prefix for units of measurement, one thousandth part (i.e. 10^{-3}); symbol m.

milling The term usually refers to the conversion of cereal grain into its derivative, e.g. wheat into flour, brown rice to white rice.

Flour milling involves two types of rollers: i) break rollers are corrugated and exert shear pressure and forces which break up the wheat grain and permit sieving into fractions containing varying proportions of *germ, *bran, and *endosperm; ii) reducing rollers are smooth and subdivide the endosperm into fine particles. *See also* FLOUR, EXTRACTION RATE.

milling, attrition *See* PEARLING.

milo Drought resistant *sorghum, especially *Sorghum bicolor*.

milt (melt) Soft roe (testes) of male fish. Also *spleen of animals.

miltone A toned milk (*see* MILK, TONED) developed in India in which peanut protein is added to buffalo or cow's milk to extend supplies.

mimosa American name for a mixture of sparkling wine and orange juice, known in the UK as buck's fizz.

Minamata disease Poisoning by organic mercury compounds, named after Minamata Bay in Japan, where fish contained high levels of organic mercury compounds after waste water from mercury processing was passed into the estuary (between 1953–6).

minarine Name sometimes given to low-fat *spreads with less than the statutory amount of fat in a *margarine.

mince 1. To chop or cut into small pieces with a knife or, more commonly, in a mincing machine or electric grinder. **2.** Meat which is finely divided by chopping or passing through a mincing machine; known as ground meat in the USA.

mincemeat A traditional product made from apple, sugar, vine fruits, and citrus peel with suet, spices, and acetic acid, coloured with caramel. Preserved by the sugar content and acid. Also called fruit mince. Originally contained meat; in the USA a spiced mixture of chopped meat, apples, and raisins.

mince pie Small pastry tart, filled with *mincemeat, traditionally eaten at Christmas.

mineola A *citrus fruit.

mineralocorticoids The *steroid *hormones secreted by the adrenal cortex that control the excretion of salt and water. *See also* WATER BALANCE.

mineral salts The inorganic salts, including sodium, potassium, calcium, chloride, phosphate, sulphate, etc. So called because they are (or originally were) obtained by mining.

minerals, trace Those *mineral salts present in the body, and required in the diet, in small amounts (parts per million): *copper, *chromium, *iodine, *manganese, *molybdenum, *selenium; although required in larger amounts, *zinc and *iron are sometimes included with the trace minerals.

minerals, ultra-trace Those *mineral salts present in the body, and required in the diet, in extremely small amounts (parts per thousand million or less); known to be dietary essentials, although rarely if ever a cause for concern since the amounts required are small and they are widely distributed in foods and water, e.g. *cobalt, *manganese, *molybdenum, *silicon, *tin, *vanadium.

miners' cramp Cramp due to loss of *salt from the body caused by excessive sweating. Occurs in tropical climates and with severe exercise; mining often combines the two.

minestra Italian; vegetable soup, thinner than *minestrone.

minestrone Italian; thick mixed vegetable soup with pasta or rice.

mint Aromatic herbs, *Mentha* spp., including spearmint (garden mint), *M. spicata*; peppermint, *M. piperita*; field or Japanese mint, *M. arvensis*. Oil of peppermint is distilled from stem and leaves of *M. piperita*, and used both pharmaceutically and as a flavour. Vietnamese mint is *laksa.

mint jelly Apple jelly flavoured with spearmint (*Mentha spicata*), often eaten with lamb.

mint julep *See* JULEP.

mint sauce Mint (spearmint, *Mentha spicata*) chopped in vinegar, sometimes with sugar added; traditionally eaten with lamb in Britain.

mirabelle French; spirit prepared by distillation of fermented yellow-green mirabelle plums; strong fruity aroma, not sweetened. Similar to the German *quetsch.

miracle berry (synsepalum) The fruit of the West African bush *Synsepalum dulcificum* (syn. *Richardella dulcifica*). It contains a taste-modifying *glycoprotein (miraculin) that causes sour foods to taste sweet.

miraculin The taste-modifying *glycoprotein of the *miracle berry.

mirepoix Mixture of finely chopped carrots, celery, and onions, fried in butter and used to flavour meat dishes.

mirin Japanese; sweet alcoholic condiment made from rice fermented by addition of *koji.

miso Japanese; sauce prepared from autoclaved soya beans mixed with cooked rice and partly fermented with *Aspergillus oryzae* and *A. sojae* to form *koji. Salt is added to stop further mould growth; bacterial fermentation continues for 1–2 months with the addition of *Lactobacillus*.

mistelle French; partially fermented grape juice.

misua South-East Asian; noodles made from wheat flour, eggs, and soda ash.

mitochondrion (pl. mitochondria) The subcellular organelles in all cells apart from red blood cells in which the major oxidative reactions of *metabolism occur, linked to the formation of *ATP from ADP.

mitsuba Japanese wild parsley, *Cryptotaenia japonica* syn. *C. canadensis* var. *japonica*; grown for the long slender petioles and leaflets, which are eaten raw or cooked.

mixiria Process of preserving meat and fish by roasting them in their own fat and preserving in jars covered with a layer of fat.

mocca Mixture of coffee and cocoa used in bakery and confectionery products.

mocha 1. Variety of arabica coffee. 2. Flavoured with coffee. 3. A hot drink that combines coffee, chocolate, and milk. *See also* MOCCA.

mock brawn *See* HEAD CHEESE.

mock fritters *See* FRENCH TOAST.

mock goose North of England; beef heart simmered in stock until tender, then stuffed, wrapped in fatty bacon, and roasted.

mock turtle soup Gelatinous soup made from calf's head, beef, bacon, and veal; similar to turtle soup, but without the *turtle; mock turtle is a calf's head dressed to resemble a turtle.

mode, à la Bœuf à la mode is beef braised in the classic way; also (in USA) fruit or other sweet pie served with ice cream.

MODY Maturity onset diabetes of the young; a rare type of *diabetes mellitus that develops in children, but unlike type I (insulin-dependent) diabetes, there is no destruction of β-islet cells of the *pancreas. Basal insulin secretion is more or less normal, but the affected children are unable to secrete additional insulin in response to a glucose load.

mogroside Triterpenoid glycoside from the fruit of the Chinese plant *Momordica grosvenori*, 300 times as sweet as sucrose, and marketed as an intense sweetener.

moinmoin *See* AKARA.

molasses The residue left after repeated crystallization of sugar; it will not crystallize. Contains 67% sucrose, together with glucose and fructose and (if from beet) raffinose and small quantities of dextrans; 260 kcal (1 100 kJ)/100 g; more than 500 mg iron per 100 g, with traces of other minerals.

mole **1.** Mexican; sauce made from sweet pepper, avocado, tomato, and sesame, flavoured with aniseed, garlic, coriander, cinnamon, cloves, chilli, and grated chocolate. **2.** Chemical term (abbreviated to mol); 1 mol of a compound is equivalent to its molecular mass in grams.

molluscs Marine bivalve shellfish with soft unsegmented bodies; most are enclosed in a hard shell; they include *abalone, *clams, *cockles, *mussels, *oysters, *scallops, *whelks, *winkles.

molokhiya Egyptian; the leaves of *Corchorus olioturus*; also a traditional soup prepared with those leaves. *See* MELOUKHIA.

molybdenum A dietary essential mineral, required for a number of enzymes, including xanthine, aldehyde, and pyridoxal oxidases, where it forms the functional part of the coenzyme molybdopterin. Deficiency is unknown; US/Canadian RDA is 45 μ/day.

molybdopterin *See* MOLYBDENUM.

momojiko Japanese; salted roe of Alaskan pollack, also known as tarako.

momoni West African; various fish left to start fermenting in tropical heat for 6–10 hours, then salted for 1–2 days and sun dried. Known in Ghana as stinking fish.

momos Tibetan; dumplings stuffed with yak meat or vegetables and flavoured with Szechwan pepper, garlic, ginger, and onion.

monascin (monascorubin) Orange and red pigments produced by the filamentous fungus *Monascus ruber*.

mondogo Caribbean (Puerto Rico); tripe stew.

monellin A sweet protein from the *serendipity berry, 1500–2000 times as sweet as sucrose.

monethanolamine *See* ETHANOLAMINE.

mongogo *See* MANKETTI.

monkey orange Fruit of the southern African tree *Strychnos cocculoides*.

monkfish Marine fish, also known as angler fish; *Lophius piscatorius*, *L. americanus*, *L. caulinarus*, *L. budegassa*. Cape monkfish is *L. vomerinus*, Pacific monkfish is *L. litulon*.

monoacylglycerol *See* FATS, SUPERGLYCERINATED.

monoamine oxidase *Enzyme that oxidises *amines; inhibitors have been used clinically as antidepressant drugs, and consumption of amine-rich foods such as cheese may cause a hypertensive crisis in people taking the drugs.

monocalcium phosphate *See* CALCIUM ACID PHOSPHATE.

monocytes Large phagocytic white blood cells with a single nucleus; 3–8% of the circulating white blood cells.

monogenic Diseases or disorders involving a single gene variant or abnormality. May be inherited in a simple Mendelian manner, or expression of the disease *phenotype may involve interactions with diet or other environmental factors. *See also* GENETIC DISEASE; OLIGOGENIC; POLYGENIC.

monoglycerides *See* FATS, SUPERGLYCERINATED.

monokines *Cytokines secreted by *monocytes.

monophagia Desire for one type of food.

monosaccharides Group name of the simplest sugars, including those composed of three carbon atoms (trioses), four (tetroses), five (pentoses), six (hexoses), and seven (heptoses). The units from which *disaccharides, *oligosaccharides, and *polysaccharides are formed.

monosodium glutamate (MSG) The sodium salt of *glutamic acid, used to enhance the flavour of savoury dishes and often added to canned meat and soups. First isolated from seaweed by Tokyo chemist Kimunae Ikeda in 1908; he called it *ajinomoto*, meaning 'the essence of taste'. *See also* FLAVOUR ENHANCERS; UMAMI.

mono-unsaturates Commonly used short term for mono-unsaturated *fatty acids.

monstera Fruit of the tropical climbing plant (the Swiss cheese plant), *Monstera deliciosa*, also known as fruit salad fruit (Australia), delicious fruit or monster, and ceriman.

Monterey jack American Cheddar-type cheese.

montmorency, à la Sweet dishes and cakes which include cherries.

montmorillonite *See* FULLER'S EARTH.

mook Korean; starch jelly from food made from beans, *buckwheat, or *acorns.

mooli Long, white *radish; oriental variety of *Raphanus sativa*.

moonfish Marine fish, *Lampris* spp., also known as opah. Peruvian moonfish is *Selene peruviana*.

moonshine American; illicit home-distilled spirit. *See also* POTEEN.

moorfowl (moorcock, moorgame) Scottish name for *grouse.

morcilla Spanish; *black pudding.

morel Edible fungus *Morchella esculenta*, much prized for its delicate flavour; *see* MUSHROOMS.

Moreton Bay bug (bay lobster) A variety of sand *lobster found in Australia.

moringa Fruit of the tropical kelor tree *Moringa oleifera*; the leaves and seed pods are edible and are reported to taste like *asparagus. The crushed seeds have antibacterial activity and can be used to purify drinking water. Ben oil from the seeds is rich in oleic acid. Also known as the horseradish tree (because its bulbous roots taste like horseradish), ben tree, and drumstick tree.

mornay, à la Dish served with béchamel cheese sauce (mornay sauce).

moroheiya *See* EWEDU.

moromi Eastern Asian; thick mash of cereal, or cereal and soy bean, left to undergo slow fermentation with bacteria, yeasts, and moulds. *See also* MISO; SAKÉ; SOY SAUCE.

mortadella *See* SAUSAGE.

mortality rate In epidemiology, crude mortality rate (CMR) is the number of deaths (overall or from a specific cause) in the study population expressed as a proportion of the population. Standardized mortality rate (SMR) is the crude mortality rate expressed as a ratio of the expected mortality rate in the population under study.

mortoban *See* PASTRY, PHYLLO.

morue French; *cod, especially salt dried cod.

morwong Marine fish from the Pacific and Indian oceans, *Nemadactylus macropterus*; grey morwong is *N. douglasi* and banded morwong is *Cheilodactylus spectablis*.

moss, Irish *See* CARRAGEENAN.

mother of vinegar *See* VINEGAR.

motilin A small *peptide *hormone secreted by the small intestine that increases gastro-intestinal motility.

mottled teeth *See* FLUORIDE.

motza *See* MATZO.

mould bran A fungal *amylase preparation produced by growing mould on moist wheat bran.

mould inhibitors *See* ANTIMYCOTICS.

moulds *Fungi characterized by their branched filamentous structure (mycelium), including *mushrooms and smaller fungi.
  i) They can cause food spoilage very rapidly, e.g. white *Mucor*, grey-green *Penicillium*, black *Aspergillus*. Many also produce *mycotoxins. ii) Some are used for large-scale manufacture of citric acid (*Aspergillus niger*), ripening of cheeses (*Penicillium* spp.), and as sources of enzymes for industrial use. iii) A number of foods are fermented with moulds. iv) The mycelium of *Fusarium* spp. is used as *mycoprotein. v) Most of the antibiotics are mould products.

moule French for *mussel.

mountain chicken *See* CRAPAUD.

moussaka Greek, eastern Mediterranean; minced lamb, potatoes, onions, and aubergine (and sometimes tomatoes), topped with *béchamel sauce and baked.

mousse Light, frothy dish based on white or custard sauce or fruit purée to which eggs, whipped cream, and sometimes gelatine are added. May be sweet or savoury, served hot or cold.

mousseline French; general term for light, fluffy dish. Mousseline sauce is Hollandaise sauce to which beaten egg-white or whipped cream is added just before serving, to give a frothy texture.

mowrah butter *See* BUTTER, VEGETABLE.

mowrala Freshwater fish *Amblypharyngodon mola*, a member of the *carp family.

mozzarella Italian, now made elsewhere; soft white curd *cheese, originally made from buffalo milk, now normally from cow's milk. Mainly used as a topping for *pizza, although also eaten uncooked.

MPD Modified *polydextrose.

MRM *See* MEAT, MECHANICALLY RECOVERED.

MSG *See* MONOSODIUM GLUTAMATE.

MSM Mechanically separated meat. *See* MEAT, MECHANICALLY RECOVERED.

MSNF Milk solids, non-fat; the *lactose, proteins, and *minerals from *milk.

MUAC *See* MID-UPPER-ARM CIRCUMFERENCE.

mucilages Soluble but undigested polysaccharides of arabinose and xylose found in seeds and seaweeds; used as thickening and stabilizing agents in food processing because of their water-holding properties and viscosity. *See also* GUM; ISPAGHULA.

mucin Viscous *mucoprotein secreted in the saliva and throughout the intestinal tract; the main constituent of *mucus. Resistant to hydrolysis by digestive enzymes.

mucopolysaccharides *Polysaccharides containing an amino sugar and uronic acid; constituent of the *mucoproteins of cartilage, tendons, connective tissue, cornea, heparin, and blood-group substances.

mucoproteins *Glycoproteins containing a sugar, usually chondroitin sulphate, combined with amino acids or peptides.

Mucor *See* MOULDS.

mucosa Moist tissue, lining, for example, the mouth (buccal mucosa), stomach (gastric mucosa), intestines, and respiratory tract.

mucous colitis *See* IRRITABLE BOWEL SYNDROME.

mucus Secretion of mucous glands, containing *mucin; protects epithelia.

muesli Breakfast cereal; a mixture of raw cereal flakes (oats, wheat, rye barley, and millet) together with dried fruit, apple flakes, nuts, sugar, bran, and wheatgerm. Originated in Switzerland in the late 19th century.

muffins *See* DOUGH CAKES.

mugwort Leaves of *Artemisia* spp., used as a herb.

mulberry Dark purple-red fruit of the tree *Morus nigra*, slightly sweet and acid, similar in shape and size to a raspberry or loganberry. The white mulberry (*M. alba*) is grown mainly as a food source for silkworms, but also for the fruits, which are dried. Indian mulberry is *noni.

mulled ale Beer that has been spiced and heated, traditionally by plunging a red-hot poker into it.

mulled wine Wine mixed with fruit juice, sweetened and flavoured with spices (especially cinnamon, cloves, and ginger), served hot.

müller-thurgau A *grape variety widely used for *wine making, not one of the classic varieties. The major variety in Rheinhessen and Pfalz in Germany.

mullet Marine fish; red mullet (also known as goatfish) are species of the family *Mullidae*, grey mullet are species of the family *Mugilidae*. Thin-lipped grey mullet is *Liza ramada*, golden grey mullet is *L. aurata*, and striped or black mullet is *Mugil cephalus*. Roe of several species is used to make *caviar.

mulligatawny Anglo-Indian; *curry-flavoured soup made with meat or chicken stock.

mulsum Roman; mixture of wine and honey, commonly drunk with the first course of a meal.

multiple sclerosis A slowly progressive disease involving nerve degeneration; it may take many years to develop to the stage of paralysis, and it is subject to random periods of spontaneous remission. There is some evidence that supplements of polyunsaturated *fatty acids slow its progression.

munster Strong soft cheese made in wheel shapes with an orange-red rind. Originally French, now made in several countries.

muscadet A *grape variety widely used for *wine making, not one of the classic varieties; makes light, very dry wines; also known as melon de bourgogne.

muscat A *grape variety widely used for *wine making, not one of the classic varieties; mostly perfumed, sweet, white wines.

muscatel Made by drying the large seed-containing grapes grown almost exclusively around Malaga in Spain. They are partially dried in the sun and drying is completed indoors; they are left on the stalk and pressed flat for sale. Muscatel is a sweet wine made from the grapes.

muscle The contractile unit of skeletal muscle is the cylindrical fibre, composed of many myofibrils. Muscle consists of three main proteins: actin, myosin, and tropomyosin. Actin is a globular protein, and actin molecules are arranged along the fibrous protein tropomyosin, interspersed with molecules of the calcium-binding regulatory protein, troponin. Myosin is a fibrous protein, with ATPase activity in the head region. The head region binds to actin; contraction of muscle involves hydrolysis of ATP by myosin and movement of myosin to bind to another actin molecule further along the chain.

The muscle fibre is surrounded by a thin membrane, the sarcolemma; within the muscle fibre, surrounding the myofibrils, is the sarcoplasm. Individual fibres are separated by a thin network of *connective tissue, the endomysium, and bound together in bundles by thicker sheets of connective tissue, the perimysium.

mush American; cakes of boiled ground rice served cold or fried.

mushrooms Various edible *fungi (botanically both mushrooms and toadstools); correctly the fruiting bodies of the fungi. Altogether some 1100 species are sold, fresh or dried, in markets around the world; most of these are gathered wild rather than cultivated. 340 are poisonous to one degree or another (10 are fatal, 6 hallucinogenic); 250 have (potential) medicinal uses.

The common cultivated mushroom, including flat, cup, and button mushrooms, is *Agaricus bisporus*, as is the chestnut or Paris mushroom. Other cultivated mushrooms include shiitake (or Black Forest mushroom, *Lentinula edodes*); oyster mushroom, *Pleurotus ostreatus*; Chinese straw mushroom, *Volvariella volvacea*.

Some wild species are especially prized, including field mushroom, *Agaricus campestris*; horse mushroom, *Agaricus arvensis*; parasol mushroom, *Macrolepiota procera*; beefsteak fungus, *Fistulina hepatica*; blewits and wood blewits, *Clitocybe* spp. syn. *Lepista* spp; cep or boletus, *Boletus edulis*; chanterelle or girolle, *Cantharellus cibarius*; matsutake, *Tricholoma matsutake* syn. *T. nauseosum*; puffballs, *Calvatia* spp.; morels, *Morchella* spp.; *truffles, *Tuber* spp.; wood-ears (or Chinese black fungus), *Auricularia polytricha*. Many other wild fungi are also edible, but many are poisonous.

A 50-g portion provides 1.5g of dietary fibre and is a rich *source of copper; a source of vitamin B_2, niacin, folate, and selenium; supplies 6kcal (25kJ).

muskellunge (musky) Freshwater fish *Esox masquinongy*, related to the pike.

mussels Various marine bivalve molluscs, of the family *Mytilidae*, especially *Mytilus edulis*, *M. californianus*. A 100-g portion of boiled flesh (330g with shell) is an exceptionally rich *source of iodine; a rich source of protein, iron, copper, and selenium; a good source of calcium, vitamin B_2, and niacin; a source of zinc; and contains 200mg of sodium; supplies 90kcal (380kJ).

Greenshell or green lipped mussels (*Perna canaliculus*), so called because of their emerald green shell markings, are native to New Zealand.

MUST Malnutrition universal screening tool, developed by *BAPEN, for detection of malnutrition in adults, based on weight and height, unplanned weight loss, and disease status.

(((●))) SEE WEB LINKS

• The MUST's homepage.

mustard Powdered seeds of black or brown mustard (*Brassica nigra* or *B. juncea*), or white or yellow mustard (*Sinapis alba*), or a mixture. English mustard contains not more than 10% wheat flour and turmeric (still referred to in parts of England as Durham mustard, after Mrs Clements of Durham who produced the first commercial dried mustard in 1722).

French mustard is made from dehusked seeds (the light-coloured Dijon) or black or brown seeds with salt, spices, and white wine or unripe grape juice. Bordeaux (usually called French mustard) is black and brown seeds mixed with sugar, vinegar, and herbs. Meaux mustard is grainy and made with mixed seeds.

American mustard, mild and sweet, is made with white seeds, sugar, vinegar, and turmeric.

mustard and cress Salad herb mixture of leaves of mustard (*Brassica alba*) and garden cress (*Lepidium sativum*). Often mustard is replaced with rape (*Brassica napus* var. *oleifera*)—a different strain from that used for *rape seed oil—it has a larger leaf and grows faster than mustard.

mustard, Chinese (gai choy, kaai tsoi) Small dark green leaves of *Brassica juncea* var. *rugosa* with a peppery taste used mainly as a vegetable, but also for pickling.

mustard, Ethiopian *Brassica carinata*, eaten as a green leafy vegetable. Of little use as an oilseed crop because of the high content of *glucosinolates in the seeds and *erucic acid in the oil.

mustard oil Oil from mustard *Brassica juncea*; oil from varieties low in glucosinolates and erucic acid is known as canola or canbra oil.

mutagen Compound that causes mutations and may be carcinogenic; *see also* AMES TEST.

mutton Meat from the fully grown sheep, *Ovis aries*. (*Lamb is from animals under 1 year old.) Depending on the cut, protein ranges are 12–18%; fat, 13–32%; energy, 195–380 kcal (820–1600 kJ). A 150-g portion of fillet (5% fat) is a rich *source of protein and niacin; a good source of vitamin B_2; a source of iron and vitamin B_1; supplies 180 kcal (750 kJ).

mwenge *See* ORUBISI.

mycelium Mass of fine branching threads that make up the vegetative part of a fungus that produces a *mushroom or toadstool as a fruiting body.

Mycobacterium avium An animal pathogen that causes chronic enteritis (Johne's disease) in cattle. Subclinical infection is widespread in dairy herds, sheep, and goats (leading to reduced milk and meat production), as well as in rabbits and deer. Has been tentatively implicated in the aetiology of *Crohn's disease in human beings. Infection may be acquired from unpasteurized milk.

mycoprotein Name given to mould mycelium used as a food ingredient; *see also* QUORN.

mycose *See* TREHALOSE.

mycotoxins Toxins produced by filamentous *fungi (moulds, so excluding mushroom toxins), especially *Aspergillus* spp. under tropical conditions and *Penicillium* and *Fusarium* species under temperate conditions. The problem is caused by storage of food under damp conditions which favour the growth of moulds. Mycotoxins include aflatoxin (on nuts and cereals), ochratoxin (on meat products and pulses), patulin (on fruit products), zearalenone, and stigmatocystin.

myenteric plexus Part of the *enteric nervous system, between the longitudinal and circular layers of muscle, responsible for control of gut motility. Also known as Auerbach's plexus.

myocommas Connective tissue between *myotomes in fish flesh.

myocytes Muscle cells; in skeletal muscle the myocytes are elongated multi-nuclear cells; cardiomyocytes in heart muscle are mononuclear.

myogenin Protein expressed in post-proliferative differentiating skeletal muscle cells (myoblasts).

myo-inositol *See* INOSITOL.

myosin *See* MUSCLE.

myostatin A protein secreted by skeletal muscle cells that slows the proliferation and differentiation of muscle stem cells, and so limits further muscle growth.

myotomes The main part of *fish flesh, consisting of long muscles divided into 'leaves' of a more or less conical shape, with the tip directed towards the head.

myristic acid A medium-chain *saturated fatty acid (C14:0).

myristicin A methylene dioxyphenyl compound found in *nutmeg and other essential oils (*see* OILS, ESSENTIAL); at high levels of intake (above what would be obtained from use of herbs and spices) it is hallucinogenic and potentially neurotoxic.

myrobalan Fruit of the tree *Prunus cerasifera*, closely related to the *bullace (*P. insititia*) and wild plum (*P. domestica*). *See also* PLUM.

myrtle An evergreen aromatic shrub, *Myrtus communis*; the leaves and berries are used to flavour foods, and the essential oil (*see* OILS, ESSENTIAL) from the leaves is used in perfumery.

mysost *See* GJETOST.

myxoedema Low metabolic rate as a result of *hypothyroidism, commonly the result of *iodine deficiency.

NAADP Nicotinic acid adenine dinucleotide phosphate; a derivative of *NAD that has a role in release of *calcium from intracellular stores in response to *hormone and nerve stimulation.

naartjie Afrikaans; a small tangerine; *see* CITRUS.

NAASO North American Association for the Study of Obesity.

((∰)) SEE WEB LINKS

• The NAASO's homepage.

NACNE National Advisory Committee on Nutrition Education (UK). An *ad hoc* working party that published a discussion paper on nutritional guidelines in 1983. *See* DIETARY GUIDELINES; NUTRITIONAL RECOMMENDATIONS.

NAD, NADP Nicotinamide adenine dinucleotide and its phosphate, the coenzymes derived from *niacin, involved as hydrogen acceptors in a wide variety of oxidation and reduction reactions.

NADH The reduced form of *NAD.

NAD(H) Abbreviation used to mean either the oxidized or reduced form of *NAD.

NAD(P) Abbreviation used to mean either of the nicotinamide nucleotides, *NAD or NADP.

NADP(H) Abbreviation used to mean either the oxidized or reduced form of NADP. *See* NAD, NADP.

nam pla Thai; salted paste made from shrimps and small fish.

nan Indian flat bread, an egg dough prepared with white flour and leavened with sodium bicarbonate, normally baked in a *tandoor.

nano Prefix for units of measurement, one thousand-millionth part (i.e. 10^{-9}), symbol n; e.g. nanogram, ng.

nanobacteria The smallest cell-walled bacteria (0.2–0.5nm), found in marine limestone, fresh water and water pipes, and also in human and animal blood. They form crystals of apatite (calcium phosphate) on the cell envelope. Nanobacteria resemble the smallest apatite units in kidney stones, and it has been suggested that they may provide nuclei for the crystallization of minerals in the kidney; a number of studies have demonstrated their presence in kidney stones.

nanofiltration *Ultrafiltration using membranes with pores 1–100 nm, which will remove compounds with M_r 300–1000 Da.

nantua, à la Dish garnished with crayfish.

naphthoquinone The chemical ring structure of *vitamin K; the various *vitamers of vitamin K can be referred to as substituted naphthoquinones.

napolitaine, à la Dish garnished with spaghetti, cheese, and tomato sauce.

naranjilla Orange-coloured fruit of the South American shrub *Solanum quitoense* (syn. *S. angulatum*), mainly used for juice.

nargizi *See* KOFTA.

naringenin *See* NARINGIN.

naringin A *glycoside (trihydroxyflavonone rhamnoglucoside) found in grapefruit, especially in the immature fruit. It is extremely bitter, and can be detected at a dilution of 1 part in 10000 of water. Sometimes found in canned grapefruit segments as tiny, white beads. Hydrolysed to the aglycone, naringenin, which is not bitter.

naseberry Fruit of the tropical South American tree *Manilkara zapotilla*.

nashi *See* PEAR, ASIAN.

nasi campur Indonesian; a dish of steamed rice topped with vegetables, meat, pickles, and *krupuk.

nasi goreng Malaysian, Dutch, Indonesian; fried rice with chicken, prawns, etc., topped with strips of omelette.

nasogastric tube Fine plastic tube inserted through the nose and thence into the stomach for *enteral nutrition.

nasturtium Both the leaves and seeds of *Tropaeolum officinalis* (syn. *T. majus*) can be eaten; they have a hot flavour. The seeds can be pickled as a substitute for *capers, and the flowers can be used to decorate salads. The tubers of *T. tuberosum* (the tuber nasturtium) are dried and eaten like potatoes in the Andes.

nata Filipino; thick gelatinous film grown on the surface of juice from coconut, sugar cane, or fruit by fermentation with *Acetobacter aceti*, which produces an extracellular polymer. Eaten as a dessert.

natamycin A polyene antifungal agent, from *Streptomyces natalensis*, used as a coating on the surface of cheeses to prevent the growth of mould or yeast. Also known as pimaricin.

National Dietary and Nutrition Survey (NDNS) A rolling series of surveys of different age groups in the UK with weighed diet records, anthropometric data, health questionnaires, and blood and urine tests.

National Food Survey An annual survey of randomly selected households in the UK with a one-week record of food purchases and consumption.

National Fruit Collection, British Maintained by the Brogdale Horticultural Trust; the largest collection of varieties of fruit trees in the world.

(⊕) SEE WEB LINKS

• The Brogdale Horticultural Trust's homepage.

natto Japanese; soya bean fermented using *Bacillus subtilis* (syn. *B. natto*).

nature-identical Food *additives synthesized in the laboratory that are chemically identical to those that occur in nature.

naturel, au Plain; uncooked, or very simply cooked.

navarin French; ragoût of mutton with potatoes and onions or spring vegetables.

navet French; turnip, *Brassica napus*.

N balance (equilibrium) *See* NITROGEN BALANCE.

NCHS standards Tables of height and weight for age used as reference values for the assessment of growth and nutritional status of children, based on data collected by the US National Center for Health Statistics in the 1970s. The most comprehensive such set of data, and used in most countries of the world.

N conversion factor *See* NITROGEN CONVERSION FACTOR.

NDNS *See* NATIONAL DIETARY AND NUTRITION SURVEY.

NDpCal *See* NET DIETARY PROTEIN ENERGY RATIO.

neapolitan ice Block of ice cream in layers of different colours and flavours.

NEAT Non-exercise activity thermogenesis; *see* THERMOGENESIS, NON-EXERCISE ACTIVITY.

neat's foot Ox or calf's foot used for making soups and jellies. Now called cow heels.

neat's-foot oil Oil obtained from the knucklebones of cattle; used in leather working and for canning sardines.

nebbiolo A *grape variety widely used for *wine making, not one of the classic varieties.

necrosis Accidental death of cells or tissues. *See also* APOPTOSIS.

nectarine Smooth-skinned peach (*Prunus persica* var. *nectarina*). One medium-sized fruit, 150 g weighed with stone, provides 3 g of dietary fibre and is a rich *source of vitamin A (as carotene); a good source of vitamin C; a source of copper; supplies 70 kcal (300 kJ).

NEDF Non-essential dietary factors. *See also* FOODS, FUNCTIONAL; NUTRACEUTICAL.

neep Scottish name for root vegetables; now used for *turnip (and sometimes for *swede in England).

NEFA Non-esterified *fatty acids, also called free fatty acids.

negus Drink made from port or sherry with spices, sugar, and hot water.

NEL *See* NO EFFECT LEVEL.

nem Vietnamese; *spring rolls.

NEO-DHC *See* NEOHESPERIDIN DIHYDROCHALCONE.

neohesperidin dihydrochalcone (NEO-DHC) A non-nutritive *sweetener, 1 000 times as sweet as sucrose; formed by hydrogenation of the naturally occurring *flavonoid neohesperidin.

neomycin *Antibiotic isolated in 1949 from *Streptomyces fradii*; has a broad spectrum of activity, and is not absorbed from the gut; commonly used to treat serious intestinal bacterial infections.

neoplasia Abnormal and uncontrolled cell growth, cancer. *See also* HYPERPLASIA; HYPERTROPHY.

neotame Synthetic intense sweetener, 8 000 times as sweet as sucrose, N-[N-(3,3-dimethylbutyl)-L-α-aspartyl]-L-phenylalanine 1-methyl ester. *See also* ASPARTAME.

nephelometry Measurement of the size and concentration of cells or particles in a solution by light-scattering.

neroli oil Prepared from blossoms of the bitter orange (*see* ORANGE, BITTER) by steam distillation. Yellowish oil with intense odour of orange blossom.

nesselrode Implies the use of chestnuts; nesselrode pudding is made from chestnuts, custard cream, and candied fruit.

net dietary protein calories *See* NET DIETARY PROTEIN ENERGY RATIO.

net dietary protein energy ratio (NDpE) A way of expressing the protein content of a diet or food taking into account both the amount of protein (relative to total energy intake) and the *protein quality. It is protein energy multiplied by *net protein utilization divided by total energy. If energy is expressed in kcal and the result expressed as a percentage, this is net dietary protein calories per cent, NDpCal%.

net protein ratio (NPR) A measure of *protein quality.

net protein utilization (NPU) A measure of *protein quality.

net protein value A way of expressing the amount and quality of the protein in a food; the product of *net protein utilization and protein content per cent.

nettle The young leaves of the stinging nettle, *Urtica dioica*, can be cooked as a vegetable and used to make nettle beer.

neufchâtel French soft mild-flavoured cheese.

neural tube defect (NTD) Congenital malformations of the spinal cord caused by the failure of the closure of the neural tube in early embryonic development. Supplements of *folic acid (400 µg/day) begun before conception reduce the risk.

neurolathyrism *See* LATHYRISM.

neuromedin U A hypothalamic *neuropeptide that reduces food intake and increases energy expenditure; its secretion is increased by *leptin.

neuropeptide Any of the many small *peptides (30–50 amino acids) that are secreted by and/or act on the nervous system.

neuropeptide Y A *peptide neurotransmitter that is important in the control of appetite and feeding behaviour, especially in response to *leptin.

neurotensin A peptide *hormone secreted by the small intestinal mucosa that inhibits secretion of gastric acid and delays gastric emptying.

neutron activation analysis A technique for determining whole body content of minerals (especially *calcium) that form short-lived radioactive isotopes when the body is irradiated with a beam of fast neutrons.

NFE *See* NITROGEN-FREE EXTRACT.

NFLEA US National Food Labelling and Education Act, 1993, the basis of *nutritional labelling of foods and health claims that may be made.

NFS *See* NATIONAL FOOD SURVEY.

nham South-East Asian; semi-dry uncooked pork or beef sausage left to undergo lactic acid bacterial fermentation for 4–5 days.

NHANES National Health and Nutrition Examination Surveys, conducted by the National Center for Health Statistics (NCHS), Centers for Disease Control and Prevention, designed to collect information about the health and diet of people in the USA.

niacin A *vitamin; one of the B vitamins without a numerical designation. It is sometimes (incorrectly) referred to as vitamin B_3 or B_5, and formerly vitamin PP (pellagra preventative). Deficiency leads to *pellagra, which is fatal if untreated. Niacin is the *generic descriptor for two compounds that have the biological activity of the vitamin: nicotinic acid and its amide, nicotinamide. In USA niacin is used specifically to mean nicotinic acid, and niacinamide for nicotinamide.

The metabolic function of niacin is in the *coenzymes NAD (nicotinamide adenine dinucleotide) and NADP (nicotinamide adenine dinucleotide phosphate), which act as intermediate hydrogen carriers in a wide variety of oxidation and reduction reactions.

Niacin can also be formed in the body from the amino acid *tryptophan; on average 60 mg of dietary tryptophan is equivalent to 1 mg of preformed niacin. The total niacin content of foods is generally expressed as mg niacin equivalents; the sum of preformed niacin plus one-sixtieth of the tryptophan. This means that most foods that are good sources of protein are also good sources of niacin. In cereals niacin is largely present as *niacytin, which is not biologically *available; therefore the preformed niacin content of cereals is generally ignored when calculating intakes. Free niacin is added to white flour and enriched breakfast cereals in many countries.

niacinamide American name for nicotinamide, the amide form of the vitamin *niacin.

niacinogens Name given to protein–niacin complexes found in cereals; *see* NIACYTIN.

niacin toxicity High doses of nicotinic acid have been used to treat *hypercholesterolaemia; they can cause an acute flushing reaction, with vasodilatation and severe itching (nicotinamide does not have this effect, but is not useful for treatment of hypercholesterolaemia). Intakes of niacin above 500 mg/day (the reference intake is 17 mg/day) can cause liver damage over a period of months; the risk is greater with sustained-release preparations of niacin.

niacytin The bound forms of the vitamin *niacin, found in cereals. Complexes of niacin with polysaccharides and peptides or glycopeptides; not hydrolysed by intestinal enzymes, so biologically unavailable, but can be liberated by acid or alkaline hydrolysis or by baking the cereal, especially with an alkaline baking powder.

nib *See* CHOCOLATE.

niceritol A derivative of the vitamin *niacin (penta-erythritol tetranicotinate) used to treat *hypercholesterolaemia.

nickel An ultra-trace *mineral; known to be essential for experimental animals, although its function is not known. There is no information on requirements. Metallic nickel is used as a catalyst in the *hydrogenation of oils.

niçoise 1. A garnish for meat with tomatoes, olives, and French beans. 2. Soup garnished with tomato, flageolets, and diced potato. 3. A sauce made from concentrated tomato purée blended with demi-glace. 4. Salade niçoise contains tuna, anchovy, hard-boiled egg, tomatoes, lettuce, and olives.

nicotinamide One of the vitamers of *niacin.

nicotinamide adenine dinucleotide (phosphate) *See* NAD.

nicotinate, sodium Sodium salt of *nicotinic acid; has been used, among other purposes, to preserve the red colour in meats.

nicotinic acid One of the vitamers of *niacin.

NIDDK National Institute of Diabetes and Digestive and Kidney Diseases.

(())) SEE WEB LINKS

• The NIDDK's homepage.

NIDDM Non-insulin-dependent *diabetes mellitus.

nigella *See* KALONJI.

Nigerian berry *See* SERENDIPITY BERRY.

nigerseed (nug) Seeds of the Ethiopean annual herb *Guizotia abyssinica*, grown mainly as an oilseed, although the seeds can also be eaten.

night blindness Nyctalopia. Inability to see in dim light as a result of *vitamin A deficiency. *See also* DARK ADAPTATION; VISION.

nim *See* CURRY PLANT.

ninhydrin test For the amino group of amino acids. Pink, purple, or blue colour is developed on heating an amino acid or peptide with ninhydrin.

nioigome Perfumed rice.

nisin *Antibiotic isolated in 1944 from lactic streptococci group N; inhibits some but not all *Clostridium* spp.; not used medically. Used as a food preservative. It is naturally present in cheese, being produced by a number of strains of cheese *starter organisms. It lowers the resistance of many *thermophilic bacteria to heat and so permits a reduction in the time and/or temperature of heating when processing canned vegetables. *See also* LANTIBIOTICS.

nitrates Plant nutrients and natural constituents of plants; found in soils and included in fertilizer. The amount in crops depends on the amount in soil. Found in drinking water as a result of excessive use of fertilizers.

Health problems can arise because, within a day or two of harvesting some crops, nitrates are converted into *nitrites which can react with the *haemoglobin (especially fetal haemoglobin) in the blood to produce *methaemoglobin which cannot transport oxygen. Maximum levels have been established for nitrate levels in drinking water (an upper limit of 45–50 mg nitrate/L has been recommended for infants).

Nitrates are also used, together with nitrites, for *curing meat products. *See also* NITROSAMINES.

nitrites Found in many plant foods, since they are rapidly formed by the reduction of naturally occurring *nitrate. Nitrite is the essential agent in preserving meat by pickling, since it inhibits the growth of clostridia; it also combines with the *myoglobin of meat to form the characteristic red *nitrosomyoglobin. *See also* NITROSAMINES.

nitrogen A gas comprising about 80% of the atmosphere; in agriculture the term 'nitrogen' is used to refer to ammonium salts and nitrates as plant fertilizers; in nutrition to proteins and amino acids as nutrients, and to urea and ammonium salts as excretory products.

nitrogen balance (N balance) The difference between the dietary intake of nitrogen (mainly protein) and its excretion (as urea and other waste products). Healthy adults excrete the same amount as is ingested, and so are in N equilibrium.

During growth and tissue repair (convalescence) the body is in positive N balance, i.e. intake is greater than loss and there is an increase in the total body pool of protein. In fevers, fasting, and wasting diseases the loss is greater than the intake and the individual is in negative balance; there is a net loss of protein from the body.

nitrogen conversion factor Factor by which nitrogen content of a foodstuff is multiplied to determine the *protein content; it depends on the amino acid composition of the protein. For wheat and most cereals it is 5.8; rice, 5.95; soya, 5.7; most legumes and nuts, 5.3; milk, 6.38; other foods, 6.25. In mixtures of proteins, as in dishes and diets, the factor of 6.25 is used. 'Crude protein' is defined as N × 6.25. *See also* KJELDAHL DETERMINATION.

nitrogen equilibrium *See* NITROGEN BALANCE.

nitrogen-free extract (NFE) In the analysis of foods and animal feedingstuffs, the fraction that contains the sugars and starches plus small amounts of other materials.

nitrogen, metabolic Nitrogen in the faeces derived from internal or endogenous sources, as distinct from nitrogen-containing dietary sources (exogenous nitrogen): unabsorbed digestive juices, the shed lining of the gastro-intestinal tract, and intestinal bacteria.

nitrosamines *N*-Nitroso derivatives of *amines. Found in trace amounts in mushrooms, fermented fish meal and smoked fish, and in pickled foods, where they are formed by reaction between *nitrite and amines. They cause cancer in experimental animals, but it is not known whether the small amounts in foods affect human beings, especially since they have also been found in human gastric juice, possibly formed by reaction between amines and nitrites from the diet.

nitrosomyoglobin The red colour of cured meat. It is formed by the reaction of *nitrite from the pickling salts with *myoglobin in the meat. Fades in light to yellow-brown metmyoglobin.

nitrous oxide A gas used as a propellant in pressurized containers, e.g. to eject cream or salad dressing from containers.

nivalenol Trichothecene *mycotoxin produced by *Fusarium* spp. (especially *F. nivale*) growing on cereals.

nixtamal The paste produced by steeping *maize in calcium hydroxide solution to make tortillas and tacos; the process is nixtamalization.

NLEA US Nutrition Labeling and Education Act (1990), the basis of current US *nutritional labelling.

NMES Non-milk extrinsic sugars; sugars in free solution in a food or beverage, other than *lactose from milk.

NMR Nuclear magnetic resonance.

NOAE With respect to food additives, No Adverse Effect Level, equivalent to *No Effect Level.

noble rot White grapes affected by the fungus *Botrytis cinerea*. It spoils the grapes if they are damaged by rain, but if they are ripe and healthy, and the weather is sunny, it causes them to shrivel and concentrates the sugar, so that top quality sweet wines can be made. *See also* TOKAY; WINE CLASSIFICATION, GERMANY.

nocino Italian; liqueur made from walnuts steeped in brandy or other spirit.

nockerln Austrian, German; small oval dumplings served with soups, stews, goulash, etc., known as noques in Alsace. Butternockerln are made with butter. Lebernockerln contain fried, finely chopped liver.

No Effect Level (NEL) With respect to food *additives, the maximum dose of an additive that has no detectable adverse effects. *See also* ACCEPTABLE DAILY INTAKE.

noggin Traditional measure of volume of liquor = ¼ pint (140 mL); also known as a quartern.

noisette **1.** Small portion, the size of a hazelnut. **2.** French liqueur made from hazelnuts. **3.** Flavoured or made with hazelnuts.

non admis *See* WINE CLASSIFICATION, LUXEMBOURG.

non-enzymic browning *See* MAILLARD REACTION.

non-essential amino acids Those *amino acids that can be synthesized in the body and therefore are not dietary essentials.

non-esterified fatty acids (NEFA) *See* FATTY ACIDS, FREE.

noni (Indian mulberry) Fruit of the South Pacific evergreen shrub *Morinda citrifolia*, with an unpleasant odour; the juice is claimed to have healing properties and to be beneficial in treatment of diabetes, heart disease, and cancer, with little evidence of efficacy.

non-nutritive sweeteners *See* SWEETENERS, INTENSE.

non-pareils The silver beads used to decorate confectionery, made from sugar coated with silver foil or aluminium–copper alloy.

non-starch polysaccharides (NSP) Those *polysaccharides (complex *carbohydrates), other than starches, found in foods. They are the major part of dietary *fibre and can be measured more precisely than total dietary fibre; they include *cellulose, *pectins, *glucans, *gums, *mucilages, *inulin, and *chitin (and exclude lignin). The NSP in wheat, maize, and rice are mainly insoluble and have a laxative effect, while those in oats, barley, rye, and beans are mainly soluble and have a cholesterol lowering effect. In vegetables the proportions of soluble to insoluble are roughly equal but vary in fruits. It is recommended that the average intake should be increased from 13 to 18g per day.

noodles Type of *pasta made with flour and water, sometimes with added egg, the flour being made from various grains such as rice, wheat, buckwheat, and mung bean starch. Made into a wide range of shapes and sizes.

noodles, cellophane Chinese; transparent *noodles made from mung bean starch.

noodles, fish Minced fish mixed with flour, extruded through tubular holes to form long strands which are dried in hot air.

nopal (nopalitos) Mexican; flattened stem segments of cacti (*Opuntia* spp., especially *O. cochenillifera*, the food plant of the *cochineal insect) eaten as a vegetable.

noques *See* NOCKERLN.

nor- Chemical prefix to the name of a compound, indicating: i) one methyl (CH$_3$) group has been replaced by hydrogen (e.g. *noradrenaline can be considered to be a demethylated derivative of adrenaline); ii) an analogue of a compound containing one fewer methylene (CH_2) groups than the parent compound; iii) an isomer with an unbranched side-chain (e.g. norleucine, norvaline).

noradrenaline Hormone secreted by the adrenal medulla together with *adrenaline; also a neurotransmitter. Physiological effects similar to those of adrenaline. Also known as norepinephrine.

norepinephrine *See* NORADRENALINE.

nori Japanese; dried *seaweed, *Porphyra* spp., especially *P. tenera*, *P. umbilicalis*, and *P. yezoensis*.

norite Activated *charcoal used to decolorize solutions.

normande, à la Dish containing apples, served (for meat: veal, etc.) with a mushroom and cream sauce or (for fish) with *Normandy sauce and garnished with shrimps, truffles, crayfish, or mussels.

Normandy pippins Whole peeled and cored dried apples.

Normandy sauce White sauce made with fish stock, butter, and egg.

normocytes Normal red blood cells.

Norwalk virus Cause of non-bacterial gastroenteritis, probably accounting for about 80% of *food-borne disease. Shellfish and salad vegetables are the foods most often implicated in outbreaks; raw clams and oysters pose a high risk for infection. Foods other than shellfish are contaminated by food handlers; commonly transmitted by faecal–oral route and contamination of water, but may also be spread by aerosol from vomiting.

Norwegian omelette *See* BAKED ALASKA.

NOS Nitric oxide synthase.

notatin *See* GLUCOSE OXIDASE.

nouet French; small muslin bag containing spices and herbs which is cooked in liquids to impart flavour without leaving solid particles. Also known as mignonette.

nougat Sweetmeat made from a mixture of gelatine or egg albumin with sugar and starch syrup, and the whole thoroughly aerated. Originated in Montélimar in southern France.

noyau Liqueur made from peach, apricot, plum, or cherry kernels, with a flavour of almonds.

NPR Net Protein Ratio, a measure of *protein quality.

NPU Net Protein Utilization, a measure of *protein quality.

NPV Net Protein Value, a measure of *protein quality.

NSAIDs Non-steroidal anti-inflammatory drugs, e.g. aspirin, iboprufen.

NSP *See* NON-STARCH POLYSACCHARIDES.

NTD *See* NEURAL TUBE DEFECT.

nubbing Term used in the canning industry for 'topping and tailing' of gooseberries.

nucellar layer Of *wheat, the layer of cells that surrounds the endosperm and protects it from the entry of moisture.

nucleic acids Polymers of *purine and *pyrimidine sugar phosphates; two main classes: ribonucleic acid (RNA) and deoxyribonucleic acid (*DNA). Collectively the purines and pyrimidines are called bases. DNA is a double-stranded polymer (the so-called 'double helix') containing the five-carbon sugar deoxyribose. RNA is a single-stranded polymer containing the sugar ribose.

They are not nutritionally important, since dietary nucleic acids are hydrolysed to their bases, ribose and phosphate, in the intestinal tract; purines and pyrimidines can readily be synthesized in the body, and are not dietary essentials.

nucleoproteins The complex of proteins and *nucleic acids found in the cell nucleus.

nucleosides Compounds of purine or pyrimidine bases with a sugar, most commonly ribose. For example, *adenine plus ribose forms adenosine. Phosphorylated nucleosides are nucleotides.

nucleotides Compounds of purine or pyrimidine base with a sugar phosphate. Natural constituents of human milk, often used to supplement infant formulae. *See also* NUCLEOSIDES.

nug *See* NIGERSEED.

nukazuke Japanese; vegetables pickled by a lactic acid fermentation in a rice bran paste.

nun's beads Scottish; small fried pastries filled with cheese.

nuoc mam Vietnamese, Cambodian; fermented fish sauce. The fish is digested by autolytic *enzymes in the presence of salt added to inhibit bacterial growth.

nutmeg Dried ripe seed of the tropical evergreen tree *Myristica fragrans*; mace is the seed coat (arillus) of the same species. Both mace and nutmeg are used as flavourings in meat products and bakery goods. African nutmeg is the seed of *Monodora myristica*. *See also* MYRISTICIN.

nutraceutical Any substance that is a food or part of a food that provides medical or health benefits, including the prevention and treatment of disease, or a product produced from foods but sold as a supplement, and demonstrated to have physiological benefits or provide protection against chronic disease. *See also* FOODS, FUNCTIONAL.

nutria *See* COYPU.

nutrient density A way of expressing the nutrient content of a food or diet relative to the energy yield (i.e. /1000kcal or /MJ) rather than per unit weight.

nutrient enemata Rectal feeding can be carried out with nutrient solutions as the colon can absorb 1–2 litres of solution per day; maximum daily amount of glucose that can be given is 75g (equivalent to 300kcal, 1260kJ), and 1g of nitrogen, in the form of hydrolysed protein (equivalent to 6g of protein). *See also* NUTRITION, ENTERAL; NUTRITION, PARENTERAL.

nutrients Essential dietary factors: *vitamins, *minerals, *amino acids, and *fatty acids. Metabolic fuels (sources of energy) are not termed nutrients so that a commonly used phrase is 'energy and nutrients'. *See also* MACRONUTRIENTS; MICRONUTRIENTS.

nutrient standards Average daily amounts of nutrients estimated on the basis of available scientific knowledge to be adequate to meet the physiological needs of nearly all healthy persons. *See also* REFERENCE INTAKE.

nutrification The addition of nutrients to foods at such a level as to make a major contribution to the diet.

nutrigenetics The study of the effects of *genotype on nutrient requirements and the effects of diet on health. *See also* NUTRIGENOMICS.

nutrigenomics The study of how nutrients interact with the *genome, and identification of nutrient-sensitive genes. *See also* NUTRIGENETICS.

nutrition The process by which living organisms take in and use food for the maintenance of life, growth, and the functioning of organs and tissues; the branch of science that studies these processes.

nutritional claim Any representation that states, suggests, or implies that a food has particular nutrition-related health properties. The extent of such claims on food *labelling and advertising are controlled by law in most countries.

nutritional disorder Any morbid process or functional abnormality of the body due to the consumption of a diet not conforming to physiological requirements, or to failure of absorption or utilization of the food after ingestion.

nutritional epidemiology Studies relating nutrition to health or disease risk.

nutritional genomics General term to include both *nutrigenetics and *nutrigenomics.

nutritional labelling In the EU nutritional information of foods must be given /100 g (or /100 mL), and may also, optionally, be given per serving of a stated size. In USA information must be given in a standard format per serving (as defined by the Food and Drug Administration), and may optionally be given /100 g or /100 mL.

nutritional melalgia *See* BURNING FOOT SYNDROME.

nutritional recommendations Recommendations comprising nutrient goals, food goals, and dietary guidelines. In addition to *reference intakes of nutrients, key recommendations in developed countries are reduction of total *fat intake to 30% of energy intake, with a more severe restriction of *saturated fats (to 10% of energy intake); increase of *carbohydrate intake to 55% of energy intake (with a reduction of sugars to 10% of energy intake); increased intake of *non-starch polysaccharides; and reduced intake of *salt. *See also* EATWELL PLATE; DIETARY GUIDELINES; FOOD PYRAMID.

nutritional status The condition of the body in those respects influenced by the diet; the levels of nutrients in the body and the ability of those levels to maintain normal metabolic integrity.

For adults, general adequacy is assessed by measuring weight and height; the result is commonly expressed as the *body mass index, the ratio of weight (kg) to height^2 (m). Body fat may also be estimated, by measuring *skinfold thickness, and muscle diameter is also measured.

For children, weight and height for age are compared with standard data for adequately nourished children. The increase in the circumference of the head and the development of bones may also be measured.

Status with respect to individual vitamins and minerals is normally determined by laboratory tests, either measuring the blood and urine concentrations of the nutrients and their metabolites, or by testing for specific metabolic responses. *See also* ANTHROPOMETRY; ENZYME ACTIVATION ASSAYS.

nutrition, enteral Tube-feeding with a liquid diet directly into the stomach or small intestine. *See also* GASTROSTOMY FEEDING; NASOGASTRIC TUBE; NUTRIENT ENEMATA; NUTRITION, PARENTERAL.

nutrition, intravenous *See* NUTRITION, PARENTERAL.

nutritionist According to the US Department of Labor, Dictionary of Occupational Titles, one who applies the science of nutrition to the promotion of health and control of disease, instructs auxiliary medical personnel, and participates in surveys. Not legally defined in the UK, but there is a Register of Accredited Nutritionists maintained by the Nutrition Society. *See also* DIETITIAN.

nutrition, parenteral Feeding other than through the gastro-intestinal tract; by intravenous or intra-rectal infusion. This may be partial, to supplement food and nutrient intake, or total (TPN, total parenteral nutrition), providing the sole source of energy and nutrients for patients with major intestinal problems. Parenteral means not enteral, i.e. not through the intestinal tract; *see also* NUTRIENT ENEMATA; NUTRITION, ENTERAL.

nutrition policy (nutrition planning) A set of concerted actions, based on a governmental mandate, intended to ensure good health in the population through informed access to safe, healthy, and adequate food.

nutrition, public health The discipline that focuses on the promotion of good health through nutrition and the primary prevention of nutrition-related illness in the population.

nutrition surveillance Monitoring the state of health, nutrition, eating behaviour, and nutrition knowledge of the population for the purpose of planning and evaluating *nutrition policy. Especially in developing countries, monitoring may include factors that may give early warning of nutritional emergencies.

nutrition transition The change from diseases associated with undernutrition to those associated with over-nutrition as countries develop. There has been a demographic transition, from high fertility associated with high mortality, to low fertility and low mortality, with increasing industrialization. At the same time there has been an epidemiological transition from a pattern of high levels of infectious disease associated with undernutrition and poor sanitation to a high *prevalence of the chronic non-communicable diseases that were formerly known as the diseases of affluence.

nutritive ratio In animal feeding; a measure of the value of a feeding ration for growth (or milk production) compared with its fattening value. It is the sum of the digestible carbohydrate, protein, and 2.3 × fat, divided by digestible protein. (Energy yield of fat is 2.3 times that of carbohydrate and protein.) Value 4–5 for growth, 7–8 for fattening.

nutritive value index In animal feeding; intake of digestible energy expressed as energy digestibility multiplied by voluntary intake of dry matter of a particular feed, divided by metabolic weight (weight$^{0.75}$; *see* WEIGHT, METABOLIC), compared with standard feed.

nutro-biscuit Indian; biscuit baked from a mixture of 60% wheat flour and 40% peanut flour; contains 16–17% protein.

nutro-macaroni Indian; mixture of 80 parts wheat flour and 20 parts defatted peanut meal; contains 19% protein.

nuts Hard-shelled fruit of a wide variety of trees, e.g. *almonds, *Brazil, *cashew, *peanut, *walnut: all have high fat content, 45–60%; high protein content, 15–20%; 15–20% carbohydrate. The *chestnut is an exception, with 3% fat and 3% protein, being largely carbohydrate, 37%. A number of nuts are grown specially for their oils; *see* OILSEED.

nyctalopia *See* NIGHT BLINDNESS.

oats Grain from *Avena* spp., the three best-known being *A. sativa*, *A. steritis*, and *A. strigosa*. A 100-g portion (raw) is a rich *source of vitamin B$_1$; a good source of protein, iron, and zinc; a source of niacin; contains 9g of fat of which 20% is saturated and 40% polyunsaturated, and 7g of dietary fibre; supplies 375kcal (1580kJ).

Oatmeal is ground oats; oatflour is ground oats with the bran removed; groats are husked oats; Embden groats are crushed groats; Scotch oats are groats cut into granules of various sizes; Sussex ground oats are very finely ground oats; rolled oats are crushed by rollers and partially precooked.

obesity Excessive accumulation of body fat. A *body mass index above 30 is considered to be obesity (and above 40 gross obesity). The desirable range of BMI for optimum life expectancy is 20–25; between 25 and 30 is considered to be *overweight rather than obesity. People more than 50% above desirable weight (*see* WEIGHT, DESIRABLE) are twice as likely to die prematurely as those within the desirable weight range.

obesity, dietary In experimental animals, obesity induced by overfeeding, as opposed to pharmacological treatment or as a result of genetic defects.

obesity drugs *See* ANORECTIC DRUGS.

Ob gene The gene that is defective in the *ob/ob* obese mutant mouse; it codes for the *hormone *leptin.

obstipation Extreme and persistent *constipation caused by obstruction of the intestinal tract.

oca Tuberous root of the perennial herb *Oxalis tuberosa*, an important food of the Andean highlanders and now cultivated in Mexico, where it is known as papa roja (red potato), and New Zealand, where it is known as New Zealand yam.

ochratoxin *Mycotoxin produced by *Penicillium verrucosum* growing on cereals in temperate climates and by various *Aspergillus* spp., especially *A. ochraceus*, in warmer regions. In tropical and subtropical regions a wider range of foodstuffs may be contaminated, including coffee, cocoa, vine fruits, and spices. Primarily a nephrotoxin, it has been associated with Balkan endemic nephropathy, which in turn is associated with urinary tract tumours.

octave A cask for wine containing one-eighth of a *pipe, about 13 imperial gallons (59 L).

octopus Marine cephalopod (*Octopus* spp.) with beak-like mouth surrounded by eight tentacles bearing suckers.

odds ratio In statistics, the ratio of the probability of an event or condition occurring in one group (e.g. an experimental group) compared with that in another group (e.g. a control group). An odds ratio of 1.0 means that the event or condition will occur equally in both groups, >1 that it will occur in the experimental group more frequently than in the control group, and <1 that it will occur less frequently in the experimental group than the control.

ODS Office of Dietary Supplements of the US National Institute of Health.

(🌐) SEE WEB LINKS

• The ODS's homepage.

oedema Excessive retention of fluid in the body; may be caused by cardiac, renal, or hepatic failure, or by starvation (famine oedema).

oenagarum Roman; salad dressing made from *liquamen mixed with wine.

oenin An anthocyanidin from the skin of purple grapes.

***Oenococcus oeni* (syn. *Leuconostoc oenos.*)** A highly acid- and alcohol-tolerant *lactic acid bacterium found in fruit mashes. It converts malate to lactate (a malolactic fermentation), and is used in wine making to reduce acidity and improve the stability and quality of wines.

oesophagus The muscular tube between the mouth and stomach; *see* GASTRO-INTESTINAL TRACT.

oestrogens (estrogens) The female sex *hormones; chemically they are *steroids, although non-steroidal compounds also have oestrogen activity, including the synthetic compounds stilboestrol and hexoestrol. These have been used for chemical caponization of cockerels and to increase the growth rate of cattle. *See also* CAPON.

Non-steroidal compounds with oestrogenic activity are found in a variety of plants; collectively these are known as *phytoestrogens.

offal Corruption of 'off-fall': i) with reference to meat, the term includes all parts that are cut away when the carcass is dressed, including liver, kidneys, brain, spleen, pancreas, thymus, tripe, and tongue. Known in the USA as organ meats or variety meat; ii) with reference to wheat, offal is the bran discarded when milled to white flour (*see* WHEATFEED).

ogi West African; porridge prepared from fermented *maize, *sorghum, or *millet.

ogiri West African; condiment made from fermented oilseeds (especially castor beans, melon, or sesame seeds).

oil *Triacylglycerols that have a low melting point and are liquid at room temperature. *See also* FAT.

oil bean, African Seeds of the tropical African leguminous tree *Pentaclethra macrophylla*. A source of oil; the cooked seeds are sliced and fermented to produce ugba, used as the basis of salads.

oil, fish Fish oils contain long-chain polyunsaturated *fatty acids which are protective against heart disease and stroke. The two main fatty acids are EPA (eicosapentaenoic acid; C20:5 ω3) and DHA (docosahexaenoic acid; C22:6 ω3). Fish oil concentrates containing these fatty acids are sold as pharmaceutical preparations. *See also* COD LIVER OIL; HALIBUT LIVER OIL; MENHADEN.

oil, frying; oil, heavy duty Virtually any edible oil or fat can be used to fry foods; heavy duty oils can be used commercially for prolonged periods because they have been processed to minimise damage by heat and air.

oil, hydrogenated Liquid oils hardened by *hydrogenation.

oillette The oil expressed from *poppy seeds.

oil, microbial Food oils produced from phytoplankton and other unicellular organisms; an alternative to fish oils (*see* OIL, FISH) as a source of long-chain ω3 polyunsaturated *fatty acids.

oils, brominated Oils from a variety of sources, including peach and apricot kernels, olives, and soya beans, that have been reacted with *bromine (which adds across the double bonds of unsaturated fatty acids). They are used to stabilize emulsions of flavouring substances in soft drinks. Also known as weighting oils.

oilseed A wide variety of seeds are grown as a source of oils, e.g. cottonseed, sesame, groundnut, sunflower, soya, and nuts such as coconut, groundnut, and palm nut. After extraction of the oil the residue (oilseed cake or presscake) is a valuable source of protein, especially for animal feedingstuffs.

oils, essential Volatile, aromatic, or odoriferous oils prepared by distillation from plant material, and used for flavouring foods. Chemically distinct from the edible oils, since they are not glycerol esters. *See also* OLEORESINS; TERPENES.

oils, fixed *Triacylglycerols, the edible oils, as distinct from the volatile or essential oils (*see* OILS, ESSENTIAL).

oil, single-cell Fats produced by fungi or bacteria growing on a non-fat substrate.

oil, terpeneless *See* TERPENES.

okara Fibre- and protein-rich remainder after extraction of *soy milk from ground *soya beans.

oke (okolehao) Hawaiian; liqueur made by distillation of fermented extract of the ti tree (*Melaleuca alternifolia*).

okra Also known as gumbo, bamya, bamies, and ladies' fingers; edible seed pods of *Hibiscus esculentus* (syn. *Abelmoschus esculentis*). Small ridged mucilaginous pods containing numerous round seeds, originally West African, now widely grown in subtropical regions, and used in soups and stews. There are two varieties: gomba are oblong, bamya are round. A 100-g portion (raw) is a rich *source of vitamin C; a good source of calcium; a source of carotene (500 µg), vitamin B_1, and folate; contains 4 g of dietary fibre; supplies 30 kcal (125 kJ).

Rainy season okra is *A. caillei*, aibikia is *A. manihot*, and musk seed or ambrette is *A. moschatus*.

okra, bush *See* EWEDU.

okroschka Russian; sour, cold soup made from sour cream, soured milk, and *kvass (rye beer).

olallie berry Cross between *loganberry and *youngberry.

old clothes stew (Spanish: *Ropa vieja*) Castilian; dish prepared from left-over cooked meat simmered with a *sofrito made from onions, red or green peppers, aubergines, tomatoes, and garlic.

old fashioned *Cocktail made from whisky, sugar, bitters, and soda water.

oleic acid Mono-unsaturated *fatty acid (C18:1 ω9); found to some extent in most fats; olive and rapeseed oils are especially rich sources. By far the most abundant of the unsaturated fatty acids.

oleomargarine *See* MARGARINE.

oleo oil *See* PREMIER JUS; TALLOW, RENDERED.

oleoresins In the preparation of some spices such as pepper, ginger, and capsicum, the aromatic material is extracted with solvents which are evaporated off, leaving behind thick oily products known as oleoresins. *See also* OILS, ESSENTIAL.

oleostearin *See* PREMIER JUS; TALLOW, RENDERED.

oleovitamin Preparation of fish liver oil or vegetable oil containing one or more of the fat-soluble *vitamins.

olestra Sucrose ester of fatty acids, used as a *fat replacer because it is not absorbed to any significant extent, and is stable to frying. Trade name Olean.

oligodynamic Sterilizing effect of traces of certain metals. For example, *silver at a concentration of 1 in 5 million will kill *Escherichia coli* and staphylococci in 3 hours.

oligodipsia Reduced sense of thirst.

oligogenic Diseases or disorders involving a small number of variant genes, which may also require interaction with diet and or other environmental factors for expression of the disease *phenotype. *See also* MONOGENIC; POLYGENIC.

oligopeptides Polymers of 4 or more amino acids; more than about 20–50 are termed polypeptides, and more than about 100 are considered to be proteins.

oligosaccharides Carbohydrates composed of 3–10 monosaccharide units (with more than 10 units they are termed *polysaccharides). Those composed of fructose, galactose, or isomaltose have *prebiotic action and encourage the growth of beneficial intestinal bacteria.

olive Fruit of the evergreen tree, *Olea europea*; picked unripe when green or ripe when they have turned dark blue or purplish, and usually pickled in brine. Olives have been known since ancient times. The tree is extremely slow-growing and continues to fruit for many years; there are claims that trees are still fruiting after one thousand years.

A 50-g portion (ten olives weighed with stones) contains 700 mg of sodium and 5 g of fat, of which 20% is saturated and 65% mono-unsaturated; supplies 40 kcal (170 kJ).

See also OLIVE OIL.

olive, African Fruit of the West African aiele tree (*Canarium schweinfurthii*); the pulp and kernel are rich in oleic and palmitic acids. Also known as aiele or mbeu.

olive oil Pressed from ripe *olives, the fruit of *Olea europea*. Virgin olive oil is not refined and the flavour varies enormously with the locality where it is grown. Extra virgin olive oil contains less than 1% acidity. Other types have been refined to varying extents. Used in cooking, as salad oil, for canning sardines, and for margarine manufacture. Apart from the special flavour of olive oil it is valued nutritionally because of its high content, 70%, of mono-unsaturates (mainly oleic acid) and its low content, 15%, of *saturates.

olives, beef *See* BEEF OLIVES.

olla podrida *See* MADRID STEW.

oloroso *See* SHERRY.

omasum *See* RUMINANT.

omega-3 fatty acids, omega-6 fatty acids, omega-9 fatty acids (ω3 fatty acids, ω6 fatty acids, ω9 fatty acids) Three series of long-chain polyunsaturated *fatty acids derived respectively from linolenic, linoleic, and oleic acids. Omega (ω) or n being the position of the first double bond counting from the terminal methyl group.

omega-3 marine triacylglycerols (ω3 marine triacylglycerols) A mixture of triacylglycerols rich in two polyunsaturated *fatty acids, eicosapentaenoic acid (EPA, C20:5 ω3) and docosohexaenoic (DHA, C22:6 ω3). *See also* OIL, FISH.

omelette (omelet) Egg whisked and fried. May be plain or filled with mushrooms, bacon, cheese, etc. Spanish omelette (*tortilla) is filled with potato. Name probably derived from a dish of eggs with honey and pepper prepared by Apicius, which he called *ovemele* (egg honey). *See also* SOUFFLÉ.

omelette, Norwegian *See* BAKED ALASKA.

omija Fruit of the Chinese vine *Schisandra chinensis*, also called the five taste tree (sweetness, sourness, bitterness, saltiness, and pungence). Used in fruit punch and fruit tea.

OMNI Organising Medical Networked Information, now known as Intute Health and Life Sciences.

((⊕)) SEE WEB LINKS

• The Intute Health and Life Sciences' homepage.

omophagia Eating of raw or uncooked food.

oncom (ontjom) Indonesian; fermented groundnut and soybean *presscake with cassava, fermented with moulds: *Neurospora sitophila* to produce a red product or *Rhizopus oligosporus* for a grey product.

onglet French; cut of beef corresponding to the top of the skirt.

onion Bulb of *Allium cepa*; there are many varieties with white, brown, and red (purple) skins. A 60-g portion, raw, supplies 20 kcal (80 kJ).

onion, Egyptian (tree onion) *Allium cepa*, proliform group. A type that produces clusters of aerial bulbs which develop shoots to form a multi-tiered plant; the aerial bulbs are cropped.

onion, everlasting *Allium perutile*, similar to Welsh onion (*see* ONION, WELSH).

onion, green *See* ONION, SPRING; ONION, WELSH.

onion, Japanese bunching *Allium fistulosum*, similar to Welsh onion (*see* ONION, WELSH), but larger.

onion, perennial *See* ONION, WELSH.

onion, spring Young plants of *Allium cepa*, generally eaten whole (the developing bulb and leaves) as a salad vegetable. Also known as salad onions or scallions. A 60-g portion (three onions) is a rich *source of vitamin C; a source of folate, calcium, and iron; contains 400 µg of carotene; provides 1.8 g of dietary fibre; supplies 15 kcal (65 kJ).

onion, Welsh The perennial onion, *Allium cepa perutile*, the leaves of which are cropped, leaving the plant to grow. Similar to, but smaller than, the Japanese bunching onion, *Allium fistulosum*. Also sometimes used as an alternative name for the *leek.

ONL Obligatory nitrogen loss. *See* NITROGEN BALANCE.

ontjom *See* ONCOM.

opah *See* MOONFISH.

opisthorchiasis Infection with the *trematode *Opisthorchis viverrini* acquired from infected freshwater fish, leading to liver and gall bladder disease.

opsomania Craving for special or unusual food.

optic Dispenser attached to bottles of spirits, etc., in bars to ensure delivery of a precise volume.

optical activity The ability of some compounds to rotate the plane of polarized light because of the asymmetry of the molecule. If the plane of light is rotated to the right, the substance is dextrorotatory and is designated by the prefix (+); if laevorotatory (rotated to the left), the prefix is (−). A mixture of the two forms is optically inactive and is termed racemic.

Sucrose is dextrorotatory but is hydrolysed to glucose (dextrorotatory) and fructose, which is more strongly laevorotatory so hydrolysis changes optical activity from (+) to (−); hence, the mixture of glucose and fructose is termed invert sugar.

(The obsolete notation for (+) was d- and for (−) was l-; this is distinct from D- and L-, which are used to designate stereo-isomerism; *see* D-, L-, AND DL-.)

optical rotation *See* OPTICAL ACTIVITY.

opuntia *See* NOPAL.

orange *Citrus fruit, from the subtropical tree *Citrus sinensis*. Of nutritional value mainly because of its vitamin C content of 40–60 mg/100 g. Blood oranges are coloured by the presence of *anthocyanins in the juice vesicles. One medium orange (160 g) is a rich *source of vitamin C; a good source of folate; a source of vitamins A (as carotene) and B_1; contains 3.2 g of dietary fibre; supplies 60 kcal (250 kJ).

orangeade Carbonated beverage flavoured with orange juice and orange peel oil.

orange, bitter The fruit of the subtropical tree *Citrus aurantium*; known as Seville orange in Spain, bigaradier in France, melangolo in Italy, and khush-khash in Israel.

It is used mainly as root stock, because of its resistance to the gummosis disease of citrus. The fruit is too acid to be edible, but is used in the manufacture of *marmalade; the peel oil is used in the liqueur curaçao. *Neroli oil is prepared from the flowers, *petit-grain oil from the twigs; both are used in perfumery.

orange butter Chopped whole orange, cooked, sweetened, and homogenized.

orange pekoe *See* TEA.

orange roughy A deep-water marine fish (*Hoplostethus atlanticus*) that turns orange after being caught; mainly caught around New Zealand.

orange, Seville *See* ORANGE, BITTER.

orcanella *See* ALKANNET.

oregano (oreganum) Aromatic *herb, *Oreganum vulgare*, also known as wild *marjoram and Mexican sage.

orektika *See* MEZZETHAKIA.

orexigenic Stimulating appetite. *See also* ANOREXIA.

orexins Two small peptide *hormones produced by nerve cells in the lateral hypothalamus, believed to be involved in stimulation of feeding. Also known as hypocretins.

organic **1.** Chemically, any compound containing carbon, with the exception of carbonates and cyanides. Compounds of animal and vegetable origin are organic; *minerals are *inorganic. **2.** The term organic foods refers to 'organically grown foods', meaning plants grown without the use of (synthetic) pesticides, fungicides, or inorganic fertilizers, and prepared without the use of preservatives. Foodstuffs must be grown on land that has not been treated with chemical fertilizers, herbicides, or pesticides for at least three years. Organic meat is from animals fed on organically grown crops without the use of growth promoters, with only a limited number of medicines to treat disease, and commonly maintained under traditional, non-intensive, conditions. Within the EU foods may be labelled as organic if they contain at least 95% organic ingredients and not more than 0.9% *GM ingredients.

organic acids *Acids occurring naturally in foods that contain, as do all *organic compounds, carbon; e.g. *acetic, *citric, fumaric, *lactic, *malic acids;

most, but not all, are carboxylic acids. Unlike the inorganic (mineral) acids such as hydrochloric and sulphuric acids, they can be metabolized; the energy yield of different acids differs, but for labelling purposes a value of 8 kJ (2 kcal)/g is used for all organic acids.

organ meat *See* OFFAL.

organoleptic Sensory properties, i.e. those that can be detected by the sense organs. For foods, it is used particularly of the combination of *taste, texture, and astringency (perceived in the mouth), and aroma (perceived in the nose).

orientale, à l' Fish, eggs, or vegetables, cooked with tomatoes and flavoured with garlic and saffron.

orlistat Drug used in the treatment of *obesity; it inhibits gastric and pancreatic *lipase and prevents absorption of much of the dietary fat. Trade name Xenical.

ormer *See* ABALONE.

ornithine An *amino acid that occurs as a metabolic intermediate in the synthesis of *urea, but not involved in protein synthesis, and of no nutritional importance.

ornithine–arginine cycle The metabolic pathway for the synthesis of *urea.

orotic acid An intermediate in the biosynthesis of *pyrimidines; a growth factor for some micro-organisms and at one time called vitamin B_{13}. There is no evidence that it is a human dietary requirement.

orphan crops Food crops that are widely consumed by poor populations, for which there is little commercial market, including *cassava, some *legumes, and coarse varieties of *millet.

orphan receptors Proteins that resemble *hormone receptors and affect gene expression, but whose physiological ligand has not been identified.

orris root Peeled rhizomes of *Iris germanica* used as a flavouring in ice cream, confectionery, and baked goods.

ortanique A Jamaican *citrus fruit; a cross between orange and tangerine.

orthophenylphenol (OPP) A compound used for the treatment of *citrus fruit and *nuts after harvesting to prevent the growth of moulds.

ortolan Small wild song bird, a bunting, *Emberiza hortulana*, still caught in the wild and eaten in parts of Europe, where it is prized for its delicate flavour.

orubisi Tanzanian; traditional effervescent, opaque, slightly sour *beer produced by fermentation of bananas and sorghum. Also known as amarwa; Kenyan urwaga and Ugandan mwenge are similar.

oryzenin The major protein of *rice.

orzata Italian; *see* HORCHATA DE CHUFAS.

Oslo breakfast A breakfast requiring no preparation, introduced in Oslo, Norway, in 1929 for schoolchildren before classes started. It consisted of rye-biscuit, brown bread, butter or vitaminized margarine, whey cheese, cod liver oil paste, ⅓ litre of milk, raw carrot, apple, and half an orange.

osmazome Obsolete name given to *meat extract regarded as the 'pure essence of meat', supposed to give to soup and broth their characteristic flavour and aroma.

osmolality Concentration of osmotically active solute per unit mass of solvent. *See also* OSMOLARITY.

osmolarity Concentration of osmotically active solute per unit volume of solvent. *See also* OSMOLALITY.

osmophiles Micro-organisms that can flourish at high *osmolarity, e.g. in jams, honey, brine pickles; especially *yeasts (also called xerophilic yeasts).

osmosis The passage of water through a semi-permeable membrane (*see* MEMBRANE, SEMI-PERMEABLE), from a region of low concentration of solutes to one of higher concentration. *See also* OSMOTIC PRESSURE.

osmosis, reverse The passage of water from a more concentrated to a less concentrated solution through a semi-permeable membrane by the application of hydrostatic pressure to overcome the *osmotic pressure. Used for desalination of sea water, concentration of fruit juices, and processing of *whey. The membranes commonly used are cellulose acetate or polyamide of very small pore size, 10^{-4}-10^{-3} μm.

osmotic pressure The pressure required to prevent the passage of water through a semi-permeable membrane (*see* MEMBRANE, SEMI-PERMEABLE) from a region of low concentration of solutes to one of higher concentration, by *osmosis.

ossein The organic matrix of the bone left when the mineral salts have been dissolved in dilute acid. Mainly *collagen and hydrolysed by boiling in water to *gelatine.

osseomucoid Mucoid substance forming part of the structure of bone.

osso bucco Italian; veal stew.

osteoblasts Cells that synthesize new *bone; they become embedded in the organic matrix they have synthesized and mature into osteocytes.

osteocalcin A calcium-binding protein in *bone, essential for the normal mineralization of bone. Its synthesis requires *vitamin K, and is controlled by *vitamin D.

osteoclasts Cells that break down *bone tissue, for replacement by the activity of *osteoblasts. Osteoclast activity is stimulated by *vitamin D in response to hypocalcaemia.

osteocytes *See* OSTEOBLASTS.

osteolathyrism *See* LATHYRISM.

osteomalacia The adult equivalent of *rickets; a *bone disorder due to deficiency of *vitamin D, which leads to inadequate absorption of calcium and loss of calcium from the bones.

osteopenia *Bone mineral density lower than normal, but not so low as to be considered to be *osteoporosis.

osteoporosis Degeneration of the bones with advancing age due to loss of bone mineral and protein as a result of decreased secretion of *hormones (oestrogens in women and testosterone in men). A high calcium intake in early life may be beneficial, since this results in greater bone density at maturity, so that clinically significant loss is delayed.

oud(e) Dutch; old or matured. The term applies to cheese, *gin (oude jenever), beer, etc.

ouzo Greek; herb liqueur flavoured with *anise. Turkish equivalent is raki; Arabic arak.

ovalbumin The albumin of egg-white; comprises 55% of the total solids. A phosphoglycoprotein, containing 3.5% carbohydrate. It contains four free sulphydryl groups and two disulphide bridges; during storage sulphydryl groups are oxidized to disulphide bridges, forming 'S-ovalbumin', which comprises 5% of the total at the time of laying, and up to 80% after storage for six months.

oven, Dutch A semicircular metal shield which may be placed close to an open fire; fitted with shelves on which food is roasted. It may also be clamped to the fire bars.

oven spring The sudden increases in the volume of a dough during the first 10–12 minutes of baking, due to increased rate of fermentation and expansion of gases.

overrun In ice cream manufacture, the percentage increase in the volume of the mix caused by the beating-in of air. Optimum overrun, 70–100%. To prevent excessive aeration US regulations state that ice cream must weigh 4.5 lb per gallon (0.48 kg/L).

overweight Excessive accumulation of body fat, but not so great as to be classified as *obesity.

ovo-lacto-vegetarians *See* VEGETARIANS.

ovomucin A carbohydrate–protein complex in egg-white, responsible for its firmness. Comprises 1–3% of the total solids.

ovomucoid A protein of egg-white, 12% of the total solids. It inhibits the digestive *enzyme *trypsin, but is hydrolysed and so inactivated by *pepsin in the stomach.

ovotransferrin *See* CONALBUMIN.

oxalates Salts of *oxalic acid.

oxalic acid A dicarboxylic acid, COOH—COOH. Poisonous in large amounts; present especially in spinach, chocolate, rhubarb, and nuts. The toxicity of rhubarb leaves is due to their high content of oxalic acid.

High concentrations of oxalates in the urine can form kidney stones; while most of these oxalates are of endogenous metabolic origin, patients with *hyperoxaluria are advised to avoid dietary sources of oxalates.

oxaloacetate A metabolic intermediate in the *citric acid cycle, and an important substrate for *gluconeogenesis; the keto acid of *aspartic acid.

Oxfam Non-governmental organization concerned with famine relief and improvement of food resources in less developed countries. Originally founded by Gilbert Murray in 1942 as the Oxford Committee for Famine Relief.

((())) SEE WEB LINKS

• Oxfam's homepage.

oxidases (oxygenases) *Enzymes that oxidize compounds by removing hydrogen and reacting directly with oxygen to form water or hydrogen peroxide. They thus differ from dehydrogenases, which transfer the hydrogen to a *coenzyme. *See also* PHENOL OXIDASES.

oxidation The chemical process of removing electrons from an element or compound (e.g. the oxidation of iron compounds from ferrous, Fe^{2+}, to ferric, Fe^{3+}); frequently together with the removal of hydrogen ions (H^+). The reverse process, the addition of electrons or hydrogen, is reduction.

In biological oxidation and reduction reactions, *cytochromes act to transfer electrons, while *coenzymes derived from the vitamins *niacin and *vitamin B_2 are intermediate hydrogen acceptors, transferring both electrons and H^+ ions.

oxtail Classed as *offal; a 150-g portion of stewed lean meat is a rich *source of iron, vitamin B_2, protein, and niacin; contains 20 g of fat; and supplies 360 kcal (1500 kJ).

oxycalorimeter Instrument for measuring the oxygen consumed and carbon dioxide produced when a food is burned, as distinct from the *calorimeter, which measures the heat produced.

oxygenases *See* OXIDASES.

oxyhaemoglobin *Haemoglobin with oxygen bound; the form in which oxygen is transported in the blood.

oxymel Medicinal syrup or beverage made from honey and vinegar.

oxymyoglobin Myoglobin is the oxygen-binding protein in muscle; it takes up oxygen to form oxymyoglobin, which is bright red, while myoglobin itself is purplish-red. The surface of fresh meat that is exposed to oxygen is bright red from the oxymyoglobin, while the interior of the meat is darker in colour where the myoglobin is not oxygenated.

oxyntic cells Or parietal cells; cells in the stomach mucosa that produce and secrete hydrochloric acid and *intrinsic factor.

oxyntomodulin Peptide *hormone released post-prandially from cells of the gastro-intestinal mucosa in proportion to energy intake. It is derived from *proglucagon, and inhibits food intake. Circulating concentrations are increased in *anorexia.

oxytetracycline *See* TETRACYCLINE.

oyster Marine bivalve *mollusc, *Ostreidae* and *Crassostrea* spp. Portuguese oyster is *C. angulata*, Pacific or rock oyster is *C. gigas*, native oyster is *O. edulis*. One dozen oysters (120 g of the edible portion) are an exceptionally rich *source of vitamin B_{12}; a rich source of iron, iodine, selenium, and vitamin D; a good source of protein and niacin; a source of vitamins A, B_1, and B_2; and supply 85 kcal (360 kJ).

oyster crabs American; small young crabs found inside oysters, cooked and eaten whole, including the soft shell.

oyster nut Seeds of the perennial African gourd vines *Telfairia pedata* and *T. occidentalis*.

oyster plant (vegetable oyster) *See* SALSIFY.

ozone Composed of three atoms of oxygen, O_3. A powerful germicide, used to sterilize water and in antiseptic ice for preserving fish.

P.4000 A class of synthetic *sweeteners, nitro-amino alkoxybenzenes. One member of the group, propoxy-amino nitrobenzene, also known as Aros, is 4100 times as sweet as saccharin, but these compounds are not considered harmless and are not permitted in foods.

paak South-East Asian; salty fish paste made by fermenting fish or shrimps with rice.

PABA *See* PARA-AMINO BENZOIC ACID.

pabda A *catfish, *Ompok pabda*.

pacificarins Compounds present in foods that resist micro-organisms; they may be of microbial origin or synthesized by the plant itself. Also known as phytoncides.

packaging, active Packaging that changes the condition of the packed food to extend its shelf life or improve safety or sensory properties, while maintaining quality. May include oxygen scavengers, desiccants, antimicrobial compounds, etc.

packaging, green Use of biodegradable materials to replace conventional plastics in food packaging. *See also* PET; STARCH, THERMOPLASTIC.

packaging, intelligent Packaging system that monitors the condition of packaged foods to give information about its quality during transport and storage. May include a variety of chemical, enzymic, or immunological sensors to detect temperature, oxygen, products of spoilage, and specific micro-organisms.

packaging, modified atmosphere Storage of fruits, vegetables, and prepacked red meat in a controlled atmosphere in which a proportion of the oxygen is replaced by carbon dioxide, sometimes with the addition of other gases such as argon and nitrous oxide. For some products a high oxygen atmosphere is used, to reduce enzymic *browning and anaerobic spoilage. The product may be sealed in a selectively permeable polymer and allowed to undergo metabolism until the desired gas composition has been achieved (the passive process); in the active process the package is evacuated, then flushed with the desired gas mixture before sealing.

pacu Brazilian freshwater fish *Piaractus mesopotamicu,* and also *Colossoma* spp., *Acnodon* spp., and *Ossubtus* spp., commonly produced by aquaculture.

paddlefish North American freshwater fish *Polyodon spathula*; the roe is used as a *caviar substitute.

paddy *Rice in the husk after threshing; also known as rough rice.

paella Spanish (Valencian) rice dish, seasoned with saffron, containing seafood and chicken.

PAHs polycyclic aromatic hydrocarbons.

pain perdu *See* FRENCH TOAST.

pair feeding Restricting the intake of a group of control animals to match that of those receiving an experimental diet, so as to eliminate differences due to total amount of food consumed.

pak choy Chinese cabbage or Chinese leaves, *Brassica chinensis*.

pakora Indian; vegetables, shrimps, etc., deep fried in batter made from chickpea flour.

PAL *See* PHYSICAL ACTIVITY LEVEL.

palak *See* SPINACH.

palatinose A *disaccharide of glucose and fructose linked α-1,6 (*sucrose is linked α-1,2).

palatone *See* MALTOL.

Palestine bee *See* BEE WINE.

Palestine soup English, 19th century; made from Jerusalem *artichokes and named in the mistaken belief that the artichokes came from Jerusalem.

palmarosa The east Indian geranium, *Cymbopogon martini*; the essential oil (*see* OILS, ESSENTIAL) is used as a flavouring, and the leaves are used as a herb.

palm, heart of *See* PEJIBAYE.

palmier Cake made from puff *pastry sandwiched with cream or jam. Also small sweet biscuits made from puff pastry.

palmitic acid A saturated *fatty acid (C16:0); occurs in many fats and oils.

palmitoleic acid A mono-unsaturated fatty acid (C16:1 ω9); occurs in many fats and oils.

palm kernel oil One of the major oils of commerce, widely used in cooking fats and margarines; oil extracted from the kernel of the nut of the oil palm,

Elaeis guineensis, pale in colour in contrast with 'red' *palm oil from the outer part of the nut; about 80% saturated and 15% mono-unsaturated.

palm oil From outer fibrous pulp of the fruit of the oil palm, *Elaeis guineensis*. Coloured red because of very high content of α-carotene (30 mg per 100 g) and β-carotene (30 mg, together with about 60 mg vitamin E), but these are usually removed to produce a pale oil; 45% *saturated and 40% mono-unsaturated, 10% polyunsaturated.

palm stew West African; prepared by stewing the entire head of nuts of the oil palm *Elaeis guineensis*, and skimming off the oil as it separates. Although most of the oil is removed, the final dish has a deep red colour because of the high content of carotenes of *palm oil.

palm, wild date *Phoenix sylvestris*, a relative of the true date palm, *P. dactylifera*; grown in India as a source of sugar, obtained from the sap.

palm wine Fermented sap from various palm trees, especially date and coconut palms.

palomino A *grape variety widely used for *wine making, not one of the classic varieties.

palynology The study of pollens and spores. *See also* MELISSOPALYNOLOGY.

pan *See* BETEL.

panada Mixture of fat, flour, and liquid (stock or milk) mixed to a thick paste; used to bind mixtures such as chopped meat, and also as the basis of soufflés and choux *pastry.

panage French; to coat food with breadcrumbs before frying or grilling. Food so treated is *pané*.

pan broil American; to cook food in a pan on top of the stove, dry and with only enough oil to prevent it sticking.

pancake Batter fried on a lightly greased griddle. Served plain (with lemon and sugar) or filled with sweet or savoury mixture.

pancake rolls *See* SPRING ROLLS.

pancetta Italian; spiced pickled *bacon, rolled in the form of a long sausage.

panch phoron Bengali five-spice: *fennel, black *mustard, *cumin, nigella seeds (*see* KALONJI), and *fenugreek.

pancreas A gland in the abdomen with two functions: the endocrine pancreas (the islets of Langerhans) secretes the *hormones *insulin, *amylin, *glucagon, *somatostatin, *gastrin, and *pancreatic polypeptide; the exocrine pancreas secretes the *pancreatic juice. Known by the butcher as sweetbread or gut sweetbread, as distinct from chest sweetbread which is thymus.

pancreatic juice The alkaline digestive juice produced by the *pancreas and secreted into the duodenum. It contains the inactive precursors of a number of *protein digestive enzymes. Trypsinogen is activated to trypsin by *enteropeptidase in the intestinal lumen; in turn, trypsin activates the other enzyme precursors: chymotrypsinogen to chymotrypsin, pro-elastase to elastase, procarboxypeptidase to carboxypeptidase. Also contains *lipase, *amylase, and nucleases.

pancreatic polypeptide (PP) A *hormone released from the *pancreas in response to food ingestion; it remains elevated for several hours after a meal, and intravenous infusion reduces food intake, suggesting it may be a satiety hormone.

pancreatin Preparation made from the pancreas of animals containing the enzymes of *pancreatic juice. Used to replace pancreatic enzymes in *cystic fibrosis as an aid to digestion.

pandan The leaves of the palm-like tree *Pandanus amaryllifolius*, used in Thai, Malasian, and Indonesian cuisine; rice is often steamed in baskets of pandan leaves.

pandemain (payndemaine) Medieval English; fine white bread made from sifted flour.

pandemic An *epidemic that affects people in many different countries, or even worldwide.

pan dowdy American; baked apple sponge pudding, served with the apple side up.

paneer (panir) Indian, Middle Eastern; soft mild-flavoured cheese made by acid coagulation of heated buffalo milk. Milk is left to ferment for 6–12 hours, then heated to separate the curd.

panettone Italian, originally Milanese; a cake made from yeast-leavened dough with candied peel and sultanas; there is a long proving time to give a light fluffy texture. Traditionally eaten at Christmas.

panga (pangasius) Freshwater fish, *Pangasius* spp., also called panga *catfish.

pangamic acid The N-di-isopropyl derivative of glucuronic acid. Claimed to be an *antioxidant, and to speed recovery from fatigue. Sometimes called vitamin B_{15}, but there is no evidence that it is a dietary essential, nor that it has any metabolic function.

panir *See* PANEER.

panne French; the fat surrounding the pig's kidneys. *See* LARD.

pannfisch German; large fried fishcake.

panocha Candy made from brown sugar, milk, butter, and nuts.

panoufle French; the underpart of the top of a sirloin of beef.

panperdy (pain perdu) *See* FRENCH TOAST.

panthenol The alcohol form of *pantothenic acid; biologically active.

pantothenic acid A vitamin of the B complex with no numerical designation. The β-alanine derivative of pantoic acid. Required for the synthesis of *coenzyme A (and hence essential for the metabolism of fats, carbohydrates, and amino acids) and of acyl carrier protein (and hence essential for the synthesis of fatty acids).

Dietary deficiency is unknown; it is widely distributed in all living cells, the best sources being liver, kidney, yeast, and fresh vegetables. Human requirements are not known with any certainty; the US/Canadian *adequate intake is 5 mg/day.

Experimental deficiency signs in rats include greying of the hair (hence at one time known as the anti-grey-hair factor; there is no evidence that it affects greying of human hair with age). Experimental deficiency in human beings leads to fatigue, headache, muscle weakness, and gastro-intestinal disturbances. *See also* BURNING FOOT SYNDROME.

pao-tzu Chinese; steamed buns.

papain *Proteolytic *enzyme from the juice of the *papaya (*Carica papaya*) used in tenderizing meat; sometimes called vegetable pepsin. The enzyme is obtained as the dried latex on the skin of the fruit by scratching it while still on the tree, and collecting the flow. In the tropics meat is traditionally tenderized by wrapping in papaya leaves.

The rate of reaction is slow at room temperature, increasing to maximum activity at 80°C and rapidly inactivated at higher temperatures, so it continues to act during the early stages of cooking.

papa seca *See* CHUÑO.

papaw Purple fruit of *Asiminia triloba*, related to the *custard apple; distinct from the pawpaw or *papaya.

papaya (pawpaw) Large green or yellow melon-like fruit of the tropical tree *Carica papaya*, widely grown in all tropical regions. Fruit of the formosa variety weigh as much as 1.5–3 kg. The proteolytic enzyme, *papain, is derived from the fruit. A 150-g portion is a rich *source of vitamin C; a good source of vitamin A (as carotene); supplies 55 kcal (230 kJ). *See also* BABACO.

papillote, en Made or served in a paper case.

papoutsakia Greek; stuffed aubergines (literally 'little shoes').

paprika *See* PEPPER.

PAR *See* PHYSICAL ACTIVITY RATIO.

para-amino benzoic acid (PABA) Essential growth factor for micro-organisms. It forms part of the molecule of *folic acid and is therefore required for the synthesis of this vitamin. Mammals cannot synthesize folic acid, and PABA has no other known function; there is no evidence that it is a human dietary requirement.

Sulphanilamides (sulpha drugs) are chemical analogues of PABA, and have antibacterial action because they antagonize utilization of PABA.

parabens Methyl, ethyl, and propyl esters of *p*-hydroxybenzoic acid used together with their sodium salts as antimicrobial agents in food. Effective over a wide range of *pH; more effective against moulds and yeast than against bacteria.

paracrine A compound secreted by a cell that acts on nearby cells, sometimes called local hormones. *See also* AUTOCRINE; ENDOCRINE GLANDS; HORMONE; JUXTACRINE.

paradise nut *See* BRAZIL NUT.

paraffin, medicinal (liquid paraffin) A mineral oil of no nutritional value since it passes through the intestine unchanged. Used as a mild *laxative because of its lubricant properties.

parageusia Abnormality of the sense of *taste.

paragonimiasis Infection with the *trematode *Paragonimus westermani* acquired from infected shellfish, leading mainly to lung lesions, but sometimes also to brain lesions.

parakeratosis Disease of swine characterized by cessation of growth, erythema, seborrhoea, and hyperkeratosis of the skin; due to *zinc deficiency and possibly to changes in essential *fatty acid metabolism.

paralactic acid *See* SARCOLACTIC ACID.

paralytic shellfish poisoning *See* SHELLFISH POISONING.

paratha Indian; wholewheat unleavened bread. The dough is rolled and brushed repeatedly with melted butter before cooking on a buttered griddle. Frequently stuffed with spiced potato or other vegetables.

parathormone Commonly used as an abbreviation for the *parathyroid *hormone; correctly a trade name for a pharmaceutical preparation of the hormone.

parathyroid hormone The hormone secreted by the parathyroid glands; four glands situated in the neck near to the thyroid gland. The hormone is secreted in response to a fall in plasma *calcium, and acts on the kidney to increase the formation of the active metabolite of *vitamin D (calcitriol), leading to an increase in plasma calcium by increasing intestinal absorption and mobilizing the mineral from bones. It also reduces urinary excretion of phosphate.

parboil Partially cook. Parboiling of brown rice, i.e. steaming it in the husk before milling, leads to water-soluble vitamins diffusing from the husk into the grain; when the rice is polished, it contains more of these vitamins than polished raw rice.

parch To brown in dry heat.

parcha Indian; foods cooked en papillote; wrapped in parchment or banana leaf.

parchita *See* PASSION FRUIT.

pare To peel or trim.

parenteral nutrition *See* NUTRITION, PARENTERAL.

pareve (parve) Jewish term for dishes containing neither milk nor meat. Orthodox Jewish law prohibits mixing of milk and meat foods or the consumption of milk products for 3 hours after a meat meal. *See also* MILCHIG; FLEISHIG.

parevine USA; a frozen dessert resembling ice cream, but containing no dairy or meat products (such as gelatine), to conform with Jewish dietary laws. *See also* PAREVE.

parfait Frozen dessert, similar to a *mousse but lighter. American parfait is ice cream and whipped cream served in a tall narrow glass (a parfait glass).

parietal cells *See* OXYNTIC CELLS.

parillin Highly toxic glycoside from *sarsaparilla root; consists of glucose, rhamnose, and parigenin. Also known as smilacin.

parkin English (Yorkshire); oatmeal, ginger, and treacle cake.

parlies Scottish; ginger cakes, believed to be so named because they were eaten by members of the Scottish parliament.

parmentier French; made or served with potatoes, named after Antoine-Auguste Parmentier (1737–1813), who popularized the potato in France. Pommes parmentier are diced and fried; parmentier soup is a leek and potato soup.

parmesan English (and French) name for the hard Italian cheese parmigiano reggiano (protected designation of origin). Made from semi-skimmed cow's milk cooked with rennet, and dried for six months. When at least 2 years old it is called vecchio; stravecchio is 3 years old; stravecchione, 4 years old. It is hard and usually served on dishes grated; it cooks without becoming sticky. A 25-g portion is a rich *source of calcium; a good source of protein; a source of vitamin A and niacin; contains 8g of fat and 250mg of sodium; and supplies 110kcal (460kJ).

parmigiana Made or served with *parmesan cheese.

PARNUTS EU term for foods prepared for particular nutritional purposes (intended for people with disturbed metabolism, or in special physiological conditions, or for young children). Also called dietetic foods.

parosmia Any disorder of the sense of smell.

parrotfish Marine fish, species of the family *Scaridae*.

parsipan (persipan) Similar to *marzipan, made using apricot kernels rather than almonds.

parsley Leaves of the herb *Petroselinum crispum, P. hertense*, or *P. sativum*. Since it is largely used as a garnish and for flavouring, the nutrients per serving are negligible. Chinese parsley is *coriander.

parsley, Hamburg Root of *Petroselinum crispum* var. *tuberosum*, grown for its root (also called turnip-rooted parsley); similar in appearance to *parsnip. A 100-g portion is a rich source of vitamin C and supplies 40kcal (170kJ).

parsnip Root of the biennial herb *Pastinaca sativa*, eaten as a vegetable. A 100-g portion, boiled, is a good *source of folate; a source of vitamin C; contains 5g of dietary fibre; supplies 70kcal (290kJ). Peruvian parsnip is *arracache.

parson's nose The small fatty joint holding the tail feathers of poultry. Also known as pope's nose.

parthenocarpic Plants that are able to develop fruits without fertilization, so that the fruit is seedless.

partridge *Game bird, *Perdix perdix* and related spp. The chukar partridge is *Alectoris chukar*; mainly a game bird, but also farmed. A 150-g portion is a rich *source of protein and iron; contains 10g of fat of which one-third is saturated; and supplies 200kcal (840kJ).

parts per million (ppm) Method of describing small concentrations which means exactly what the term says; mg per kg is also ppm. Usually used with regard to traces of contaminants and food additives.

paselli *Maltodextrin from corn, potatoes, wheat, or tapioca. Used as a *fat replacer and bulking agent in foods.

pasendah *See* PURSINDAH.

paskha (paska) Russian; dessert of curd cheese with cream, almonds, and dried fruit; an Easter speciality.

passion fruit Fruit of the tropical American vine, *Passiflora* spp; purple passion fruit is *Passiflora edulis*, yellow is *P. flavicarpa*, and banana passion fruit or curuba is *P. mollisima*. A 100-g portion (four fruits, 60g of edible flesh and pips) is a good *source of vitamin C; supplies 20 kcal (85 kJ). Also known as parchita, granadilla, and water lemon.

Passover The Jewish festival celebrating the Exodus from slavery in Egypt. There was no time to allow bread dough to rise, and unleavened bread was eaten. In commemoration, Jews abstain from leavened bread for the week of Passover, eating *matzo instead, and using matzo meal or potato flour for baking. Foods certified free from leavened bread are known as 'kosher for Passover'. *See also* KOSHER.

pasta Dried dough, traditionally made with hard wheat (semolina) but soft wheat may be added, sometimes with egg and milk. Spinach, tomato, or squid ink may be added to the dough to give a green, red, or black colour. The dough is partly dried in hot air, then more slowly. Sold both completely dry, when it can be stored for a long period, or 'fresh', i.e. less dried and keeping for a week or so only. A 230-g portion (boiled) is a good *source of copper; a source of protein; contains 4.6g of dietary fibre and 0.7g of fat of which 33% is saturated; supplies 280 kcal (1180 kJ).

It is made in numerous shapes: spaghetti is a solid rod about 2mm in diameter; vermicelli is about one-third this thickness; ravioli (envelopes stuffed with meat or cheese), tagliatelle, fettucine, and linguini (ribbons); and a range of twists, spirals, and other shapes. Macaroni is tubular shaped, about 5mm in diameter; at 10mm it is known as zitoni, and at 15mm fovantini or maccaroncelli. Cannelloni are tubes 1.5–2 cm wide and 10 cm long, stuffed with meat; penne are nib-shaped. Lasagne is sheets of pasta.

pasterma Middle Eastern; spiced dry cured beef or camel meat. Also known as pastirma, bastirma, basterma, or basturma.

pasteurization A means of prolonging the storage time of foods for a limited time, by killing the vegetative forms of many pathogenic organisms. This is achieved by mild heat treatment, whereas destruction of all bacteria and spores (sterilization) requires higher temperatures for longer periods, often spoiling the product in the process.

Pasteurization of milk destroys all pathogens, and although it will sour within a day or two, this is not a source of disease. It is achieved either by heating to 63–66°C for 30 minutes (holder method), followed by immediate cooling, or (the high-temperature short-time process) heating to 71°C for 15 seconds. *See also* ULTRA-PASTEURIZATION.

pasteurization, flash The product is held at a higher temperature, but for a shorter time, than in conventional *pasteurization, so that there is less development of a cooked flavour.

pasteurization, HTST High-temperature, short-time *pasteurization, ranging from a few seconds to about one minute; at higher temperatures bacteria are destroyed more rapidly than damage occurs to nutrients and texture.

pasteurization, LTLT Low-temperature, long-time batch *pasteurization (the holder method at 63°C, for 30 minutes) before cooling and bottling.

pasteurizer Equipment used to pasteurize liquids such as milk, fruit juices, etc. The material is passed continuously over heated plates, or through pipes, where it is heated to the required temperature, maintained for the required time, then immediately cooled. *See also* PASTEURIZATION.

pastillage Paste used to make edible decorations on cakes, made from icing sugar with gum tragacanth or gelatine and cornflour.

pastille Round, flat sweet, often coated with sugar, sometimes medicated.

pastis French; spirit prepared by distilling anise and liquorice, as opposed to *anise, which is prepared by steeping the herbs in spirit.

pastourma Greek and Turkish; black-rinded smoked bacon, highly flavoured with garlic; generally fried until crisp.

pastrami Middle-European (especially Romanian-Jewish); smoked and seasoned beef, also made from turkey. Known in Canada as smoked beef.

pastry Baked dough of flour, fat, and water. There are six basic types: shortcrust, in which the fat is rubbed into the flour; suet crust, in which chopped suet is mixed with the flour; puff and flaky, in which the fat is rolled into the dough; hotwater crust and choux, in which the fat is melted in hot water before being added to the flour.

Suet pastry is raised using baking powder or self-raising flour; puff, flaky, and choux pastry are raised by the steam trapped between layers of dough.

pastry, choux (chou) Light, airy pastry, invented by the French chef Marie-Antoine Carême (1784–1833), used in *éclairs and *profiteroles. The pastry, made with eggs, is whisked to a paste, then precooked in a saucepan before baking. The name comes from the French for cabbage, *chou*, because of the characteristic shape of the cream-filled puffs.

pastry, Danish Rich, sweet, yeast pastry confection filled with fruit or nuts. Originally Viennese, not Danish; indeed known in Danish as *Wienerbrod*.

pastry, phyllo (filo pastry) Plain paper-thin pastry made from flour and water only, rolled into small balls then tossed in the air and stretched until it forms an extremely thin sheet. Multiple layers are used as the basis for Greek and Middle Eastern pastry dishes (e.g. *baklava). Known as mortoban in South-East Asia.

pasty Individual dish enclosed in pastry, folded over, and baked on a flat tray.

patabaim Freshwater fish, *Macrognathus aculeatus*.

patatas bravas Spanish; fried slices of potato eaten with a garlic *mayonnaise.

pâte French for paste; used for pastry, dough, or batter; also for *pasta.

pâté Literally, French for a savoury pie, now used almost exclusively to mean a savoury paste of liver, meat, fish, or vegetables.

pâté, Strasbourg Gourmet pâté de fois gras, prepared from the livers of geese which have been force-fed to achieve a very high fat content.

pathogens Disease-causing bacteria, as distinct from those that are harmless.

pâtisserie French; ornate small cakes and pastries.

patsa Greek tripe soup.

patty Small savoury pie, normally made with shortcrust pastry; also (in the USA) small cakes of minced meat or poultry, like croquettes but not dipped in breadcrumbs before cooking.

patulin *Mycotoxin produced by *Penicillium*, *Aspergillus*, and *Byssochlamys* spp. In foods the most important is *Penicillium expansum*, which causes soft rot of apples and a number of other fruits. A problem especially with apple juice.

patum peperium *See* RELISH.

paua *See* ABALONE.

paunching To remove the entrails of rabbits, hares, etc.

paupiette Small, thinly cut piece of meat wrapped round a filling of forcemeat and braised.

pavé French; sweet or savoury cold dish made in a square or rectangular mould. Pavé de bœuf is a thick slice of beef fillet.

pavlova Australian; meringue cake topped with fruit and whipped cream; created in honour of the Russian ballerina Anna Pavlova on her visit to Australia in the 1920s.

pawpaw *See* PAPAYA.

paysanne, à la Peasant or simple country style. Meat or poultry, usually braised and accompanied by a garnish of mixed vegetables, bacon, etc.

payusnaya Russian, Eastern European; coarse, pressed *caviar including skins of ovaries.

PBI Protein-bound iodine; *see* IODINE, PROTEIN BOUND.

PBM Peak bone mass.

PCM *See* PROTEIN-ENERGY MALNUTRITION.

PCR *See* POLYMERASE CHAIN REACTION.

PDCAAS Protein digestibility corrected amino acid score; a measure of *protein quality based on amino acid score, corrected for the digestibility of the protein.

pea, asparagus Edible pods of the southern European plant *Lotus tetragonolobus*, harvested before maturity.

peach Fruit of the tree *Prunus persica*. A 120-g serving is a rich *source of vitamin C; provides 2.5g of dietary fibre; and supplies 36kcal (150kJ).

pea, chickling *Lathyris sativus*, also known as chickling vetch or grass pea; *see* LATHYRISM.

peanut Fruit of *Arachis hypogaea*, also known as groundnut, earth-nut, arachis nut, monkey nut, and, in southern USA, goober pea (derived from the Swahili *nguba*); originally a native of South America, it was introduced into the USA by slaves from East Africa. The French peanut is the Malabar chestnut (*see* CHESTNUT, MALABAR). A 60-g portion (sixty nuts) is a rich *source of protein, niacin, and vitamins E and B_1; a good source of copper and zinc; and a source of protein, vitamin B_6, folate, and iron. When dry-roasted or roasted and salted some of the vitamin B_1 is damaged and the nuts are only a source of this vitamin; dry-roasted peanuts usually contain about 500mg of sodium per 60-g portion, and roast and salted about 250mg. All three types contain 30g of fat per portion of which 20% is *saturated and 50% mono-unsaturated; and supply 350kcal (1470kJ).

peanut butter Ground, roasted peanuts, first marketed in 1904; commonly prepared from a mixture of Spanish and Virginia peanuts, since the first alone are too oily and the second are too dry. Separation of the oil is prevented by partial *hydrogenation of the oil and the addition of *emulsifiers. A 20-g portion (as thickly spread on one slice of bread) is a *source of protein, copper, and niacin; contains 1.5g of dietary fibre and 11g of fat, of which 20% is saturated; supplies 120kcal (500kJ).

peanut oil Oil extracted from the *peanut, *Arachis hypogaea*: 20% *saturated, 50% mono-unsaturated (*oleic acid), 30% polyunsaturated (*linoleic acid), less than 1% linolenic acid. Also known as groundnut oil or arachis oil.

pea, pigeon Tropical *legume, *Cajanus cajan*, also known as red gram.

pear Fruit of many species of *Pyrus*; cultivated varieties all descended from *P. communis*; the British *National Fruit Collection has 469 varieties of dessert and cooking pears, and a further 20 varieties of *perry pears. A 200-g portion (an average fruit) is a *source of vitamins B_6 and C and copper; contains 4–5g of dietary fibre; supplies 80kcal (340kJ). *See also* POIRE WILLIAMS.

pear, alligator *See* AVOCADO.

pear, Asian (nashi) Fruit of *Pyrus pyrifolia* (syn. *P. serotina*), more apple shaped than the European pear, with a crisp texture.

pear, balsam *See* GOURD, BITTER.

pearling The removal of indigestible hulls, aleurone, and germ layers from cereals by abrasion. Also known as attrition milling and abrasive debranning.

pear, prickly *See* PRICKLY PEAR.

pease pudding English; a dish prepared from dried peas that are soaked, boiled, mashed, and sieved, traditionally served with baked ham.

peas, garden (green peas) Seeds of the *legume *Pisum sativum*. Widely available frozen, dried, and canned. A 75-g portion, boiled, is a rich source of vitamin B_1; a good source of vitamin C; a source of protein, niacin, and folate; contains 3g of dietary fibre; supplies 60kcal (250kJ). *See also* MANGE-TOUT.

peas, mushy Northern English; a dish prepared from processed peas (*see* PEAS, PROCESSED), boiled and sometimes mashed to give a smooth texture. A 100-g portion is a *source of protein; supplies 80kcal (340kJ).

peas, processed Garden peas *see* PEAS, GARDEN) that have matured on the plant and are then canned. A 75-g portion is a *source of protein; contains 3.5g of dietary fibre; supplies 75kcal (320kJ).

pecan nuts From the American tree *Carya illinoinensis*, a species of hickory nut. A 60-g portion (ten nuts) is a rich *source of selenium, vitamin E, and niacin; a good source of vitamin B_1 and zinc; a source of protein and iron; contains 40g of fat, of which 10% is *saturated and 60% mono-unsaturated; supplies 400kcal (1700kJ).

pecorino Italian; hard sheep's milk cheese with a grainy texture.

pectase An *enzyme in the pith (albedo) of *citrus fruits which removes the methoxyl groups from *pectin to form water-insoluble pectic acid. The intermediate compounds, with varying numbers of methoxyl groups, are pectinic acids. Also known as pectin esterase, pectin methyl esterase, and pectin methoxylase; distinct from *pectinase.

pectic acid Demethylated *pectin.

pectin Plant tissues contain hemicelluloses (polymers of galacturonic acid) known as protopectins, which cement the cell walls together. As fruit ripens, there is maximum protopectin present; thereafter it breaks down to pectin, pectinic acid, and, finally, pectic acid, and the fruit softens as the adhesive between the cells breaks down.

Pectin is the setting agent in *jam; it forms a gel with sugar under acid conditions. Soft fruits, such as strawberry, raspberry, and cherry, are low in pectin; plums, apples, and oranges are rich. Apple pulp and orange pith are the commercial sources of pectin. Added to jams, confectionery, chocolate, and ice cream as an emulsifier and stabilizer instead of *agar; used in making jellies, and as an anti-staling agent in cakes. Included in *non-starch polysaccharides.

pectin, amidated The low-methoxyl pectin formed when pectin is demethylated using ammonia (as opposed to use of *pectase), forming amides to replace the methoxyl groups.

pectinase An enzyme present in the pith (albedo) of citrus fruits, which hydrolyses *pectin or pectic acids into smaller polygalacturonic acids, and finally galacturonic acid and its methyl ester. Used to clarify fruit juices. Also known as pectolase, pectozyme, and polygalacturonase. Distinct from *pectase.

pectinic acid Partially demethylated *pectin; *see* PECTIN, LOW METHOXYL.

pectin, low methoxyl Partially demethylated *pectin which can form a gel with little or no sugar and is therefore used in low-calorie *jam, etc. *See also* PECTASE; PECTIN, AMIDATED.

pectolase (pectozyme) *See* PECTINASE.

pectosase (pectosinase) *See* PROTOPECTINASE.

***Pediococcus* spp.** *Homofermentative *lactic acid bacteria. *P. pentosaceus* and *P. acidilactici* are used as *starter cultures for fermented sausages, vegetables, and soy milk, as well as for inoculation of silage. *P. pentosaceus* produces *bacteriocins.

pejibaye The Amazonian peach palm, *Bactris gasipaes* (syn. *B. speciosa*, *Guilielma gasipaes*, *G. speciosa*, *G. utilis*); bears clusters of 50–100 ovoid fruits, each 2.5–5 cm long. The fruit is caustic when raw, is usually boiled for several hours before sale, and is used mainly as a source of flour for baking. Mainly cultivated for the stem tips, which are eaten as a vegetable (heart of palm).

pekmez Turkish; thick jelly made by evaporating grape juice, the basis of *Turkish delight and other sugar confectionery. Also the general Balkan name for jam.

pekoe See TEA.

pelagic Fish that swim near the surface, compared with demersal fish, which live on the sea bottom. Pelagic fish are mostly of the oily type such as herring, mackerel, and pilchard, containing up to 20% oil.

pellagra The disease due to deficiency of the *vitamin *niacin and the *amino acid *tryptophan. Signs include a characteristic symmetrical photosensitive dermatitis (especially on the face and back of the hands), resembling severe sunburn; mental disturbances (a depressive psychosis sometimes called dementia); and digestive disorders (most commonly diarrhoea); fatal if untreated.

Most commonly associated with a diet based on *maize or *sorghum, which are poor sources of both tryptophan and niacin, with little meat or other vegetables.

PEM See PROTEIN-ENERGY MALNUTRITION.

pemmican Mixture of dried, powdered meat and fat, with berries, used as a concentrated food source by native Americans (the name derives from the Cree for grease). First reported use on an expedition was by Scottish fur trader Alexander Mackenzie when he crossed North America in 1793.

Penicillium A genus of *moulds; apart from the production of the antibiotic penicillin, several species are valuable in the ripening of *cheeses.

pentane breath test See BREATH TEST, ETHANE AND PENTANE.

pentosans *Polysaccharides of five-carbon sugars (*pentoses). Widely distributed in plants, e.g. fruit, wood, corncobs, oat hulls. Not digested, and hence a component of *non-starch polysaccharides and *dietary fibre.

pentose phosphate pathway See GLUCOSE METABOLISM.

pentoses *Monosaccharide *sugars with five carbon atoms. The most important is ribose.

pentosuria The excretion of *pentose sugars in the urine. Idiopathic pentosuria is an inherited metabolic disorder almost wholly restricted to Ashkenazi (north European) Jews, which has no adverse effects. Consumption of fruits rich in pentoses (e.g. pears) can also lead to (temporary) pentosuria.

penuche Candy made from brown sugar and beaten until it is smooth and creamy.

pepino Fruit of the South American shrub *Solanum muricatum*. Also known as melon pear.

pepper **1.** Fruit of the annual plant *Capsicum annuum*, variously known as bell pepper, bullnose pepper, capsicum, paprika, sweet pepper; Spanish name *pimiento* (not the same as pimento or *allspice). Red, yellow, purple, or brown fruits, often eaten raw in salads; very variable in size and shape; some varieties can be spicy but most are non-pungent. One-quarter of a green pepper (45g) is a rich *source of vitamin C; contains 0.4g of dietary fibre and 0.2g of fat; supplies 6kcal (25kJ). **2.** Red pepper, chilli (or chili); small red fruit of the bushy perennial plant *Capsicum frutescens*. Very pungent, an ingredient of *curry powder, pickles, and *tabasco sauce. Cayenne pepper is made from the powdered dried fruits. Unripe (green) chillis are also very pungent. **3.** Black and white pepper, fruit of the tropical climbing vine, *Piper nigrum*; the fruits are peppercorns. Black pepper is made from sun-dried, unripe peppercorns when the red outer skin turns black. White pepper is made by soaking ripe berries and rubbing off the outer skin. Usually ground as a condiment. Green peppercorns are dried or pickled unripe fruit. Pungency due to the alkaloids piperine, piperdine, and chavicine.

peppercorn *See* PEPPER (3).

pepper dulse Red aromatic *seaweed (*Laurencia pinnatifida*), dried and used as a spice in Scotland.

peppergrass Peppery-tasting cress (*Lepidium sativum*), also known as pepperwort and (in the USA) peppermint.

pepper, guinea *See* PEPPER, MELEGUETA.

pepper, Jamaican *See* ALLSPICE.

pepper, Java *See* CUBEB.

pepper, melegueta Seeds of the West African tree *Amomum melegueta* (syn. *Xylopia aethiopica*), also known as guinea pepper or grains of paradise.

peppermint A hybrid (*Mentha* × *piperita*) between *M. aquatica* and *M. spicata* (spearmint). Not used for flavouring dishes but grown for the essential oil (*see* OILS, ESSENTIAL) which is used in confectionery and medicinally. *See also* MINT.

pepperoni *See* SAUSAGE.

pepper, pink Seeds of the South American pepper tree *Schinus molle*.

pepperpot Caribbean (originally native American); stew flavoured with *cassareep.

pepper, Szechwan Seeds of *Zanthoxylum piperitum*; the pungent flavour develops gradually after biting into the seeds. Also known as Japan pepper or fagara. *See also* SANSHO.

pepper, tailed *See* CUBEB.

pepperwort *See* PEPPERGRASS.

pepsin An *enzyme in the *gastric juice which hydrolyses proteins to give smaller polypeptides (sometimes called peptones); an *endopeptidase. Active only at acid *pH, 1.5–2.5. Secreted as the inactive precursor pepsinogen, which is activated by gastric acid or active pepsin.

pepsinogen The inactive form (*zymogen) in which *pepsin is secreted; activated by the action of *gastric acid or active pepsin.

pepsin, vegetable *See* PAPAIN.

peptic ulcer *See* ULCER.

peptidases *Enzymes that hydrolyse proteins, and therefore important in *protein digestion. *See also* ENDOPEPTIDASES; EXOPEPTIDASES.

peptide bond The bond formed by condensation between the carboxyl group of one *amino acid and the amino group of another (—CO—NH—).

peptides Compounds formed when *amino acids are linked together through the —CO—NH— (peptide) linkage. Two amino acids so linked form a dipeptide, three a tripeptide, etc.; medium-length chains of amino acids (four up to about 50) are known as oligopeptides, longer chains are polypeptides or proteins.

peptides, bioactive *Peptides from plant or animal proteins with biological activity (e.g. opioid, immunostimulatory, or antihypertensive activity).

peptide YY *Hormone secreted by *endocrine cells of the *gastro-intestinal tract in proportion to the energy yield of a meal; it acts on the hypothalamus to signal satiety and decrease food intake. It also inhibits intestinal motility and gastric secretion.

peptones Small polypeptides that are intermediate products in the hydrolysis of proteins. The term is often used for any partial hydrolysate of proteins as, e.g., bacteriological peptone, which is used as a medium for the growth of micro-organisms.

PER Protein Efficiency Ratio, a measure of *protein quality.

perch Fish; freshwater perch is *Perca fluviatilis*, yellow perch is *P. flavescens*; Nile perch is *Lates niloticus*, widely distributed in lakes and rivers in Central

Africa. Marine perch include Pacific perch, *Sebastes alutus*, and torpedo sand perch, *Diplectrum maximum*. *See also* REDFISH.

percomorph oil Prepared from the liver of fish of the order Percomorphi (the *perch family), containing standardized amounts of vitamins A and D.

pericarp 1. The fibrous layers next to the outer husk of cereal grains and outside the testa; of low digestibility and removed from grain during milling. The major constituent of bran. **2.** The tissue surrounding the seed in a fruit. In fleshy fruits there are generally three layers of pericarp: the exocarp (or peel, sometims called the epicarp), the mesocarp (the fleshy part that is normally eaten), and the endocarp, which directly surrounds the seed, and may be membranous or thick and hard (as in the 'stones' of cherries, plums, etc.).

périgord, à la (à la périgueux, à la périgourdine) Dish made or served with *truffles and sometimes *foie gras.

perilipin The major protein coating lipid droplets in *adipose tissue; acts to regulate the access of *lipase to the lipids, and may be the target of phosphorylation in response to hormones that result in increased activity of intracellullar lipases. *See also* ADIPOPHILIN; DESNUTRIN; LIPASE, HORMONE-SENSITIVE.

perilla Eastern Asian herb, *Perilla frutescens*; the leaves are used fresh or pickled as a vegetable. The seeds are a minor source of oil, and important as a source of *perillartine.

perillartine Non-nutritive *sweetener extracted from *perilla seeds, 2000 times as sweet as sucrose.

perimysium *See* MUSCLE.

periodontitis Inflammation of the gums, periodontal ligament, and eventually the alveolar bone, leading to loosening and loss of teeth. *See also* GINGIVITIS.

peristalsis The rhythmic alternating contraction and relaxation of smooth muscle that forces food through the intestinal tract in peristaltic waves.

peritonitis Inflammatory disease of the peritoneum, commonly as a result of perforation of the large intestine.

periwinkle *See* WINKLE.

peroxide Any compound with the peroxy (—O—O—) group; oxidation of unsaturated *fatty acids produces peroxides. Also used to mean specifically hydrogen peroxide (H_2O_2).

peroxide number (peroxide value) A measure of the oxidative rancidity of fats by determination of the lipid peroxides present.

peroxisomes Intracellular organelles that contain *catalase, peroxidases, and *superoxide dismutase as well as various oxidative enzymes that produce hydrogen peroxide or superoxide.

perry Fermented pear juice (in the UK it may include not more than 25% apple juice) analogous to *cider from apples. Sparkling perry is sometimes known as champagne perry.

Persian apple *See* CITRON.

persimmon Fruit of *Diospyros virginiana* (American persimmon or Virginia date) and *D. kaki* (Japanese persimmon, date plum, or kaki). Kaki may be eaten raw or cooked; American persimmon develops a sour flavour if cooked.

pescetarian *Vegetarian who will eat fish, but not meat.

pesto Italian; basil and garlic sauce.

PET Polyethylene terephthalate; clear plastic used in packaging, especially bottles for drinks. Biodegradable within about eight weeks when composted.

petai The large (1 m long) bean-like seed pods of the Malaysian tree *Parkia speciosa*, eaten raw, cooked, or pickled; they have a garlic-like flavour with a bitter aftertaste. *P. biglobosa* is the locust bean, an important food in the Carribbean, and *P. filicoidea* is the African locust bean.

petechiae (petechial haemorrhages) Small, pin-point bleeding under the skin; one of the signs of *scurvy.

pétillant French; lightly sparkling wines, equivalent to Italian frizzante.

petit-grain oils Prepared from twigs and leaves of the bitter orange (*see* ORANGE, BITTER) by steam distillation.

petit pois Small *peas, picked when young.

petit salé French; salted belly or flank of pork.

petits fours Small, rich, sweet cakes and biscuits served after a meal.

PEU Protein-energy undernutrition *See* PROTEIN-ENERGY MALNUTRITION.

Peyer's patches Areas of thickening of the intestinal muosa in the ileum (*see* GASTRO-INTESTINAL TRACT) that are lymphoid tissue, producing antibodies against potentially pathogenic intestinal bacteria. Part of the gut-associated lymphoid tissue (*see* GALT).

PGA Pteroylglutamic acid; *see* FOLIC ACID.

pH Potential hydrogen, a measure of acidity or alkalinity. Defined as the negative logarithm of the hydrogen-ion concentration. The scale runs from 0, which is very strongly acid, to 14, which is very strongly alkaline. Pure water is pH 7, which is neutral; below 7 is acid, above is alkaline. *See also* ACID; BUFFER.

phaeophytin Brownish-green derivative of *chlorophyll, due to the loss of the *magnesium in acid conditions. The formation of phaeophytin accounts for the colour change when green vegetables are cooked.

phage *See* BACTERIOPHAGE.

phagocytosis Uptake into white blood cells (phagocytes, macrophages) of large particles (e.g. bacteria) by *endocytosis.

phagomania Morbid obsession with food; also known as sitomania.

phagophobia Fear of food; also known as sitophobia.

phalsa Fruit of the Himalayan shrub *Grewia subinaequalis* or *G. asiatica*.

pharmafoods *See* FOODS, FUNCTIONAL.

phase inversion *Cream is an emulsion of fat in water; *butter is an emulsion of water in fat. The change from cream to butter is termed phase inversion.

phaseolin Globulin protein in kidney or haricot *bean (*Phaseolus vulgaris*).

phaseolunatin *Cyanogenic (cyanide-forming) *glucoside found in *legumes such as *lima bean, *chickpea, common vetch.

phasin Originally the *lectin from the bean *Phaseolus vulgaris*, now used for plant lectins in general.

PHB ester *See* PARABENS.

pheasant *Game bird, *Phasianus colchicus* and related spp. Total weight 1.5 kg; traditionally sold as a brace, i.e. cock and hen, although now commonly available as single birds; usually hung for 3 days (up to 3 weeks in very cold weather) to develop flavour. A 150-g portion is an extremely rich *source of iron; a rich source of protein, niacin, and vitamin B_2; contains about 15 g of fat of which one-third is saturated; and supplies 330 kcal (1400 kJ).

phenetylurea *See* DULCIN.

phenol oxidases Enzymes that oxidize phenolic compounds to quinones. For example, monophenol oxidase in mushrooms and polyphenol oxidases in potato and apple are responsible for the development of the brown colour when the cut surface is exposed to air; tyrosinase in plants and animals forms the brown and black pigment melanin.

phenotype The physical or biochemical characteristics of an organism, as determined by the *genotype and interactions of genotype with environmental factors.

phentermine An *appetite suppressant drug used in the treatment of obesity, especially in combination with *fenfluramine (fen-phen); withdrawn in 1995 because of reports of heart valve damage.

phenylalanine An essential *amino acid; in addition to its role in protein synthesis, it is the metabolic precursor of *tyrosine (and hence *noradrenaline, *adrenaline, and the *thyroid hormones). Dietary tyrosine spares phenylalanine, so reducing the requirement.

phenylethylamine The *amine formed by decarboxylation of the *amino acid *phenylalanine.

phenylketonuria A genetic disease affecting the metabolism of *phenylalanine, which is normally metabolized to *tyrosine, catalysed by phenylalanine hydroxylase. Impairment of this reaction leads to a considerable accumulation of phenylalanine in plasma and tissues (up to 100 times the normal concentration) and metabolism to phenylpyruvate, phenyllactate, and phenylacetate, collectively known as phenylketones, which are excreted in the urine.

The very high plasma concentration of phenylalanine causes disruption of brain development, and if untreated there is severe mental retardation. Infants are screened for phenylketonuria shortly after birth (by measurement of plasma phenylalanine); treatment is by very strict limitation of phenylalanine intake, only providing sufficient to meet requirements for protein synthesis. Once brain development is complete (between the ages of 8 and 12 years) dietary restriction can be relaxed to a considerable extent, since high concentrations of phenylalanine seem to have little adverse effect on the developed brain. There may, however, be benefits from continuing dietary restriction into adult life, and phenylketonuric women require extremely careful dietary control through pregnancy to avoid damage to the fetus's developing brain.

phitosite High-calorie food.

phosphatase test For the adequacy of *pasteurization of milk. The *enzyme phosphatase, normally present in milk, is denatured at a temperature slightly greater than that required to destroy the tubercle bacillus and other pathogens; therefore the presence of detectable phosphatase activity indicates inadequate pasteurization. The test can detect 0.2% raw milk in pasteurized milk.

phosphates Salts of *phosphoric acid; the form in which the element *phosphorus is normally present in foods and body tissues. *See also* POLYPHOSPHATES.

phosphatides *See* PHOSPHOLIPIDS.

phosphatidic acid Glycerol esterified to two molecules of fatty acid, with the third hydroxyl group esterified to phosphate (diacylglycerol phosphate); intermediate in the metabolism of *phospholipids.

phosphatidylcholine A *phospholipid containing *choline; *see* LECITHIN.

phosphatidylethanolamine A *phospholipid containing ethanolamine.

phosphatidylinositol A *phospholipid containing *inositol.

phosphatidylserine A *phospholipid containing *serine.

phospholipids (phosphatides, phospholipins) Glycerol esterified to two molecules of *fatty acid, one of which is commonly polyunsaturated. The third hydroxyl group is esterified to phosphate and one of a number of water-soluble compounds, including *serine (phosphatidylserine), ethanolamine (phosphatidylethanolamine), *choline (phosphatidylcholine, also known as *lecithin), and *inositol (phosphatidylinositol).

Cell membranes consist of a double layer of phospholipids with the fatty acid side-chains on the inside; the water-soluble compound esterified to the phosphate interacts with water. Phospholipids can be used to emulsify oils and fats in water, and are commonly used in food manufacture as *emulsifiers.

Metabolically they can be regarded as being equivalent to simple fats (*triacylglycerols); they also provide a dietary source of choline and inositol, neither of which is a dietary essential.

phospholipins *See* PHOSPHOLIPIDS.

phosphoproteins Proteins containing phosphate, other than as *nucleic acids (nucleoproteins) or phospholipids (lipoproteins), e.g. *casein from milk, ovovitellin from egg yolk.

phosphoric acid May be one of three types: orthophosphoric acid (H_3PO_4), metaphosphoric acid (HPO_3), or pyrophosphoric acid ($H_4P_2O_7$). Orthophosphoric acid and its salts are used as *acidity regulators and in acid-fruit-flavoured beverages.

phosphorus An essential element, occurring in tissues and foods as phosphate (salts of *phosphoric acid), *phospholipids, and *phosphoproteins. In the body most (80%) is present in the skeleton and teeth as calcium phosphate (hydroxyapatite, $Ca_{10}(PO_4)_6(OH)_2$); the remainder is in the *phospholipids of cell membranes, in *nucleic acids, and in a variety of metabolic intermediates, including *ATP. The *parathyroid hormone controls the concentration of phosphate in the blood, mainly by modifying its excretion in the urine.

Adult needs (about 1.3 g per day) are always met. The *calcium to phosphate ratio of infant foods is, however, important. Phosphate deficiency is not uncommon in livestock and gives rise to *osteomalacia (also known as sweeny or creeping sickness).

photolysis Cleavage of covalent bonds due to the absorption of energy from light.

photo-oxidation Oxidation reactions initiated by light.

photosynthesis The synthesis of carbohydrates from carbon dioxide and water by plants in sunlight, with the release of oxygen.

phrynoderma Blocked pores or 'toad-skin' (follicular hyperkeratosis of the skin) often encountered in malnourished people. Originally thought to be due to *vitamin A deficiency but possibly due to other deficiencies, and also occurs in adequately nourished people.

phulka See CHAPATTI.

phulouri Caribbean; fritters made from dried split peas.

PHV Peak height velocity, the time of most rapid linear growth (increase in height) during the adolescent growth spurt.

phycotoxins Marine biotoxins that accumulate in fish and shellfish from their diet (causing *shellfish poisoning and *ciguatera poisoning when the fish are eaten), as distinct from toxins naturally present (*tetramine poisoning). See also RED TIDE.

phyllodulcin An isocoumarin derivative extracted from the leaves of *Hydrangea thunbergii*; about 350 times as sweet as sucrose, but with a liquorice-like aftertaste.

phylloquinone See VITAMIN K.

phylloxera An aphid that threatened to destroy the vineyards of Europe in the middle of the 19th century. They were saved by grafting susceptible varieties on to resistant American vine rootstock.

physalin A *carotenoid pigment in the fruits of the Cape gooseberry, *Physalis* spp.; zeaxanthin dipalmitate.

physalis Fruit of the herbaceous perennial Chinese lantern *Physalis peruviana*, *P. pubescens*, or *P. edulis*, resembling a small cherry, surrounded by a dry, bladder-like calyx. Also known as Cape gooseberry, golden berry, and Peruvian cherry. A 100-g portion is a rich *source of vitamin C; a source of vitamin A (as carotene); supplies 70 kcal (295 kJ).

Dwarf Cape gooseberry (strawberry tomato or ground cherry) is *P. pruinosa*. Tomatillo, ground tomato, or jamberry is *P. ixocarpa*.

physical activity level (PAL) Total *energy cost of physical activity throughout the day, expressed as a ratio of *basal metabolic rate. Calculated from the *physical activity ratio for each activity, multiplied by the time spent in that activity. A desirable PAL for health is considered to be 1.7; the average in the UK is 1.4.

physical activity ratio (PAR) *Energy cost of physical activity expressed as a ratio of *basal metabolic rate.

physin Name given to a growth factor in liver, later found to be vitamin B_{12}.

phytase An *enzyme (a phosphatase) that hydrolyses *phytate to *inositol and phosphate. Present in yeast, liver, blood, malt, and seeds. If enough yeast is used in baking high extraction flours, some of the phytate is broken down.

phytate Salts of phytic acid, which is *inositol hexaphosphate, present in cereals, particularly in the bran, in dried legumes, and some nuts as both water-soluble salts (sodium and potassium) and insoluble salts of calcium and magnesium. Magnesium calcium phytate is phytin.

   Phytate forms insoluble complexes with calcium, iron, and zinc; it is not clear how far it reduces the availability of these minerals from the diet, since there is *phytase in yeast and *legumes (and possibly in the human gut) that may liberate these minerals.

phytic acid See PHYTATE.

phytin Magnesium calcium *phytate.

phytoalexins Toxic compounds synthesized by plants in response to stress by physical damage, exposure to ultraviolet light, etc.

phytobezoar See BEZOAR.

phytochemicals Various compounds in plant foods that may have beneficial or adverse effects. See FOODS, FUNCTIONAL.

phytoestrogens (phyto-oestrogens) Compounds in plant foods, especially *soy bean, that have both oestrogenic and anti-oestrogenic action; may be protective against hormone-dependent cancer and *osteoporosis. See also LIGNANS; OESTROGENS.

phytoncides See PACIFICARINS.

phytonutrients Various compounds in plant foods that have protective effects against diseases (especially cardiovascular disease and cancer) but are not dietary essentials and hence are not classified as *nutrients.

phytoplankton See PLANKTON.

phytoprotectants Various compounds in plant foods that have protective effects against diseases (especially cardiovascular disease and cancer) but are not dietary essentials and hence are not classified as *nutrients.

phytostanols See STANOLS.

phytosterol General name given to *sterols occurring in plants. *See also* SITOSTEROL.

phytotoxin Any poisonous substance produced by a plant.

phytylmenaquinone *See* VITAMIN K.

pica An unnatural desire for foods; alternative words are cissa, cittosis, and allotriophagy. Also a perverted appetite (eating of earth, sand, clay, paper, etc.).

picarel Marine fish, *Spicara smaris*.

piccalilli Mixture of chopped, brine-preserved vegetables, usually in *mustard sauce (mustard and *vinegar, thickened with *tapioca starch, plus *turmeric and other spices).

piccata Italian; small thin slices of veal.

pickles, dill Pickles (commonly cucumber) fermented in a mixture of brine, *dill weed, spices, and vinegar.

pickling Also called *brining. Vegetables immersed in 5–10% salt solution (brine) undergo lactic acid fermentation, while the salt prevents the growth of undesirable organisms. The sugars in the vegetables are converted to lactic acid; at 25°C the process takes a few weeks, finishing at 1% acidity. *See also* BRINE; BRINING; CURING OF MEAT; HALOPHILES.

picklizes Caribbean (esp. Haitian); pickled mixed vegetables; *piccalilli.

picnic shoulder American name for hand of pork.

pico Prefix for units of measurement, one million-millionth part (i.e. 10^{-12}); symbol p.

pidan *See* EGGS, CHINESE.

pie Food cooked in a dish and covered with pastry; may be sweet or savoury. Also savoury dishes with a crust of mashed potato.

piernik Polish; spiced honey cake.

pierogi Polish; envelopes of dough stuffed with minced meat, cheese, vegetables, or fruit; similar to *ravioli.

pigeon Game bird, *Columbia livia*; young about 4 weeks old is a squab. A 150-g portion is an extremely rich *source of iron; a rich source of protein, niacin, and vitamins B_1 and B_2; contains 20g of fat; supplies 350kcal (1500kJ).

pignoli (pignolias, pinoli) *See* PINE NUTS.

pignut *See* EARTH-NUT.

pig's fry *See* HASLET.

pike Freshwater fish, *Esox lucius*. Pike-perch is *Stizostedion lucioperca*, also known as zander.

pikelets *See* DOUGH CAKES.

pilafi Greek; rice dishes.

pilau (pilaf) Dish of rice cooked in stock, with vegetables, meat, or fish added.

pilchard Oily marine fish, *Sardina* (*Clupea*) *pilchardus*; young is the *sardine. Pacific, South American, or south Atlantic pilchard is *Sardinops sagax*.

piles *See* HAEMORRHOIDS.

pils Pale type of lager originally made in Czechoslovakia. *See* BEER.

pimaricin *See* NATAMYCIN.

pimento *See* ALLSPICE.

pimentón Spanish; powdered, dried red *pepper. Pimentón picante (hot) is cayenne; pimentón dulce (sweet) is paprika.

pimiento *See* PEPPER.

pimpernel *See* BURNET.

piña colada A long drink made from rum, pineapple juice, and coconut milk; also the trade name for a sweet liqueur made from rum, pineapple, and coconut.

pinang *See* BETEL.

pineapple Fruit of the tropical plant *Ananas sativus* (syn. *A. comosus*), one of the bromeliad family. The fruit contains the proteolytic *enzyme bromelain, which has been used (like *papain) to tenderize meat. A 100-g portion is a rich *source of vitamin C; a source of copper; provides 0.8 g of dietary fibre; supplies 30 kcal (125 kJ).

pineau French; mixture of grape must and cognac; about 17% alcohol.

pine nuts (pine kernels, pignoli) Edible seeds of various species of pine cone, especially Mediterranean stone pine, *Pinus pinea*, and piñon, *P. edulis*.

pinhão Seeds of the Brazilian pine *Araucaria angustifolia* (*A. brasiliensis*) eaten in southern Brazil either boiled or milled to flour.

pinocchio Pine kernels; *see* PINE NUTS.

pinocytosis The process by which cells take up liquids and water-soluble compounds without passing through the cell membrane; a process of *endocytosis.

pinot Three varieties of *grape used for *wine making; pinot noir is one of the nine 'classic' varieties, but is used especially in champagne; pinot blanc and pinot gris are also widely used.

pinotage A South African *grape variety used for *wine making, a cross between the *cinsaut and *pinot noir varieties.

piononos Caribbean (Puerto Rico); stuffed plantains.

pipe Cask for wine; the volume varies with the type of wine, e.g. port, 115 gallons (517L); Tenerife, 100 gal (450L); marsala, 90 gal (418L).

piping To force a smooth mixture (e.g. icing or mashed potato) through a narrow nozzle to form fancy shapes to decorate a dish.

pipis Edible *mollusc, *Plebidonas deltoides*, widely distributed around the Australian coastline.

piri-piri Small red chillies (*see* PEPPER) about 1 cm long, extremely pungent. Piri-piri seasoning is Portuguese: crushed chillies, citrus peel, onion, garlic, pepper, salt, lemon juice, bay leaves, paprika, pimiento, basil, oregano, and tarragon.

pirozhki (pirogi) Russian; small baked pasties of yeast dough filled with chopped fish, meat, etc.

pisco South American; *brandy made by distilling wine made from muscat grapes.

pissaladière French (Provençal); savoury tart similar to *pizza.

pissenlit French; *dandelion leaves, eaten raw or cooked. So called because of the diuretic effect.

pistachio Fruit of the deciduous tree *Pistacchio vera*; yellow-green coloured nut. May be roasted and salted or used as flavouring for ice cream and (Indian) hot, sweet, milk beverage. A 60-g portion (weighed with shells) is a *source of protein, vitamins B_1 and E, and niacin; contains 18 g of fat, of which 10% is saturated and 50% mono-unsaturated; supplies 200 kcal (840 kJ).

pisto manchego Spanish (Castilian); vegetable hash.

pitahaya Fruit of a variety of warm-climate cactus fruits, especially *Cereus peruvianus*, and *Hylocereus* and *Selenicereus* spp., also known as dragon fruit.

pitanga Surinam cherry, *Eugenia uniflora* or *E. michelii*; small, round fruit, deeply ribbed, cherry-like with a single stone. A 100-g portion is a rich *source of vitamin C.

pitaya Fruit of the large South American cactus *Cereus peruvianus*, also known as cactus apple or koubo.

pitch lake pudding Caribbean (Barbadian, Trinidadian); dark rum and chocolate mousse.

pith *See* ALBEDO.

pito African alcoholic beverages made by fermentation of cereal mash.

pits Stones from cherries, plums, peaches, and apricots. Oil extracted from these pits is used in cosmetics, pharmaceuticals, for canning sardines, and as table oil. The presscake left behind contains *amygdalin.

pitta (pita) Middle Eastern; sourdough flat bread, baked as an oval or circle, which can be opened up as an envelope. Also known as pocket, balady, or burr bread.

pitting Removing the stones (*pits) from cherries, olives, etc.

pitz Swiss; raw tomatoes stuffed with minced apple and celeriac.

PIVKA Protein induced by vitamin K absence; old name for pre-prothrombin, the precursor of *prothrombin before the *vitamin K dependent carboxylation of glutamate residues to form γ-carboxyglutamate.

pizza Originally Italian; savoury tart on a base of yeast dough, traditionally cooked in a wood-burning oven; the first pizzeria in the USA opened in New York in 1895. The topping varies with the region and may contain tomatoes, cheese, salami, seafood, etc.

plaice Marine flatfish; European plaice is *Pleuronectus platessa*, Alaska plaice is *P. quadrituberculatus*, and American plaice is *Hippoglossoides platessoides*.

plaki Greek; fish baked or braised with vegetables.

plancha, a la Spanish; cooking 'on the plate'. The plancha is a thick iron or aluminium plate, traditionally incorporated into the stove, an oiled hotplate or griddle.

planking Cooking (and usually serving) meat or fish on a small board of oiled hardwood.

plankton Minute organisms, both plant (phytoplankton) and animal (zooplankton), drifting in the sea, which form the basis of the marine *food chain.

plansifter A nest of sieves mounted together so that material being sieved is divided into a number of fractions of different size. Widely used in flour milling.

plantago *See* PSYLLIUM.

plantain Adam's fig; variety of *banana (*Musa* spp.) with higher starch and lower sugar content than dessert bananas, cooked because it is picked when the flesh is too hard to be eaten raw. Some varieties become sweet if left to ripen, others never develop a high sugar content. A 200-g portion is a rich *source of vitamins B_6 and C; a good source of folate and copper; a source of selenium; provides 12g of dietary fibre; supplies 240kcal (1000kJ).

plaque Dental plaque is a layer of bacteria in an organic matrix on the surface of teeth, especially around the neck of each tooth. May lead to development of gingivitis, periodontal disease, and caries. Atherosclerotic plaque is the development of fatty streaks in the walls of blood vessels; *see also* ATHEROSCLEROSIS.

plasma, blood *See* BLOOD PLASMA.

plasmid Small circular region of extra-chromosomal bacterial *DNA which has an origin of replication and is therefore maintained in a cell line. Especially amenable to the introduction of foreign genes, and widely used in genetic engineering. Between 5–90kb in size.

plasticizer Chemical added to plastic films to make them more flexible.

plate count To estimate the number of bacteria in a sample, it is poured on to an *agar plate, when each cell multiplies to produce a colony that is visible to the naked eye. A count of the number of colonies gives the number of bacteria in the sample.

plonk Colloquial term for cheap, indifferent wine; originated in Australia.

ploughman's lunch Originally cheese, bread, and pickle, now an English pub lunch; cheese (or sometimes pâté or ham) with salad and crusty bread.

pluck Butchers' term for heart, liver, and lungs of an animal.

plum Originally used as a name for all dried fruit (*see* FRUIT, DRIED), now used specifically for fruit of various species of *Prunus*, which were originally called *prunes. Common European plums are *P. domestica*; blackthorn or sloe is *P. spinosa*; bullace is *P. insititia*; damson is *P. damascena*; gages are *P. italica*; myrobalan is *Prunus cerasifera*; beach plum is a wild plum, *Prunus maritime*. The British *National Fruit Collection has 304 varieties of plum. A 200-g portion of dessert plums (four medium-size fruits weighed without stones) is a *source of vitamin C; provides 3g of dietary fibre; supplies 100kcal (420kJ).

plum, Japanese Fruit of *Prunus salicina*; also alternative name for *loquat (*Eriobotrya japonica*).

plumcot A cross between *plum and *apricot.

plum sauce Chinese; sauce made from plums, apricots, chilli, vinegar, and sugar.

PMN Polymorphonuclear leukocytes. *See* BLOOD CELLS.

poach To cook for a short time in a shallow layer of liquid kept at a temperature just below boiling point.

POEMS (polyoxyethylene monostearate) *See* CRUMB-SOFTENERS.

poffertjes Dutch; small pancakes served hot with icing sugar and butter.

poi Hawaiian; bread baked from dough made with starchy fruit or tubers, unripe banana, taro, or cocoyam that is left for several days or weeks to undergo a lactic acid fermentation before drying or baking.

poire williams *Pear liqueur prepared by steeping williams pears in pear brandy (eau-de-vie prepared by distillation of *perry). Traditionally a bottle is placed over the developing fruit bud on the tree; when the fruit has ripened it is then steeped in pear brandy in the bottle in which it has grown.

polenta Italian; porridge made from maize meal, often with cheese added; it may be further cooked by baking or frying. Also the Italian name for coarsely ground maize meal; *see also* HOMINY.

policosanols Long-chain (C24–30) aliphatic alcohols from hydrolysis of sugar-cane wax that lower *LDL cholesterol, increase *HDL, prevent platelet aggregation, and may inhibit *foam cell formation from *macrophages.

pollack (pollock) Marine fish, *Pollachius virens*, also known as coalfish or lythe. Pacific or Alaska pollack is *P. pollachius*.

pollan Freshwater fish, *Coregonus autumnalis*, also known as arctic cisco.

pollards *See* WHEATFEED.

polonaise, à la Dishes made with soured cream, beetroot, and red cabbage.

polony Smoked pork and veal sausage, ready to slice and eat; also known as bologna. A 150-g portion is a good *source of protein, vitamin B_1, and niacin; a source of iron; contains 30 g of fat and 1200 mg of sodium; supplies 320 kcal (1280 kJ).

polvorones Spanish (Andalusian); *shortbread.

polydextrose, modified A randomly bonded glucose polymer prepared by heating *glucose and *sorbitol with citric acid. It is resistant to enzymic digestion and 60% is excreted in faeces, so providing only about 1 kcal (4 kJ)/g; hence termed 'non-sweetening sucrose replacement', or *bulking agent.

polydipsia Abnormally intense thirst; a typical symptom of *diabetes.

polygalacturonase *See* PECTINASE.

polygenic Diseases or disorders involving the simultaneous action of many variant genes, each of individually small effect, which may also require interaction with diet and/or other environmental factors for expression of the disease *phenotype. *See also* MONOGENIC; OLIGOGENIC.

polyglucose *See* POLYDEXTROSE.

polymerase chain reaction (PCR) An *in vitro* method for rapid amplification of DNA sequences. Starting from minute amounts of DNA, repetitive cycles of template denaturation, primer annealing, and the extension of the annealed primers by DNA polymerase result in almost exponential accumulation of DNA; 10^6-fold in 20 cycles, each of which takes 4 minutes. The basis of DNA fingerprinting techniques, and widely used for rapid identification of pathogenic micro-organisms in foods.

Reverse transcriptase PCR has an initial step using reverse transcriptase to convert mRNA to DNA, which is then amplified in the usual way. This avoids the false positive results from microbial contamination of foods that occurs using conventional PCR, since DNA from dead micro-organisms is stable and is detected by PCR. By contrast, microbial mRNA is lost rapidly after cell death, so dead micro-organisms are not detected.

Real-time or quantitative PCR involves measuring the amount of DNA formed in each cycle of the reaction, so as to permit estimation of the amount of DNA (or mRNA) initially present.

polymorphism **1.** The ability to crystallize in two or more different forms. For example, depending on the conditions under which it is solidified, the fat tristearin can form three kinds of crystals, each of which has a different melting point, namely, 54, 65, and 71 °C. **2.** In genetics, the occurrence of variants of a gene relatively frequently in the population.

polymyxins Antibiotics isolated from *Bacillus polymyxin* (syn. *B. aerosporin*); polymyxin A is aerosporin. They are polypeptides, active against coliform bacteria; apart from clinical use, they are of value in controlling infection in brewing.

polyols *See* SUGAR ALCOHOLS.

polyose *See* POLYSACCHARIDE.

polyoxyethylene *See* CRUMB-SOFTENERS.

polypeptides *See* PEPTIDES.

polyphagia Excessive or continuous eating.

polyphenols A variety of aromatic compounds in plant foods that have multiple hydroxyl groups; they are generally considered to have beneficial *antioxidant action.

polyphosphates Complex *phosphates added to foods as *emulsifiers, *buffers, or *sequestrants. They prevent discoloration of sausages and aid mixing of the fat, speed penetration of the brine in curing, and hold water in meat and fish products.

polysaccharides Complex *carbohydrates formed by the condensation of large numbers of *monosaccharide units, e.g. *starch, *glycogen, *cellulose, *dextrins, *inulin. On hydrolysis the simple sugar is liberated. *See also* NON-STARCH POLYSACCHARIDES.

polysaccharose Alternative name for *polysaccharides.

polysorbates *See* CRUMB-SOFTENERS.

polyunsaturates Commonly used short term for polyunsaturated *fatty acids.

pomace Residue of fruit pulp after expressing juice; also applied to fish from which oil has been expressed.

pomarrosa *See* APPLE, ROSE.

pombé African *beer prepared from *millet; also known as kaffir beer. Commonly associated with *iron overload, since it is frequently brewed in iron drums, and alcohol increases the absorption of iron.

POMC *See* PRO-OPIOMELANOCORTIN.

pomegranate The fruit of the subtropical tree *Punica granatum*. The juice is contained in a pulpy sac surrounding each of a mass of seeds; the outer skin contains tannin and is therefore bitter. The sweet juice is used to prepare *grenadine syrup for alcoholic and fruit drinks. *See also* ANARDANA.

pomelo (pomeloe, pummelo) Fruit of *Citrus grandis*, from which the *grapefruit is descended; also called shaddock, after Captain Shaddock, who introduced it into Barbados in the 16th century. *See* CITRUS.

pomerac *See* APPLE, MALAY.

pomes Botanical name for fruits such as apple or pear, formed by the enlargement of the receptacle which becomes fleshy and surrounds the carpels.

pomfret Marine fish, *Brama*, *Stromachus*, and *Pampus* spp. Pomfret or black sea bream is *B. brama*, Pacific pomfret is *B. japonica*, bigscale pomfret or longfinned bream is *Taracticthys longipinnis*, and black pomfret is *Paratromateus niger*. *See also* BUTTERFISH; PONTEFRACT CAKE

pompano Oily fish, *Trachinotus carolinus*, related to *mackerel.

ponceau (ponceau 4R) Strawberry-red colour, E124.

ponderal index An index of fatness, used as a measure of *obesity: the cube root of body weight divided by height. Confusingly, the index is higher for thin people, and lower for fat people. *See also* BODY MASS INDEX.

ponderocrescive Foods tending to increase weight: easily gaining weight; the opposite of ponderoperditive.

ponderoperditive Stimulating weight loss.

pone bread Colloquial name for corn bread in the southern states of the USA. (Corn pone are small corn cakes, a speciality of Alabama.)

Pontefract cake A round, flat sweetmeat made from *liquorice, originally made in Pontefract in England; also called pomfret.

poonac The residue of *coconut after the extraction of the oil.

poor man's goose Casserole dish of liver and potatoes.

popcorn Variety of *maize (parch maize, *Zea mays* var. *everta*) that expands on heating, also the name of the fluffy white mass so formed. The first microwaveable popcorn was introduced in the USA in 1986.

pope's eye The small circle of fat in the centre of a leg of pork or mutton.

pope's nose *See* PARSON'S NOSE.

popover Individual *batter pudding; small *Yorkshire pudding.

poppadom Indian; thin roasted or fried crisps made from lentil flour; may be spiced.

poppy seed Seeds of the opium poppy, *Papaver somniferum*, used mixed with honey in cakes, and as a flavouring on the crust of bread and rolls. Also called maw seed.

popsicle American name for *ice lolly.

Population Reference Intake (PRI) *See* REFERENCE INTAKES.

porgy American term for various food and game fish of the sea bream family (*see* BREAM, SEA), including *Pagrus* (red porgy) and *Senostomus* spp. *See also* POMFRET; SCUP.

pork Meat from the pig (swine, hog), *Suidae* spp., eaten fresh, as opposed to *bacon and *ham, which are cured; pigs (known in the USA as hogs) were first introduced into the USA by Hernando de Soto in 1539. By far the richest of all meat sources of vitamin B_1, a 150-g portion supplying more than the average daily requirement; a rich *source of protein, niacin, vitamin B_{12}, copper, and selenium; a good source of vitamins B_2 and B_6, zinc, and iron; depending on the joint contains 30–45g of fat of which one-third is saturated; supplies 430–500kcal (1800–2100kJ).

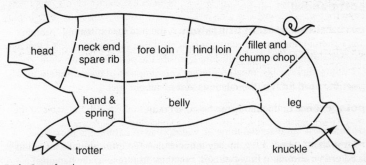

Pork. Cuts of pork

pork, hand of The foreleg of *pork; usually salted and boiled.

***Porphyra* spp.** Red *seaweed used to make *laverbread.

porridge Oatmeal cooked in water or milk as a breakfast dish; originally Scottish. Also similar thick soups made with other cereals. *See* OATS.

port Fortified wines from the upper Douro valley of north-east Portugal. Mostly aged in wood and bottled when ready for drinking; vintage port is aged in wood for 2 years, then in the bottle for at least 10; late bottled vintage is aged less than 6 years. Crusted port is blended from quality vintages bottled young, and develops a sediment (crust) in the bottle. Ruby port is young; old tawny is aged for 10 or more years; fine old tawny is a blend of young and old wines. Tawny port is aged in wood, vintage in the bottle. White port is made from white grapes; generally served chilled as an apéritif. Around 16% alcohol by volume, 12% sugars; 160kcal (670kJ)/100mL.

porter *See* BEER.

porterhouse American term originally for large beef steak cut from the rear end of sirloin and including some fillet: served with beer (porter) in porterhouses. Now a thick slice cut from the wing-rib of *beef.

portugaise, à la Dishes made with tomato, onion, and garlic.

poshte *See* CUSTARD APPLE.

Poskitt index Index of fatness in children; per cent of expected weight for age.

posset Drink made from hot milk curdled with ale or wine, sometimes thickened with breadcrumbs and spiced. Formerly used as a remedy for colds; popular in the later Middle Ages.

postprandial Occurring after a meal.

postprandial protein utilization A method for estimating *protein and essential *amino acid requirements from measurements of $[^{13}C]$ leucine balance during a constant infusion; losses in the post-absorptive state (12 hours after the last meal) represent consumption of tissue protein to meet the need for *gluconeogenesis and metabolic fuel.

potage French; thick soup. *See also* POTTAGE.

potassium An essential mineral, widespread in nature; the human body contains about 125 g, mostly intracellular. *Reference intake for adults is 3.5 g/day; abundant in vegetables, potatoes, fruit (especially bananas).

potassium nitrate *See* NITRATES; SALTPETRE.

potassium sorbate Potassium salt of *sorbic acid (E202).

potato, air Tubers of *Dioscorea bulbifera*, the aerial *yam.

potato crisps Flavoured, thin slices of potato, deep fried and eaten cold, sometimes as an accompaniment to meals, more commonly as a snack. Called chips in the USA. Reputedly invented by George Crum, a chef in Saratoga Springs, NY (1853), as a mocking response to customers who complained his French fries were too thick.

potatoes, duchesse Sieved boiled potato mixed with cream and egg, glazed with beaten egg, and baked until browned.

potatoes, straw *See* ALLUMETTES.

potato, fairy *See* EARTH-NUT.

potato flour Dried potato tuber.

potato, Irish The 'ordinary' potato, tuber of *Solanum tuberosum*. Discovered in Peru by the Spanish explorer Gonzalo Jiminez de Quesada in 1530, and introduced into Spain in 1539. Later introduced into France, initially as an ornamental plant. Believed to have been introduced into Ireland in 1588 among wreckage of ships from the Spanish Armada. Introduced to North America by Irish immigrants to Boston in 1718, and hence known as in the USA as Irish potatoes. Growing potatoes was banned in Burgundy in 1618 in the belief that eating them was the cause of leprosy. A 200-g portion is a rich *source of vitamin B_6; a good source of vitamins B_1 and C (new potatoes are a rich source of vitamin C), and folate; a source of niacin; provides 2.5 g of dietary fibre, 560 mg of potassium; supplies 140 kcal (590 kJ).

potato, Livingstone Tubers of the South African perennial herb *Plectranthus esculentis*, also known as African or Hausa potato (*see also* POTATO, SUDAN).

potato, red *See* OCA.

potato starch Also called farina. Prepared from potato tuber and widely used as a stabilizing agent when gelatinized by heat.

potato, Sudan Tubers of the African perennial herb *Plectranthus rotundifolius* (syn. *Solenostemon rotundifolius*), also known as Zulu round potato or Hausa potato (*see also* POTATO, LIVINGSTONE).

potato, sweet Tubers of the herbaceous climbing plant *Ipomoea batatas*, known in Britain before the Irish potato (*see* POTATO, IRISH). Also known as kumara. The flesh may be white, yellow, or pink (if carotene is present); the leaves are also edible. A 200-g portion is a rich *source of vitamins A (as carotene if pink) and C; a source of iron and vitamin B_1; provides 4.5g of dietary fibre; contains 0.4g of fat, of which 16% is saturated; supplies 170kcal (700kJ).

potato, tule *See* ARROWHEAD.

pot-au-feu French; large deep earthenware casserole or *marmite; also a traditional stew of beef and vegetables.

poteen Irish; illicit home-distilled spirit. *See also* MOONSHINE.

pot herb Any plant with stalks and leaves that can be boiled as a vegetable or used in soups and stews (in larger amounts than *herbs used for flavouring).

pot liquor Liquid left in the pan after cooking vegetables.

pot pie American; meat or poultry pie baked in an uncovered vessel with a crust of pastry or biscuit dough.

pot roasting A method of cooking joints of meat in a saucepan or casserole with fat and a small amount of liquid.

pottage Thick, well-seasoned meat or vegetable soup, usually containing barley or other cereal or a pulse (e.g. lentils). *See also* POTAGE.

pottle Traditional English wine measure; ½ gallon (= 2.25L).

poularde A neutered hen bird.

poulette, sauce Rich white sauce, with egg yolks and lemon juice.

poultry General term for farmyard birds (as opposed to wild *game birds) kept for eggs and/or meat; *chicken, *duck, *goose, *guinea fowl, *pigeon, and *turkey.

poultry, New York dressed Poultry that have been slaughtered and plucked but not eviscerated.

pound cake American; *Madeira cake; rich cake containing a pound, or equal quantities, of each of the major ingredients: flour, sugar, and butter, with added eggs.

poussin Young *chicken, 4–6 weeks old, weighing 250–300g.

pout Marine fish, *Trisopterus luscus*, also known as pout whiting, pouting, or bib.

powdor fort, powdor douce Medieval English; mixed spices. Powdor fort was hot, containing ginger, pepper, and mace; powdor douce was milder, containing ginger, cinnamon, nutmeg, and cloves.

power calculation In statistics, an estimate of the number of observations or subjects needed in order to detect a given size of effect.

pozol Latin American; balls of fermented maize dough mixed with water and eaten as a porridge; various bacteria and yeasts are involved in the fermentation. Chorote is similar, but ground cocoa beans are mixed with the dough.

PP *See* PANCREATIC POLYPEPTIDE.

PPAR Peroxisome proliferation activated receptor. A nuclear receptor that regulates the expression of specific genes; the physiological ligand is an *eicosanoid or other derivative of a long-chain polyunsaturated *fatty acid.

ppm Parts per million (= mg/kg).

PPU *See* POST-PRANDIAL PROTEIN UTILIZATION.

Prader-Willi syndrome Rare *genetic disease due to loss of several genes on (paternally derived) chromosome 15. Signs include short stature, small hands and feet, poor muscle development with *hypotonia, genital hypoplasia and infertility, and excessive central accumulation of fat, as a result of both increased appetite and low energy expenditure.

prahoc Cambodian; fermented fish paste prepared by pressing fish under banana leaves before salting and sun-drying.

prairie chicken American *game bird, *Tympanuchus cupido* and *T. pallidicinctus*.

prairie oyster Traditional cure for a hangover; a raw egg with *Worcestershire sauce and brandy; the egg is swirled with the liquid but the yolk remains intact.

praline **1.** Confection of nuts and partially caramelized sugar, often used as a centre for chocolates. **2.** In France, a sugar-coated almond.

prawn (shrimp) Small crustaceans, various species of the families *Aristaeidae, Palaemonidae, Penaeidae*, and *Pandalidae*. Traditionally small fish are called shrimps and larger ones prawns; by EU regulations fish which when cooked have a count of less than 397/kg (or peeled tails <1 323/kg) are called either prawns or shrimp. Those that have a count of less than 123/kg with head and shell on (or <242/kg with head and shell removed) are king prawns. The deep-water prawn is *Pandalus borealis*; common pink shrimp is *Pandalus montagui*; brown shrimp is *Crangon* spp.; kuruma prawn is *Penaeus japonicus*; tiger prawn (the largest of the commercially important prawns) is *Penaeus* spp.

See also DUBLIN BAY PRAWN; LOBSTER; SCAMPI.

PRE Protein Retention Efficiency, a measure of *protein quality.

prebiotics Non-digestible *oligosaccharides that support the growth of colonies of certain bacteria in the colon. They include derivatives of *fructose and *galactose, and lead to the growth of bifidobacteria, so changing and possibly improving the colonic flora. *Probiotics and prebiotics are sometimes termed synbiotics. They are considered to play a role as functional foods (*see* FOODS, FUNCTIONAL).

prechurpi *See* CHURPI.

precursors, enzyme *See* ZYMOGENS.

prediabetes *See* METABOLIC SYNDROME.

pregnancy, nutritional needs in Pregnant women have slightly increased energy and protein requirements compared with their needs before pregnancy, although there are metabolic adaptations in early pregnancy which result in laying down increased reserves for the metabolic stress of the last trimester, and high requirements for iron and calcium. These increased needs are reflected in the increased *reference intakes for pregnancy.

premier cru *See* WINE CLASSIFICATION, LUXEMBOURG.

premier jus Best-quality *suet prepared from beef and sheep kidneys. The fat is chilled, shredded, and heated at moderate temperature. When pressed, premier jus separates into a liquid fraction (oleo oil or liquid oleo) and a solid fraction (oleostearin or solid tallow).

pré-salé French; mutton or lamb from sheep raised on saltmarshes; prized for its flavour.

preservation Protection of food from deterioration by micro-organisms, enzymes, and oxidation: by cooling, destroying the micro-organisms and enzymes by heat treatment or *irradiation, reducing their activity through dehydration or the addition of chemical *preservatives, and by smoking, *salting, and *pickling.

preservatives Substances capable of retarding or arresting the deterioration of food; examples are *sulphur dioxide, *benzoic acid, specified *antibiotics, *salt, acids, and essential oils (*see* OILS, ESSENTIAL).

presscake The residue of oilseeds when the oil has been pressed out. Valuable as animal feed and in a number of fermented foods, including *bongkrek, *dagé, and *oncom. Also called expeller cake.

pressure, blood *See* HYPERTENSION.

pressure cooking By cooking under pressure, it is possible to achieve a higher temperature, and therefore boil or steam foods faster than in an open pan. *See also* AUTOCLAVE.

pressure, osmotic *See* OSMOTIC PRESSURE.

pretzels German; hard, brittle biscuits in the shape of a knot, made from flour, water, shortening, yeast, and salt. Fresh pretzels are bigger in size and are soft bread. Also called bretzels.

prevalence Of a disease, the total number of cases in the population.

prevalence, lifetime The proportion of people in a population who will have a particular disease at some stage in their life.

prevalence, point The proportion of people in a population who have a particular disease at a particular time. The one-year period prevalence rate is the point prevalence rate plus the annual *incidence rate.

PRI Population Reference Intake of nutrients; *see* REFERENCE INTAKES.

prickly ash Bark and berries of *Zanthoxylum americanum* and *Z. clava-herculis*, used as a food flavour, reputed to be a circulatory stimulant, and antirheumatic. Also known as toothache bark.

prickly pear Fruit of the cactus *Opuntia* spp., also called Indian fig, barberry fig, and tuna; an important part of the diet in some areas of Mexico. A 150-g portion is a rich *source of vitamin C; supplies 60 kcal (245 kJ). *See also* NOPAL.

primeur French; early forced vegetables and fruits. Also used for young, early wine.

princesse, à la Dish with a garnish of asparagus tips and truffles or noisette potatoes.

principal component analysis Mathematical technique for condensing a *metabolomic spectrum to a single point on a graph, permitting rapid comparison between different species, experimental and control groups, etc.

printanière, à la Spring-style dish containing, or garnished with, small, young vegetables.

prion The infective agent(s) responsible for Creutzfeld—Jakob disease, kuru and possibly other degenerative diseases of the brain in human beings, scrapie in sheep, and bovine spongiform encephalopathy (*BSE). They are simple proteins, and unlike viruses do not contain any nucleic acid. Transmission occurs by ingestion of infected tissue.

Pritikin programme Low-fat, low-cholesterol diet combined with exercise, to prevent heart disease, developed by Nathan Pritikin, 1979.

probiotics Preparations of live micro-organisms added to food (or used as animal feed), claimed to be beneficial to health by restoring microbial balance in the intestine. The organisms commonly involved are lactobacilli, bifidobacteria, streptococci, and some yeasts and moulds, alone or as mixtures. The idea that friendly bacteria in yoghurt will crowd out pathogenic organisms was originally propounded by Russian-French bacteriologist Ilya Metchnikoff (1845–1916) in *The Prolongation of Life* (1907). *See also* ACIDOPHILUS THERAPY; BACTERIOCINS; PREBIOTICS.

procarcinogen A compound that is not itself carcinogenic, but undergoes metabolic activation in the body to yield a *carcinogen.

processing Any and all processes to which food is subjected after harvesting for the purposes of improving its appearance, texture, palatability, nutritional value, keeping properties, and ease of preparation, and for eliminating micro-organisms, toxins, and other undesirable constituents.

processing aids Compounds used in manufacturing to enhance the appeal or utility of a food or component: clarifying and clouding agents, catalysts, flocculants, filtration aids, crystallization inhibitors, etc.

pro-elastase The inactive form (*zymogen) in which *elastase is secreted; activated by *trypsin.

pro-enzymes *See* ZYMOGENS.

profiterole Originally a light cake baked on hot ashes and filled with cream; now a small case of choux pastry (*see* PASTRY, CHOUX), baked, filled with cream, and served with chocolate sauce. Also small rounds of choux pastry used as a garnish for clear soups or consommés.

proglucagon Precursor of the *peptide *hormone *glucagon, synthesized in α-islet cells of the *pancreas and endocrine cells of the *gastro-intestinal tract; post-synthetic modification leads to formation of *glucagon, *oxyntomodulin, and *GLP-1.

progoitrins Substances found in plant foods which are precursors of *goitrogens.

programming, metabolic The idea that nutrition *in utero* (and hence maternal nutrition) and early post-natal life leads to *epigenetic programming of metabolism, and predisposes to chronic disease in later life. Sometimes known as the Barker hypothesis, since it was first enunciated by David Barker. *See also* EPIGENETICS.

prolamins Storage proteins of cereal grains that are soluble in 65–75% alcohol; also known as gliadins.

proline A non-essential *amino acid.

promoter Of a *gene, a region about 25–30 base pairs upstream of the gene that signals the location of a gene to be transcribed; includes the TATA box, a region containing the sequence TATA. Transcription factors bind to this TATA box, resulting in activation of RNA polymerase, and initiation of *transcription some 25–30 base pairs downstream.

Pronutro Protein-rich baby food (22% protein) developed in South Africa; made from maize, skimmed-milk powder, groundnut flour, soya flour, and fish protein concentrate with added vitamins.

proof spirit An old method of describing the *alcohol content of *spirits; originally defined as a solution of alcohol of such strength that it will ignite when mixed with gunpowder. Proof spirit contains 57.07% alcohol by volume or 49.24% by weight in the UK. In the USA it contains 50% alcohol by volume. Pure (absolute) alcohol is 175.25° proof UK or 200° proof USA. Now largely replaced by % alcohol by volume.

pro-opiomelanocortin (POMC) *Peptide *hormone precursor that is normally modified by *carboxypeptidase E. POMC neurons in the central nervous system mediate feeding behaviour and affect *insulin levels, and peptides derived from POMC are ligands for the hypothalamic melanocortin receptor, which inhibits feeding behaviour. *See also* AGOUTI MOUSE; FAT MOUSE.

pro-oxidant nutrients Any nutrients that can, under appropriate conditions, serve as a source of *radicals. Most of those that are considered to be *antioxidants can also have pro-oxidant action, either forming radicals non-enzymically, or because their antioxidant action is due to the formation of stable radicals that survive long enough to penetrate deeper into tissues or plasma lipoproteins, perpetuating radical damage. *See also* ANTIOXIDANT PARADOX.

propionates Salts of propionic acid, CH_3CH_2COOH, a normal metabolic intermediate. The free acid and salts are used as mould inhibitors, e.g. on cheese surfaces, and to inhibit *rope in bread and baked goods.

propolis Waxy substance produced by bees, used to seal the hive; has antioxidant and antibacterial activities, and is sold as a nutritional supplement, with little evidence of efficacy.

propyl gallate An *antioxidant.

prosciutto Italian for *ham; in English it means specifically smoked, spiced, Italian ham, eaten thinly sliced (prosciutto crudo in Italian).

prostacyclins *Eicosanoids synthesized by the cyclo-oxygenase pathway.

prostaglandins *Eicosanoids synthesized by the cyclo-oxygenase pathway.

prosthetic group Non-protein part of an *enzyme molecule; either a *coenzyme or a metal ion. Essential for catalytic activity. The enzyme protein without its prosthetic group is the apo-enzyme and is catalytically inactive. With the prosthetic group, it is known as the holo-enzyme. *See also* ENZYME ACTIVATION ASSAYS.

proteans Slightly altered proteins that have become insoluble, probably an early stage of denaturation.

proteases Enzymes that hydrolyse *proteins; *see also* ENDOPEPTIDASES; EXOPEPTIDASES.

proteasome A multi-enzyme complex that catalyses the ATP-dependent hydrolysis of tissue proteins labelled with *ubiquitin. The ATP is hydrolysed in the process of unfolding target proteins to permit hydrolysis.

protein All living tissues contain proteins; they are polymers of *amino acids, joined by *peptide bonds. The name was coined by the Dutch chemist Gerard Johann Mulder in 1838, meaning 'of the first importance'. There are twenty main amino acids in proteins, and any one protein may contain several hundred or over a thousand amino acids, so an enormous variety of different proteins occur in nature, i.e. in foods and our bodies.

Generally a polymer of relatively few amino acids is referred to as a peptide (e.g. di-, tri-, and tetrapeptides); oligopeptides contain up to about 50 amino acids; larger molecules are polypeptides or proteins.

The sequence of the amino acids in a protein determines its overall structure and function: many proteins are *enzymes; others are structural (e.g. *collagen in connective tissue and *keratin in hair and nails); many *hormones are polypeptides.

Proteins are constituents of all living cells and are dietary essentials. Chemically they are distinguished from fats and carbohydrates by containing nitrogen. They are composed of carbon, hydrogen, oxygen, nitrogen, sulphur, and sometimes phosphorus.

proteinases Enzymes that hydrolyse *proteins, also known as peptidases and proteases. *See also* ENDOPEPTIDASES; EXOPEPTIDASES.

protein-calorie malnutrition *See* PROTEIN-ENERGY MALNUTRITION.

protein calories per cent *See* PROTEIN-ENERGY RATIO.

protein conversion factor *See* NITROGEN CONVERSION FACTOR.

protein, crude Total *nitrogen multiplied by the *nitrogen conversion factor = 6.25. *See also* KJELDAHL DETERMINATION.

Protein Efficiency Ratio (PER) A measure of *protein quality.

protein-energy malnutrition (PEM) A spectrum of disorders, especially in children, due to inadequate feeding. Marasmus is severe wasting and can also occur in adults; it is the result of a food intake inadequate to meet energy expenditure. Kwashiorkor affects only young children and includes severe oedema, fatty infiltration of the liver, and a sooty dermatitis; it is likely that deficiency of *antioxidant nutrients and the stress of infection may be involved. Marasmic kwashiorkor is the most severe form of protein-energy malnutrition in children, with weight for height less than 60% of that expected, and with oedema and other signs of kwashiorkor. Emaciation, similar to that seen in marasmus, occurs in patients with advanced cancer, AIDS, and other chronic inflammatory diseases; in this case it is known as *cachexia.

protein-energy ratio The protein content of a food or diet expressed as the proportion of the total energy provided by protein (17kJ, 4kcal/gram). The average requirement for protein is about 7–8% of total energy intake; average Western diets provide about 14%.

protein equivalent A measure of the digestible nitrogen of an animal feedingstuff in terms of protein. It is measured by direct feeding or calculated from the digestible pure protein plus half the digestible non-protein nitrogen.

protein, first class An obsolete system of classifying proteins into first and second class, to indicate their relative nutritional value or *protein quality. Generally, but not invariably, animal proteins were considered 'first class' and plant proteins 'second class', but this classification has no validity in the diet as a whole.

protein hydrolysate Mixture of *amino acids and *polypeptides prepared by hydrolysis of *proteins with acid, alkali, or *proteases, used in *enteral and *parenteral nutrition and in supplements.

protein intolerance An adverse reaction to one or more specific proteins in foods, commonly the result of an allergy. General protein intolerance may be due to a variety of genetic diseases affecting amino acid metabolism. Treatment is normally by severe restriction of protein intake or avoidance of the offending foods. *See also* AMINO ACID DISORDERS; FOOD, ADVERSE REACTIONS; HYPERAMMONAEMIA.

protein kinases *Enzymes that catalyse phosphorylation of target enzymes in cells in response to the action of *hormones and neurotransmitters. Protein kinase A is activated by 5′-AMP, protein kinase B by the activated *insulin receptor substrate, protein kinase C by cyclic AMP; MAP kinases are activated by a variety of mitogenic hormones.

protein milk Partially skimmed lactic acid milk plus milk curd (prepared from whole milk by *rennet precipitation); richer in protein and lower in fat than ordinary milk, and supposed to be better tolerated in digestive disorders. Also known as albumin milk and eiweiss milch.

protein quality A measure of the usefulness of a dietary protein for growth and maintenance of tissue, and, in animals, production of meat, eggs, wool, and milk. It is important only if the total intake of protein barely meets the requirement. The quality of individual proteins is unimportant in mixed diets, because of *complementation between different proteins.

Two types of measurement are used to estimate protein quality: (a) biological assays and (b) chemical analysis.

(a) Biological Value (BV) is the proportion of absorbed protein retained in the body (i.e. taking no account of digestibility). A protein that is completely useable (e.g. egg and human milk) has BV = 0.9–1.0; meat and fish have BV = 0.75–0.8; wheat protein, 0.5; gelatine, 0.

Net Protein Utilization (NPU) is the proportion of dietary protein that is retained in the body under specified experimental conditions (i.e. it takes account of digestibility; NPU = BV × digestibility). By convention NPU is measured at 10% dietary protein (NPU_{10}) at which level the protein synthetic mechanism of the animal can utilize all of the protein so long as the balance of *essential amino acids is correct. When fed at 4% dietary protein, the result is NPU standardized. If the food or diet is fed as it is normally eaten, the result is NPU operative (NPU_{op}).

Protein Efficiency Ratio (PER) is the gain in weight of growing animals per gram of protein eaten.

Net Protein Retention (NPR) is the weight gain of animals fed the test protein, minus the weight loss of a group fed a protein-free diet, divided by the protein consumed.

Protein Retention Efficiency (PRE) is the NPR converted into a percentage scale by multiplying by 16: it then becomes numerically the same as Net Protein Utilization.

Relative Protein Value (RPV) is the ability of a test protein, fed at various levels of intake, to support *nitrogen balance, relative to a standard protein.

(b) Chemical Score is based on chemical analysis of the protein; it is the amount of the limiting *amino acid compared with the amount of the same amino acid in egg protein.

Protein Score is similar to Chemical Score, but uses an amino acid mixture as the standard, also known as amino acid score. Protein digestibility-corrected amino acid score (PDCAAS) takes account of the digestibility of the protein as well as its amino acid composition.

Essential amino acid index is the sum of all the essential amino acids compared with those in egg protein or the amino acid target mixture.

protein rating Used in Canadian food labelling regulations to assess the overall protein quality of a food. It is Protein Efficiency Ratio multiplied by the protein content of food (per cent) multiplied by the amount of the food that is reasonably consumed. Foods with a rating above 40 may be designated excellent dietary sources; foods with a rating below 20 are considered to be insignificant sources; 20–40 may be described as good sources.

protein, reference A theoretical concept of the perfect protein which is used with 100% efficiency at whatever level it is fed in the diet. Used as a means of expressing recommended intakes. The nearest approach to this theoretical protein are egg and human milk proteins, which are used with 90–100% efficiency when fed at low levels in the diet (4%), but not when fed at high levels (10–15%).

Protein Retention Efficiency (PRE) A measure of *protein quality.

proteins, antifreeze Naturally occurring proteins (especially in cold-water fish), which prevent freezing of tissues on exposure to low temperatures. Of potential use in the food industry for lowering the freezing point of foods and inhibiting recrystallization of ice.

proteins, conjugated Proteins that include a non-protein *prosthetic group.

protein score A measure of *protein quality based on chemical analysis.

protein, second class *See* PROTEIN, FIRST CLASS.

protein, single-cell Collective term used for biomass of bacteria, algae, and yeast, and also (incorrectly) moulds, of potential use as animal or human food.

protein-static signals *See* AMINOSTATIC SIGNALS.

protein turnover *See* HALF-LIFE.

proteoglycans *Glycosaminoglycans esterified to proteins.

proteolysis The hydrolysis of proteins to their constituent *amino acids, catalysed by alkali, acid, or enzymes.

proteome *See* PROTEOMICS.

proteomics Identification of all the proteins present in a cell, tissue, or organism. The proteome cannot be predicted from the transcriptome, because of post-translational modifications such as glycosylation, esterification, and phosphorylation that are involved in the synthesis of many proteins. *See also* GENOMICS, NUTRITIONAL; TRANSCRIPTOMICS.

proteoses Partial degradation products of proteins.

prothrombin Protein in plasma involved in coagulation of *blood. The prothrombin time is an index of the coagulability of blood (and hence of vitamin K nutritional status) based on the time taken for a citrated sample of blood to clot when calcium ions and thromboplastin are added.

protoalkaloids Amines synthesized by decarboxylation of amino acids. *See also* ALKALOIDS; PSEUDOALKALOIDS.

protopectin *See* PECTIN.

protopectinase The enzyme in the pith of citrus fruits which converts protopectin into *pectin with the resultant separation of the plant cells from one another. Also known as pectosinase and pectosase.

provençale, à la Containing olive oil, garlic, and often tomato. Normally flavoured with mixed provençal herbs.

proving The stage in bread making when the dough is left to rise.

provitamin A substance that is converted into a vitamin, such as 7-dehydrocholesterol, which is converted into *vitamin D, or those *carotenes that can be converted to *vitamin A.

provolone Italian; smoked curd cheese, originally made from buffalo's milk, now mainly cow's milk.

proximate analysis *See* ANALYSIS, PROXIMATE.

prunelle French name for *sloe; also a liqueur made from sloes, similar to sloe gin.

prune Originally used as a general name for *plums, now specifically used for dried plums. *See* FRUIT, DRIED.

prunin *See* NARINGIN.

Prunus Genus of plants including *plums, *peaches, *nectarines, *cherries, and *almonds.

Pruteen Trade name for microbial protein produced by growing bacteria, *Methylophilus methylotrophus*, on methanol (derived from methane or natural gas); 70% protein in dry weight.

pseudoalkaloids Pharmacologically active compounds in plants; unlike *alkaloids and *protoalkaloids, they are not derived from amino acids. Two major groups: steroid and terpene derivatives, and purines (e.g. *caffeine).

pseudocereal Plants that produce seeds that are used in the same way as cereal grain to make flour, but are not grasses or true cereals, e.g. *amaranth, *buckwheat, and *quinoa.

psoralens Toxic secondary metabolites found in many fruits and vegetables; potent photosensitizers.

PSP Paralytic *shellfish poisoning.

P/S ratio The ratio between polyunsaturated and saturated *fatty acids. In Western diets the ratio is about 0.6; it is suggested that increasing it to near 1.0 would reduce the risk of atherosclerosis and coronary heart disease.

psychrophilic organisms Bacteria and fungi that tolerate low temperatures. Their preferred temperature range is 15–20 °C, but they will grow at or below 0 °C; the temperature must be reduced to about −10 °C before growth stops, but the organisms are not killed and will regrow when the temperature rises.

Bacteria of the genera *Achromobacter, Flavobacterium, Pseudomonas,* and *Micrococcus; Torulopsis* yeasts; and moulds of the genera *Penicillium, Cladosporium, Mucor,* and *Thamnidium* are psychrophiles.

psychrotrophic organisms Micro-organisms that can grow at relatively low temperatures, but grow optimally within the temperature range of 15 to 20 °C.

psyllium Small, dark reddish-brown seeds of *Plantago psyllium* or *P. ovata,* also known as plantago, flea seed; the source of *ispaghula *gum. The seeds form a mucilaginous mass with water, taken medicinally to assist the passage of intestinal contents. Aqueous extracts of psyllium reduce hyperglycaemia in *diabetes mellitus by inhibiting the intestinal absorption of glucose.

pteroylglutamic acid (pteroylglutamate, pteroyl-polyglutamic acid (pteroylpolyglutamate)) *See* FOLIC ACID.

PTFE Polytetrafluoroethylene, resistant to heat and many chemicals, and with low friction, used to make non-stick coatings for cooking utensils. Discovered by Roy Plunkett, working for Du Pont in 1938; marketed as Teflon and Fluon.

PTH *See* PARATHYROID HORMONE.

ptomaines Loosely used term for amines formed by decarboxylation of *amino acids during putrefaction of proteins, coined by Italian toxicologist Francesco Selmi, 1870: putrescine from arginine, cadaverine from lysine, muscarine in mushrooms, neurine formed by dehydration of choline. They have an unpleasant smell and were formerly thought to cause *food poisoning.

ptyalin Obsolete name for salivary *amylase.

ptyalism Excessive flow of *saliva.

puberty, delayed The normal onset of puberty in boys is between the ages of 12–15; a number of factors may delay this, especially deficiency of *zinc. Severely zinc-deficient boys of 20 are still prepubertal.

puchero Spanish, Latin American; stew of beans, meat, and sausages.

pudding A baked or steamed sponge or suet dish, usually sweet and served as a dessert, but also savoury suet puddings (e.g. steak and kidney). Also milk puddings, made by baking rice, semolina, or sago in milk. *See also* BLACK PUDDING; HASTY PUDDING.

PUFA Polyunsaturated *fatty acids.

puffballs Edible wild fungi; mosaic puffball *Calvatia* (*Lycoperdon*) *caelata*, and giant puffball *C. gigantea* (may grow to 30 cm in diameter), normally eaten while still relatively small and fleshy. Much prized for their delicate flavour. *See also* MUSHROOMS.

puffer fish *See* FUGA; TETRODONTIN POISONING.

pulasan *See* RAMBUTAN.

pulpeta Caribbean (Cuban); meat loaf, served hot or cold.

pulque Latin American; sourish beer produced by the rapid natural fermentation of aquamiel, the sweet, mucilaginous sap of the agave (American aloe or century plant, *Agave americana*). Contains 6% alcohol by volume.

puls (pulmentus) Roman; barley or wheat that has been roasted, pounded, and boiled to make a gruel; probably a precursor of *polenta.

pulses Name given to the dried seeds (matured on the plant) of *legumes such as *peas, *beans, and *lentils. In the fresh, wet form they contain about 90% water, but the dried form contains about 10% water and can be stored.

pumpernickel Dense, sour-flavoured black *bread made from *rye, originating from Germany. A 100-g portion is a *source of protein; contains 1 g of fat; provides 10 g of dietary fibre; supplies 200 kcal (850 kJ). Also used in the USA for any rye bread.

pumpkin A *gourd, fruit of *Cucurbita maxima*; a 90-g portion provides 1.8 g of dietary fibre and is a rich *source of vitamin A (as carotene); supplies 15 kcal (65 kJ).

punch A drink, hot or cold, made from wine and spirit, lemons and other fruit, spices, and sugar.

punchnep Welsh; mashed potato and turnip with small holes punched into the top, into which cream is poured.

punti Freshwater fish, a member of the *carp family, *Punctius sarana*.

purée Fruit, vegetable, meat, or fish that has been pounded or sieved (usually after cooking) to give a smooth, finely divided pulp. Also a soup made by sieving vegetables with the liquor in which they were cooked.

purgative *See* LAXATIVE.

puri (poori) Indian; unleavened wholewheat bread prepared from a butter-rich dough, shaped into small pancakes and deep fried in hot oil.

purines Nitrogenous compounds (bases) that occur in *nucleic acids (adenine and guanine) and their precursors and metabolites; inosine, caffeine, and theobromine are also purines. They are not dietary essentials; both dietary and endogenously formed purines are excreted as *uric acid. *See also* GOUT.

Sweetbread (pancreas) is rich in purines, as is fish roe; there are moderate amounts in sardines and anchovies, lesser amounts in other fish and meat; little in vegetables, fruits, and cereals.

purl Old English winter drink; warmed ale with bitters and brandy or milk, sugar, and spirit.

pursindah (pasendah) Indian; roast tender fillets of meat, cut into thin strips and beaten flat; normally cooked on skewers over *charcoal.

purslane Common purslane is *Portulaca oleracea*, a flowering succulent with edible leaves that are normally cooked. Sea purslane is *Halimione portulacoides*, a halophyte of saltmarshes and coastal dunes; the leaves may be eaten raw or cooked. Winter purslane is *Montia perfoliata*, also known as miner's lettuce and Cuban spinach.

puto South-East Asian; steamed bread made from rice that has been allowed to undergo a lactic acid fermentation. *Leuconostoc mesenteroides* and yeasts produce carbon dioxide as a raising agent.

putromaine Any toxin produced by the decay of food within the body.

pyrazines Derivatives of six-membered heterocyclic aromatic compounds with two N atoms in the ring that impart nutty, roasted, green, and fruity flavours to foods.

pyridine nucleotides Obsolete name for the *coenzymes *NAD and NADP.

pyridorin Term used for pyridoxamine (*see* VITAMIN B$_6$) when used to inhibit the Amadori reaction (the rearrangement of the initial product of protein glycation to the advanced glycation end-product); potentially useful in preventing the adverse effects of poor glycaemic control in *diabetes mellitus.

pyridoxal, pyridoxamine, pyridoxine *See* VITAMIN B$_6$.

pyridoxyllysine The product of reaction between pyridoxal (*see* VITAMIN B$_6$) and the ε-amino side-chains of *lysine residues in proteins, which renders both the vitamin and the lysine unavailable.

pyrimidines Nitrogenous compounds (bases) that occur in *nucleic acids: cytosine, thymidine, and uracil.

pyrocarbonate *See* DIETHYL PYROCARBONATE.

pyrolysis Degradation of a compound by heat; pyrolysis products of proteins formed in roasting and grilling meat adds much of the flavour, although there is evidence that some pyrolysis products are potentially carcinogenic.

pyrroles Derivatives of five-membered heterocyclic compounds (C_4H_4NH) that impart a 'burnt' flavour to foods, mainly formed by the *Maillard reaction.

pyruvate Salts of *pyruvic acid.

pyruvic acid An intermediate in the metabolism of carbohydrates, formed by the anaerobic *metabolism of *glucose. It may then either be converted to acetyl CoA, and oxidized through the *citric acid cycle, or be reduced to lactic acid. The oxidation to acetyl CoA is *thiamin dependent, and blood concentrations of pyruvate and lactate rise in thiamin deficiency.

p

Q

QbA Qualitätswein bestimmer Anbaugebeite; *see* WINE CLASSIFICATION, GERMANY.

QmP Qualitätswein mit Prädikat; *see* WINE CLASSIFICATION, GERMANY.

QPM Quality protein *maize.

QUAC stick Quaker arm circumference measuring stick. A stick used to measure height which also shows the 80th and 85th centiles of expected *mid-upper-arm circumference. Developed by a Quaker Service Team in Nigeria in the 1960s as a rapid and simple tool for assessment of nutritional status.

quahog American bivalve *shellfish, *Venus mercenaria*.

quail Formerly a *game bird, now so endangered in the wild that shooting is prohibited, but it is farmed. Two main species, *Bonasa umbellus* and *Colinus virginianus*; Californian quail is *Lophortyx californica*. The small eggs are prized as a delicacy. A 150-g portion (whole bird) is a rich *source of protein and niacin; a good source of vitamins B_1 and B_2; contains 3g of fat; and supplies 180kcal (760kJ).

qualitätswein *See* WINE CLASSIFICATION, GERMANY.

quamash (camash) Starchy roots of *Camassia quamash*, the staple food of west coast native Americans.

quantitative ingredients declaration (QUID) Obligatory on food labels in the EU since February 2000; previously legislation required only declaration of ingredients in descending order of quantity, not specific declaration of the amount of each ingredient present.

quark (quarg) Originally German; very low-fat cheese made from skimmed milk; contains 80% water; a 100-g portion is a good *source of protein and vitamin B_{12}; a source of vitamin B_2; with only a trace of fat, contains 40mg of sodium and 90mg of calcium; and supplies 80kcal (325kJ).

quart Imperial measure of volume, equal to ¼ imperial gallon or 2 pints (i.e. 1.1L).

quart, reputed The traditional 'bottle' of wine or spirits; approximately ⅔ imperial quart, or 26⅔ fl oz (730 mL). Reputed pint is 13⅓ fl oz.

quartern *See* NOGGIN.

queen cake Individual, small, light, rich cakes containing dried fruit.

queen fish Freshwater fish, *Botia dario*.

queen of puddings *Pudding made from custard and breadcrumbs, flavoured with lemon rind and vanilla, topped with jam or sliced fruit and meringue.

queen substance *See* ROYAL JELLY.

quenelle Dumpling made from finely pounded meat or fish.

quercitin A flavone (*see* FLAVONOIDS), found in onion skins, tea, hops, and horse chestnuts.

quercitol A sweet compound isolated from *acorns, sometimes called acorn sugar.

quercitron A *flavin.

querns Pair of grinding stones used for pulverizing grain (from about 4000–2000 BC). The lower stone was slightly hollowed and the upper stone was rolled by hand on the lower one.

Quetelet's index *See* BODY MASS INDEX.

quetsch German; plum brandy prepared by distillation of fermented plums. Similar to *slivovitz and *mirabelle. Sometimes called zwetschgenwasser or zwetschenwasser.

quiche Savoury egg custard tart in a pastry case containing a wide variety of vegetable, meat, or fish fillings. Speciality of Alsace and Lorraine in France.

quick breads Baked goods such as biscuits, muffins, popovers, griddles, cakes, waffles, and dumplings, in which no yeast is used, but the raising is carried out quickly with baking powder or other chemical agents.

QUID *See* QUANTITATIVE INGREDIENTS DECLARATION.

quillaja (quillaia) Also known as soapbark; the dried bark of the shrub *Quillaja saponaria*, which contains *saponins and *tannins. Used to produce foam in soft drinks, shampoos, and fire extinguishers.

quinazolidine alkaloids A group of about 100 bitter compounds found in lupin seeds; modern varieties are called sweet because the *alkaloid content has been reduced very considerably by selective breeding.

quince Pear-shaped fruit of *Cydonia oblongata*, with flesh similar to that of the apple; sour but strong aromatic flavour when cooked; rich in pectin and used chiefly in jams and jellies; formerly known as 'the apple and the vine'. The British *National Fruit Collection has twenty varieties. Japanese quince is the fruit of the ornamental shrub *Chaenomelis lagenaria*, hard, sour and aromatic, used in preserves and jellies.

quince, Bengal (Indian quince) *See* BAEL.

quinine Bitter *alkaloid extracted from the bark of the cinchona tree (*Cinchona officinalis*), used to treat or prevent malaria and in apéritif wines, *bitters, and *tonic water.

quinoa Glutinous seeds of the South American plant *Chenopodium quinoa* (syn. *C. album*), used in Chile and Peru to make bread. A 100-g portion is a rich *source of iron and vitamin B_1; a good source of protein; a source of calcium, vitamin B_2, and niacin; supplies 350 kcal (1470 kJ). *See also* KAÑIWA.

quinquina French; bitter *vermouths based on partially fermented grape juice (mistelle) and *quinine; trade names include Byrrh, Dubonnet, and St Raphaël.

quintal 100 kg (220 lb).

Quorn Trade name for *mycoprotein from the mould *Fusarium graminearum*. A 150-g portion is a good *source of protein and niacin; a source of vitamin B_2; contains 4 g of fat, of which a quarter is saturated and half polyunsaturated; provides 7 g of dietary fibre; supplies 130 kcal (550 kJ).

q

R- and S- Prefixes to chemical names to denote the three-dimensional arrangement of the molecule based on rigorous chemical rules. *See* D-, L-, AND DL-.

rabbit *Lepus cuniculus*; both wild and farmed rabbits are eaten. A 150-g portion is a rich *source of protein, niacin, vitamins B_2, B_6, and B_{12}, selenium, and iron; a source of vitamin B_1, zinc, and copper; contains about 12g of fat, of which about 40% is *saturated and 20% mono-unsaturated; supplies 270 kcal (1100 kJ).

rabri Indian; concentrated, sweetened buffalo milk product with a flaky texture. Milk is heated and the clotted cream is removed; sugar is added to the concentrated milk, then the clotted cream is added back.

racasse Marine fish, *Scorpaema porcus*, also known as black scorpionfish.

racemic The mixture of the *D- and L-isomers of a compound, commonly shown as DL-.

rack Rib chops of lamb or mutton, left in one piece for roasting.

raclette French, Swiss; cheese melted over a fire, eaten with boiled potatoes.

racuszki Polish; deep-fried puffs made from mashed potato, served with sugar and sour cream.

radappertization Sterilization of food by high-dose irradiation for complete destruction of (virtually) all organisms. *See also* RADICIDATION; RADURIZATION; STERILE.

radicals Highly reactive molecules with an unpaired electron. *See* ANTIOXIDANT NUTRIENTS.

radicchio Red *chicory.

radicidation Low-level irradiation treatment to kill non-spore-forming pathogens and prevent food poisoning. *See also* RADAPPERTIZATION; RADURIZATION.

radioallergosorbent tests (RAST) Tests for food allergy. *See* FOOD, ADVERSE REACTIONS.

radio frequency heating *See* MICROWAVE COOKING.

radiolysis Chemical changes caused by irradiation, producing compounds that have antibacterial activity.

radish The root of *Raphanus* spp. An 80-g portion is a good *source of vitamin C; supplies 10kcal (40kJ).

radish, Japanese Oriental variety of *Raphanus sativus* with a long root and mild flavour. Sold in the UK as mouli or rettich. Also known as daikon.

radurization *Pasteurization of food by low-dose irradiation to destroy a sufficient number of yeasts, moulds, and non-spore-forming bacteria to prolong shelf life. *See also* RADAPPERTIZATION; RADICIDATION.

RAE *See* RETINOL ACTIVITY EQUIVALENT.

raffinade Best-quality refined sugar.

raffinose A trisaccharide, galactosyl-glucosyl-fructose, not hydrolysed by intestinal enzymes, and a substrate for bacterial fermentation, leading to *flatulence. Has 23% of the sweetness of sucrose. Also known as melitose or melitriose.

raftiline Preparation of *inulin from chicory roots. Used as a fat replacer and bulking agent.

ragi **1.** Dried balls of starter containing moulds, yeast, and bacteria on cereal or starch, used as a starter inoculation for production of *lao-chao, *saké, *tapé, and other fermented foods. **2.** Finger *millet, *Eleusine coracana*.

ragoût Stew of meat or poultry and vegetables, browned in a little fat then gently simmered.

rainbow runner Marine fish, *Elagatis bipinnulata*.

raisin Dried seedless grapes of several kinds. Valencia raisins from Spanish grapes; Thompson seedless raisins produced mainly in California from the sultanina grape (the skins are coarser than the sultana). Raisins are also produced in Australia and South Africa. A 20-g portion provides 1.4g of dietary fibre and supplies 50kcal (210kJ). *See also* CURRANTS, DRIED; DRIED FRUIT; SULTANAS.

Raisin oil is extracted from the seeds of muscat *grapes, which are removed before drying them to yield raisins. The oil is used primarily to coat the raisins to prevent them sticking together, to render them soft and pliable and less subject to insect infestation.

raising powder *See* BAKING POWDER.

raita Indian; yoghurt with chopped cucumber, onion, garlic, and spices.

raki *See* OUZO.

rambutan Fruit of the evergreen tree *Nephelium lappaceum*; covered with yellowish-red, soft spines with large seed surrounded by white juicy flesh, similar to *lychee, and sometimes called hairy lychee. The name means 'hairy man of the jungle' in Bahasa-Malay, reflecting the appearance of the fruit. The pulasan (*N. rambutan-ake* syn. *N. mutabile*) is similar.

ramekin **1.** Porcelain or earthenware mould in which mixture is baked and then brought to the table, or the savoury served in a ramekin dish. Paper soufflé cases are called ramekin cases. **2.** Formerly the name given to toasted cheese; now tarts filled with cream cheese.

rancidity The development of unpleasant flavours in oils and fats as a result of oxidation or lipolysis (*see* RANCIDITY, LIPOLYTIC).

rancidity, ketonic Some moulds (*Penicillium* and *Aspergillus* spp.) attack fats containing short-chain fatty acids and produce *ketones with a characteristic odour and taste. Butter, coconut, and palm kernel oils are most susceptible.

rancidity, lipolytic Spoilage of foods as a result of *hydrolysis of fats to free fatty acids on storage by the action of *lipase either from bacteria or naturally present in the food.

randomization of fats *See* INTERESTERIFICATION.

rape *Brassica napus* and *B. rapa*, also known as cole, coleseed, or colza. Grown for its seed, as source of oil for both industrial and food use. Varieties low in *erucic acid are termed '0' or single low; varieties also low in glucosinolates are termed '00' or double low, both these being undesirable constituents of ordinary rapeseed. The oil is very rich in mono-unsaturates (60%), contains 33% polyunsaturates, and only 7% saturates. *See also* CANOLA.

RAR Retinoic acid receptor; *see* VITAMIN A.

RARE Retinoic acid *response element; *see* VITAMIN A.

rarebit *See* WELSH RAREBIT.

ras el hanout Moroccan; spice mixture containing 30 or more ingredients. The name means 'top of the shop', implying that the spice merchant takes special pride in his blend.

rasgulla Indian; dessert of small balls of milk curd, ground almond, and semolina boiled in syrup.

rasher Slice of *bacon or *ham.

raspberry Fruit of *Rubus idaeus*. An 80-g portion is a rich *source of vitamin C; a source of folate and copper; supplies 6.4g of dietary fibre; supplies 20kcal (85kJ). Black raspberry is *R. occidentalis*, native of the eastern USA. *See also* WINEBERRY.

raspings Finely ground breadcrumbs, used for coating rissoles, fishcakes, etc.

RAST Radioallergosorbent tests for food allergy. *See* FOOD, ADVERSE REACTIONS.

rastons Medieval English; small round loaves made from sweetened bread dough with egg. After baking the top was cut off and the crumb removed; the hollow shell was filled with finely chopped crumb mixed with butter, the top replaced, and the dish served hot.

rastrello Sharp-edged spoon used to cut out the pulp from halved oranges or other *citrus fruit.

ratafia 1. Flavouring essence made from bitter almonds. 2. Small macaroon-like biscuits flavoured with almonds. 3. Almond-flavoured liqueur.

ratatouille French, Provençal; casserole or stew of aubergine, onions, peppers, courgettes, and tomatoes.

ravigote butter *See* BUTTER, RAVIGOTE.

ravigote sauce French; 1. *salad dressing containing pounded hard-boiled egg, highly flavoured with garlic and chopped herbs. 2. Sauce made from ravigote butter (*see* BUTTER, RAVIGOTE) melted in wine and vinegar added to a *velouté sauce; served with boiled poultry.

ravioli Square envelope of *pasta stuffed with minced meat or cheese.

ray Cartilaginous fish, *Raja* spp. Thornback ray is *R. clavata*, starry ray is *R. asterias*, and shagreen ray is *Leucoraja fullonica*. Often used synonymously with *skate.

RBC Red *blood cells.

RBP *See* RETINOL BINDING PROTEIN.

RCT Randomized controlled trial—the gold standard for intervention trials; neither the subjects nor the investigators know the allocation of active treatment or placebo, and allocation to one treatment or the other is by use of random number tables.

RD Região demarcada; *see* WINE CLASSIFICATION, PORTUGAL.

RDA Recommended daily (or dietary) allowance (or amount) of nutrients; first US RDA published in 1943; *see* REFERENCE INTAKES.

RE Retinol equivalents; *see* VITAMIN A.

rebaudioside Very sweet substance extracted from the leaves of *Stevia rebaudiana* (same source as *stevioside); 400 times as sweet as sucrose.

réchauffé Made-up dish of reheated food; literally 'reheated' (French).

reciprocal ponderal index An index of adiposity; height divided by cube root of weight. *See also* PONDERAL INDEX.

Recommended Daily Amount (Recommended Daily Allowance, RDA) *See* REFERENCE INTAKES.

recrystallization Changes in shape, size, or orientation of ice crystals in frozen foods that cause a loss of quality.

rectal feeding *See* NUTRIENT ENEMATA.

red blood cells *See* BLOOD CELLS.

red colours *Amaranth, *carmoisine, *cochineal, *erythrosine, *ponceau 4R, red 2G.

red cooking Chinese method of cooking; meat or poultry is first *stir fried, then simmered in broth or water with *soy sauce, *herbs, and spices.

redcurrants Fruit of *Ribes sativum* (same species as whitecurrants); the British *National Fruit Collection has 70 varieties of redcurrant and 20 of whitecurrant. An 80-g portion is a rich *source of vitamin C; a source of copper; provides 5.6 g of dietary fibre; supplies 15 kcal (65 kJ).

redfish Marine fish, *Sebastes* spp. and *Helicolenus* spp. Also known as ocean perch or rose fish.

redox potential Oxidation/reduction potential, the tendency of a compound to undergo reduction.

red tide Sudden, unexplained increase in numbers of toxic organisms (dinoflagellates) in the sea which cause fish and shellfish feeding on them to become toxic. *See also* CIGUATERA; PHYCOTOXINS; SHELLFISH POISONING.

r

reduce The process of boiling a mixture (especially when making a sauce, soup, or syrup) in an uncovered pan to evaporate surplus liquid and give a more concentrated product.

reduced EU and US legislation state that for a food label or advertising to bear a claim that it contains a reduced amount of fat, saturates, cholesterol, sodium, or alcohol it must contain 25% less of the specified nutrient than a reference product for which no claim is made. A food may not claim to have a reduced content of a nutrient if it is already classified as *low in or *free from that nutrient.

Reductil Trade name for *sibutramine, an *anorectic drug used in the treatment of obesity.

reduction The opposite of *oxidation; chemical reactions resulting in a gain of electrons, or hydrogen, or the loss of oxygen.

reduction rolls *See* MILLING.

reference intakes (of nutrients) Amounts of nutrients greater than the requirements of almost all members of the population, determined on the basis of the average requirement plus twice the standard deviation, to allow for individual variation in requirements and thus cover the theoretical needs of 97.5% of the population.

Reference intakes for energy are based on the average requirement, without the allowance for individual variation. Used for planning institutional catering and assessing the adequacy of diets of groups of people, but not strictly applicable to individuals. Tables of reference intakes published by different national and international authorities differ because of differences in the interpretation of the available data.

Variously called, in different countries and by different expert committees: RDA, the Recommended Daily (or Dietary) Amount (or Allowance); RDI, Recommended Daily (or Dietary) Intake; RNI, Reference Nutrient Intake; PRI, Population Reference Intake; safe allowances. *See* APPENDICES IV–VIII.

Levels of intake below that at which health and metabolic integrity are likely to be maintained are generally taken as the average requirement minus twice the standard deviation. Variously known as Minimum Safe Intake (MSI), Lower Reference Nutrient Intake (LRNI), and Lowest Threshold Intake.

reference man/woman An arbitrary physiological standard; defined as a person aged 25, weighing 65 kg, living in a temperate zone of a mean annual temperature of 10 °C. Reference man performs medium work, with an average daily energy requirement of 13.5 MJ (3200 kcal). Reference woman is engaged in general household duties or light industry, with an average daily requirement of 9.7 MJ (2300 kcal).

Reference Nutrient Intake (RNI) *See* REFERENCE INTAKES.

reference protein *See* PROTEIN, REFERENCE.

reform sauce *Espagnole sauce enriched with port and *redcurrant jelly; originated at the Reform Club in London as an accompaniment for breaded and fried lamb cutlets.

refractive index Measure of the bending or refraction of a beam of light on entering a denser medium (the ratio between the sine of the angle of incidence of the ray of light and the sine of the angle of refraction). It is constant for pure substances under standard conditions. Used as a measure of sugar or total solids in solution, purity of oils, etc.

refractometer Instrument to measure the *refractive index.

refreshing A process used by cooks when preparing vegetables. After the vegetables have been cooked, cold water is poured over them to preserve the colour; they are then reheated before serving.

região demarcada (RD) *See* WINE CLASSIFICATION, PORTUGAL.

regional enteritis *See* CROHN'S DISEASE.

Register of Accredited Nutritionists A register of those with approved qualifications in nutrition maintained by the British Nutrition Society. There are also separate registers of public health nutritionists and sports nutritionists.

reine, à la *See* BOUCHÉE.

Relative Protein Value (RPV) A measure of *protein quality.

relative risk In epidemiology, the ratio of the incidence of a disease or condition in a group exposed to an environmental factor or experimental condition to that in a control group.

release agents Substances applied to tinned or enamelled surfaces or plastic films to prevent the food adhering, e.g. fatty acid amides, microcrystalline waxes, starch, methyl cellulose.

relish Culinary term for any spicy or piquant preparation used to enhance flavour of plain food. In the UK, a thin pickle or sauce with a vinegar base; in the USA it includes finely chopped fruit or vegetables with a dressing of salt, sugar, and vinegar, sometimes eaten as a first course (termed apple, garden, or salad relish).

Gentleman's relish is a trade name for a paste of anchovies, butter, cereal, salt, and spices developed in the UK in the 19th century; also called patum peperium.

rémoulade sauce Mayonnaise with added mustard and finely chopped capers, gherkins, parsley, and chervil. *See also* SALAD DRESSING.

remove Obsolete term for the main course of dinner.

renal failure Inability of the kidneys to excrete waste, as a result of kidney disease. Especially in advanced cases, as well as haemodialysis, treatment includes feeding a very low protein diet, so as to minimize the amount of nitrogenous waste that must be excreted.

renal threshold Concentration of a compound in the blood above which it is not reabsorbed by the kidney, and so is excreted in the urine.

rendering The process of liberating the fat from the cells that constitute the adipose tissue. Dry rendering, heating the fat dry, or wet rendering, when water is present.

renin The *enzyme that converts angiotensinogen to *angiotensin.

rennet Extract of calf stomach; contains the enzyme *chymosin (rennin) which clots milk. Used in cheese making and for *junket.

rennet, vegetable The name given to proteolytic enzymes derived from plants, such as bromelain (from the pineapple) and ficin (from the fig), as well as biosynthetic *chymosin. Used for the preparation of 'vegetarian' cheeses.

rennin See CHYMOSIN.

renversé Turned out of a mould, as for a cream or jelly.

repression (of enzymes) Decreased synthesis of an *enzyme in response to a *hormone or other stimulus that decreases *transcription (and hence expression) of the gene for that enzyme. See also INDUCTION.

resazurin test See MILK, DYE REDUCTION TEST OF.

resins, ion-exchange See ION-EXCHANGE RESINS.

resistin Small protein secreted by adipose tissue that antagonizes *insulin action in the liver and acts on *adipose tissue to inhibit differentiation of pre-adipocytes. Expression is low in *diabetes mellitus and during food deprivation, increased on refeeding, administration of insulin, and in obesity. Also known as adipocyte secreted factor.

respiratory quotient (RQ) Ratio of the volume of carbon dioxide produced when a substance is oxidized, to the volume of oxygen used. The oxidation of carbohydrate results in an RQ of 1.0; of fat, 0.7; and of protein, 0.8.

respirometer See SPIROMETER.

response element A region in *DNA that may be up- or downstream of a *gene; it binds a *hormone receptor or other ligand and serves to increase or decrease the rate at which the gene is transcribed (see TRANSCRIPTION).

restoration The addition of nutrients to replace those lost in processing, as in milling of cereals. See also FORTIFICATION.

restriction enzymes Endonucleases isolated from bacteria, used to cut *DNA molecules into smaller pieces. Many act at palindromic sequences, and so produce 'sticky ends', permitting insertion of new DNA into a bacterial or other *genome.

reticulocyte Immature precursor of the red blood cell in which the remains of the nucleus are visible as a reticulum. Very few are seen in normal blood as they are retained in the marrow until mature, but on remission of anaemia, when there is a high rate of production, reticulocytes appear in the bloodstream (reticulocytosis).

reticulum See RUMINANT.

retinal (retinaldehyde; retinene, retinoic acid) *See* VITAMIN A.

retinoid receptors Intracellular proteins that bind the vitamers of *vitamin A (retinol, retinoic acid, and other *retinoids), resulting in the modulation of gene expression, and hence the basis of the actions of the vitamin other than in vision.

retinoids Compounds chemically related to, or derived from, *vitamin A, which display some of the biological activities of the vitamin, but have lower toxicity; they are used for treatment of severe skin disorders and some cancers.

retinol *See* VITAMIN A.

retinol activity equivalent (RAE) Alternative to *retinol equivalent, taking into account more recent data on the *bioefficacy of *carotenoids as precursors of *vitamin A. 1 µg RAE = 1 µg preformed retinol, 2 µg β-carotene supplement in oil, 12 µg β-carotene, or 24 µg other pro-vitamin A carotenoids.

retinol binding protein The protein required for transport of *vitamin A from liver reserves to tissues.

retinol equivalent The *vitamin A content of foods is expressed as retinol equivalents, i.e. retinol plus carotene; 1 µg retinol = 6 µg β-carotene = 12 µg other active carotenoids = 3.33 *international units. *See also* RETINOL ACTIVITY EQUIVALENT.

retort In food technology, an *autoclave.

retrogradation The crystalline structure of starch is lost in baking, and subsequently the starch recrystallizes—this is the process of retrogradation. As a result bread crumb loses its softness and the bread goes stale. Retrogradation can be delayed by *emulsifying agents such as monoglycerides, which are known as *crumb-softeners.

retsina Greek dry white wine, with a strong resinous flavour due to the addition of pine resin as a preservative.

reverse osmosis *See* OSMOSIS, REVERSE.

reverse transcription PCR *See* POLYMERASE CHAIN REACTION.

rexinoids Compounds chemically related to *vitamin A, that bind to the retinoid X receptor but not the retinoic acid receptor.

RF heating *See* MICROWAVE HEATING.

RFLP Restriction fragment length *polymorphism, variation in the length of DNA fragments produced by the action of *restriction enzymes.

rhamnose A methylated pentose (five-carbon) sugar; it has 33% of the sweetness of sucrose, and is widely distributed in plant foods.

rheology Study of deformation and flow of materials; in food technology it involves plasticity of fats, doughs, milk curd, etc. It provides a scientific basis for subjective measurements such as mouth feel, spreadability, pourability.

rhizome Botanical term for swollen stem that produces roots and leafy shoots.

rhizopterin Obsolete name for *folic acid.

rhodopsin The pigment in the rod cells of the retina of the eye, also known as visual purple, consisting of the protein opsin and retinaldehyde, which is responsible for the visual process. In cone cells of the retina the equivalent protein is iodopsin. *See* VITAMIN A; DARK ADAPTATION; VISION.

Rhodotorula Yeasts that may cause red, pink, or yellow discolouration in foods.

rhubarb Leaf-stalks of the perennial plant, *Rheum rhabarbarum*. Has a high content of *oxalic acid (the leaves contain even more, and are toxic). A 200-g portion (stewed without sugar) is a *source of vitamin C; contains 2.5 g of dietary fibre; supplies 15 kcal (65 kJ).

riboflavin *See* VITAMIN B_2.

ribonucleic acid (RNA) *See* NUCLEIC ACIDS.

ribose A pentose (five-carbon) sugar which occurs as an intermediate in the metabolism of glucose; especially important in the *nucleic acids and various *coenzymes; occurs widely in foods.

ribosomes The intracellular organelles on which proteins are synthesized.

ribotyping Method for identification of bacteria using DNA probes to identify their ribosomal RNA.

rice Grain of *Oryza sativa* (African rice is *O. glaberrima*); the major food in many countries. Rice when threshed is known as paddy, and is covered with a fibrous husk comprising nearly 40% of the grain. When the husk has been removed, brown rice is left. When the outer bran layers up to the endosperm and germ are removed, the ordinary white rice of commerce or polished rice is obtained (usually polished with glucose and talc). There are many thousands of varieties, in two main groups: long-grained *indica* and short-grained glutinous *japonica*.

A 200-g portion of boiled brown rice is a good *source of niacin and copper; a source of protein, vitamin B_1, and selenium; provides 1.6 g of dietary fibre; supplies 280 kcal (1180 kJ). A 200-g portion of boiled white rice is a source of niacin and protein; supplies 280 kcal (1180 kJ).

rice, American *See* BULGUR.

rice cones Granular rice particles the size of sand grains; the rice equivalent of *semolina.

rice, fermented South American; whole rice is moistened and left to ferment for 10–15 days, then dried and milled. Bacterial and fungal fermentation reduces the time required for cooking—there is some loss of protein, but synthesis of *vitamin B_2. Also known as arroz fermentado, arroz amarillo, or sierra rice.

rice, glutinous Rice that is rich is soluble starch, dextrin, and maltose, so that on boiling the grains adhere in a sticky mass; used mainly for sweetmeats and cakes, also *sushi. For most dishes, separate rice grains that do not stick together are preferred.

rice, golden Variety of rice genetically engineered to contain large amounts of *carotene.

rice grass, Indian Perennial, growing wild in the USA, *Oryzopsis hymenoides*; tolerant to drought. The seeds, which resemble *millet, are small, round, and dark in colour, covered with white hairs. Traditionally used by native Americans for flour, now used almost exclusively for forage.

rice, hungry A variety of *millet, *Digitaria exilis*, important in West Africa; also known as fonio.

rice, maize (mealie rice) *See* MAIZE RICE.

rice paper Smooth edible white 'paper' made from the pith of the Taiwanese shrub *Tetrapanax papyriferus* and the Indo-Pacific shrub *Scaevola sericea*. Macaroons and similar biscuits are baked on it and the paper can be eaten with the biscuits.

rice, parboiled *See* PARBOIL.

rice, red West African rice, *Oryza glaberrima*, with red bran layer.

rice, sierra *See* RICE, FERMENTED.

rice, synthetic *See* TAPIOCA-MACARONI.

rice, Tuscarora *See* RICE, WILD.

rice, unpolished American term; rice that has been under-milled in that the husk, germ, and bran layers have been only partially removed.

rice vinegar Japanese; *vinegar prepared from *saké.

rice, wild *Zizania aquatica*, native to eastern North America, grows 12 feet high; it has a long, thin, greenish grain; little is grown and it is difficult to harvest. Also known as zizanie, Tuscarora rice, Indian rice, and American wild rice (American rice is bulgur); called wild oats by some early travellers. Higher in protein content than ordinary rice at 14%.

rice wine *See* SAKÉ.

Richelieu, à la Dish made with Richelieu sauce (a rich brown Madeira sauce) or garnished with mushrooms, artichokes, or stuffed tomatoes, etc.

ricin A *lectin in the *castor oil bean.

ricing Culinary term: cutting into small pieces about the size of rice grains.

ricinoleic acid A hydroxylated mono-unsaturated *fatty acid in *castor oil.

rickets Malformation of the bones in growing children due to deficiency of *vitamin D, leading to poor absorption of calcium. In adults the equivalent is *osteomalacia.

rickets, refractory (vitamin D resistant rickets) *Rickets that does not respond to normal amounts of vitamin D but requires massive doses. Usually a result of a congenital defect in the vitamin D receptor, or the metabolism of the vitamin; it can also be due to poisoning with strontium.

rickey Long drink made from liqueur or spirit with ginger ale and fresh fruit.

ricotta Italian; *cheese made originally from the *whey left by cheese making, but now often with milk added.

riddle bread Yorkshire; griddle cakes made from oatmeal mixed with water and left overnight to ferment, then baked on one side on a griddle.

riesling One of the nine 'classic' *grape varieties used for *wine making; the wines have a flowery aroma when young.

rigor mortis Stiffening of muscle that occurs after death. As the flow of blood ceases, anaerobic metabolism leads to the formation of lactic acid and the soft, pliable muscle becomes stiff and rigid. If meat is hung in a cool place for a few days ('conditioned'), the meat softens again. Fish similarly undergo rigor mortis but it is usually of shorter duration than in mammals. *See also* MEAT CONDITIONING; MEAT, DFD.

rijsttaffel Dutch, Indonesian; meal consisting of twenty or more different dishes served at the same time.

rillauds French; potted pork, goose, or rabbit made from very small pieces, flavoured, seasoned, and cooked very slowly in stock. Rillettes and rillons are modifications of the procedure.

rillettes, rillons *See* RILLAUDS.

rimonabant Appetite suppressant drug used to treat *obesity and the *metabolic syndrome; it acts as a cannibinoid receptor antagonist.

rioja Wines from the Rioja region of Spain; white or red. Traditionally matured in oak casks, so have a strong 'oaky' flavour.

risk, attributable In epidemiology, the difference in the incidence of the condition under investigation between the exposed group and those unexposed to a particular hazard. It estimates the proportion of disease incidence that may be due to a particular exposure or risk factor. *See also* RISK, RELATIVE.

risk factor In epidemiology, something that can be measured (perhaps as a surrogate) as an index of the hazard of an exposure; it does not imply cause and effect, and reducing the risk factor may not reduce the incidence of disease.

risk, relative In epidemiology, the ratio of the incidence of the condition under investigation in the exposed group (or those receiving an experimental treatment) to those unexposed (or the control group). A relative risk of 1 shows that there is no difference between the groups; a value >1 shows a hazard of the exposure or treatment; a value <1 shows a beneficial effect of the exposure or treatment. *See also* RISK, ATTRIBUTABLE.

risotto Italian; rice dishes cooked with meat, poultry, vegetables, etc.

rissole Small round cake of cooked minced meat, bound with mashed potato, coated in egg and breadcrumbs, and fried. Originally enclosed in an envelope of thin pastry before frying.

rissolé Roasted or fried and well browned.

river cobbler Freshwater fish, *Pangasius* spp.

RMR Resting metabolic rate; *see* BASAL METABOLIC RATE.

RNA Ribonucleic acid; *see* NUCLEIC ACIDS.

RNAi (RNA interference) A technique for silencing the expression of specific genes by use of double-stranded *RNA; it serves as an antiviral defence mechanism and may play a role in the formation and maintenance of heterochromatin during cell division.

RNI Reference Nutrient Intake; *see* REFERENCE INTAKES.

roach Freshwater fish, a member of the *carp family, *Rutilus rutilus*.

roast Originally meant to cook meat over an open fire on a spit; now refers to cooking in an enclosed oven, and so is 'dry heating'. With meat the juices evaporate on the surface, producing the *Maillard complex characteristic of roasted meat.

robert sauce Piquant sauce containing onion, white wine, vinegar, mustard, and espagnole or demi-glace sauce; served with meat.

r

rocambole Mild variety of *garlic, *Allium scordoprasum*, also called sand leek.

rock (mint-rock) Traditional English seaside sugar confectionery, made by pulling melted sugar. It is white, with an outer coloured layer (traditionally pink) and an inner ring of coloured sugar that spells out the name of the town where it is sold or of which it is a souvenir.

rock cake Plain buns containing fruit and spice, baked in small heaps on a tin or baking sheet.

rock candy Large clear crystals of sugar made by suspending strings in sugar syrup.

rock eel, rock salmon Alternative names for *dogfish.

rocket Cruciferous plant, *Eruca sativa*, with small spear-shaped leaves and peppery taste, eaten raw in salads or cooked. Also called arugula, rucola, Italian cress. Grown as an oilseed crop (jamba oil) in some countries.

rock fish Saltwater *fish, *Sebastodes* spp., with a flavour resembling crab.

rock lobster New Zealand salt-water *crayfish (*Jasus edwardsii*).

rocou *See* ANNATTO.

roe Hard roe is the eggs of the female fish. A 100-g portion of (fried) cod roe is a rich *source of protein, vitamins B_1, B_2, and C; a good source of niacin; a source of iron; contains 10g of fat, of which 10% is saturated and 50% unsaturated; supplies 200kcal (840kJ). Soft roe is from the male fish, also known as milt. A 100-g portion of (fried) herring roe is a rich source of protein, vitamin B_2, and niacin; a source of vitamin B_1, and iron; contains 15g of fat, of which 10% is saturated and 50% polyunsaturated; supplies 240kcal (1000kJ). Hard roe of sturgeon, lumpfish, and other fishes are used to make *caviare.

rohu Freshwater fish *Labeo rohita*; carp family.

rohwurst German; raw, fermented, dry sausages.

roker Marine fish, *Raja clavata*.

roller mill Pairs of horizontal cylindrical rollers, separated by only a small gap and revolving at different speeds. The material is thus ground and crushed in one operation. Used in flour milling.

rollmop Filleted uncooked *herring pickled in spiced vinegar.

roll-on closure (RO) Aluminium or lacquered tinplate cap for sealing on to narrow-necked bottles with a threaded neck. The unthreaded cap is moulded on to the neck of the bottle and forms an airtight seal.

roly-poly Sweet suet *pudding filled with jam.

romaine French and American name for cos *lettuce.

romesco sauce Spanish (Catalan); pungent red sauce made from small red peppers, tomatoes, almonds, olive oil, garlic, and cayenne pepper.

root beer American; non-alcoholic carbonated beverage flavoured with extract of *sassafras root and oil of wintergreen.

ropa vieja *See* OLD CLOTHES STEW.

rope Spore-forming bacteria (*Bacillus mesentericus* and *B. subtilis*) occurring on wheat and hence in flour. The spores can survive baking and then are present in the bread. Under the right conditions of warmth and moisture the spores germinate and the bacteria convert the bread into sticky, yellowish patches which can be pulled out into rope-like threads, hence the term 'ropy' bread. The bacterial growth is inhibited by acids. Can also occur in milk, called long milk in Scandinavia.

roquefort French; green-blue marbled *cheese made in Roquefort-sur-Soulzon from cow's milk; ripened in limestone caves where the mould *Penicillium roquefortii* is present and the cheese thus inoculated. A 30-g portion is a *source of vitamins B_{12}, B_2, and protein; contains 9 g of fat, 200 mg of calcium, 500 mg of sodium; supplies 115 kcal (475 kJ).

ROS **1.** Reactive oxygen species; *see* ANTIOXIDANT NUTRIENTS. **2.** Resistant oligosaccharides; *see* GLYCAEMIC INDEX.

rosado Portuguese, Spanish; rosé wines.

rosato Italian; rosé wines.

rosé Pink-coloured *wines, either made from red grapes, allowing the skin to remain in the fermentation for only 12–36 hours, or by mixing red and white wines. Known as blush wines in the USA.

rose fish *See* REDFISH.

rose hips The fruit of the rose (*Rosa* spp.); a rich source of vitamin C. Rose-hip syrup is extract of rose hips with added sugar.

roselle Caribbean (originally African) plant, *Hibiscus sabdariffa*, grown for its fleshy red sepals, used to make drinks, jams, and jelly; the leaves are also eaten. Also known as Jamaica sorrel, flor de Jamaica.

rosemary An evergreen bushy shrub, *Rosmarinus officinalis*, cultivated commercially for its essential oil (*see* OILS, ESSENTIAL), used in medicine and perfumery. The leaves are used to flavour soups, sauces and meat.

rose water Fragrant water made by distillation or extraction of the essential oils (*see* OILS, ESSENTIAL) of rose petals. Used in confectionery (especially *Turkish delight) and baking.

r

rösti Swiss; potatoes are partly baked or boiled, then sliced and fried in hot fat to form a cake with a golden crust.

rotaviruses Three main groups of viruses that cause *food-borne infection (vomiting and diarrhoea). The primary mode of transmission is the faecal–oral route, which can occur directly, through contact with an infected individual, or indirectly, through contaminated water or food. Globally the main cause of diarrhoea in children. Infection results in partial (temporary) destruction of the intestinal mucosa, with loss of microvilli, and subsequent changes in the composition of the intestinal microflora.

roti *See* CHAPATTI.

rôtisserie Method of cooking which developed from the traditional rotating spit above an open fire; the food is rotated while roasting, so bastes itself.

rotmos Swedish; mashed boiled potatoes and swedes.

rotten pot *See* MADRID STEW.

roughage *See* FIBRE, DIETARY.

rouille French, Provençal; sauce made from red chillies, garlic, olive oil, and potatoes or breadcrumbs, served with fish dishes.

roulade French; meat roll or galantine.

roux The foundation of most sauces; prepared by cooking together equal amounts of fat and plain flour, for a short time for white sauces, and longer for blond or brown sauces. The sauce is then prepared by stirring in milk or stock.

Rovimix Trade name for stabilized forms of vitamins, including A, D, and E as beadlets coated with a gelatine–starch mixture, used to enrich foods.

rowan Fruit of the rowan tree (mountain ash, *Sorbus aucuparia*) can be used to make a bitter-sweet jelly served with *game.

royal jelly The food on which bee larvae are fed and which causes them to develop into queen bees. Although it is a rich source of *pantothenic acid and other vitamins, in the amounts consumed it would make a negligible contribution to human intakes. Of its dry weight, 2% is hydroxy-decenoic acid, which is believed to be the active queen substance. Claimed, without foundation, to have rejuvenating properties for human beings.

RPV Relative Protein Value, a measure of *protein quality.

RQ *See* RESPIRATORY QUOTIENT.

RR Relative risk; *see* RISK, RELATIVE.

rRNA Ribosomal *RNA.

RS Resistant starch; *see* STARCH, RESISTANT.

RTE Ready to eat.

rubané Dish made from food cut into ribbon-like layers.

rubbing-in Method of incorporating fat into flour for pastry, etc.; the fat is cut into small pieces and gently rubbed into the flour by hand.

rue Leaves of the perennial shrub *Ruta graveolans* used as a *pot herb and to flavour meat; Mediterranean or Aleppo rue is *R. chalepensis*.

ruhi Freshwater fish, a member of the *carp family, *Labeo rohita*.

rum *Spirit distilled from fermented *sugar-cane juice or *molasses; may be colourless and light-tasting or dark and with a strong flavour. Traditionally rum is darker and more strongly flavoured the further south in the Caribbean it is made.

There are three main categories—Cuban, Jamaican, and Dutch East Indian—and several types: aguardiente (Spain, Portugal, and S. America), Bacardi (trade name, originally from Cuba), cachaca (Brazil), cane spirit (S. Africa), Demerara rum (Guyana); 35–60% alcohol by volume, 250–420 kcal (1.0–1.8 MJ) per 100 mL.

rumen *See* RUMINANT.

ruminant Animals such as the cow, sheep, and goat, which possess four stomachs, as distinct from monogastric animals, such as human beings, pig, dog, and rat. The four are: the rumen, or first stomach, where bacterial fermentation produces volatile fatty acids, and whence the food is returned to the mouth for further mastication (chewing the cud); the reticulum, where further bacterial fermentation produces volatile fatty acids; the omasum; and the abomasum or true stomach. The bacterial fermentation allows ruminants to obtain nourishment from grass and hay which cannot be digested by monogastric animals.

rumpbone Cut of meat: in the USA it is called the aitchbone, in the UK, the loin or haunch.

rush nut *See* TIGER NUT.

rusk **1.** Sweetened biscuit or piece of bread or cake crisped in the oven, especially as food for young children when teething. **2.** Cereal added to *sausages and *hamburgers.

russe, à la Containing beetroot and/or sour cream. Originally the Russian practice of serving meals in separate courses rather than placing many dishes on the table at once.

Russian dressing *See* SALAD DRESSING.

rutabaga American name for *swede.

rutin A *flavonoid, the disaccharide derivative of *quercitin, containing *glucose and *rhamnose.

RXR The retinoid X receptor, so called because its ligand was originally unknown, now known to be 9-*cis*-retinoic acid. *See* VITAMIN A.

rye Grain of *Secale cereale*, the predominant cereal in some parts of Europe; very hardy and withstands adverse conditions better than *wheat. Rye flour is dark and the dough lacks elasticity; rye bread is usually made with sourdough (*see* BREAD, SOURDOUGH) rather than yeast. *See also* BREAD, RYE; CRISPBREADS; ERGOT; ERGOTISM; PUMPERNICKEL; TRITICALE.

rye whisky *See* WHISKY.

r

S- and *R*- *See* R- AND S-.

saba nut *See* CHESTNUT, MALABAR.

sabayon French; *see* ZABAGLIONE.

sablé Biscuit paste made with butter and flour; sweet or savoury.

sablefish Marine fish, *Anoplopoma fimbria,* distributed across the north Pacific.

sabra Israeli name for the *prickly pear. Also an Israeli liqueur flavoured with bitter oranges and chocolate.

sabre fish Marine fish, *Lepidopus caudatus,* also known as scabbard fish.

saccharases *Enzymes that hydrolyse sugars to liberate their constituent *monosaccharides. *See also* INVERTASE; SUCRASE.

saccharic acid The dicarboxylic acid derived from glucose.

saccharimeter Polarimeter used to determine the purity of sugar; graduated on the International Sugar Scale in degrees sugar (distinct from *saccharometer).

saccharin A synthetic intense *sweetener, benzoic sulphimide, 300–550 times as sweet as *sucrose. Soluble saccharin is the sodium salt. Discovered in the USA in 1879.

saccharometer Floating device used to determine the specific gravity of sugar solutions (distinct from *saccharimeter).

saccharose Alternative name for *sucrose.

sachertorte Austrian; chocolate sponge cake with rich chocolate icing and whipped cream.

sack Old name for a variety of white wines from Spain and the Canaries, e.g. *sherry.

SACN Scientific Advisory Committee on Nutrition of the UK Food Standards Agency (*see* FSA).

sacristan Cake made from trimmings of puff pastry, dusted with sugar, and baked in twisted strips.

saddle The whole back of the animal (e.g. *lamb, *venison, *hare), from the end of the loin to the best end of the neck.

safe allowances *See* REFERENCE INTAKES.

safe and adequate intake *See* ADEQUATE INTAKE; REFERENCE INTAKES.

safflower oil Vegetable oil extracted from the seeds of the annual herb *Carthamus tinctoria*, 75% polyunsaturated fatty acids. *See also* SAFFRON, MEXICAN.

saffron Orange powder from the stigmata of the saffron crocus, *Crocus sativus*; 1 g requires the stigmata of 1500 flowers and yields about 50 mg of extract. Used as natural food colour and spice. Very soluble in water.

saffron, Indian *See* TURMERIC.

saffron, Mexican Substitute for *saffron made from the stigmata of *Carthamus tinctoria* (family *Compositae*), also known as the safflower; the seeds are the source of *safflower oil.

sage Leaf of the perennial herb, *Salvia officinalis* (Dalmatian sage); fragrant and spicy; used to flavour meat and fish dishes, and in poultry stuffing. Other sages differ in flavour; clary sage is *S. sclarea*, Greek sage is *S. fructicosa*, and pineapple sage (with a pineapple flavour) is *S. elegans*.

sago Starchy grains prepared from the pith of the sago palm (*Metroxylon sagu*), the sugar palm (*Arenga pinnuta*), and the toddy palm (*Caryota urens*); almost pure starch and sugars (sucrose, glucose, and fructose), free from protein.

sailfish Marine fish, *Istiophorus* spp., from Pacific and Indian oceans. Atlantic sailfish is *I. albicans*, Pacific sailfish is *I. greyi*, and Indo-Pacific sailfish is *I. gladius*.

St Anthony's fire *See* ERGOT.

St Germain, à la Dish made with green peas.

St John's bread *See* CAROB.

saithe Also known as coley and coal fish, *Polachius virens*. Apart from being eaten cooked, it is smoked, salted, and dyed red, to resemble smoked salmon.

saké Japanese; fermented beverage made from rice; although commonly called rice wine, it is technically a beer, since it is made from a cereal, although it does not contain gas. The fungus *Aspergillus oryzae* (*koji) is used as a source of amylase, then yeast is added; the final product contains 14–20% alcohol. Normally drunk warm and traditionally served in conical ceramic cups.

sakuradai Marine fish *Odontanthias rhodopeplus*, sea *bass family.

salad Originally derived from the Latin *sal* for salt, meaning something dipped into salt. Now normally a dish of uncooked vegetables; either a mixed salad or just one item (commonly lettuce or tomato). In France it can mean a small, hot, savoury dish, e.g. of chicken liver, etc.

salad burnet *See* BURNET.

salad, caesar Cos lettuce, fried croûtons, chopped anchovies, Parmesan cheese, and raw egg, tossed in dressing. Reputedly invented by Alex and Caesar Cardini in Tijuana, Mexico, in 1924, when a party of Americans arrived at their hotel on 4 July, and these were the only ingredients available to feed them.

salad, château French-Canadian; cooked frogs' legs with shredded lettuce and watercress, garnished with hard-boiled egg and lemon.

salad dressing Emulsions of oil and vinegar, which may or may not contain other flavourings. French dressing (vinaigrette) is a temporary *emulsion of oil and vinegar; heavy French dressing is stabilized with *pectin or vegetable *gum.

Mayonnaise is a stable emulsion of vinegar in oil, made with egg. Salad cream was originally developed as a commercial substitute for mayonnaise (mid 19th century); an emulsion made from vegetable oil, vinegar, salt, and spices, emulsified with egg yolk and thickened. Legally, in the UK, it must contain not less than 25% by weight of vegetable oil and not less than 1.35% egg-yolk solids. Mayonnaise usually contains more oil, and less carbohydrate and water. By US regulations salad dressing contains 30% vegetable oil and 4% egg yolk; mayonnaise contains 65% oil plus egg yolk. Low fat mayonnaise and salad cream are widely available.

Red mayonnaise is prepared by adding beetroot juice and the coral (eggs) of lobster to mayonnaise; an accompaniment to seafood dishes.

Russian dressing is in fact American; made from mayonnaise with pimento, chilli sauce, green pepper, and celery, or sometimes by mixing mayonnaise with tomato ketchup. Thousand Island dressing is made from equal parts of mayonnaise and Russian dressing, with whipped cream.

salades composées French regional specialities, mixed salads containing meat, fish, eggs, etc.; for example, salade Niçoise contains hard-boiled egg, anchovy fillets, tuna, and olives as well as lettuce and tomatoes.

salad, Russian Cooked diced vegetables, ham, prawns, etc., in aspic.

salad, Waldorf Apple, walnuts, and celery with mayonnaise; created by Swiss chef Oscar Tschirsky ('Oscar of the Waldorf') at the Waldorf Hotel, New York, about 1894.

salak Fruit of the South-East Asian palm *Salacca zalacca*, with a crisp texture, usually eaten raw.

salamander Traditional round metal cooking implement, heated in the fire until red hot and held over the surface of pastry and other foods to brown it.

salami Type of *sausage speckled with pieces of fat and flavoured with garlic; originally Italian.

salatrims *S*hort- *a*nd *l*ong-chain *a*cid *tri*acylglycerol *m*olecules. Family of triacylglycerols prepared from hydrogenated *soya or *canola oil and short-chain triacylglycerols by *interesterification; only partially absorbed and used as a *fat replacer.

salchichón Spanish; dried sausage similar to *salami.

salep (Greek: *salepi*.) Turkish beverage prepared from orchid tubers; milky white in appearance, with only a slight flavour.

sal fat Vegetable butter prepared from seeds of the Indian sal tree (*Shorea robusta*). *See also* COCOA BUTTER EQUIVALENTS.

salinometer (salimeter, salometer) Hydrometer to measure concentration of salt solutions by density.

saliva Secretion of the *salivary glands in the mouth: 1–1.5 L secreted daily. A dilute solution of the protein mucin (which lubricates food) and the enzymes *amylase (which hydrolyses starch) and *lysozyme, with small quantities of urea, potassium thiocyanate, sodium chloride, and bicarbonate.

salivary glands Three pairs of glands in the mouth, which secrete *saliva: parotid (producing watery saliva with *amylase but little *mucus), submandibular (producing mucus and *lysozyme, but little amylase), and submaxillary glands (producing a thick mucous secretion).

Sally Lunn A sweet, spongy, yeast cake, named after a girl who sold her tea cakes in Bath in the 18th century. In southern states of the USA, a variety of yeast and soda breads.

salmagundi (salamagundi) Old English dish consisting of diced fresh and salt meats mixed with hard-boiled eggs, pickled vegetables, and spices, arranged on a bed of salad.

salmi *Ragoût made from game or poultry.

salmon Marine fish that spawn in fresh water. Atlantic salmon is *Salmo salar*; others are *Oncorhynchus* spp.: cherry or Pacific salmon is *O. masou*

masou, Chum or keta salmon is *O. keta*, coho, silver, or medium red salmon is *O. kisutch*, pink salmon is *O. gorbuscha*, red or sockeye salmon is *O. nerka*, spring, king, or chinook salmon is *O. tshawytscha*. Although wild salmon are caught on a large scale, most of the salmon available in Europe is farmed in deep inlets of the sea, especially in Scotland and Norway.

A 150-g portion is an exceptionally rich *source of vitamin B_{12}; a rich source of protein, niacin, vitamin B_6, copper, and selenium; a good source of vitamin B_1; a source of vitamin B_2 and folate; contains 160mg of sodium and 20g of fat, of which 20% is *saturated and 50% is mono-unsaturated; supplies 300kcal (1260kJ). Pacific salmon may be a source of vitamin A and a rich source of vitamin D; canned salmon, in which the softened bones are edible, is also a source of calcium.

salmon berry Fruit of American wild raspberry, *Ribes spectabilis*.

Salmonella Genus of bacteria of family *Enterobacteriaceae*. Common cause of *food-borne disease. Found in eggs from infected hens, sausages, etc.; can survive in brine and in the refrigerator; destroyed by adequate heating. The principal symptoms of salmonellosis are fever, headache, nausea, abdominal pain, and diarrhoea.

salmon, rock Alternative name for *dogfish.

salometer *See* SALINOMETER.

salpicon French; various mixtures of chopped meat, fish, or vegetables in a sauce, used as stuffing or filling.

salsa Literally, the Spanish name for sauce. In culinary terms, the term refers to sauces prepared from chopped vegetables, lemon juices or lime juices, and spices. The most common type is tomato-based salsa.

salsa amarilla Spanish (literally 'yellow sauce'); made from hard-boiled eggs blended with *Madeira wine, oil, and mustard.

salsa Española Spanish sauce; basically a thick brown *roux sauce, diluted with stock made from meat or bones, onion, carrot, garlic, and herbs.

salsa mahonesa Spanish (Balearic) mayonnaise; *see* SALAD DRESSING.

salsa romesco *See* ROMESCO SAUCE.

salsify Long, white, tapering root of the biennial plant *Tragopogon porrifolius*, also known as oyster plant or vegetable oyster. Black salsify or scorzonera is the root of the hardy perennial, *Scorzonera hispanica* (sometimes used roasted as coffee substitute).

salt Chemically any product of reaction between an *acid and an *alkali is a salt. Table salt (or common salt) is *sodium chloride. The main sources are either mines in areas where there are rich deposits of crystalline salt, or deposits left by the evaporation of sea water in shallow pans (known as sea salt). *See also* BUFFERS; DIET, SALT-FREE; ELECTROLYTES.

salt, dendritic A form of ordinary table salt with branched or star-like (dendritic) crystals instead of the normal cubes. This is claimed to have a number of advantages: lower bulk density, more rapid solution, and an unusually high capacity to absorb moisture before becoming wet.

salt, iodized Usually 1 part of iodate in 25000–50000 parts of salt, as a means of ensuring adequate *iodine intake in regions where deficiency is a problem. *See also* GOITRE.

saltimbocca Italian; thin slices of veal wrapped in ham (literally 'jump in the mouth').

salting Method of preserving meat, fish, and some vegetables using *salt and *saltpetre.

saltlicks An adequate intake of *sodium is necessary to all animals. Grass is relatively poor in sodium, and its high potassium content increases sodium excretion. This loss causes a craving for sodium which is satisfied by licking on natural outcrops of salt-rich rock or artificial salt crystals.

salt, light (lite salt) Mixtures of *sodium chloride with potassium chloride and/or other substances to reduce the intake of *sodium.

saltpetre (Bengal saltpetre) Potassium *nitrate.

salts, bile *See* BILE.

salts, Indian Ancient Greek and Roman name for sugar.

sambal South-East Asian; mixture of chillies and spices, or a relish of raw vegetables or fruit in spiced vinegar. *See also* TRASSI.

sambol Indian, South-East Asian; *curry of fairly solid consistency.

sambuca Italian; liqueur flavoured with liquorice and *elderberry (*Sambucus nigra*). Traditionally served with coffee beans in the glass, and set alight.

SAMI Socially acceptable monitoring instrument. A small heart-rate counting apparatus used to estimate *energy expenditure.

samna *See* BUTTER, CLARIFIED.

samosa Indian; deep-fried stuffed pancakes, rolled into a cone or folded into an envelope. The filling is normally spiced; it may be meat or vegetables.

samp Coarsely cut portions of *maize with bran and germ partly removed. *See also* HOMINY.

samphire **1.** Rock samphire, St Peter's herb, succulent plant of cliffs and saltmarshes (*Crithmum maritimum*, member of carrot family); grows on coastal rocks, and has fleshy aromatic leaves which may be eaten raw, boiled, or pickled. Also known as sea fennel. **2.** Marsh samphire (glasswort, sea asparagus), *Salicornia* spp., grows in saltmarshes, is salty, and is eaten cooked as a vegetable.

samsa *See* AKKRA.

Samso Danish hard cheese, similar to *Emmental.

sancoche Caribbean (Trinidadian); casseroled salt pork, beef, and vegetables.

sandeel Marine fish, *Ammodytes tobianus*.

sanding In sugar confectionery, coating with sugar crystals.

sand leek *See* ROCAMBOLE.

sandwich Two slices of bread enclosing a filling (meat, cheese, fish, etc.). Invention attributed to the 4th Earl of Sandwich (1718–92) who spent long periods at the gaming table and carried a portable meal of beef sandwiched with bread.

   Decker sandwiches consist of several layers of bread, each separated by filling; Neapolitan sandwiches are decker sandwiches made with alternating slices of white and brown bread. Open sandwiches (*belegte brote, *smørrebrød) consist of a single slice of bread, biscuit, or small roll. *See also* BOCADILLO; CROQUE MONSIEUR; UITSMIJTER.

sandwich, club American; double-decker sandwich made with toast, turkey, lettuce, bacon, and mayonnaise.

sandwich, Reuben American; salt beef (corned beef) with cheese and sauerkraut, on rye bread, served hot. Originated in 1956 as the winner of a competition for novel sandwiches; probably named after the New York entrepreneur Arnold Reuben, who opened his first sandwich shop on upper Broadway in 1913.

sangak Iranian; large flat bread made from wholewheat sourdough.

sangaree Caribbean; drink made from spiced and sweetened port and brandy, diluted with crushed ice.

sangiovese A *grape variety widely used for *wine making, not one of the classic varieties.

sangría Spanish; fruit cup prepared from red wine fortified with brandy, in which fruit has been marinated, diluted with carbonated water and served with ice.

sansa oil Oil that is extracted chemically from *olive press residue.

sansho Japanese; the dried and powdered leaves of *Zanthoxylum piperitum* (*see* PEPPER, SZECHWAN) used to season noodle dishes and soups.

santalins Three stable red *flavonoid pigments, isolated from sandalwood. Used in foods to produce an orange-red colour below, and purple above, *pH 5.0.

sapid Full of flavour.

sapodilla Fruit of the Central American evergreen tree *Manilkara zapote*, syn. *Achras sapota*; with rough-grained, yellow to greyish pulp. *Chicle, the basis of *chewing gum, is made from the latex of the tree. Also known as chickoo and sapota.

saponification *Hydrolysis of *fat (*triacylglycerol) into its constituent *glycerol and *fatty acids by boiling with alkali. The fatty acids will be present as the sodium salts or soaps. Waxes, alkanes, sterols, and fat-soluble vitamins are the unsaponifiable fraction of lipids in a food.

saponins Compounds that occur in plants and can produce a soapy lather with water. Extracted commercially from soapwort (*Saponaria officinalis*) or soapbark (*Quillaja saponaria*) and used as a foam producer in beverages and fire extinguishers, as detergents, and for emulsifying oils. Bitter in flavour. *See also* QUILLAJA.

sapota *See* SAPODILLA; SAPOTE.

sapote Originally the Aztec name for any soft sweet fruit. Black sapote is the fruit of *Diospyros digyna*, a Central American *persimmon, also known as chocolate fruit or black persimmon; it has a chocolate flavour when ripe, but is bitter when unripe. Mamey sapote is the fruit of *Pouteria sapota*, which is unrelated to the *mamey apple. White sapote is the fruit of *Casimiroa edulis*, shaped like a persimmon, with creamy white flesh and a custard-like flavour. *See also* ABIU; CANISTEL; SAPODILLA; STAR APPLE.

sapsago Swiss cheese made from soured skimmed milk and whole milk; clover is added to the curd, giving it a green colour.

sapucaia nut *See* BRAZIL NUT.

saracen corn *See* BUCKWHEAT.

saran Generic name for thermoplastic materials made from polymers of vinylidene chloride and vinyl chloride. They are clear, transparent films (cling film) used for wrapping food; resistant to oils and chemicals; can be heat-shrunk on to the product.

sarcocarp *See* MESOCARP.

sarcolactic acid Obsolete name for (+) lactic acid (which rotates the plane of polarized light to the right), found in muscle, as distinct from the optically inactive *lactic acid (a mixture of (+) and (−) isomers) found in sour milk. Also known as paralactic acid. *See also* MEAT CONDITIONING; MEAT, DFD; RIGOR MORTIS.

sarcolemma *See* MUSCLE.

sarcosine An intermediate in the metabolism of *choline, *N*-methylglycine. Found in relatively large amounts in starfish and sea urchins; used in the synthesis of antienzyme agents in toothpaste.

sardell *See* ANCHOVY.

sardellina Marine fish, *Sardellina* spp.

sardine Young *pilchard, *Sardina* (*Clupea*) *pilchardus*; commonly canned in oil, brine, or tomato paste. Norwegian canned sardines are salted and smoked before canning; French are salted and steamed. A 100-g portion (canned in oil and drained, or canned in brine or tomato sauce) is an exceptionally rich *source of vitamin B_{12}; a rich source of protein, niacin, calcium, selenium, and vitamin D; a good source of vitamins B_2 and, B_6, iron, zinc, and copper; a source of iodine; contains 13 g of fat, of which one-third is *saturated and one-third mono-unsaturated; supplies 200 kcal (850 kJ).

sardine, Monterey Marine fish, *Sardinops sagax* subspp. *caeruleus,* from the Pacific Ocean off the coast of California. Other subspecies of *S. sagax* (South American pilchard) are found in various areas of the Pacific Ocean.

Saridele Protein-rich baby food (26–30% protein) developed in Indonesia; extract of soya bean with sugar, calcium carbonate, thiamin, and vitamins B_{12} and C.

sarsaparilla A carbonated beverage flavoured with an extract of oil of *sassafras and oil of either wintergreen or sweet birch, and roots of the South American plant *Smilax officinalis*, both of which are also called sarsparilla.

sashimi Japanese; thin slices of raw fish.

Saskatoon berry *See* SERVICE BERRY.

sassafras American tree (*Sassafras albidum*) with aromatic bark and leaves. The root is used to make *root beer and the young leaves are powdered to make filé powder, an essential flavouring of *gumbo. Sassafras oil from the root-bark is used medicinally and as a flavour in beverages, but is banned in some countries because of its toxicity.

saté (sateh, satay) Indonesian, Malaysian; a spicy peanut sauce.

satiety The sensation of fullness after a meal.

satsuma *See* CITRUS.

saturated With reference to *fatty acids means that the carbon chain carries its full complement of hydrogen atoms, as compared with mono-unsaturated and polyunsaturated. Where the nutrient content of foods is described in these entries the total amount of fat is listed, together with the proportion of saturates. Where mono-unsaturates are sufficiently important this is also quoted and the polyunsaturates can be calculated by difference from the total. Where the amounts of mono-unsaturates are small the entry lists the proportion of polyunsaturates and the mono-unsaturates can be calculated by difference from the total.

saturates Commonly used short term for *saturated *fatty acids.

sauce Used to flavour, coat, or accompany a dish, or may be used in the cooking to bind ingredients together; may be sweet or savoury. Thick sauces may be: i) *roux sauces based on flour heated with fat; ii) thickened with starch (*arrowroot, *cornflour, *custard powder) or *modified starch (gravy granules, thickening granules); iii) thickened with egg (*Hollandaise sauce, *custard); iv) thickened by reduction.

sauce, table Condiment or relish eaten with food; there are two main types: brown sauce, a (usually secret) blend of herbs, spices, and vegetables in vinegar; and tomato sauce or *ketchup.

sauce, Worcestershire *See* WORCESTERSHIRE SAUCE.

sauerbraten German; beef marinated for several days in wine vinegar, then braised and served with sour cream.

sauerkraut German, Dutch, Alsatian; prepared by lactic fermentation of shredded cabbage. In the presence of 2–3% salt, acid-forming bacteria thrive and convert sugars in the cabbage into acetic and lactic acids, which then act as preservatives.

sauermilchkase German cheeses made from low fat milk using a lactic acid starter and no *rennet.

sauerteig Sourdough; *see* BREAD, SOURDOUGH.

saury Marine fish; Atlantic saury is *Scomberesox saurus*, Pacific saury is *Coloabis saira*.

sausage Chopped meat, mostly beef or pork, seasoned with salt and spices, mixed with cereal (usually wheat rusk prepared from crumbed unleavened biscuits), and packed into casings made from the connective tissue of animal intestines or cellulose.

There are six main types: fresh, smoked, cooked, smoked and cooked, semi-dry, and dry. Frankfurters, Bologna (*polony), Polish, and Berliner sausages are made from cured meat and are smoked and cooked. Thuringer, soft salami, mortadella, and soft cervelat, are semi-dry sausages. Pepperoni, chorizo, dry salami, dry cervelat are slowly dried to a hard texture.

In the UK pork sausages must be 65%, and beef sausages 50%, meat ('meat' includes flesh and the skin, gristle, rind, and sinew 'naturally associated with the flesh'). A 150-g portion of standard British varieties of pork or beef sausages, grilled, is a rich *source of protein, niacin, and iron; beef sausage contains 25 g of fat, of which 40% is saturated and 50% mono-unsaturated; supplies 400 kcal (1700 kJ); pork sausage contains 35 g of fat of which 40% is saturated and 50% mono-unsaturated; supplies 450 kcal (1900 kJ).

sausage casings Natural casings are made from hog intestines for fresh frying sausages, and from sheep intestines for chipolatas and frankfurters. Now mainly replaced by artificial casings made from cellulose, polyvinyl dichloride, or collagen. Skinless sausages are prepared in cellulose casing, which is then peeled off.

sausage factor *See* MEAT FACTOR.

sausage, Glamorgan Welsh; Caerphilly cheese, breadcrumbs, and egg, fried in a sausage shape.

sausage meat Mixture of meats as used to make *sausages, *pies, and *stuffing.

sausages, emulsion Sausages made from a meat mixture that is finely chopped with added water and salt. Much of the fat is liberated but remains emulsified by the lean meat mixture, giving a homogeneous paste (known in German as *brat*) that gels on heating to a firm sliceable mass.

sausage, summer *See* CERVELAT.

sausage toad Sausages baked in batter, also known as toad-in-the-hole.

sauté To toss in hot fat, from the French *sauter*, to jump. Sauté potatoes are usually boiled, cut into slices, and cooked in a little fat until lightly browned.

sauvignon blanc One of the nine 'classic' *grape varieties used for *wine making; the wines are distinctively aromatic and sometimes smokey.

savarin *See* BABA.

saveloy Highly seasoned smoked *sausage; the addition of saltpetre gives it a bright red colour. Originally a sausage made from pig brains.

savory Herb with strongly flavoured leaves used as seasoning in sauces, soups, and salad dishes. Summer savory is an annual, *Satureja hortensis*; winter savory is a perennial, *S. montana*.

savoury Foods with a savoury or salty flavour; may be small titbits eaten with the fingers (cocktail savouries) or a savoury dish served after the sweet course and before the dessert at a formal banquet. *See also* TASTE; UMAMI.

savoy Variety of *cabbage (*Brassica oleracea* var. *capitata*) with crimped leaves; said to have a more delicate flavour than ordinary cabbage.

savoy biscuits Small sponge fingers.

saw palmetto North American palm (*Serenoa repens, S. serrulata*); the berries were eaten by native Americans, and there is some evidence that the oil may have beneficial effects in treatment of benign prostate enlargement. It also contains *sterols.

saxitoxin *Mycotoxin produced by *Alexandrium tamarense*.

sbrinz Swiss hard cheese similar to *parmesan.

scabbard fish Marine fish, *Lepidopus caudatus*, also known as sabre fish.

scad *See* MACKEREL, HORSE.

scald **1.** To pour boiling water over a food to clean it, loosen hairs (e.g. on a joint of pork), or remove the skin of fruit, tomatoes, etc. *See also* BLANCHING. **2.** To heat milk almost to boiling point, to retard souring or to make clotted *cream. **3.** Defect occurring in stored apples; the formation of brown patches under the skin, with browning and softening of the tissue underneath. Due to accumulation of gases given off during ripening.

scaldfish *See* MEGRIM.

scallion Small *onion that has not developed a bulb, widely used in Chinese cooking; also used for shallots and spring onion (especially in the USA). *See also* ONION, SPRING.

scalloped dishes Food (often previously cooked) baked in a scallop shell or similar small container, usually combined with a creamy sauce, topped with breadcrumbs, and surrounded by a border of piped potato.

scalloping A way of decorating the double edge of the pastry covering of a pie by making horizontal cuts with a knife close together round the edge of the pie, then, using the back of the knife, pulling the edge up vertically at regular intervals to form scallops.

scallops Marine bivalve *molluscs, various species of the family *Pectinidae*; king scallop is *Pecten maximus*, queen scallop is *Chamys* (*Aequipecten*) *opercularis*, Atlantic scallop is *Placopecten magellanicus*. A 100-g portion is a rich *source of protein, niacin, and vitamin B_{12}; a source of iron; supplies 70 kcal (290 kJ).

scampi *Shellfish, Norway lobster or Dublin Bay prawn, *Nephrops norvegicus*; *see* LOBSTER. Pacific scampi are *Metanephrops* spp.

scenedesmus *See* ALGAE.

Schiedam *See* GIN.

Schilling Test A test of *vitamin B_{12} absorption by giving an intravenous loading dose of non-radioactive vitamin followed by an oral dose of radioactive vitamin and measuring the excretion of the radioactive label in the urine.

schinkenhäger *See* GIN.

schmaltz Jewish name for dripping (rendered fat), especially from chicken or goose.

schnapps (snaps) *See* AQUAVIT.

schnitzel Austrian, German; cutlet or escalope of veal or pork. The most common one, wienerschnitzel, is veal coated in egg and breadcrumbs and fried, then served with various garnishes.
   Bismarck schnitzel is garnished with plovers' eggs, mushrooms, truffles, and tomato sauce; holsteiner schnitzel with fried egg, capers, olives, and anchovies; rahmschnitzel with paprika-flavoured cream sauce; zigeuner schnitzel with tomato sauce, mushrooms, and smoked ox tongue.

schug Yemeni, Middle Eastern; pungent paste or dip made from green chillies, with coriander and mint, also known as harrief.

schweitzer kraut German; chopped cooked marigold leaves.

scifers Cornish name for Welsh onion (*see* ONION, WELSH).

sclerosis Hardening of a tissue.

scombroid poisoning Also known as skipjack reaction, caused by eating fish, including many of the *Scombridae* (*tuna, bonito, *mackerel) but also non-scombroid fish and other foods, that have undergone bacterial spoilage leading to the formation of *histamine. Symptoms include skin rash, nausea, and tingling.

scone A variety of tea cake originally made from white flour or barley meal and sour milk or buttermilk in Scone, Scotland; baked on a griddle and cut in quarters. A drop scone (Scotch pancake) is a small pancake made by dropping spoonfuls of batter on to a griddle.

scorbutic *See* SCURVY.

score To make shallow cuts in the surface of food in order to improve its flavour and appearance or to cook more quickly.

scorzonera *See* SALSIFY.

Scotch broth Mutton and vegetable broth with pearl barley.

Scotch bun Spiced plum cake with pastry crust, traditionally eaten in Scotland at Hogmanay (New Year's Eve). Also known as black bun.

Scotch pancake *See* SCONE.

SCP *See* SINGLE CELL PROTEIN.

scrapple American; meat dish prepared from pork carcass trimmings, maize meal, flour, salt, and spices, and cooked to a thick consistency.

scratchings, pork Small pieces of crisply cooked pork skin.

screwdriver A cocktail; half a measure of vodka with four measures of orange juice.

scrod Young *cod or *haddock.

scrumpy Rough, unsweetened *cider.

scup American term for various food and game fish of the sea bream family, especially *Senostomus* spp. *See also* PORGY.

scuppernong The most widely cultivated of the muscadine *grapes, used chiefly in wine rather than as a dessert grape.

scurvy Deficiency of *vitamin C, fatal if untreated. Nowadays extremely rare, but in the past was a major problem in winter, when there were few sources of the vitamin. It was especially a problem of long sea voyages during the 16th and 17th centuries; when fresh supplies of fruit and vegetables were not available the majority of the crew often succumbed to scurvy. James Lind discovered the role of citrus fruits in preventing or curing the disease; he published *Treatise on the Scurvy* in 1753.

scurvy, alpine *See* PELLAGRA.

scurvy grass A herb, *Cochlearia officinalis*, recommended as far back as the late 16th century as a remedy for *scurvy.

scutellum Area surrounding the embryo of the cereal grain; scutellum plus embryo is the germ; rich in vitamins.

scybalum Lump or mass of hard *faeces.

SD Standard deviation.

SDA Specific dynamic action; *see* THERMOGENESIS, DIET-INDUCED.

SDS gel electrophoresis *See* ELECTROPHORESIS.

seaberry *See* SEA BUCKTHORN.

sea bream *See* PORGY.

sea buckthorn Fruit of the perennial shrub *Hippophae rhamnoides*, a rich source of vitamin C, but acidic with an unpleasant flavour on its own.

sea crayfish Shellfish, family *Palinuridae*; *see* LOBSTER.

sea cucumber Various marine invertebrates with soft cylindrical bodies, especially *Stichopus* spp. and *Cucumaria* spp. Also known as bêche de mer, trepang, and sea slug.

sea fennel *See* SAMPHIRE.

seafood A general term to include crustaceans and *shellfish, sometimes also *fish.

seafood stick Characteristically pink and white sticks of cooked fish, eaten cold in salads and buffet meals, mainly made from cod or other white fish and containing little or no *shellfish. Also known as crab sticks or fish sticks.

sea kale Coastal plant, *Crambe maritime*; the tender shoots are eaten like asparagus. Sea kale beet is Swiss chard (*see* CHARD, SWISS).

sea lettuce Various green *seaweeds, *Ulva* spp.

sea mustard The brown *seaweed *Undaria pinnatifida*, a source of edible starch gels.

sea pie Beef stew with a suet-crust lid.

sear To brown meat quickly in a little fat before grilling or roasting. The term is sometimes used when vegetables are browned in fat before being used to make soup or sauce.

sea slug *See* SEA CUCUMBER.

seasoning Normally used to mean salt and pepper, but may include any herbs, spices, and condiments added to a savoury dish.

sea truffle *Shellfish, a bivalve *mollusc, *Venus verrucosa*.

seaweed Marine algae of interest as food include *Irish moss, *laver bread, and *kelp, which are eaten to some extent in different communities and serve as a mineral supplement in animal feed.

secco Italian; dry wines.

seco Portuguese, Spanish; dry wines.

second messenger An intracellular metabolite produced in response to binding of a *hormone or other ligand to a cell surface receptor; cAMP, cGMP, and inositol trisphosphate are formed in response to various hormones and activate *protein kinases that phosphorylate target enzymes to modify their activity.

secretagogue A compound that regulates the secretion of a *hormone or other secretion.

secretin A peptide *hormone secreted by the intestinal mucosa that stimulates pancreatic secretion and inhibits secretion of *gastric acid and *gastrin.

sedoheptulose (sedoheptose) A seven-carbon sugar which is an intermediate in *glucose metabolism by the pentose phosphate pathway.

seed cake A sponge or *Madeira cake containing caraway seeds, mace, and nutmeg. Tipperary seed cake contains orange-flower water and caraway seeds, but no mace or nutmeg.

seek kababs Indian; minced meat croquettes shaped over an iron skewer (the seek) and cooked rapidly by grilling.

Seitz filter A filter disc (originally of asbestos) with pores so fine that they will not permit passage of bacteria; solutions emerge bacteriologically sterile, although viruses will pass through the filter.

sekt German; sparkling *wine, usually dry, made by tank fermentation, not the *méthode champenoise.

selenium A dietary essential mineral, which is part of *enzymes *glutathione peroxidase and thyroxine deiodinase (*see* THYRODOXIN REDUCTASE; THYROID HORMONES). Through its role in glutathione peroxidase it acts as an *antioxidant, and to some extent can compensate for *vitamin E deficiency. Similarly, vitamin E can compensate for selenium deficiency to some extent.

Requirements are of the order of 50 µg/day; in parts of New Zealand, Finland, and China soils are especially poor in selenium and deficiency occurs. In China selenium deficiency is associated with *Keshan disease and *Kashin–Beck syndrome. Rich *sources include fish and shellfish, mung (dahl) and red kidney beans, Brazil nuts, bread, kidney, lentils, liver, pork, rabbit, veal.

Selenium is toxic in excess; mild selenium intoxication results in production of foul-smelling hydrogen selenide, which is excreted on the breath and through the skin. Intakes above 400 µg/day are considered hazardous.

selenoprotein P *Selenium-containing plasma protein, synthesized in various tissues; it turns over rapidly and is believed to be important in transport of selenium from the liver to peripheral tissues, and possibly also in removal of surplus selenium from tissues. Potentially a more sensitive index of selenium status than measurement of *glutathione peroxidase or total blood selenium.

self-raising flour *See* FLOUR, SELF-RAISING.

seltzer Effervescent mineral water, originally from Niederselters, Germany. *See also* SODA WATER.

SEM Standard error of the mean.

sémillon One of the nine 'classic' *grape varieties used for *wine making, especially the great sauternes, graves, and white Bordeaux. Traditionally called riesling in some parts of Australia.

seminose *See* MANNOSE.

semi-seco Spanish; medium dry wines.

semolina The inner, granular, starchy endosperm of hard or durum wheat (not yet ground into flour); used to make *pasta and semolina milk pudding.

SENECA Survey Europe on Nutrition in the Elderly: a Concerted Action. A multicentre European study of nutrition and health in the elderly, begun in 1998.

sensitization The process of producing antibodies (IgE) against an environmental antigen—the basis of food allergies (*see* FOOD, ADVERSE REACTIONS).

sensory properties *See* ORGANOLEPTIC.

sequestrants Compounds that form soluble complexes with polyvalent metal ions, preventing them from undergoing reactions, and so improving the quality and stability of the product. *See also* CHELATING AGENTS.

sercial *See* MADEIRA WINES.

sereh powder *See* LEMON GRASS.

serendipity berry Or Nigerian berry, fruit of the West African plant *Dioscoreophyllum cumminsii*. It has an extremely sweet taste; the active principle is a protein, monellin.

serine A non-essential *amino acid.

serotonin *See* 5-HYDROXYTRYPTAMINE.

serum Clear liquid left after the protein in a solution has been clotted; the serum from milk, occasionally referred to as lacto-serum, is *whey.

   Blood serum is *blood plasma without the fibrinogen. When blood clots, the fibrinogen is converted to fibrin, which is deposited in strands that trap the red cells and form the clot. The clear liquid that is exuded is the serum. *See also* BLOOD CLOTTING.

serum butter *See* WHEY.

service berry Fruit of the wild service tree, *Sorbus torminalis*, formerly used to flavour and preserve beer. The fruit of *S. domestica* is also known as service berry; the Saskatoon service berry (or juneberry) is the fruit of the North American shrub *Amelanchier alnifolia*.

serving US food labelling legislation requires that nutrients be shown per standard serving of the food. The Food and Drug Administration has defined serving or portion sizes, based on surveys of amounts customarily eaten, so the definition of portions is not left to the manufacturer.

sesame A tropical and subtropical plant, *Sesamum indicum*. Known as sim-sim in East Africa, benniseed in West Africa, gingelly and til in Asia. Seeds are small and, in most varieties, white; used whole in sweetmeats, in stews, and to decorate cakes and bread, and for extraction of the oil, which is used as a seasoning. The seeds contain 60% oil, of which 15% is saturated and 45% polyunsaturated. It has a strong nutty flavour and is used more as a seasoning than a cooking oil. *See also* TAHINI.

setback (of starch) *See* RETROGRADATION.

seto fuumi Japanese; seasoning consisting of dried *seaweed, tuna, sesame seed, and *monosodium glutamate.

Seville orange *See* ORANGE, BITTER.

sfogato Greek; minced meat casserole.

sfumatrice Machine for obtaining the oil from the peel of citrus fruit. Based on the principle that the natural turgor of the oil sacs forces out the oil when the peel is folded.

SGLT The family of glucose transport proteins that permit uptake of glucose into cells against a concentration gradient, linked to uptake of sodium ions. *See also* GLUT; TRANSPORT, ACTIVE.

shad Oily *fish, *Alosa* spp. (American shad is *A. sapidissima*), related to *herring, that spawn in fresh water. The roe is especially prized. Indian or hilsa shad is *Tenualosa ilisha*.

shaddock *See* POMELO.

shakaria *See* POTATO, SWEET.

shallot Bulb of the plant *Allium escalonium* (*A. cepa aggregatum* group) related to the *onion, with essentially the same flavour but less pungency; each plant has a cluster of small bulbs rather than the single large bulb of the onion.

shandy A mixture of lemonade and *beer, originally shandy-gaff. Ginger beer may be used for ginger beer shandy.

shark Cartilaginous marine fish; silky shark is *Carcharhinus falciformis*, blacktip shark is *C. limbatus*, sandbar shark is *C. plumbeus*, basking shark is *Cetorhinus maximus*, shortfin mako is *Isurus oxyrinchus*, porbeagle is *Lamna nasus*, blue shark is *Prionace glauca*, whale shark is *Rhincodon typus*.

sharon fruit Alternative name for the sweet *persimmon or *kaki.

sharps *See* WHEATFEED.

shashlik *See* KEBAB.

shawarma Arabic name for *döner kebab.

shchi Russian; green vegetable soup, sometimes called Russian cabbage soup.

shea butter Vegetable butter from the nuts of the shea tree (*Butyrospermum parkii*) which grows wild in West and Central Africa. It contains 10% non-saponifiable lipids (*see* SAPONIFICATION). *See also* COCOA BUTTER EQUIVALENTS.

shearling 15–18-month-old sheep. *See* LAMB.

sheatfish Freshwater catfish *Silurus glanis*.

sheepshead Saltwater fish; *see* PORGY.

sheer (kheer) Indian; creamed-rice dessert.

shellfish A wide range of marine molluscs (*abalone, *clams, *cockles, *mussels, *scallops, *oysters, *whelks, *winkles) and crustacea (members of the zoological order Decapoda: *crayfish, *crabs, *lobsters, *prawns, *shrimps).

shellfish poisoning Paralysis caused by eating shellfish contaminated with toxic organisms (dinoflagellates) that contain saxitoxin and related toxins. *See also* CIGUATERA; PHYCOTOXINS; RED TIDE.

shepherd's pie Dish made from minced lamb or mutton with a crust of mashed potato, baked. Cottage pie is made with minced beef.

sherbet **1.** Arabic name for water-ice (sugar, water, and flavouring), also known by French name, *sorbet, and the Italian name, granita. Used to be served between courses during a meal to refresh the palate. **2.** Originally a Middle Eastern drink made from fruit juice, often chilled with snow. Modern version is made with sodium bicarbonate and tartaric acid (to fizz) with sugar and flavours. Sherbet powder is the same mixture in dry form. **3.** In the USA a frozen dessert containing 1–2% milk fat, 2–5% dairy solids; as opposed to sorbet, which contains no dairy solids.

sherry Fortified wines (around 15% *alcohol by volume) from the south-west of Spain, around Jerez and Cadiz. Matured by the solera process rather than by discrete vintages; each year 30% of the wine in the oldest barrel is drawn off for bottling and replaced with wine from the next oldest; this in turn is replaced from the next barrel, and so on.

In order of increasing sweetness, sherries are: fino (very dry); manzanilla; amontillado; oloroso (may be medium-dry or sweetened and more highly fortified); amoroso or cream. Dry sherry contains 1–2% sugar and 100mL supplies 120kcal (500kJ); medium sherry, 3–4% sugar, supplies 125kcal (530kJ); sweet sherry, 7% sugar, supplies 140kcal (590kJ).

Sherry-type wines are also produced in other countries, including South Africa, Cyprus, and Britain (made from imported grape juice), and may legally be described as sherry as long as the country of origin is clearly shown.

shiga toxin Cytotoxic (and possibly also neurotoxic) protein produced by invasive strains of *Shigella dysenteria*. *See* SHIGELLA SPP.

***Shigella* spp.** Invasive pathogens, causing bacterial dysentery. Cells multiply in the lumen of the colon and penetrate the epithelium by receptor-mediated *endocytosis. A wide variety of different foods may be vehicles for infection, as a result of poor hygiene in food handling.

shigellosis Infection with *Shigella* spp.

shir To bake food (usually eggs) in a small shallow container or ramekin dish.

shirataki Chinese, Japanese; noodles made from tubers of the devil's tongue plant *Amorphallus rivieri*.

shishkebab *See* KEBAB.

shol Freshwater fish, *Channa striata*.

shoo-fly pie American; pie with sweet filling made from molasses, brown sugar, and flour.

shortbread Sweet biscuit baked with a high proportion of butter to flour. Sometimes called shortcake in the USA.

shortcake American; rich cake with a filling of fruit and cream. *See also* SHORTBREAD.

shortcrust *See* PASTRY.

shortening Soft fats that produce a crisp, flaky effect in baked products. *Lard possesses the correct properties to a greater extent than any other single fat. Shortenings compounded from mixtures of fats or prepared by *hydrogenation of oils are called lard compounds or lard substitutes.

Unlike oils, shortenings are plastic and disperse as a film through the batter, preventing the formation of a hard, tough mass.

shoti *See* ZEDOARY ROOT.

shoyu *See* SOY SAUCE.

shred To slice a food such as cheese or raw vegetables into very fine pieces, which often curl as they are cut.

shrimp *See* PRAWN.

shrub A bottled cordial made from various fruits, spirits, and sugar.

sialogogue Substance that stimulates the flow of saliva.

sialorrhoea Excessive flow of saliva.

sibutramine *Anorectic drug used in the treatment of *obesity that acts by inhibiting reuptake of *serotonin and *noradrenaline, so decreasing food intake by increasing *satiety; it also increases serum *HDL. Trade name Reductil.

sidemeats *See* OFFAL.

siderophilin *See* IRON TRANSPORT.

siderosis Accumulation of the iron-storage protein, haemosiderin, in liver, spleen, and bone marrow in cases of excessive red cell destruction and on diets exceptionally rich in *iron. It is common among the Bantu, apparently due to intakes of about 100 mg of iron daily from iron cooking pots and *pombé. *See also* HAEMOCHROMATOSIS; IRON STORAGE.

sierra rice *See* RICE, FERMENTED.

sift To shake flour, sugar, etc., through a sieve.

sild Young *herrings (*Clupea harengus*) and young *sprats (*Sprattus sprattus*) when canned; they are caught together and cannot readily be separated. When fresh or frozen the mixture is called whitebait.

silica gel A drying agent, sodium silicate, used in food packaging. It can be regenerated by heating to drive off adsorbed water.

silicones Organic compounds of silicon; in the food field they are used as antifoaming agents, as semi-permanent glazes on baking tins and other metal containers, and on non-stick wrapping paper.

sillabub *See* SYLLABUB.

silvaner A *grape variety widely used for *wine making, not one of the classic varieties.

silver Not of interest in foods apart from its use in covering *non-pareils, the silver beads used to decorate confectionery. Present in traces in all plant and animal tissues but not known to be a dietary essential, and has no known function, nor is enough ever absorbed to cause toxicity. *See also* OLIGODYNAMIC.

silver beet *See* CHARD, SWISS.

silverside **1.** Boned joint of *beef cut from the top part of the hind leg, commonly boiled or salted, although it can be roasted. **2.** A marine fish, species of the family *Atherinida*, also known as sandsmelt.

simmer A method of cooking in water slightly below boiling point (also known as coddling).

simnel cake Fruit cake with a layer of almond paste on top and sometimes another baked in the middle. Originally baked for Mothering Sunday, now normally eaten at Easter.

sim-sim *See* SESAME.

singe To pass a plucked bird quickly over a flame to burn off the down.

singing hinnie (singin' hinny) Northern British (Northumberland); large, round, currant scone baked on a girdle (*see* GRIDDLE) or hotplate, usually cut in half, buttered, and eaten hot. The name comes from the hissing noise it makes as it cooks.

sinharanut *See* CHESTNUT.

sippet A small piece of bread, fried or toasted, served as a garnish to a mince or hash.

sirloin Upper part of the hind loin of *beef.

sirtuins A family of *enzymes that catalyse NAD-dependent deacetylation of *histones and other proteins. There is some evidence that activation of sirtuins is responsible for the observed increase in lifespan of animals maintained on an energy-restricted diet.

sitapophasis Refusal to eat as expression of mental disorder.

sitology Science of food (from the Greek *sitos*, food).

sitomania Mania for eating, morbid obsession with food; also known as phagomania.

sitophobia Fear of food; also known as phagophobia.

sitosterol The main *sterol found in vegetable oils; inhibits the absorption of cholesterol from the intestinal tract and has been used in treatment of *hyperlipidaemia.

skate Various marine cartilaginous fish; big skate is *Raja binoculata*, longnose skate is *R. oxyrhinchus*, and smooth skate is *R. innominita*. Often used synonymously with *ray.

skillet Frying pan (especially in the USA).

skim To remove fat from the surface of stock, gravy, stews, etc., or scum from jams, etc., while they are cooking.

skinfold thickness Index of subcutaneous fat and hence body fat content. Measured at four sites: biceps (midpoint of front upper arm), triceps (midpoint of back upper arm), subscapular (directly below point of shoulder blade at angle of 45 degrees), supra-iliac (directly above iliac crest in mid-axillary line). Rapid surveys often involve only biceps. *See also* ANTHROPOMETRY.

skink Irish, Scottish; originally an essence or extract, now a thick soup-stew of meat and vegetables.

skipjack reaction *See* SCOMBROID POISONING.

skirlie Scottish; cakes of oatmeal and onion fried in pork dripping. Sold commercially in a skin, also known as mealie pudding.

skorthalia Greek; sauce with garlic, lemon, and nuts.

skyr *See* MILK, FERMENTED.

slapjack *See* FLAPJACK.

slimming clubs Groups which provide help and support for *overweight and *obese people trying to lose weight, including nutritional counselling and provision of clear, easy-to-follow, weight-reducing diets. The most successful groups are often those in which the counsellors were once obese people themselves, and understand the problems involved in losing excess weight.

sling Drink made from gin and fruit juice.

slivovitz (sliwowitz) East European (originally Yugoslavian); distilled spirit made from fermented plums; similar to German *quetsch and French *mirabelle. Some of the stones are included with the fruit and produce a characteristic bitter flavour from the hydrocyanic acid (0.008% cyanide is present in the finished brandy).

sloe Wild *plum, fruit of the blackthorn (*Prunus spinosa*) with a sour and astringent flavour; almost the only use for it is for the preparation of sloe gin, a liqueur made by steeping *sloes in gin or neutral spirit, known in France as prunelle.

sloke *See* LAVER.

slott Shetland; dumplings made from pounded cod roe and flour.

SMA Trade name (Scientific Milk Adaptation) for a milk preparation for infant feeding modified to resemble the composition of human milk. *See* FORMULA, INFANT; MILK, HUMANIZED.

smallage Wild celery, *Apium graveolens*; its seeds, herb, and root are said to have medicinal properties.

smell *See* ORGANOLEPTIC.

smelt Marine oily fish, *Osmerus* spp., also known as sparling.

smen Moroccan; clarified butter (*see* BUTTER, CLARIFIED) with dried herbs and salt. Aged in earthenware pots until it acquires a consistency and aroma similar to Roquefort cheese.

smetana Thin, sour cream, originally Russian.

smilacin *See* PARILLIN.

smoked beef *See* PASTRAMI.

smoke, liquid Either condensate from wood smoke or an aqueous extract of smoke, applied to the surface of foods as an alternative to traditional *smoking.

smoke point The temperature at which the decomposition products of frying oils become visible as bluish smoke. The temperature varies with different fats, ranging between 160 and 260°C. *See also* FIRE POINT; FLASH POINT.

smoking The process of flavouring and preserving meat or fish by drying slowly in the smoke from a wood fire; the type of wood used affects the flavour of the final smoked product. *See also* SMOKE, LIQUID.

smoking, cold Raw food is dried at approximately 30°C, then smoked at 24–27°C for several hours or days.

smoking, hot Hot smoked products are cooked, usually after drying at between 30–40°C, then smoked for 1–2 hours as the temperature rises to 70–80°C.

smoothies Thick and smooth textured beverages made by blending fruits with yoghurt, milk, ice, ice cream, or frozen yoghurt.

smörgåsbord Scandinavian; buffet table laden with delicacies as a traditional gesture of hospitality, a traditional way of serving meals. *See also* SMØRREBRØD.

smørrebrød Scandinavian; open *sandwiches, often on rye bread, with a variety of toppings and garnishes. Literally 'smeared bread'. *See also* SMÖRGÅSBORD.

SMS Sucrose monostearate. *See* SUCROSE ESTERS.

smut Group of fungi that attack wheat; includes loose or common smut (*Ustilago tritici*) and stinking smut or bunt (*Tilletia tritici*). Corn smut is *huitlacoche.

snail The small snail eaten in Europe is *Helix pomatia*; the giant African snail (which weighs several hundred grams) is *Achatima fulica*.

snap pea *See* MANGE-TOUT.

snapper Marine fish, *Aphareus* spp., *Aprion* spp., and *Pristimoides* spp. Also known as jobfish.

snaps *See* AQUAVIT.

snibbing Topping and tailing of *gooseberries.

snook Marine fish, *Centropomus* spp.

snow Mixture of sweetened fruit pulp with whisked egg-white, normally served with sponge fingers or biscuits, or on a bed of sponge cake soaked in fruit juice.

snow pea *See* MANGE-TOUT.

SNP Single nucleotide *polymorphism.

SO₂ *See* SULPHUR DIOXIDE.

soapbark *See* QUILLAJA.

soapstock In the refining of crude edible oils the free fatty acids are removed by agitation with alkali. The fatty acids settle to the bottom as alkali soaps and are known as soapstock or 'foots'.

soba Japanese; noodles made from *buckwheat.

sobresada Spanish (Mallorquin); spiced sausage containing pork, tripe, paprika, and cayenne pepper; large in diameter and soft in texture, so it can be spread like a pâté. A firmer variety, which requires cooking, is longaniza.

SOD *See* SUPEROXIDE DISMUTASE.

soda water Artificially carbonated water, also known as club soda; if sodium bicarbonate is also added, the product is *seltzer water.

sodium A dietary essential mineral; requirements are almost invariably satisfied by the normal diet. The body contains about 100 g of sodium and the average diet contains 3–6 g, equivalent to 7.5–15 g of sodium chloride (*salt); the requirement is less than 0.5 g sodium/day. The intake varies widely between individuals and excretion varies accordingly. Excessive intake of sodium is associated with *hypertension. *See also* DIET, SALT-FREE; SALT LICK; SODIUM–POTASSIUM RATIO; WATER BALANCE.

sodium bicarbonate Also known as baking soda or bicarbonate of soda (NaHCO₃); liberates carbon dioxide when in contact with acid. Used as a raising agent in baking flour confectionery. *See also* BAKING POWDER.

   A small pinch of sodium bicarbonate preserves the green colour in cooked vegetables (too much destroys the vitamin C). Also helps to reduce acidity when stewing sour plums or rhubarb.

sodium chloride Common *salt, the commonest form in which *sodium is consumed. *See also* DIET, SALT-FREE.

sodium glutamate *See* GLUTAMATE; MONOSODIUM GLUTAMATE.

sodium–potassium ratio In the body, the ratio of sodium (in the extracellular fluid) to the potassium (in intracellular fluid) is about 2 : 3. The ratio in unprocessed food, no salt added, is much lower, and when salt is added during processing it is much higher. Fruits and vegetables are relatively low in sodium and rich in potassium. Animal foods are rich in sodium. Unproven suggestions have been made for the benefits of controlling the sodium–potassium ratio in the diet.

sodium pump Sodium ions are expelled from cells by two ATP-dependent processes: the sodium–potassium ATPase, which exchanges three Na^+ for two K^+ linked to hydrolysis of ATP to ADP and phosphate; and the proton pump, which creates an H^+ gradient across the cell membrane linked to the hydrolysis of ATP. The protons then re-enter the cell in exchange for Na^+ ions. The Na^+ ions then re-enter the cell together with amino acids, sugars, and other compounds being transported against their concentration gradient. *See also* SGLT; TRANSPORT, ACTIVE.

sofrito Spanish; sauce prepared from onions, tomatoes, garlic, and other vegetables fried gently in oil.

soft drinks Term applied to non-alcoholic drinks, usually fruit juice or fruit-flavoured, but also a variety of *carbonated beverages. Various concentrations and preparations are termed squash, crush, and cordial, which usually require dilution before drinking; others are ready to drink. In the USA *cider (sometimes soft cider) means unfermented apple juice (a soft drink), while the fermented product is hard cider.

soft swell *See* SWELLS.

sol A colloidal solution, i.e. a suspension of particles intermediate in size between ordinary molecules (as in a solution) and coarse particles (as in a suspension). A jelly-like sol is a gel.

Solanaceae Family of plants including *aubergine (*Solanum melongena*), *physalis (or Cape gooseberry, *Physalis* spp.), *potato (*Solanum tuberosum*), *tomato (*Lycopersicon esculentum*).

solanine Heat-stable toxic compound (a *glycoside of the *alkaloid solanidine), found in small amounts in potatoes, and in larger and sometimes toxic amounts in sprouted potatoes and when they become green through exposure to light. Causes gastro-intestinal disturbances and neurological disorders; 20 mg solanine per 100 g fresh weight of potato tissue is the upper acceptable limit.

sole Marine flatfish, *Solea* spp. Dover or common sole is *Solea solea*, butter sole is *Isopsetta isolepsis*, Californian sole is *Parophrys vetulus*, eyed sole is *Microchirus variegates*, lemon sole is *Microstomus kitt*, petrale sole is *Eopsetta jordani*, rex or long-finned sole is *Glyptocephalus zachirus*, rock sole is *Lepidopsetta bilineata*, Pacific sole is *Microstomus pacificus*, Torbay sole or witch is *Glyptocephalus cynoglossus*, yellow sole is *Buglossidium luteum*.

solera *See* SHERRY.

soltelte Medieval English; carved sugar sculpture presented to high table at banquets.

solyanka Russian; fish or meat stew with salted or pickled vegetables.

somatostatin *Peptide *hormone secreted by the hypothalamus, stomach, intestinal mucosa, and δ-cells of the *pancreas; it acts to inhibit secretion of growth hormone (*see* SOMATOTROPHIN), thyrotropin, and a variety of gastro-intestinal peptides. Also known as growth hormone inhibiting hormone (GHIH) or somatotropin release-inhibiting hormone (SRIF).

somatotrophin Also known as growth hormone; a *peptide *hormone secreted by the pituitary gland that indirectly promotes growth of bone and soft tissues by increasing the synthesis and secretion of insulin-like growth factors. Its direct actions include reducing glucose uptake and metabolism, by down-regulating *insulin receptors, increasing lipolysis (because of this it has been promoted as an aid to weight reduction, with little evidence of efficacy), increased amino acid transport and protein synthesis, and increased differentiation of fibroblasts. Sometimes abbreviated to hGH (human growth hormone); growth hormone from other mammals differs in structure and activity. *See also* SOMATOTROPHIN, BOVINE; SOMATOSTATIN.

somatotrophin, bovine (BST) The natural growth hormone of cattle; biosynthetic BST is used in some dairy herds to increase milk production (approved for use in the USA in 1993, prohibited in the EU).

somen Japanese; thin fine white noodles made from wheat.

soncoya *See* CUSTARD APPLE.

soondth *See* GINGER.

soonf *See* FENNEL.

sopa de gandules Creole; soup made from green pigeon peas.

sorbestrin Fatty acid esters of *sorbitol, developed as a *fat replacer because it is only partially absorbed from foods.

sorbet A water-ice containing sugar, water, and flavouring (commonly fruit juice or pulp). Also known as *sherbet (from the Arabic) and granita (Italian).

Believed to originate from *charbet*, made with fruit and snow from the mountains of Lebanon, and offered to Richard I by Saladin as a peace offering.

sorbic acid Hexadienoic acid. Used together with its sodium, potassium, and calcium salts to inhibit growth of fungi in wine, cheese, soft drinks, low-sugar jams, flour, confectionery, etc.

sorbitan esters Fatty acid esters of *sorbitol (mainly the monostearate) used as an *emulsifying agent.

sorbitol (glycitol, glucitol) A six-carbon *sugar alcohol found in some fruits and manufactured by reduction of glucose. Although it is metabolized in the body, it is only slowly absorbed from the intestine and is tolerated by diabetics. It is 50–60% as sweet as sucrose. Used in baked products, jam, and confectionery suitable for diabetics.

sorcerers' milk *See* MILK, WITCHES'.

sorghum *Sorghum vulgare, S. bicolor*; cereals that thrive in semi-arid regions and provide important food in tropical Africa, central and north India, and China. Sorghum produced in the USA and Australia is used mainly for animal feed. Also known as kaffir corn (in South Africa), guinea corn (in West Africa), jowar (in India), Indian millet, and millo maize. The white-grain variety is eaten as meal; the red-grained has a bitter taste and is used for beer; sugar syrup is obtained from the crushed stems of the sweet sorghum. A 200-g portion is a rich *source of protein, vitamin B_1, niacin, and iron; a good source of zinc; a source of vitamin B_2; provides 14g of dietary fibre; supplies 660kcal (2800kJ). *See also* MILLET.

sorrel A common wild plant (*Rumex acetosa*); the leaves have a strong acid flavour, and are cooked together with spinach or cabbage, used to make soup (*see* BORSCHT), and used in salads. *See also* ROSELLE. French sorrel is *R. scutatus*.

soubise Dish flavoured with onion or garnished with onion purée; soubise sauce is a white sauce containing onion.

souchet (souchy) 1. English, 19th-century method of poaching fish (especially trout) in the oven with fish stock, onions, and sliced roots of Hamburg parsley (*see* PARSLEY, HAMBURG). **2.** Fish broth flavoured with onions and thickened with potatoes.

souchong *See* TEA.

soufflé Light, fluffy, baked dish of eggs, flour, and butter with various fillings; may be sweet or savoury.

soul food Afro-Caribbean term for food with traditional or cultural links, having emotional significance.

sourballs See ACID DROPS.

source In this book foods are listed as sources of nutrients. A rich source of a nutrient means that 30% or more of the recommended daily amount (*see* REFERENCE INTAKES) of the nutrient is supplied in the stated portion; a good source has 20%; and a source, 10%. Although amounts smaller than 10% are not mentioned, the foods may still make a useful contribution to the diet.

sourdough See BREAD, SOURDOUGH.

soursop See CUSTARD APPLE.

souse **1.** To cook or steep food in vinegar; especially oily *fish such as *herring and *mackerel. **2.** Pork in gelatine with vinegar, dill pickles, and sweet peppers.

sous vide French-originated term describing a method of treating food by partial cooking followed by vacuum-sealing and chilling, giving the food a shelf-life of weeks; claimed also to retain flavour and nutrients.

souvlaki (souvlakia) Greek; *kebabs, especially shishkebab (from the Greek *souvla*, skewer).

sowans Shetland; thick beverage made from oat and wheat meal, steeped in water for several days until sour, then strained. Also called virpa.

sow thistle A wild plant *Sonchus oleraceus*; the young leaves can be used in salads, and the roots can be roasted or boiled, and eaten in the same way as *salsify. Also known as milk weed or hare's lettuce.

soya (soy) A *bean (*Glycine max*) important as a source of both oil and protein. The protein is of higher nutritional value (*see* PROTEIN QUALITY) than that of many other vegetables. When raw it contains a *trypsin inhibitor, which is inactivated by heat. Native of China, where it has been cultivated for five thousand years; grows 60–100 cm high with 2–3 beans per pod. Contains indigestible sugars, *stachyose, and *raffinose, which can cause *flatulence. A 100-g portion of boiled beans is a good *source of protein and iron; a source of niacin and calcium; provides 6 g of dietary fibre; supplies 140 kcal (590 kJ). Also a rich source of *phytoestrogens.

soybean curd See TOFU.

soybean flour Dehulled, ground *soya bean. The unheated material is a rich source of *amylase and *proteinase and is useful as a baking aid. The heated material has no enzymic activity but is a valuable protein-rich food.

Full-fat soya flour is a rich *source of protein, iron, vitamin B_1, and niacin; a good source of calcium and zinc; a source of vitamin B_2; contains 24 g of fat, of which 15% is saturated and 60% polyunsaturated; provides 10 g of dietary fibre; supplies 450 kcal (1900 kJ). Low-fat flour contains 7 g of fat.

soybean milk Extract of the *soya bean. A 250-mL portion is a rich source of vitamin B_2; a source of vitamin B_1 and protein; supplies 80 kcal (340 kJ).

soy, black 1. The rat's eye bean, *Rhynchosia volubilis*, more used in oriental medicine than as a food. 2. Soybeans that have been fermented and preserved by salting, used for the preparation of black bean sauces and *meju.

soy sauce A condiment prepared from fermented soya bean, commonly used in China and Japan. Traditionally the bean, often mixed with wheat, is fermented with *Aspergillus oryzae* over a period of 1–3 years. The modern process is carried out at a high temperature or in an autoclave for a short time. Kikkoman soy sauce (trade name) was invented in Japan in 1630; the name is derived from *kikko* (tortoise shell) and *man* (10000) because the tortoise was believed to live for 10000 years

SPA Spontaneous physical activity.

spaghetti *See* PASTA.

spaghetti squash A *gourd, also called cucuzzi, calabash, suzza melon; often classed as summer squash but not a true *squash. Only after cooking does the flesh resemble spaghetti in appearance.

Spam Trade name for canned pork luncheon meat; a contraction of 'spiced ham' introduced by George A. Hormel & Company in 1937.

Spanish omelette *See* TORTILLA.

Spanish toxic oil syndrome Disease that occurred in Spain during 1981/2, with 450 deaths and many people chronically disabled, due to consumption of oil containing aniline-denatured industrial rapeseed oil, sold as olive oil. The precise cause is unknown.

Spans Trade name for non-ionic surface agents derived from fatty acids and hexahydric alcohols. They are oil-soluble, in contrast to Tweens which are water-soluble. Used in bread as crumb-softeners (anti-staling) to improve doughs, cakes, and biscuits, and as emulsifiers.

spareribs Pork ribs with most of the surrounding meat removed.

sparling Marine oily fish, *Osmerus* spp., also known as smelt.

spastic colon *See* IRRITABLE BOWEL SYNDROME.

spatchcock Small birds split down the back and flattened before grilling. Spitchcock is eel treated similarly.

spätlese *See* WINE CLASSIFICATION, GERMANY.

spätzle Austrian, German; very small noodles made by forcing noodle dough through a colander directly into boiling water.

SPE *See* SUCROSE POLYESTERS.

spearmint *See* MINT.

specific dynamic action *See* THERMOGENESIS, DIET-INDUCED.

specific gravity Of a liquid, its mass divided by the mass of the same volume of water at the same temperature, or its density divided by the density of water at the same temperature.

spelt Coarse variety of wheat, mainly used as cattle feed.

spent wash Liquor remaining in the whisky still after distilling the spirit. A source of unidentified compounds that are growth factors for chicks. When dried it is known as distillers' dried solubles.

spermyse Medieval English; soft cheese made and eaten in summer. Also called green cheese.

sphingolipids Fatty acids bound in amide linkage to the amino group of *sphingosine; the terminal hydroxyl group may be esterified to phosphate or (in *glycolipids) a carbohydrate.

sphingomyelin Complex *phospholipids found in cell membranes, and especially in brain and nerve tissue; composed of the base *sphingosine plus fatty acids, phosphoric acid, and *choline.

sphingosine A long-chain amino diol, esterified to fatty acids in *glycolipids and other *sphingolipids.

sphygmomanometer Instrument for measuring *blood pressure.

spices Distinguished from *herbs in that part, instead of the whole, of the aromatic plant is used: root, stem, or seeds. Originally used to mask putrefactive flavours. Some have a preservative effect because of their essential oils (*see* OILS, ESSENTIAL), e.g. cloves, cinnamon, and mustard.

spickgans German; goose breast, dry-brined and smoked.

spider herb, African The tropical wild plant *Cleome gynandra*, also known as cat's whiskers, mainly consumed as a leafy vegetable.

spilanthes Leaves of the South American annual herb *Spilanthes acmella*, used in salads and as a *pot herb. Also known as pará cress.

spina bifida Congenital neural tube defect due to developmental anomaly in early embryonic development. Supplements of *folic acid (400 µg/day), begun before conception, reduce the risk by about 50%.

spinach Leaves of *Spinacia oleracea*, introduced into Sicily by invading Saracens in the early 9th century. A 90-g portion is a rich *source of vitamin A (as carotene), folate, and vitamin C; provides 5.4 g of dietary fibre; and supplies

25 kcal (100 kJ). The content of *oxalic acid renders much of the iron and calcium that are presently unavailable.

spinach beet *See* CHARD, SWISS.

spinach, Ceylon (Malabar spinach) Leaves and stems of the tropical perennial herb *Basella rubra* (syn. *B. alba*). Also known as Malabar nightshade.

spinach, Chinese Leaves of *Amaranthus gangeticus* and *A. tricolor*, also known as bhaji and *callaloo. *See also* AMARANTHUS.

spinach, Cuban *See* PURSLANE.

spinach, Japanese mustard *See* KOMATSUNA.

spinach, Philippine Variety of purslane (*Talinum triangulare*) cultivated in the USA and cooked in the same way as *spinach.

spinach, water Herbaceous plant, *Ipomoea aquatica*, resembling *watercress, with small leaves. Also known as kangkong, water convolvulus, and swamp cabbage. Classified as a noxious weed in USA, with restrictions on its importation and inter-state movement.

spirits Beverages of high *alcohol content made by distillation of fermented liquors, including *brandy, *gin, *rum, *vodka, *whisky; usually 40% alcohol by volume (equivalent to 31.7 g per 100 mL). A standard measure (in the UK) was formerly one-fifth or one-sixth of a *gill; now 25 mL.

spirit, silent Highly purified *alcohol, or neutral spirit, distilled from any fermented material.

spirometer (respirometer) Apparatus used to measure the amount of oxygen consumed (and in some instances carbon dioxide produced) from which to calculate energy expenditure (indirect *calorimetry).

Spirulina Blue-green *alga which can fix atmospheric nitrogen to form proteins; eaten for centuries round Lake Chad in North Africa, and in Mexico. Many health claims are made, but are negated by the small amounts eaten.

spit Thin metal bar on which meat, poultry, or game is roasted in front of an open fire, and rotated during cooking; now also inside an oven or grill.

spitchcock Eel split down the back and flattened before grilling. *See also* SPATCHCOCK.

spleen Organ near the stomach whose main function is destruction of time-expired red blood cells and recycling the iron. As a food it is called melts. A 150-g portion of calf spleen is a rich *source of iron, vitamins B_2, niacin, and C; a good *source of vitamin A; contains 6 g of fat; supplies 150 kcal (630 kJ).

sponge Light-textured *cake made from self-raising flour beaten with butter, eggs, and sugar.

spores, bacterial Resistant resting stages in the life-cycle of bacteria, generally formed in response to adverse environmental conditions or depletion of a nutrient in the growth medium. They are resistant to conditions such as high temperatures, drying, UV and other ionizing irradiation, disinfectants, and chemical sterilants that are lethal to vegetative cells.

spotted dick (spotted dog) Steamed or boiled suet pudding containing currants and sultanas.

sprat Small oily *fish, *Sprattus* (*Clupea*) sprattus, fresh or frozen; young are canned as brisling. *See also* HERRING; KILKA; WHITEBAIT.

springers *See* SWELLS.

spring greens Young leafy *cabbage eaten before the heart has formed, or leaf sprouts formed after cutting off the head. *See also* COLLARD.

spring onion *See* ONION, SPRING.

spring rolls Chinese (and general South-East Asian); pancakes filled with quick-fried vegetables and meat; may be served as soft pancakes prepared at the table, or rolled and deep fried. Also known as pancake or imperial rolls, loempia in Indonesian, and nem in Vietnamese, cuisine.

sprouts *See* BEANSPROUTS; BRUSSELS SPROUTS.

sprue Atrophy of the *villi of the small intestine, leading to fatty diarrhoea and malabsorption, and hence weight loss and undernutrition. The aetiology is not known, but tropical sprue, which occurs in many tropical regions, is assumed to be caused by an as yet unidentified bacterial infection. *Folic acid deficiency exacerbates the condition by impairing regeneration of the damaged mucosa.

spumante Italian; sparkling wines. *See also* FRIZZANTE.

spurtle Scottish; wooden stick traditionally used to stir porridge. Also known as theevil.

squab Young *pigeon; squab pie is a west of England dish made from meat, apples, and onions.

squash Gourds, fruits of *Cucurbita* spp.

squash, fruit *See* SOFT DRINKS.

squid (calamar) Marine cephalopod with elongated body and eight arms, *Loligo* and *Illex* spp. Arrow squid is *Nototodarus* spp.

SRD State Registered Dietitian; legal qualification to practise as a *dietitian in the UK.

SRIF Somatotropin release-inhibiting hormone; *see* SOMATOSTATIN.

srikhand Indian; dessert made from fermented milk.

stabilizers Compounds that stabilize emulsions of fat and water, e.g. *gums, *agar, egg albumin, *cellulose ethers; used to produce the texture of meringues and marshmallow; *lecithin for crumb-softening in bread and confectionery, glyceryl monostearate and polyoxyethylene stearate for crumb-softening in other foods. Other compounds include superglycerinated fats (*see* FATS, SUPERGLYCERINATED), propylene glycol alginate and stearate carboxymethyl-celluloses derivatives, stearyl tartrate, and sorbitan esters of fatty acids. Bread may only contain superglycerinated fats and stearyl tartrate.
  See also EMULSIFYING AGENTS.

stachyose Tetrasaccharide, galactosyl-galactosyl-glucosyl-fructose, found in *legumes. Not hydrolysed by intestinal enzymes, and a substrate for bacterial fermentation, leading to *flatulence. Also known as mannotetrose and lupeose. About 0.28 times as sweet as *sucrose, and used as a bulk *sweetener.

stachys *See* ARTICHOKE, CHINESE.

stackburn The deterioration in colour and quality of canned foods which have not been sufficiently cooled after canning, then stored in stacks which cool slowly.

stadiometer Portable device for measuring height, with a vertical measuring board and a horizontal headboard.

staling *See* RETROGRADATION.

stamp-and-go *See* ACCRA.

stamppot Dutch; vegetable hotpot.

stanols Analogues of *sterols that inhibit the intestinal absorption of *cholesterol and are used in spreads, yoghurt, and other foods as hypocholesterolaemic agents.

***Staphylococcus* spp.** A major cause of bacterial *food-borne infection, as a result of poor hygiene in food handling, with contamination occurring through direct contact, indirectly by skin fragments, or through respiratory tract droplets. *Staphylococcus* spp. produce a variety of enterotoxins, and are also associated with skin and systemic infection.

staple food The principal food of a population or region, e.g. wheat, rice, maize, etc.

star anise *See* ANISE, STAR.

star apple Round, purple-skinned fruit of *Chrysophyllum cainito*, a member of the *sapote family, with a star-shaped array of eight segments in cross-section.

star fruit *See* CARAMBOLA.

starch *Polysaccharide, a polymer of *glucose units; the form in which carbohydrate is stored in the plant; it does not occur in animal tissue. (*Glycogen is sometimes referred to as animal starch.) Starch is broken down by acid or enzymic hydrolysis (*amylase), or during digestion, first to maltose and then glucose; it is the principal carbohydrate of the diet and hence the major source of energy. Starches from different sources (e.g. potato, maize, cereal, arrowroot, sago, etc.) have different structures, and contain different proportions of two major forms: amylose, which is a linear polymer, and amylopectin, which has a branched structure. The mixture of dietary starches consists of about one-quarter amylose and three-quarters amylopectin.

starch, A and starch, B Refers to wheat starch: A, larger granules, 25–35 μm; B, smaller particles, 2–8 μm.

starch, animal *See* GLYCOGEN.

starch, arum From the root of the arum lily (*Arum maculatum* and other spp.); similar to *sago and *arrowroot.

starch blockers Compounds that inhibit *amylase and so reduce the digestion of starch. Used as a slimming aid, with little evidence of efficacy.

starch, cold water swellable Starch that has been heated in a small amount of water so that it forms granules that will swell in cold water to form a gel, for use in instant desserts and other products.

starch, cross-linked Starch chains are cross-linked by phosphate or adipic diesters, to strengthen the granule and so control texture and provide heat, acid, and shear tolerance.

starch, derivatized Chemical derivatives of starch, such as ethers and esters, show properties such as reduced gelatinization in hot water and greater stability to acids and alkalis ('inhibited' starch); useful where food has to withstand heat treatment, as in canning or in acid foods. Further degrees of treatment can result in starch being unaffected by boiling water and losing its gel-forming properties. *See also* STARCH, PREGELATINIZED; STARCH, MODIFIED.

starch equivalent A measure of the energy value of animal feedingstuffs; the number of parts of pure starch that would be equivalent to 100 parts of the ration as a source of energy.

starch, floridean A highly branched polysaccharide resembling *glycogen, obtained from red algae (*Florideae* spp.).

starch, inhibited *See* STARCH, DERIVATIZED.

starch, modified Starch altered by physical or chemical treatment to give special properties for food processing, e.g. change in gel strength, flow properties, colour, clarity, stability of the paste. Acid-modified starch (thin boiling starch) results from acid treatment that reduces the viscosity of the paste (used in sugar confectionery). *See also* STARCH, DERIVATIZED; STARCH, PREGELATINIZED.

starch, pregelatinized Raw starch does not form a paste with cold water and therefore requires cooking if it is to be used as a food thickening agent. Pregelatinized starch, mostly from maize, has been cooked and dried. Used in instant puddings, pie fillings, soup mixes, salad dressings, sugar confectionery, and as a binder in meat products. Nutritional value is the same as that of the original starch. *See also* STARCH, MODIFIED.

starch, resistant Starch that escapes digestion in the small intestine but can be fermented by bacteria in the large intestine. According to the method of analysis used, it may be included with *dietary fibre, but not non-starch polysaccharide.

starch syrup *See* SYRUP.

starch, thermoplastic (destructurized starch) A homogeneous thermoplastic material made from native starch by swelling in a solvent (plasticizer) followed by heating and an extrusion process; used to make biodegradable packaging films and foam trays (to replace polystyrene foam).

starch, waxy Starch containing a high percentage of *amylopectin; it forms a soft paste rather than a rigid gel when *gelatinized. *See also* MAIZE STARCH, WAXY.

stargazer Marine fish, species of the family *Uranoscopidae*.

starter Culture of bacteria used to inoculate or start growth in a fermentation, e.g. milk for cheese production, or butter to develop the flavour. *See also* ADJUNCT CULTURE.

statins A family of related compounds (lovastatin, pravastatin, simvastatin) used to treat *hypercholesterolaemia. They act by inhibiting hydroxymethylglutaryl CoA reductase (HMG CoA reductase), the first and rate-limiting *enzyme of *cholesterol synthesis.

steak Piece of meat cut from the fillet, rump, sirloin, or other lean part of the animal (normally *beef). Also used for thick sections of fish such as *salmon and *cod.

steak, Salisbury American; similar to *hamburger, i.e. minced lean beef mixed with bread, eggs, milk, and seasoning, shaped into cakes and fried.

steam baking In commercial baking an even temperature is maintained in the oven by means of closed pipes through which steam circulates. This is sometimes erroneously taken to mean that the bread is baked in live steam.

steam distillation Process for removal of volatile components by passing steam through the heated mixture, followed by condensation of the steam and volatiles. May be used either to purify a volatile compound such as an essential oil (*see* OILS, ESSENTIAL) or to remove undesirable flavours from oils and fats.

steaming Method of cooking food in the steam above boiling water; there is less loss of nutrients into the cooking water than with boiling. Steaming is also carried out above 100°C by means of pressure cookers; *see* AUTOCLAVE.

stearic acid Saturated *fatty acid (C18:0); present in most animal and vegetable fats.

stearidonic acid A polyunsaturated *fatty acid (C18:4 ω3); a desaturation product of α-*linolenic acid found in a few plant seed oils. It may have anti-inflammatory properties due to inhibition of leukotriene B4 synthesis.

stearin The solid phase in *fractionation of oils.

stearyl citrate Ester of stearyl alcohol and citrate, used to *chelate metal ions that might otherwise cause *rancidity in oils.

steatopygia Accumulation of large amounts of fat in the buttocks.

steatorrhoea Excretion of faeces containing a large amount of fat, and generally foul-smelling. May be due to lack of *bile, lack of *lipase in the digestive juices, or defective absorption of fat. Treatment is by feeding low-fat diet. *See also* COELIAC DISEASE; SPRUE.

steatosis Fatty infiltration of the liver; occurs in *protein-energy malnutrition and alcoholism.

steely hair syndrome *See* MENKES SYNDROME.

steep The process of leaving a food to stand in water, either to soften it or to extract its flavour and colour. Also the preparation of fruit liqueurs by steeping fruit in *spirit.

steer Bull castrated when very young; if castrated after reaching maturity, it is known as a stag.

steinhäger *See* GIN.

stelk Irish; potatoes boiled, then mashed with milk in which spring onions have been simmered. Also called thump.

stenosis Narrowing or constriction of a blood vessel or part of the *gastro-intestinal tract.

Stephan curve A graph of the *pH of dental *plaque over a time-course of 10–20 minutes in response to different foods, used to assess the acidogenic potential of different foods, and hence their likely action in promoting dental caries.

stercobilin One of the brown pigments of the faeces; formed from the bile pigments, which, in turn, are formed as breakdown products of the *haemoglobin of old red *blood cells.

stercolith Stone formed of dried compressed *faeces.

sterculia gum *See* GUM, KARAYA.

stereo-isomerism Occurs when compounds have the same molecular and structural formula, but with the atoms arranged differently in space. There are two subdivisions: optical isomerism (*see* OPTICAL ACTIVITY) and geometrical isomerism (*see* CIS- AND TRANS-ISOMERISM).

sterigmatocystin A *mycotoxin produced by some *Aspergillus* spp.; it is a precursor of *aflatoxins as well as a toxin in its own right.

sterile Free from all micro-organisms, bacteria, moulds, and yeasts. When foods are sterilized, as in canning, they are preserved indefinitely, since they are protected against recontamination in the can, and also against enzymic deterioration.

sterility, commercial Canned foods that are not *sterile but which will not spoil during storage, because of the high acid content of the food, or the presence of pickling salts, or a high concentration of sugar.

sterilization, cold Applied to preservation with *sulphur dioxide or by *irradiation.

sterilization, HTST High-temperature, short-time. Sterilization by heat from times ranging from a few seconds to minutes; usually applied to flow sterilization, in which the process time is less than a minute; at higher temperatures bacteria are destroyed more rapidly than damage occurs to nutrients and texture. *See also* STERILIZATION, UHT.

sterilization, UHT Ultra-high-temperature. Sterilization at higher temperatures (130–150°C), and for shorter times (2–8s), than high-temperature short-time sterilization (*see* STERILIZATION, HTST).

steroids Compounds that contain the cyclopenteno-phenanthrene ring system. All the biologically important steroids are derived metabolically from *cholesterol; they include the sex *hormones (androgens, oestrogens, and

progesterone) and the hormones of the adrenal cortex. *See also*
PHYTOSTEROLS; SITOSTEROL.

sterols Alcohols derived from the *steroids; including *cholesterol,
ergosterol in yeast (the precursor for synthetic *vitamin D$_2$), *sitosterol and
stigmasterol in plants, and coprosterol in faeces. Various plant sterols inhibit
intestinal absorption of *cholesterol and are used in spreads, yoghurt, and
other foods as hypocholesterolaemic agents.

stevia leaves Leaves of the Paraguayan perennial herb, *Stevia rebaudiana*,
the source of *stevioside and *rebaudioside, also known as yerba dulce or
sugar-leaf.

stevioside Naturally occurring *glucoside of steviol, a *steroid derivative,
which is 300 times as sweet as sucrose. Isolated from leaves of the Paraguayan
shrub, yerba dulce (*Stevia rebaudiana*), the same source as *rebaudioside.

stew Meat and vegetables cooked together, also known as hotpot. Two main
types: brown stew in which meat, vegetables, and flour are fried together
before stewing, and white stew in which the ingredients are not fried first. Irish
stew is a thin white stew (i.e. not thickened with flour).

stewing Slow cooking in an enclosed pan at a temperature below boiling
point, about 90°C. Useful for low-quality meat (rich in *connective tissue),
since it slowly breaks down *collagen to gelatine and so softens the meat.

stickwater *See* FISH SOLUBLES.

stigmasterol A plant *sterol.

stilboestrol Synthetic compound with potent oestrogen activity; the first
non-steroid compound found to have oestrogen activity. Formerly used both
clinically and for chemical caponization of cockerels (*see* CAPON) and to
stimulate the growth of cattle.

Stilton Semi-hard, creamy white or blue-veined English *cheese made only
in a very restricted area of the Vale of Belvoir in Leicestershire, England, but
named after the village of Stilton, Huntingdonshire. Matured 3–4 months; for
production of blue Stilton the cheese is pricked with stainless steel wires
during ripening to encourage growth of the mould *Penicillium roquefortii*.
A 30-g portion is a rich *source of vitamin B$_{12}$; a source of protein and niacin;
contains 11 g of fat; and supplies 125 kcal (510 kJ).

stiparogenic Foods that tend to cause constipation.

stiparolytic Foods that tend to prevent or relieve constipation.

stirabout Irish name for *porridge.

stir fry Chinese method of cooking; sliced vegetables and meat fried for a short time in a small amount of oil, normally in a *wok, over high heat with constant stirring.

stirrup cup A hot *punch traditionally served to the huntsmen at the start of a hunt.

stobb Strawberry stalk.

stock The juice obtained by boiling meat, fish, or vegetables, used to prepare soups, stews, and gravy. Meat and bone contain *collagen, which is converted into *gelatine by prolonged boiling; hence, the stock may set to a jelly on cooling. The main nutritional value of stock is the mineral content.

stock cubes Ready made, dried, preparations of *stock. Most contain relatively large amounts of salt, as well as colouring and flavouring.

stocker cattle Weaned calves grazed on grass, small grain pastures, grain stubble, or legume pastures.

stockfish Unsalted fish (commonly *cod) that has been dried naturally in air and sunshine; mostly prepared in Norway. Contains 12–15% water; 4.5 kg of fresh fish yield 1 kg stockfish.

stollen German; Christmas cake made from yeast dough studded with dried fruit, sometimes filled with *marzipan. Originated in Dresden, mid 15th century.

Stomacher Trade name for a paddle-action blender used to prepare food samples for microbiological testing.

stondyng Medieval English; thick *pottage such as *frumenty.

storage, modified gas (controlled gas storage) Storage of fruits, vegetables, and prepacked meat in a controlled atmosphere in which a proportion of the oxygen has been replaced by carbon dioxide, sometimes with the addition of other gases.

stork process The process of ultra-high-temperature *sterilization of milk followed by sterilization again in the bottle.

stout *See* BEER.

stracciatella 1. Italian; soup into which beaten egg is introduced while boiling, forming curls or strands. **2.** Italian; fiordilatte ice cream with chocolate chips.

strain Horticultural term for seed-raised plants exhibiting certain desirable characteristics but which are not stable or predictable enough when propagated to be a *cultivar.

stratified analysis In epidemiology, when different subgroups of the study population are analysed separately, e.g. separating smokers and non-smokers, to avoid *confounding.

strawberry Fruit of *Fragaria* spp., a perennial herb of American origin, introduced into the UK around 1600. An 80-g portion is a rich *source of vitamin C; provides 1.6g of dietary fibre; and supplies 20kcal (85kJ). The alpine strawberry is *Fragaria vesca* var. *semperflorens*, a variety of the European wild strawberry.

strawberry tomato *See* PHYSALIS.

strawberry tree *See* ARBUTE.

strega Italian; herb-flavoured liqueur.

streptococcal poisoning *See* FOOD POISONING.

Streptococcus thermophilus Used, together with *Lactobacillus* spp., as *starter culture for the manufacture of yoghurt and some cheeses.

streptozotocin A clinically useless antibiotic produced by *Streptomyces acromogenes*; it is cytotoxic to β-islet cells of the *pancreas, and is widely used to produce an animal model of type I *diabetes mellitus.

streusel 1. Middle-European; a mixture of flour, sugar, butter, cinnamon, and chopped almonds, sprinkled over cakes and cookies. 2. Also known as chocolate vermicelli or chocolate strands, made by extruding a chocolate paste through a perforated die plate and setting the strands as they emerge.

stroganoff *See* BEEF STROGANOFF.

stroke Also known as cerebrovascular accident (CVA); damage to brain tissue by hypoxia due to blockage of a blood vessel as a result of thrombosis, atherosclerosis, or haemorrhage. The severity and nature of the effects of the stroke depend on the region of the brain affected and the extent of damage. *Hypertension and *hypercholesterolaemia are major risk factors.

strudel Austrian, German; sweet or savoury *pastry made from paper-thin dough.

struvite Small crystals of magnesium ammonium phosphate that occasionally form in canned fish, and resemble broken glass.

stuffing Savoury mixture used to give flavour to a dish; may be placed in a body cavity, as with poultry, laid flat between two portions, or rolled into boneless joint of meat. May be a mixture of breadcrumbs, flour, chestnut, etc., with herbs and spices, or may be minced meat. *See also* FORCEMEAT.

stunting Reduction in the linear growth of children, leading to lower than expected height for age, generally resulting in lifelong short stature. A common effect of *protein-energy malnutrition, and associated especially with inadequate protein intake. *See also* ANTHROPOMETRY; HARVARD STANDARD; NCHS STANDARDS; NUTRITIONAL STATUS; TANNER STANDARD; WATERLOW CLASSIFICATION.

sturgeon White *fish (*see* FISH, WHITE) of *Acipenser* spp. *See* CAVIAR.

sublimation Change in state from solid to gas without melting to a liquid.

submucosal plexus Part of the *enteric nervous system, in the submucosa; it senses the environment in the gut lumen and regulates gastro-intestinal blood flow and epithelial cell function. Also known as Meissner's plexus.

substantial equivalence Term used to denote oil, starch, etc., from genetically modified crops, that does not contain protein or *DNA, and cannot be distinguished from the same product from the unmodified crop.

substrate **1.** The compound on which an *enzyme acts. **2.** The medium on which *micro-organisms grow.

subtilin Antibiotic isolated from a strain of *Bacillus subtilis* grown on a medium containing asparagine. Used as a food preservative as it reduces the thermal resistance of bacterial *spores and so permits a reduction in the processing time (not permitted in the EU).

succory *See* CHICORY.

succotash American; dish of sweetcorn (*see* MAIZE) kernels with green or lima (butter) beans.

succus entericus *See* INTESTINAL JUICE.

suchar Activated *charcoal, used to decolorize solutions.

sucking pig Piglet aged 4–5 weeks, usually stuffed and roasted whole.

Sucralose Trade name for synthetic chlorinated sucrose (trichlorogalactosucrose), 2000 times as sweet as sucrose, stable to heat and acid.

sucrase The enzyme that hydrolyses *sucrose to yield *glucose and *fructose (*see* SUGAR, INVERT). Also known as invertase or saccharase.

sucroesters Sucrose esters of fatty acids obtained by the direct esterification of sucrose by fatty acid methyl esters, used as *emulsifiers. *See also* SUCROGLYCERIDES.

sucroglycerides Mixtures of monoglycerides and *sucroesters obtained by *transesterification of sucrose and triglycerides, used as *emulsifiers.

sucrol *See* DULCIN.

sucrose Cane or beet *sugar. A *disaccharide of *glucose and *fructose.

sucrose distearate *See* SUCROSE ESTERS.

sucrose esters Di- and trilaurates and mono- and distearates of sucrose. Used as emulsifiers, wetting agents, and surface active agents, e.g. for washing fruits and vegetables; as anti-spattering agents, antifoaming agents, and anti-staling or crumb-softening agents. *See also* SUCROESTERS; SUCROSE POLYESTERS.

sucrose intolerance *See* DISACCHARIDE INTOLERANCE.

sucrose monostearate *See* SUCROSE ESTERS.

sucrose polyesters (SPE) Mixtures of hexa-, hepta-, and octa-esters of sucrose and *fatty acids (C-12 to C-20 and above). Can replace fats and oils in foods and food preparation but pass through the gastro-intestinal tract without being absorbed, hence known as fat substitutes or *fat replacers.

suçuk Turkish; dry fermented sausages.

Sudan gum *See* GUM ARABIC.

suedoise Moulded fruit purée set with gelatine.

suet Solid white fat around the kidneys of oxen and sheep, used in baking and frying.

suet crust *See* PASTRY.

sufu Chinese; cheese made by inoculating soybean curd (*tofu) with the mould *Actinomucor elegans*; stored after adding salt and alcohol.

sugar 1. Commonly table sugar or *sucrose, which is extracted from the sugar beet (*see* BEET, SUGAR) or *sugar cane, concentrated, and refined. *Molasses is the residue left after the first stage of crystallization and is bitter and black. The residue from the second stage is *treacle, less bitter and viscous than molasses. The first crude crystals are Muscovado or Barbados sugar, brown and sticky. The next stage is light brown, Demerara sugar. Refined white sugar is essentially 100% pure sucrose; technically described in EU as semi-white, white, and extra-white. Yields 16kJ (3.9kcal)/g. Soft sugars are fine-grained and moister, white or brown (excluding large-grained Demerara sugar). **2.** Chemically a group of compounds of carbon, hydrogen, and oxygen (carbohydrates). The simplest sugars are monosaccharides. They may contain three (triose), four (tetrose), five (pentose), six (hexose), or seven (heptose) carbon atoms, with hydrogen and oxygen in the ratio $C_nH_{2n}O_n$. The nutritionally important monosaccharides are hexoses: *glucose (grape sugar), *fructose (fruit sugar), and *galactose. Two pentoses are also important: *ribose and deoxyribose. *See also* ALDOSE; DISACCHARIDES; KETOSE; OLIGOSACCHARIDES.

sugar, acorn A sweet compound (quercitol) extracted from *acorns.

sugar alcohols Also called polyols, chemical derivatives of *sugars that differ from the parent compounds in having an alcohol group (CH_2OH) instead of the aldehyde group (CHO); thus *mannitol from *mannose, *xylitol from *xylose, *lacticol from *lactulose (also *sorbitol, *isomalt, and *hydrogenated glucose syrup). Several occur naturally in fruits, vegetables, and cereals. They range in sweetness from equal to sucrose to less than half. They provide bulk in foods such as confectionery (in contrast to intense *sweeteners), and so are called bulk sweeteners. They are slowly and incompletely metabolized, and are tolerated by diabetics, and provide less energy than sugars: they are less *cariogenic than sucrose. *See also* SWEETS, TOOTH-FRIENDLY.

The energy yields differ, but the EU has adopted an average value of 10 kJ (2.4 kcal) per gram for all sugar alcohols (compared with 4 for sugars). They are considered safe and have no specified *Acceptable Daily Intake, meaning that they can be used in foods in any required amount; however, a fairly large amount, more than 20–50 g per day (varying with the rest of the diet and the individual), can cause gastro-intestinal discomfort and have a laxative effect. For labelling purposes they are included with carbohydrates, not sugars.

sugar apple *See* CUSTARD APPLE.

sugar beet *See* BEET, SUGAR.

sugar, bottlers' *See* SUGAR, CANNERS'.

sugar cane The tropical grass, *Saccharum officinarum*; the juice of the stems contains about 15% *sucrose and provides much of the world's *sugar production.

sugar, canners' Sugar with a higher standard of microbiological quality control than normal table sugar because some bacterial spores can survive the high temperatures of canning and even small numbers can damage canned food. Similarly bottlers' sugar must be virtually free from yeasts, moulds, and bacteria.

sugar, caster Ordinary *sugar (sucrose) crystallized in small crystals.

sugar confectionery A range of sugar-based products, including boiled sweets (hard glasses; *see* SWEETS, BOILED), fatty emulsions (*toffees and *caramels), soft crystalline products (fudges), fully crystalline products (fondants), and gels (gums, pastilles, and jellies).

sugar doctor To prevent the crystallization or 'graining' of *sugar in confectionery, a substance called the sugar doctor or candy doctor is added. This may be a weak acid, such as *cream of tartar, which inverts (hydrolyses) some of the sucrose during the boiling, or invert sugar (*see* SUGAR, INVERT) or a starch syrup (*see* SYRUP, CORN).

sugar, extrinsic Sugars in free solution in foods, as opposed to intrinsic sugars (*see* SUGAR, INTRINSIC). Non-milk extrinsic sugars means all free sugars apart from the *lactose in *milk.

sugar, icing Powdered *sucrose; see FROSTING.

sugaring (of dried fruits) Deterioration of dried fruit (especially prunes and figs) on storage. A sugary substance appears on the surface or under the skin, consisting of glucose and fructose, with traces of citric and malic acids, lysine, asparagine, and aspartic acid.

sugar, intrinsic Sugars in foods that are enclosed in plant cell walls, as apposed to extrinsic sugars (see SUGAR, EXTRINSIC).

sugar, invert The mixture of *glucose and *fructose produced by hydrolysis of *sucrose, 1.3 times as sweet as sucrose. So called because the , *optical activity is reversed in the process. It is important in the manufacture of sugar confectionery, and especially boiled sweets (see SWEETS, BOILED), since the presence of 10–15% invert sugar prevents the crystallization of sucrose.

sugar, London Demerara White sugar coloured with molasses to resemble partly refined sugar.

sugar, maple *See* SYRUP, MAPLE.

sugar palm *Arenga saccharifera* (syn. *A. pinhata*); grows wild in Malaysia and Indonesia; sugar (sucrose) is obtained from the sap. Various other palms are also tapped for sugar, or to make palm wine, including mokola palm (*Hyphaene petersiana*), lala palm (*H. coriacea*), palmyra or Borassus palm (*Borassus flabellifer*), nipa palm (*Nypa fruticans*), wild date palms (*Phoenix sylvestris* and *P. reclinata*), buri palm (*Corypha utan* or *C. elata*), and fishtail or toddy palm (*Caryota urens*).

sugar pea *See* MANGE-TOUT.

sugar, rainbow Crystals of *sugar that have been coloured.

sugar, raw Brown unrefined sugar, 96–98% pure, as imported for refining, contaminated with fungal spores, bacteria, cane fibre, and dirt.

sugar, reducing *Sugars that are chemically reducing agents, including *glucose, *fructose, *lactose, *pentoses, but not *sucrose.

sugar tolerance *See* GLUCOSE TOLERANCE.

sugar, turbinado Washed raw sugar, with a thin film of molasses.

sugarware Edible *seaweed, *Laminaria saccharina*.

sukha bhoona *See* BHOONA.

sulphate (sulfate) Salts and esters of sulphuric acid, H_2SO_4. *See also* SULPHUR.

sulphites (sulfites) Salts of sulphurous acid (H_2SO_3) used as sources of *sulphur dioxide (SO_2); 221–227.

sulphonylureas Oral hypoglycaemic agents used in treatment of type II *diabetes mellitus; they stimulate *insulin secretion.

sulphur (sulfur) An element that is part of the *amino acids *cystine and *methionine and is therefore present in all proteins. It is also part of the molecules of vitamin B_1 and biotin and occurs in foods and in the body as *sulphates. Apart from these amino acids and vitamins, there appears to be no requirement for sulphur in any other form and no deficiency has ever been observed, although it is essential for plants.

Not only was the old-fashioned remedy of sulphur and molasses (brimstone and treacle) unnecessary, but elemental sulphur is not metabolized.

sulphur dioxide (SO_2) Preservative used in gaseous form or as salts (*sulphites) for fruit drinks, wine, comminuted meat, and as a processing aid to control the physical properties of flour; also prevents enzymic and non-enzymic *browning. Protects vitamin C but destroys vitamin B_1. Prepared by ancient Egyptians and Romans by burning sulphur and used to disinfect wine.

sulphuring Preservation by treatment with *sulphur dioxide or sulphites; also used for treatment of vegetables prior to dehydration to prevent *browning reactions.

sultanas Made from golden sultana *grapes; the bunches are dipped in alkali, washed, sulphured, and dried. Sultanas of the European type produced in the USA are termed seedless raisins. A 20-g portion is a *source of copper; provides 1.4g of dietary fibre; supplies 50kcal (210kJ). *See also* CURRANTS, DRIED; FRUIT, DRIED; RAISINS.

sumac The berries of the spice sumac tree *Rhus coriaria* are used in Middle Eastern cuisine for their sourness and astringency.

summer pudding Cold sweet of stewed fruit cased in bread or sponge cake; traditionally summer soft fruits such as raspberries, blackberries, strawberries, and currants are used.

sum-sum *See* SESAME.

sunchokes *See* ARTICHOKES.

sundae Dessert of *ice cream and *fruit.

sunfish Various freshwater fish, especially *Lepomis* spp., and the large marine fish *Mola mola*.

sunflower Annual plant, *Helianthus annuus*, introduced into Europe from the Americas by the Spanish in 1510.

An important commercial source of edible oil (low in saturates, 12%, approximately 70% polyunsaturated); residual oilseed cake is used as animal feed.

sunlight flavour　Name given to unpleasant flavours developing in foods after exposure to sunlight. In milk it is due to the photo-oxidation of *methionine catalysed by vitamin B_2.

superchill　Cool to temperature of –1 to –4 °C (chill temperature is usually +2 °C).

supercooling　A phenomenon in which a liquid does not become solid even though the temperature is below its freezing point.

superoxide dismutase (SOD)　*Enzyme that converts the superoxide *radical to hydrogen peroxide; sometimes promoted as having useful *antioxidant properties, but would be ineffective taken by mouth since it is a protein and will be digested.

supplementation　*See* FORTIFICATION.

supplements, dietary　Legally defined in USA as including products containing vitamins, minerals, herbs, amino acids, and other dietary substances for use to supplement the diet by increasing total dietary intake. They are excluded from regulation as either food additives or drugs. (Dietary Supplement Health and Education Act (DSHEA), 1994.)

suprarenal glands　*See* ADRENAL GLANDS.

suprême　French; the best or most delicate part. A white sauce made with reduced chicken stock, cream, butter, or egg yolk; also a dish of poultry served with this sauce.

suprêmes　French; breast and wings of chicken or game birds.

suquet　Spanish (Catalan); fish stew.

sur commande　French; menu term for dishes that take time to prepare and are cooked only when ordered.

surface area　*See* BODY SURFACE AREA.

surfactants　Surface active agents; compounds that have are both *hydrophobic and *hydrophilic, and so act as *emulsifiers, e.g. soaps and detergents. Used as wetting agents to assist the reconstitution of powders, including dried foods, to clean and peel fruits and vegetables, also in baked goods and comminuted meat products.

surimi　Traditional Japanese; minced non-oily fish that has been washed with water to remove soluble proteins and odorants, leaving the myofibrillar proteins that give an elastic and chewy texture. When prepared with cryoprotectants (sucrose and sorbitol) it has a better stability to freeze denaturation than minced fish, and is used to manufacture seafood analogues such as 'crab sticks'. The main commercial sources are Alaska pollock and southern blue whiting. *See also* KAMABOKO.

sur lattes French, literally 'on wooden slats'; with reference to wines, means storage on the side so that the cork is kept moist and airtight.

surullitos Caribbean (Puerto Rican); small cylindrical biscuits made from corn meal and cheese.

susceptibility alleles The genetic variants of genes involved in the predisposition to a complex disease involving interaction between *genotype and diet and/or other environmental factors for expression of the disease *phenotype.

susceptor plates Special metallic films (usually powdered *aluminium) deposited inside the packets of foods intended for microwave cooking; they concentrate the energy on the outside of the food and brown and crisp it.

sushi Japanese; thin slices of fresh raw fish or *seaweed wrapped around a cake of boiled rice. The term is also used for dishes consisting of fresh raw fish flesh placed on boiled rice flavoured with vinegar.

süss *See* WINE SWEETNESS.

süssreserve Unfermented grape juice added to wines after fermentation to increase sweetness, especially in Germany, England, and New Zealand.

Sustagen Trade name for a food concentrate in powder form, also useable for tube feeding; mixture of whole and skimmed milk, casein, maltose, dextrins, and glucose.

swainsonine *See* LOCOWEED.

swede Root of *Brassica rutabaga,* also known as Swedish or yellow turnip; called rutabaga in the USA. A 150-g portion is a rich *source of vitamin C; a source of vitamin B_1; provides 4.5g of dietary fibre; supplies 15kcal (60kJ).

sweeney *Osteomalacia in livestock due to *phosphate deficiency.

sweetbread Butchers' term for *pancreas (gut sweetbread) or thymus (chest sweetbread).

sweet cicely (sweet chervil) A herbaceous perennial, *Myrrhis odorata*; the aniseed-flavoured leaves are used to flavour fruit cups, fruit salads, and cooked fruit; the main root can be boiled, sliced, and used in salads.

sweet clover disease Haemorrhagic disease of cattle caused by eating hay made from spoiled sweet clover (*Melilotus officinalis*), which contains dicoumarol, an antimetabolite of vitamin K.

sweetcorn *See* MAIZE.

sweeteners Four groups of compounds are used to sweeten foods: i) the *sugars, of which the commonest is *sucrose. *Fructose has 173% of the sweetness of sucrose; *glucose, 74%; *maltose, 33%; and *lactose, 16%. *Honey is a mixture of glucose and fructose; ii) bulk sweeteners, including *sugar alcohols and hydrogenated glucose syrup (*see* SYRUP, HYDROGENATED); iii) synthetic non-nutritive sweeteners (*see* SWEETENERS, INTENSE), which are many times sweeter than sucrose; iv) various other chemicals such as *glycerol and *glycine (70% as sweet as sucrose), and certain *peptides.

sweeteners, artificial *See* SWEETENERS, INTENSE.

sweeteners, intense (non-nutritive, sweeteners) Compounds that have no calorific value but are intensely sweet and so are useful as a replacement for sucrose in foods intended for diabetics and those on slimming regimes, but unlike bulk *sweeteners neither replace the bulk of sucrose nor have its preservative actions. *See also* ACESULPHAME; ASPARTAME; CYCLAMATE; MIRACLE BERRY; MONELLIN; NEOHESPERIDIN; SACCHARIN; STEVIOSIDE; THAUMATIN.

sweeteners, synthetic *See* SWEETENERS, INTENSE.

sweetness One of the five basic senses of *taste.

sweet potato *See* POTATO, SWEET.

sweets, boiled Sugar and water boiled at such a high temperature (150–166° C) that practically no water remains and a vitreous mass is formed on cooling.

sweet sop *See* CUSTARD APPLE.

sweets, tooth-friendly Name given to confectionery made with *sugar alcohols, which do not ferment in the mouth and so do not damage teeth; the term originated in Switzerland. Sugar alcohols can have a laxative effect if eaten in large quantities (more than 20–50g of sweetener per day). *See also* DIARRHOEA, OSMOTIC.

swells Infected cans of food swollen at the ends by gases produced by fermentation. A 'hard swell' has permanently extended ends. If the ends can be moved under pressure, but not forced back to the original position, they are 'soft swells'. 'Springers' can be forced back, but the opposite end bulges. A 'flipper' is a can of normal appearance in which the end flips out when the can is struck.
   Hydrogen swells are harmless, due to acid fruits attacking the can.

Swiss cheese American term for hard cheese such as Emmental and Gruyère; may be made in the USA or imported from Switzerland.

Swiss roll Thin rectangle of sponge cake, spread with jam or other filling and rolled into a cylinder. Known in the USA as jelly roll.

swordfish Oily *fish, *Xiphias gladius*.

syllabub (sillabub) Elizabethan dish made of cream curdled with wine or cider; a thickened version is used as a dessert and a thinner version as a drink.

synbiotics A combination of *probiotics and *prebiotics in a functional food (*see* FOOD, FUNCTIONAL).

syneresis Oozing of liquid from gel when cut and allowed to stand (e.g. from jelly or baked custard).

synsepalum *See* MIRACLE BERRY.

syrah One of the nine 'classic' *grape varieties used for *wine making, important in the red Rhône wines. Also known as shiraz, especially in Australia and California.

syrup A solution of sugar which may be from a variety of sources, such as maple or sorghum, or stages in refining cane and beet sugar such as top syrup, refiners' syrup, sugar syrup, golden syrup, or by hydrolysis of *starch (glucose or corn syrup).

syrup, corn The concentrated solution of sugars from the partial acid or enzymic *hydrolysis of *starch (usually maize or potato starch). 70% total solids by weight, containing glucose, maltose, and oligomers of glucose of 3, 4, or more units. Used as a sweetening agent in sugar confectionery; the higher the glucose content the sweeter the syrup. Also called corn starch hydrolysate, glucose syrup, starch syrup, confectioner's glucose, and uncrystallizable syrup. *See also* DEXTROSE EQUIVALENT VALUE; SYRUP, HIGH FRUCTOSE.

syrup, golden Light-coloured *syrup made by evaporation of cane sugar juice; *see also* SUGAR; TREACLE.

syrup, high fructose Corn syrup (*see* SYRUP, CORN) in which a proportion of the glucose has been isomerized to *fructose, which is sweeter. The higher the fructose content, the sweeter the syrup.

syrup, hydrogenated Produced by partial hydrolysis of *starch followed by *hydrogenation to yield a mixture of *sugar alcohols (especially sorbitol and maltitol) and glucose; about 0.7 times as sweet as *sucrose. Also known as hydrogenated starch hydrolysates. Used as bulk sweeteners, viscosity or bodying agents, humectants, crystallization modifiers (*see* RETROGRADATION), and rehydration aids.

syrup, lactose Made from *whey by removal of proteins by *ultrafiltration and of minerals by ion exchange chromatography. Used as sweetener in dairy products, infant formula, and sugar confectionery.

syrup, maltose Made from starch by hydrolysis with acid or bacterial maltase and a maltogenic enzyme, containing up to 75% maltose with little glucose.

syrup, maple Sap of the North American sugar maple tree *Acer saccharum*. Evaporated either to syrup (63% sucrose, 1.5% invert sugar) or to dry sugar (maple sugar) for use in confectionery.

syrup, sorghum The concentrated juice from crushed stems of sweet varieties of *sorghum.

syrup, sorrel Caribbean; syrup prepared from *roselle flowers.

T-2 toxin *Mycotoxin produced by *Fusarium sporotrichioides*.

T3 Tri-iodothyronine, one of the *thyroid hormones.

T4 Thyroxine (tetra-iodothyronine), one of the *thyroid hormones.

tabasco A thin piquant sauce prepared by fermentation of powdered dried fruits of chilli *pepper, mixed with spirit vinegar and salt. Traditionally used with Mexican and Caribbean foods; first formulated in Louisiana by Edmund McIlhenny, 1868.

tabbouleh (tabouleh) Syrian, Lebanese; *salad made with *bulgur, *parsley, *onion, *mint, *lemon juice, *oil, and *spices.

table d'hôte A meal consisting of a set number of courses at a fixed price; there is usually some choice of dishes within each course; a set menu as opposed to à la *carte.

tachycardia Rapid heartbeat, as occurs after exercise; may also occur, without undue exertion, as a result of anxiety, and in *anaemia and *vitamin B$_1$ deficiency.

tachyphagia Rapid eating.

taco Mexican; *tortilla (maize-meal pancake) filled with meat, beans, and spicy sauce, and fried.

taeniasis Intestinal infection with the *tapeworm, *Taenia solium*, acquired from undercooked infected pork, or *T. saginata*, from undercooked infected beef. *See also* CYSTICERCOSIS.

taette *See* MILK, FERMENTED.

tafelwein *See* WINE CLASSIFICATION, GERMANY.

taffy *See* TOFFEE.

tafia Spirit made from *sugar cane, similar to *rum.

TAG *Triacylglycerol.

tagatose Isomer of *fructose (D-lyxo-2-hexulose) obtained by hydrolysis of plant gums and used as a bulk *sweetener; 14 times as sweet as sucrose. Not metabolized to any significant extent, so does not raise blood sugar and has zero energy yield.

tagine (tajine) Moroccan; stew prepared by slow cooking of meat and vegetables in an earthenware dish with a conical lid that acts like an oven; also the dish itself.

tagliatelle *Pasta in ribbons 2–3 cm wide.

tahini (tahina) Middle Eastern; paste made from *sesame seeds, usually eaten as a dip; also used in preparation of *hummus. A 50-g portion is a rich *source of calcium, iron, and vitamin B_1; a good source of niacin; a source of protein and zinc; provides 4 g of dietary fibre; contains 30 g of fat, of which 15% is saturated and 45% polyunsaturated; supplies 300 kcal (1250 kJ).

tai *See* GUARANA.

tajine *See* TAGINE.

takadiastase An enzyme preparation produced by growing the fungus *Aspergillus oryzae* on bran, leaching the culture mass with water, and precipitating with alcohol. Contains a mixture of enzymes, largely diastatic (i.e. *amylases), used for the preparation of starch hydrolysates. *See also* ASPERGILLUS; KOJI.

taki Freshwater fish, *Channa punctata*.

talawa Indian term for deep-fried food.

Talin Trade name for *thaumatin, an extract of the berry *Thaumatococcus danielli*, about 3000 times as sweet as sucrose.

tallow, rendered Beef or mutton fat prepared from parts other than the kidney, by heating with water in an *autoclave. When pressed, separates to a liquid fraction, oleo oil, used in margarine, and a solid fraction, oleostearin, used for soap and candles. *See also* PREMIER JUS.

tamal (tamales) Mexican; maize-meal pancake, similar to *tortilla, but made with fat. Traditionally cooked inside the soft husks of maize.

tamarillo *See* TOMATO, ENGLISH.

tamarind Leguminous tree, *Tamarindus indica*, with pods containing seeds embedded in brown pulp, eaten fresh, used to prepare beverages and seasonings in oriental cuisine (e.g. the Indian sauce, *imli).

tambaqui Freshwater fish, *Colossoma macroponum*, also known as cachama.

tammy To squeeze a sauce through a fine woollen cloth (a tammy cloth) to strain it.

tandoor Traditional north Indian clay oven.

tandoori (tanduri) Indian term for food cooked in a clay oven (*tandoor). The meat is marinated with aromatic herbs and spices before cooking.

tangelo *See* UGLI.

tangerine A *citrus fruit, *Citrus reticulata*, also called mandarin; satsuma is a variety of tangerine. One medium-sized tangerine (70g weighed without the peel) is a rich *source of vitamin C; provides 1.5g of dietary fibre; supplies 25kcal (100kJ).

tangleberry Wild *bilberry, *Gaylusacia frondosa*.

tangors *See* CITRUS.

tanier *See* TANNIA.

tankage Residue from slaughterhouse excluding all the useful tissues; fertilizer or animal feed.

Tanner standard Tables of height and weight for age used as reference values for the assessment of growth and nutritional status in children, based on data collected in England in the 1960s. Now largely replaced by the *NCHS (US National Center for Health Statistics) standards. *See also* ANTHROPOMETRY.

tannia (tanier) The corm of *Xanthosoma sagittifolium*; known as white malanga, new cocoyam, or yautia. Yellow malanga is *X. atrivirens*.

tannic acid *See* TANNINS.

tannins Water-soluble *polyphenols (from a variety of plants) that precipitate alkaloids and proteins; so called because they were originally used in leather tanning. Present in dark-coloured sorghum, carob bean, unripe fruits, tea, etc.; they have an astringent effect in the mouth, precipitate proteins, and are used to clarify beer and wines. There are two main types: proanthocyanidins (condensed tannins) and glucose polyesters of gallic or hexahydroxydiphenic acids (hydrolysable tannins). They are potentially protective antioxidants, but also have potential antinutritional effects, reducing protein digestibility and impairing the absorption of some minerals. Also called tannic acid and gallotannin.

tanoor Iranian; thin leavened flat bread made from high-extraction wheat flour (*see* FLOUR, EXTRACTION RATE).

tanrogan Manx name for *scallops.

tansy A herb, *Tanacetum vulgare*. The leaves and young shoots are used to flavour puddings and omelettes. Tansy cakes made with eggs and young leaves used to be eaten at Easter. Tansy tea made by infusing the herb was formerly used as a tonic and for intestinal worms; may be poisonous in large amounts. The root, preserved in honey or sugar, was formerly used to treat gout.

tapas Spanish; small savoury dishes (especially seafood) served with wine in bars.

tapé Indonesian; sweet-sour alcoholic paste made from fermented cassava, millet, or maize, using a *ragi starter. Either sun-dried and used in soups and stews, or deep fried as a snack.

tapeworm Parasitic intestinal worm; infection is acquired by eating raw or undercooked infected pork (*Taenia solium*), beef (*T. saginata*), or fish (*Diphyllobothrium latum*). Eggs are shed in the faeces and infect the animal host. *Cysticercosis is infection of human beings with the larval stage by ingestion of eggs from faecal contamination of food and water.

tapioca Starch prepared from the root of the *cassava plant (*Manihot utilissima*); there are only traces of nutrients. The starch paste is heated to burst the granules, then dried either in globules resembling *sago or in flakes. The name is also used of starch in general, as in manioc tapioca and potato flour tapioca.

tapioca-macaroni A mixture of either 80–90 parts *tapioca flour, with 10–20 parts of peanut flour; or tapioca, peanut, and semolina, in proportion 60 : 15 : 25; it is baked into shapes resembling rice grains or macaroni; developed in India. Also referred to as synthetic rice.

tarako Japanese; salted roe of Alaskan pollack, also known as momojiko.

taramosalata (taramasalata) Greek; fish roe (usually smoked cod roe), whipped with oil, garlic, and lemon juice, then thickened with bread, to make a dip.

taratòr Balkan; cold soup made from yoghurt, cucumber, nuts, and garlic.

tares Traditional English name for the vetches, which are *pulses.

tarhana *See* KISHK.

tarhonya Hungarian; pea-sized balls of egg and flour dough, fried in lard then simmered in water. A traditional food of the Hungarian lowland plain.

tarka Indian; spiced ghee (*see* BUTTER, CLARIFIED) used to sear foods. Also known as chamak.

taro A starchy root vegetable, the *corm of *Colocasia esculenta* and *C. antiquorum*, traditionally a subsistence crop that thrives in wetlands and waterlogged conditions, but now grown commercially. Called eddo or dasheen in the Caribbean, old cocoyam in West Africa, and amadumbe in South Africa.

tarpon Marine fish, members of the family *Megalopidae*.

tarragon Leaves and flowering tops of the bushy perennial plant *Artemisia dracunculus*; Russian or false tarragon is *A. dranunculoides*. Has a mild anise flavour and is used to flavour pickles; it is one of the ingredients of *fines herbes. Tarragon vinegar is made by steeping the fresh herb in white wine vinegar and is used in making *tartare sauce and French *mustard.

tart, tartlet Open pastry case filled with fruit, jam, lemon curd, custard, etc.

tartan purry Scottish; finely chopped cooked kale mixed with oatmeal. The name is probably a corruption of *tarte en purée*, suggesting it may originally have been served in a pastry case.

tartar Hard gritty deposit of *plaque and minerals that accumulates on and between teeth. Originally the name given by alchemists to animal and vegetable concretions, such as wine lees, stone, gravel, and deposits on teeth, since they were all attributed to the same cause.

tartare (steak tartare) French; seasoned raw minced steak, served with a raw egg. Reputedly discovered by Marco Polo (13th century) when he saw the Tartars of Yunnan eating raw minced meat.

tartar emetic Potassium antimonyl tartrate; produces inflammation of the gastro-intestinal *mucosa and formerly used as an emetic.

tartare sauce Mayonnaise made using *tarragon vinegar, and flavoured with herbs, chopped *capers, *gherkins, etc., served with fish. *See also* SALAD DRESSING.

tartaric acid A dibasic *acid, dihydroxysuccinic acid. Occurs in fruits, the chief source being grapes; used in preparing lemonade, added to jams when the fruit is not sufficiently acidic (*citric acid also used), and in baking powder. Rochelle salt is potassium sodium tartrate. *Cream of tartar is potassium hydrogen tartrate.

tarte tatin French; apple pie baked with the pastry uppermost, then inverted before serving.

tartrazine A yellow colour, called Yellow No. 5 in the USA.

taste The tongue can distinguish five separate tastes: sweet, salt, sour (or acid), bitter, and savoury (sometimes called *umami, from the Japanese word for a savoury flavour), due to stimulation of the *taste buds. The overall taste or flavour of foods is due to these tastes, together with astringency in the mouth, *texture, and *aroma.

taste buds Situated mostly on the tongue; about 9000 elongated cells ending in minute hairlike processes, the gustatory hairs.

TATA box *See* PROMOTER.

tatary *See* BUCKWHEAT.

taurine A derivative of the *amino acid *cysteine, aminoethane sulphonic acid. Known to be a dietary essential for cats (deficient kittens are blind) and possibly essential for human beings, since the capacity for synthesis is limited, although deficiency has never been observed. In addition to its role in maintaining osmotic homeostasis in the eye and nervous system, it is important for conjugation of the *bile salts.

taurocholic acid *See* BILE.

tawa Indian; heavy iron griddle.

TBARS Thiobarbituric acid (TBA) reactive substances, an assay of the products of lipid peroxidation in plasma as a means of estimating total body *radical burden. *See also* TBA VALUE.

TBA value A measure of oxidative rancidity in fats. Thiobarbituric acid (TBA) reacts with malondialdehyde formed by oxidation of polyunsaturated fatty acids to form a coloured product.

TBK Total body *potassium.

T-bone steak Cut from the thin fillet end of a sirloin of *beef, containing a T-shaped section of bone.

TBW Total body water; *see* WATER BALANCE.

tea A beverage prepared by infusion of the young leaves, leaf buds, and internodes of varieties of *Camellia sinensis* and *C. assamica*, originating from China. Up to 30% of the dry weight may be various *polyphenols that have been associated with protection against cardiovascular disease.

   Green tea is dried without further treatment. Black tea is fermented (actually an oxidation) before drying; oolong and pouchong are lightly fermented. Among the black teas, flowering pekoe is made from the top leaf buds, orange pekoe from first opened leaf, pekoe from third leaves, and souchong from next leaves. Earl Grey is flavoured with bergamot; lapsang souchong was originally produced by burning tarry ropes near the tea during processing. Tea bags were introduced in New York by Thomas Sullivan in 1908, initially as a means of sending samples of tea to customers in muslin bags rather than tin cans.

   See also CAFFEINE; HERB TEA; XANTHINES.

tea, afternoon An afternoon meal; may consist of a light meal (especially in southern Britain), or be a substantial meal (high tea) as in northern Britain; introduced by Anna, Duchess of Bedford, in 1840 because of the long interval between a light luncheon and dinner at 8pm.

tea, anzer Dried leaves of *Thymus praecox* subsp. *caucasicus*, used as a *herb tea in Turkey.

tea, Brazilian (Paraguayan tea) See MATÉ.

tea, honeybush Herb tea prepared from fermented leaves of South African plants *Cyclopia* spp., especially *C. genistoides*, and *C. intermedia* (mountain tea).

tea, jasmine A perfumed or scented tea made by adding petals of jasmine flowers to Chinese tea; not a *herb tea or tisane.

tea, Mexican See EPAZOTE.

tea, rooibos Red-coloured *herb tea made from fermented leaves of the South African bush *Aspalathus linearis*. It contains a unique polyphenol, aspalathin, which becomes red during preparation; free from *caffeine and *theaflavin.

tea, Russian Tea without milk, served with lemon. Traditionally it is not sweetened, but is drunk by sucking through a crystal of sugar held between the teeth.

teacake Flat round cakes made from yeast dough, normally toasted and buttered.

teaseed oil Oil from the seed of *Thea sasangua*, cultivated in China; used as salad oil and for frying; similar in properties to olive oil.

TEE Total *energy expenditure.

teeth, deciduous The first set of 20 teeth that appear during infancy and are lost during childhood and early adolescence as the adult (permanent) teeth erupt. Also known as milk teeth, or first teeth.

teeth, mottled See FLUOROSIS.

teetotal Total abstinence from alcohol, advocated by Richard Turner in a speech in Preston (Lancs) in 1833; he stammered over the word 'total'.

TEF Thermic effect of food; *see* THERMOGENESIS, DIET-INDUCED.

teff A tropical *millet, *Eragrostis abyssinica* or *E. tef*, the dietary staple in Ethiopia, where it is used to make *injera; little grown elsewhere.

Teflon See PTFE.

teg A 2-year-old sheep. See LAMB.

teiglach Jewish; small biscuits made from flour, egg, and ginger, boiled in honey.

tejpat See CASSIA.

tempeh Indonesian; *soya bean fermented by a mould, *Rhizopus* spp.

temperature, absolute (Kelvin) A temperature scale starting from absolute zero; 0°K is −273°C.

temperature, endpoint The temperature to which a product must to be heated to ensure destruction of pathogens.

tempranillo A *grape variety widely used for *wine making, not one of the classic varieties; the wine of *rioja.

tempura Japanese (originally Portuguese); vegetables, fish- or shellfish, deep fried in batter.

tench Freshwater fish, a member of the *carp family, *Tinca tinca*, also known as lin.

tenderizer Usually refers to the *enzyme *papain (extracted from the *papaya), when used to tenderize meat. Similar enzymes occur in *pineapple and *figs. Weak acids such as *vinegar and lemon juice also tenderize meat.

tenderloin Fillet of *beef (especially in the USA) or *pork.

tenderometer Instrument to measure the stage of maturity of peas to determine whether they are ready for cropping. Measures the force required to effect a shearing action.

tenesmus Persistent ineffective spasms of bladder or rectum; intestinal tenesmus commonly occurs in *irritable bowel syndrome.

tengra A *catfish, *Mystus vittatus*.

tenosynovitis Inflammation of a tendon sheath caused by strain, calcium deposits, *hypercholesterolaemia, *gout, rheumatoid arthritis, etc. Claimed to be relieved by high intakes of *vitamin B$_6$, some 50 times the *reference intake, but there is little evidence. *See also* CARPAL TUNNEL SYNDROME.

tenuate *Anorectic drug, used in the treatment of *obesity; no longer recommended.

tepary bean *Phaseolus acutifolius*, also known as frijole, Mexican haricot bean, or pinto. It is drought-hardy.

tequila Mexican; *spirit (40–50% alcohol by volume) prepared by double distillation of fermented sap of the cultivated agave or maguey, *Agave tequilana*. Mescal and pulque are similar, made from various species of wild agave, and have a stronger flavour.

teratogen Substance that deforms the fetus in the womb and so induces birth defects.

terpenes Major components of the essential oils (*see* OILS, ESSENTIAL) of citrus fruits; however, they are not responsible for the characteristic flavour, and, since they readily oxidize and polymerize to produce unpleasant flavours, they are removed from citrus oils by distillation or solvent extraction, leaving the so-called terpeneless oils for flavouring foods and drinks.

terrine Oval French earthenware or china dish and also the food cooked in the dish (the latter is technically *pâté en terrine*).

testa The fibrous layer between the pericarp and the inner aleurone layer of a cereal grain.

test meal *See* FRACTIONAL TEST MEAL.

tetany Over-sensitivity of motor nerves to stimuli; particularly affects face, hands, and feet. Caused by reduction in the concentration of ionized *calcium in the bloodstream and may occur in severe *rickets.

tetracyclines A group of closely related *antibiotics including tetracycline, oxytetracycline (terramycin), and aureomycin. The last two are used in some countries for preserving food and as growth improvers, added to animal feed at the rate of a few mg per tonne.

tetraenoic acid *Fatty acid with four double bonds, e.g. *arachidonic acid.

tetrahydrofolate *See* FOLIC ACID.

tetramine poisoning Paralysis similar to that caused by curare, caused by a toxin in the salivary glands of the red whelk, *Neptunea antiqua* (distinct from the edible whelk, *Buccinum undatum*).

tetrodontin poisoning Caused by a toxin, tetrodotoxin, in fish of the *Tetrodontidae* family (puffer fish) and amphibia of the *Salamandridae* family. Occurs in Japan from Japanese puffer fish or fuga (*Fuga* spp.), eaten for gustatory and tactile pleasure since traces of the poison cause a tingling sensation in the extremities (larger doses cause respiratory failure).

tetrodotoxin *See* TETRODONTIN POISONING.

texture Combination of physical properties perceived by senses of kinaesthesis (muscle-nerve endings), touch (including mouth feel), sight, and hearing. Physical properties may include shape, size, number, and conformation of constituent structural elements.

textured vegetable protein Spun or extruded vegetable protein, usually made to simulate meat.

texture profile *Organoleptic analysis of the complex of food in terms of mechanical and geometrical characteristic and fat and moisture content, including the order in which they appear from the first bite to complete mastication.

TG Triglyceride, old name for *triacylglycerol.

thal Indian; platter of brass, copper, or silver on which food is served and eaten; a smaller dish is a thali.

thaumatin The intensely sweet protein (1600 times as sweet as sucrose) from the fruit of the African tree, *Thaumatococcus daniellii*; also known as the miraculous fruit of Sudan (not the same as *miracle berry) and called katemfe in Sierra Leone.

theaflavins Reddish-orange pigments formed in *tea during fermentation; responsible for the colour of tea extracts and part of the astringent flavour.

theanine γ-N-Ethylglutamine, the major free amino acid in tea, 1–2% dry weight of leaf.

theevil *See* SPURTLE.

theine Alternative name for *caffeine, especially when it occurs in tea.

theobromine An *alkaloid (3,7-dimethylxanthine) found in *cocoa, chemically related to *caffeine (trimethylxanthine), and with similar effects.

theophylline An *alkaloid (1,3-dimethylxanthine) found in *tea, chemically related to *caffeine (trimethylxanthine), and with similar effects.

thermic effect of food *See* THERMOGENESIS, DIET-INDUCED.

thermization Heat treatment to reduce number of micro-organisms, less severe than *pasteurization, e.g. heat treatment of milk for cheese-making.

thermoduric Bacteria that are heat resistant but not *thermophiles; they survive *pasteurization. Usually not pathogens but indicative of unsanitary conditions.

thermogenesis Increased heat production by the body, either to maintain body temperature (by shivering or non-shivering thermogenesis; *see* THERMOGENESIS, NON-SHIVERING) or in response to food intake (*see* THERMOGENESIS, DIET-INDUCED). *See also* ADIPOSE TISSUE, BROWN; UNCOUPLING PROTEINS.

thermogenesis, cold-induced Heat production as a result of increased metabolic activity in order to maintain body temperature when placed in a cold environment. *See also* ADIPOSE TISSUE, BROWN; UNCOUPLING PROTEINS.

thermogenesis, diet-induced The increase in metabolic activity and hence heat production following a meal. It is due to both the metabolic energy cost of digestion (the secretion of digestive enzymes, active transport of nutrients from the gut, and gut motility) and the energy cost of forming tissue reserves of fat, glycogen, and protein. It can be up to 10–15% of the energy intake. Also known as the specific dynamic action (SDA), thermic effect of foods, and luxus konsumption.

thermogenesis, drug-induced Caffeine, nicotine, and alcohol can all lead to increased metabolic activity and hence increased heat production.

thermogenesis, dynamic Heat production without performing physical work, due to muscle stretching, as, for example, in descending a ladder.

thermogenesis, isometric Heat production as a result of increased muscle tension without performing any physical work.

thermogenesis, non-exercise activity The increase in metabolic activity and hence heat production due to low-level involuntary physical activity (fidgeting).

thermogenesis, non-shivering Heat production as a result of increased metabolic activity rather than increased physical activity or muscle contraction. *See also* ADIPOSE TISSUE, BROWN; UNCOUPLING PROTEINS.

thermogenesis, psychological Heat production due to increased metabolic activity in response to stress, anxiety, or anticipation, mediated by increased *adrenaline secretion.

thermogenic drugs Compounds that stimulate *thermogenesis; potentially of interest in weight reduction.

thermogenin *See* UNCOUPLING PROTEINS.

thermophiles (thermophilic bacteria) Bacteria that prefer temperatures above 55°C and can tolerate temperatures up to 75–80°C. Extreme thermophiles can live in boiling water, and have been isolated from hot springs.

thiamin *See* VITAMIN B_1.

thiaminase An *enzyme present in many species of micro-organisms, plants, and fish that splits thiamin (*vitamin B_1), forming products that have anti-vitamin activity. Non-enzymic cleavage of thiamin, for example by polyphenols, is also sometimes called thiaminase action. Chastek paralysis in foxes and mink fed diets rich in raw fish, and blind staggers in horses and other animals eating bracken fern, are due to acute vitamin B_1 deficiency caused by dietary thiaminase.

thiazoles Derivatives of five-membered heterocyclic compounds containing both N and S in the ring (C_3H_3NS) that impart green, roasted, or nutty flavours to foods. May be naturally present in foods or formed by the *Maillard reaction.

thiazolindinediones Oral hypoglycaemic agents used in treatment of type II *diabetes mellitus; they increase *insulin sensitivity of tissues, activate the *PPARγ receptor, and repress the synthesis of 11β-hydroxysteroid dehydrogenase in adipocytes, so reducing the formation of cortisol in adipose tissue.

thiobarbituric acid value *See* TBA VALUE.

thiobendazole Antifungal agent used for surface treatment of bananas.

thioctic acid *See* LIPOIC ACID.

thiophenes Derivatives of five-membered heterocyclic compounds (C_4H_4S); sulphur analogues of furans that impart pungent or sweet flavours to foods.

thirst *See* WATER BALANCE.

thixotropy The reversible property of a material that enables it to stiffen rapidly on standing; on agitation it becomes a viscous fluid.

Thousand Island dressing *See* SALAD DRESSING.

threonine An essential *amino acid. It was the last of the protein amino acids to be discovered, in 1935, in studies of *nitrogen balance on subjects fed mixtures of the then known amino acids in place of proteins.

thrombin Plasma protein involved in the *coagulation of blood.

thrombokinase (thromboplastin) An *enzyme liberated from damaged tissue and blood platelets; it converts prothrombin to *thrombin in the *coagulation of blood.

thrombosis Formation of blood clots in blood vessels.

thromboxanes *Eicosanoids synthesized by the cyclo-oxygenase pathway.

thrombus A blood clot.

thump *See* STELK.

thuricide Name given to a living culture of *Bacillus thuringiensis* which is harmless to human beings but kills insect pests. Known as a microbial insecticide. Used to treat certain foods and fodder crops to destroy pests such as corn earworm, flour moth, tomato fruit worm, cabbage looper, etc. The bacillus is mass-produced and stored like a chemical. *Transgenic plants containing genes for individual insecticidal proteins produced by *B. thuringiensis* are resistant to attack by specific insect pests.

thyme The aromatic leaves and flowering tops of *Thymus* spp. used as flavouring in soup, meat, fish, poultry dressing, and sausages.

thymidine (thymine) A pyrimidine; *see* NUCLEIC ACIDS.

thymonucleic acid Obsolete name for *deoxyribonucleic acid.

thymus Chest (neck) sweetbread; a ductless gland in the chest, as distinct from gut sweetbread or *pancreas.

thyrodoxin reductase *Selenium-dependent *glutathione peroxidase in the *thyroid gland; important in the removal of peroxides formed during *thyroid hormone synthesis. Selenium deficiency may result in *atrophy of the thyroid gland as a result of oxidative damage, and so exacerbate the effects of *iodine deficiency. *See also* THYROID HORMONES.

thyroglobulin The protein in the thyroid gland that is the precursor for the synthesis of the *thyroid hormones. The thyroid-stimulating hormone of the pituitary gland stimulates hydrolysis of thyroglobulin and secretion of the *hormones into the bloodstream.

thyroid hormones The thyroid is an endocrine gland situated in the neck, which takes up *iodide from the bloodstream and synthesizes two *hormones, tri-iodothyronine (T3) and thyroxine (T4, tetraiodothyronine). The active hormone is T3; thyroxine is converted to T3 in tissues by the action of a *selenium-dependent *enzyme, thyroxine de-iodinase. T3 controls the *basal metabolic rate.

  See also GOITRE; HYPOTHYROIDISM; THYROTOXICOSIS.

thyrotoxicosis Over-activity of the thyroid gland, leading to excessive secretion of *thyroid hormones and resulting in increased *basal metabolic rate. Hyperthyroid subjects are lean and have tense nervous activity.

  Iodine-induced thyrotoxicosis affects mostly older people who have lived for a long time in iodine-deficient areas, have a long-standing *goitre, and then have been given extra iodine. Also known as Jodbasedow, or Basedow's disease.

thyroxine One of the *thyroid hormones.

TIA Transient ischaemic attack. The result of temporary obstruction of the blood supply to a region of the brain; symptoms similar to a stroke, but the patient usually recovers within 24 hours.

TIBC Total iron binding capacity. In *iron deficiency there is increased synthesis of *transferrin and hence an increase in the capacity of blood plasma to bind iron because of the presence of apo-transferrin.

tierce Obsolete measure of wine cask; ⅓ of a *pipe, i.e. about 35 imperial gallons (160 litres).

tiffin Anglo-Indian name for a light midday meal.

tiger nut Tuber of grass-like sedge, *Cyperus esculentus*; also earth or ground almond, chufa nut, rush nut, nut sedge; 5–20mm long, usually available partly dried. Mainly starch and fat (75% mono-unsaturated); a rich source of dietary fibre (19g/100g). *See also* HORCHATA DE CHUFAS.

tikka Indian; marinated chicken (or other meat) threaded on skewers and grilled.

til *See* SESAME.

tilapia Various freshwater fish, especially *Tilapia* and *Oreochromis* spp., widely distributed in rivers and lakes of Africa and widely farmed. Nile tilapia (known in Egypt as bolti) is *O. niloticus* (formerly *T. nilotica*); Mozambique tilapia is *O. mossambicus*.

tilsit Dutch, German; firm textured cheese.

timbale Round, fireproof china or tinned copper mould, used for moulding meat or fish mixtures; also the dishes cooked in the mould. For hot timbales the mould is lined with potato, pastry, or pasta; for cold the lining is *aspic.

tin A metal; a dietary essential for experimental animals, but so widely distributed in foods that no deficiency has been reported in human beings, and its function, if any, is not known. In the absence of oxygen, tin is resistant to corrosion; hence its use to plate steel cans for food.

ting South African; sour porridge made from fermented *sorghum.

tinto Portuguese, Spanish; red wines.

tipsy cake Sponge cake soaked in wine and fruit juice, made into a trifle, and reassembled into the original tall shape. The wine and fruit juice may cause the cake to topple sideways in drunken (tipsy) fashion.

tiramisù Italian; dessert made of coffee-flavoured sponge or biscuit filled with sweetened cream cheese (*mascarpone) and cream, doused with syrup.

tisane French term for an infusion made from herbs (camomile, lime blossoms, fennel seeds, etc.), believed to have medicinal properties. *See also* HERB TEA.

TK$_{ac}$ Transketolase activation coefficient, the result of the *transketolase test for *vitamin B$_1$ nutritional status, an *enzyme activation assay.

TMP Thymidine monophosphate.

TNF-α *See* TUMOUR NECROSIS FACTOR-α.

toad-in-the-hole *Sausages cooked in batter, also called sausage toad.

toad skin *See* PHRYNODERMA.

TOBEC Total body electrical conductivity, a method of measuring the proportion of fat in the body by the difference in the electrical conductivity of fat and lean tissue.

tocino Spanish; salted pork fat.

tocol, tocopherol *See* VITAMIN E.

tocopheronic acid Water-soluble metabolite isolated from the urine of animals fed with tocopherol (*vitamin E); it has vitamin E activity.

tocotrienol *See* VITAMIN E.

toddy Warming drink made from whisky with hot water and sugar.

toddy palm (kitul) *Caryota urens,* a source of palm sugar (*see* SUGAR PALM) and *sago; the sap is fermented to yield an alcoholic beverage. Young leaves are edible.

toffee A sweet made from butter or other fat, milk, and sugar boiled at a higher temperature than *caramels. Called candy or taffy in the USA (originally the UK name). Variants include butterscotch and glessie (Scots). Toffee apples are apples coated with hardened syrup (called caramel apples in the USA).

tofu Chinese, Japanese; soybean curd precipitated from the aqueous extract of the *soya bean, introduced into Japan in the 13th century from China, where it had been eaten since the 10th century. A 200-g portion is a rich *source of protein and calcium; a source of iron and niacin; supplies 8g of fat (mostly polyunsaturated); supplies 150kcal (630kJ). *See also* SUFU.

tofu skin *See* YUBA.

tokay Hungarian sweet white wine made from grapes affected by *noble rot; also a variety of grape used for wine making.

tomatillo *See* PHYSALIS.

tomato The fruit of *Lycopersicon esculentum,* introduced into England as an ornamental plant in 1596. One medium-sized tomato or six cherry tomatoes (85g) is a good *source of vitamin C; provides 1.3g of dietary fibre; supplies 13kcal (54kJ). A 100-mL portion of tomato juice is a rich source of vitamin C; a source of vitamin A (as carotene); provides 3g of dietary fibre; supplies 12kcal (50kJ).

tomato, English (tree tomato) Reddish-yellow or purple fruit of *Cyphomandra betacea,* also called tamarillo; eaten raw or stewed. Also an alternative name for *kiwano.

tomme au raisin French soft cheese covered with grape pulp, skin, and pips.

tongue From various animals, e.g. lamb, ox, sheep. A 150-g portion is an exceptionally rich *source of iron; a rich source of protein, niacin, and vitamin B_2; contains about 35g of fat; and supplies 450kcal (1900kJ).

tonic water A sweetened, carbonated beverage flavoured with quinine, commonly used as a mixer with *gin or *vodka. Originally invented by the British in India as a pleasant way of taking a daily dose of *quinine to prevent malaria; sometimes known as Indian tonic water.

toothfish Marine fish, *Dissostichus mawsoni* and *D. eleginoides*, also known as icefish.

topepo American; cross between tomato and sweet pepper.

topfen German; foods containing curd or cottage cheese.

topside Boneless cut of *beef from the top of the hind leg.

torte Open tart or rich cake mixture baked in a pastry case, filled with fruit, nuts, chocolate, cream, etc.

tortilla **1.** Mexican; thin maize pancake. Traditionally prepared by soaking the grain in alkali and pressing it to form a dough, which is then baked on a griddle. Tortillas filled with meat, beans, and spicy sauce are *tacos. *See also* TAMAL. **2.** In Spain, an omelette made by frying potatoes and onions with eggs; may be served hot or cold; also used for a variety of filled omelettes.

Torulopsis Yeasts that cause spoilage in various foods.

total parenteral nutrition (TPN) *See* NUTRITION, PARENTERAL.

tournedos Thick steak cut from the 'eye' of the fillet or undercut of beef. *See also* FILET MIGNON.

tourte **1.** French; round tart or flan topped with pastry, filled with sweet or savoury mixture. **2. (trete, treet)** Medieval English; wholewheat bread containing both flour and husk. Often used to form the *trencher.

toxic oil syndrome *See* SPANISH TOXIC OIL SYNDROME.

Toxoplasma gondii Infectious protozoan; infection may be asymptomatic, but acute disease can cause lymphadenopathy, and lymphocytosis persisting for days or weeks. Cysts can remain in muscle and brain for long periods and be reactivated. Transplacental infection may occur during pregnancy, causing stillbirth, perinatal death, or defects of the ocular, auditory, and/or central nervous system. The main source of infection is contamination of food and water by oocysts in cat faeces. Other animals are intermediate hosts and carry infectious oocysts, so that raw meat may be a source of infection even if there is no contamination with feline faeces.

TPN Total parenteral nutrition; *see* NUTRITION, PARENTERAL.

traceability Of foods, the ability to relate each batch of product both back to the individual ingredients and their suppliers, and forward to distribution to shops and consumers.

trace elements *See* MINERALS, TRACE; MINERALS, ULTRA-TRACE.

tracers *See* ISOTOPES.

traife Foods that do not conform to Jewish dietary laws; the opposite of *kosher.

trans- *See* CIS-AND TRANS-ISOMERISM.

transaminase Any *enzyme that catalyses the reaction of *transamination.

transaminase activation test An *enzyme activation test for *vitamin B_6 nutritional status, based on the fact that *transaminases require the vitamin for activity.

transamination The transfer of the amino group ($—NH_2$) from an amino acid to an acceptor (a keto-acid or oxo-acid). Pyridoxal phosphate, the metabolically active form of *vitamin B_6, acts as the intermediate carrier of the amino group (i.e. it is a *coenzyme). The enzymes catalysing the reaction are known as transaminases or aminotransferases.

transcalciferin *See* Gc GLOBULIN.

transcobalamin A family of three *vitamin B_{12} binding proteins in the bloodstream. Transcobalamin II transports the vitamin from liver to peripheral tissues, and transcobalamin III returns the vitamin and metabolites to the liver for secretion in *bile. The function of transcobalamin I (haptocorrin) is unknown, although it accounts for 85–90% of total blood vitamin B_{12}.

transcription The process of copying one strand (the template strand) of *DNA to form *mRNA.

transcriptome *See* TRANSCRIPTOMICS.

transcriptomics Apart from mutations, the *genome of an organism is constant, and analysis of a genome does not tell us which genes are expressed in which tissue, at what stage in development, or whether in response to environmental, nutritional, and hormonal stimuli. This is the science of transcriptomics—identification of which genes are active (i.e. being transcribed) in the organism, tissue, or cell at different times and under different conditions.

transduction Of genetic material; mediated by bacteriophages which, upon disintegration of the host bacteria, co-transfer the genetic material of the virus and parts of the host's DNA to a new host.

transesterification A process to modify the properties of a fat for food manufacturing purposes, by interchanging fatty acids between molecules of triacylglycerol. A chemical process using catalysts such as sodium ethylate or sodium methylate, which achieves randomization of the fatty acids at all three positions on glycerol. *See also* INTERESTERIFICATION.

trans-fatty acids *Isomers of unsaturated *fatty acids in which one or more of the double bonds is in the *trans*-conformation, unlike the majority of unsaturated fatty acids in which the double bonds are all in the *cis*-conformation (*see* CIS- AND TRANS-ISOMERISM). Small amounts occur naturally as a result of bacterial metabolism in *ruminants, and are found in ruminant fat and dairy produce; larger amounts arise as a result of isomerization of fatty acids during partial *hydrogenation to produce solid fats from liquid oils. They have at least the same adverse effect on serum *cholesterol in low density *lipoprotein (*LDL) as saturated fatty acids, and current advice is that *trans*-fatty acids should provide no more than 1% of energy intake.

transferrin *See* IRON TRANSPORT.

transgenic A micro-organism, plant, or animal modified to contain genetic material from another species, stably incorporated into the germ line. For production of transgenic animals four main techniques are available: i) microinjection of DNA into the pronucleus of a fertilized oocyte (zygote); ii) integration of a (retro)viral vector into an early embryo; iii) incorporation of genetically manipulated pluripotent stem cells into an early embryo; and iv) transfer of genetically altered nuclei into enucleated oocytes. *See also* AGROBACTERIUM TUMEFACIENS; BIOLISTICS; ELECTROPORATION; GENETIC MODIFICATION; KNOCK OUT.

transketolase test An *enzyme activation test for *vitamin B_1 nutritional status, based on the fact that the *enzyme transketolase in red blood cells requires the vitamin for activity.

translation The process of protein synthesis on the *ribosome, when the information in *mRNA is translated into the amino acid sequence of the protein.

transport, active Uptake of compounds into a cell with accumulation against a concentration gradient, linked to hydrolysis of ATP to ADP and phosphate. Some membrane transport proteins (P-type transporters) are phosphorylated to permit uptake, others (*see* ABC PROTEIN) bind and hydrolyse ATP but are not phosphorylated. In some cases ATP hydrolysis is linked to generation of a sodium ion gradient, and the transported material enters the cell against its concentration gradient, along with sodium ions down their concentration gradient. *See also* SODIUM PUMP.

transport, passive Carrier-mediated uptake of compounds into a cell, but not against a concentration gradient, so that the concentration inside and outside the cell comes to equilibrium.

transport, sodium-linked Sugars and amino acids are transported into cells against their concentration gradient together with sodium ions that have been expelled from the cell by the *sodium pump. *See also* TRANSPORT, ACTIVE.

trassi (trassi udang) Sumatran; cured salted shrimp paste; may contain potato peelings or rice bran. Cooked with chilli peppers to make the condiment *sambal goring.

treacle First product of refining of *molasses from sugar beet (*see* BEET, SUGAR) or *sugar-cane extract is black treacle, slightly less bitter; will not crystallize. A 25-g portion is a *source of calcium and iron; supplies 65 kcal (270 kJ).

trebbiano A *grape variety widely used for *wine making, not one of the classic varieties; makes the relatively thin wines of central Italy if not blended with other varieties.

trehalose Mushroom sugar, also called mycose, a *disaccharide of *glucose. Found in some fungi (*Amanita* spp.), *manna, and some insects; hydrolysed by the intestinal *enzyme trehalase.

trematodes Parasitic flatworms causing both acute and chronic disease, transmitted through contaminated aquaculture products such as raw or under processed freshwater fish (*Clonorchis sinensis, Opisthorchis viverrini*, and *O. felineus*), crustaceans (*Paragonimus westermani*), watercress, and salad plants (*Fasciola hepatica* and *F. gigantica*).

trencher Medieval English; thick slices of (normally stale) bread, partly hollowed out and used as a plate, commonly given to the poor after the meal. Later replaced by a wooden trencher.

trepang *See* SEA CUCUMBER.

triacetin Glyceryl triacetate.

triacylglycerols Sometimes called triglycerides; simple fats or *lipids consisting of glycerol esterified to three *fatty acids (acyl groups). The major component of dietary and tissue fat. Also known as saponifiable fats (*see* SAPONIFICATION), since on reaction with sodium hydroxide they yield glycerol and the sodium salts (or soaps) of the fatty acids.

Trichinella spiralis *See* TRICHINOSIS.

trichinosis (trichinellosis, trichiniasis) Infection with the parasitic roundworm *Trichinella spiralis*; initially gastro-intestinal symptoms as encysted larvae develop into adults in the intestine. Female worms produces larvae that migrate into the lymphatic system and bloodstream, then encapsulate in muscle and other tissues. In severe cases death results from myocardial failure. Acquired by consumption of undercooked meat containing encysted larvae.

trichlorogalactosucrose *See* SUCRALOSE.

Trichoderma reesei (*T. longibrachiatum*) A wood-degrading fungus that first attracted attention due to its ability to produce large amounts of *cellulases and hemicellulases. It grows well in large scale culture, and is used as an expression system for production of enzymes and other products as a result of *genetic modification.

trichothecenes *Mycotoxins produced by *Fusarium* spp. growing on cereals such as barley, wheat, and maize. They are all immunosuppressive; acute toxicity varies considerably from one member of the family to another. T-2 toxin is very toxic (and has been implicated in the aetiology of *pellagra). Deoxynivalenol (vomitoxin) is much less acutely toxic but is more common in cereals grown throughout the world.

trifle Cold dessert made from sponge cake soaked in fruit juice or sweet wine, covered with custard sauce and whipped cream, and decorated.

triglycerides *See* TRIACYLGLYCEROLS.

trigonelline A metabolite of *niacin, *N*-methylnicotinic acid, excreted in the urine in small amounts after consumption of relatively large amounts of nicotinic acid. It also occurs in some foods; it has no vitamin activity, but a considerable amount is converted to niacin during the roasting of coffee.

tri-iodothyronine One of the *thyroid hormones.

trimethylamine $(CH_3)_3N$; formed by bacterial reduction of trimethylamine oxide in marine fish as they become stale; measured as an index of freshness.

trioses Three-carbon sugars.

tripa Corsican; pudding made from beetroot, spinach, herbs, and sheep's blood, stuffed into the stomach of a sheep, and boiled.

tripe Lining of the first three stomachs of ruminants, usually calf or ox. Sold 'dressed', i.e. cleaned and treated with lime. According to the part of the stomach there are various kinds, such as blanket, honeycomb, book, monk's hood, and reed tripe. Contains a large amount of *connective tissue which forms *gelatine on boiling. A 150-g portion is a good *source of calcium; a source of protein, niacin, iron, zinc, and copper; contains 7g of fat, of which one-fifth is saturated; supplies 150kcal (630kJ).

tripeptide *See* PEPTIDES.

triple sec Sweet orange-flavoured *liqueur.

triticale Polyploid hybrid of *wheat (*Triticum* spp.) and *rye (*Secale* spp.) which combines the winter hardiness of the rye with the special baking properties of wheat.

TRL Triacylglycerol-rich *lipoproteins; *chylomicrons and *VLDL.

trocken *See* WINE SWEETNESS.

trockenbeerenauslese *See* WINE CLASSIFICATION, GERMANY.

Trolox Trade name for a water-soluble *vitamin E analogue.

tropical oils Suggested term (USA) for vegetable oils that contain little polyunsaturated fatty acid, such as coconut and palm oils.

tropical sprue *See* SPRUE.

tropomyosin *See* MUSCLE.

troponin *See* MUSCLE.

trout Marine or freshwater oily fish; brown trout is *Salmo trutta trutta* that has spent all of its life in fresh water; sea or salmon trout is *S. trutta trutta* that has spent part of its life in salt water; rainbow trout is *S. gairdneri* or *Onchorhynchus mykiss*; cutthroat trout is *O. clarki*. A 150-g portion is a rich *source of protein, vitamin B_{12}, and selenium; a good source of vitamin B_6; a source of iron and iodine; contains 7 g of fat, of which 20% is saturated; supplies 200 kcal (840 kJ). *See also* CHAR.

truffles **1.** Edible fungi growing underground, associated with roots of oak trees; very highly prized for their aroma and flavour. Most highly prized is the French black or Perigord truffle, *Tuber melanosporum*, added to pâté de foie gras. Others include white Piedmontese truffle, *T. magnatum*; summer truffle, *T. aestivum*; and violet truffle, *T. brumale; see also* MUSHROOMS. **2.** Chocolate truffles, a mixture of chocolate, sugar, cream, and often rum, covered with chocolate strands or cocoa powder.

trypsin An *endopeptidase secreted by the *pancreas that catalyses hydrolysis of the esters of basic amino acids. Secreted as the inactive precursor, trypsinogen, which is activated by *enteropeptidase.

trypsin inhibitors Proteins in *soya and other beans that inhibit *trypsin; they are *denatured and hence inactivated by heating.

trypsinogen The inactive precursor (*see* ZYMOGEN) of *trypsin, secreted in the *pancreatic juice and activated by *enteropeptidase.

tryptamine The *amine formed by decarboxylation of the *amino acid *tryptophan.

tryptophan An essential *amino acid. In addition to its role in protein synthesis, it is the precursor of the neurotransmitter *5-hydroxytryptamine (serotonin) and of *niacin. Average intakes of tryptophan are more than adequate to meet niacin requirements without the need for any preformed niacin in the diet.

It is destroyed by acid, and therefore not measured when proteins are hydrolysed by acid before analysis; determination of tryptophan requires alkaline or enzymic hydrolysis of the protein.

TSH Thyroid stimulating hormone, also called thyrotropin.

tsire West African; a mixture of *peanuts, *chilli, *ginger, *nutmeg, *cloves, and *cinnamon used as a coating for *kebabs.

TSP Textured *soya protein, prepared by extrusion through fine pores to give a fibrous, meat-like texture to the final product.

tubby mouse Genetically obese mouse that develops insulin resistance; it is also deaf and blind due to apoptosis in sensory neurons in the retina and in hair cells in the cochlear organ of Corti. The role of the *tub* gene product in the development of obesity is not known.

tube feeding *See* NUTRITION, ENTERAL.

tuber Botanical term for underground storage organ of some plants, e.g. *potato, Jerusalem *artichoke, sweet potato (*see* POTATO, SWEET), *yam.

tuberin The major protein of *potato.

tumbet Spanish (Balearic); baked vegetables and egg.

tumour necrosis factor-α (TNF-α) A *cytokine produced by mononuclear phagocytes when they are stimulated by bacterial endotoxin. It causes weight loss by impairing *insulin action, stimulating *gluconeogenesis from amino acids, and inducing *ubiquitin-dependent breakdown of tissue proteins. A major factor in *cachexia.

tun Obsolete measure; a large cask holding 216 imperial gallons (972 litres) of ale; 252 gallons (1 134 litres) of wine.

tuna *See* PRICKLY PEAR.

tuna fish (tunny) Oily marine fish, *Thunnus* spp. and *Neothunnus* spp. Albacore tuna is *T. alalunga*, yellowfin tuna is *T. albacares*, bluefin tuna is *T. thynnus*, Pacific or oriental bluefin tuna is *T. orientalis*, southern bluefin tuna is *T. maccoyii*, big eye tuna is *T. obesus*, skipjack tuna is *Katsuwonus pelamis*. A 100-g portion, canned, is a rich *source of protein, niacin, and vitamins B_{12} and D; a source of iodine. When canned in oil and drained it contains about 9 g of fat, of which 20% is *saturated and 30% mono-unsaturated; supplies 200 kcal (840 kJ). When canned in brine the fish contains little fat and the portion supplies 100 kcal (420 kJ).

tuo zaafi African; sorghum or millet gruel left overnight to undergo a lactic acid fermentation.

turbot Marine flatfish; European turbot is *Scopthalmus maximus* or *Psetta maxima*, Greenland turbot is *Reinhardtius hippoglossoides.*

turkey A poultry bird, *Meleagris gallopavo*, introduced into Europe from America by the Spaniards in 1523. The name derives from confusion with the *guinea fowl, which had recently been introduced from the eastern Mediterranean by Turkish merchants. A 150-g portion is a rich *source of protein, niacin, and vitamin B_{12}; a good source of vitamin B_6, zinc, and copper; a source of iron, vitamins B_1 and B_2, and folate; contains 4g of fat of which 40% is saturated; supplies 200 kcal (840 kJ).

turkey X disease Fatal disease of farmed turkeys caused by *aflatoxins.

Turkish delight Sweet made from gelatine and concentrated grape juice, flavoured with *rose water. Also sometimes made with marshmallow. (Turkish, *rahat lokum.*) *See also* PEKMEZ.

Turkish taffy American name for *Turkish delight.

turmeric Dried rhizome of *Curcuma longa* (ginger family), grown in India and South Asia. It is deep yellow and used both as condiment and food colour; used in curry powder and prepared mustard. Its pigment is used as a dye under the name curcumin or Indian saffron. Javanese turmeric is *C. xanthorrhiza. See also* ZEDOARY.

turnip Root of *Brassica campestris* eaten as a cooked vegetable. A 150-g portion is a good *source or vitamin C; provides 3g of dietary fibre; supplies 20 kcal (85 kJ). Swedish or yellow turnip is *swede.

turnover Small pie or pasty; the filling is placed on one half of a piece of rolled-out pastry and the other half is folded over to make a semicircular envelope.

turrón Spanish *nougat.

turtle Marine reptile; the main species for food is the green turtle, *Chelonia mydas*, so called because of the greenish tinge of its fat. It is farmed to a small extent, but mainly caught in the wild. *See also* CALIPASH; MOCK TURTLE.

tutti-frutti Mixture of soft fruits bottled in brandy. Also *ice cream containing mixed preserved fruit.

tvoroinki (tvorozhniki) Russian; cheese dumplings.

TVP *See* TEXTURED VEGETABLE PROTEIN.

tweed kettle Scottish; salmon cut into small cubes before poaching. Also called salmon hash.

Tweens *See* SPANS.

tyramine The *amine formed by decarboxylation of the amino acid *tyrosine.

tyropita Greek; cheese pie prepared with *feta and cottage *cheeses, eggs, and phyllo pastry (*see* PASTRY, PHYLO).

tyrosinase *Enzyme that oxidizes the *amino acid *tyrosine and other phenolic compounds to form brown and black pigments (melanin). Present in some fruits and vegetables, e.g. potato and apple, and is responsible for the dark colour produced when cut raw food or juice is exposed to air.

tyrosine A non-essential *amino acid, formed in the body from the essential amino acid *phenylalanine, hence it has some sparing action on phenylalanine. In addition to its role in proteins, tyrosine is the precursor for the synthesis of melanin (the black and brown pigment of skin and hair), and the hormones *adrenaline and *noradrenaline.

tzatziki Greek; grated cucumber in yoghurt, flavoured with garlic, olive oil, and vinegar.

ubiquinone *Coenzyme in the respiratory (electron transport) chain in mitochondria, also known as coenzyme Q or mitoquinone; widely distributed in nature. May have *antioxidant activity, and supplements are sometimes sold as vitamin Q, although there is no evidence that it is a dietary essential.

ubiquitin A small peptide (8.5k) that targets tissue proteins for catabolism by forming a peptide bond to the ε-amino group of lysine residues. Poly-ubiquitinylated proteins are hydrolysed by the *proteasome.

UCP *See* UNCOUPLING PROTEINS.

udon Japanese; narrow ribbon-like white or transparent noodles made from wheat.

UFA Unesterified fatty acids; *see* FATTY ACIDS, FREE.

ugba *See* OIL BEAN, AFRICAN.

ugli A *citrus fruit, a cross between *grapefruit or *pomelo and *tangerine, also called tangelo (in the USA); first produced in Jamaica in 1930.

UHT Ultra-high-temperature *sterilization.

uisge beatha (usquebaugh) *See* WHISKY.

uitsmijter Dutch; *sandwich of cooked meat or ham and fried egg.

uji *See* KOKO.

ukoy Filipino; shrimp and sweet potato fritters coloured with *annatto.

UL Tolerable upper intake level of a nutrient; maximum intake (from supplements and enriched foods) that is unlikely to pose a risk of adverse effects on health.

ulcer A crater-like lesion of the skin or of a mucous membrane resulting from tissue death associated with inflammatory disease, infection, or cancer. Peptic ulcers affect regions of the *gastro-intestinal tract exposed to gastric juices containing acid and *pepsin: gastric in the stomach and duodenal in the duodenum. Usually treated with antagonists of *histamine receptors or inhibitors of gastric acid secretion. Often caused by infection with *Helicobacter pylori*.

ulcerative colitis *See* COLITIS.

ullage Liquid left in cask or bottle after some has been removed.

ulluco Both the starchy tuber and leaves of the perennial Andean plant *Ullucus tuberosus* are eaten, although it is cultivated mainly as a root vegetable. Also known as anu, mashua, and tuberous basella.

ultrafiltration Filtration under pressure through a membrane with pores small enough to retain relatively large solutes and permit the passage of small solutes. *See also* DIALYSIS; MEMBRANE, SEMI-PERMEABLE; MICROFILTRATION.

ultra-pasteurization A process in which milk is heated to 138°C for at least 2 s, so as to produce a product that has an extended shelf life (up to 10 weeks) under refrigeration (and so distinct from UHT sterilized milk (*see* STERILIZATION, UHT), which will keep without refrigeration).

ultraviolet (UV) irradiation Light of wavelength below the visible range. Wavelength for maximal germicidal action is 260 nm; it has poor penetrating power and is of value only for surface sterilization or sterilizing air and water. Also used for tenderizing and ageing of meat, curing cheese, and prevention of mould growth on the surface of bakery products.

Ultraviolet from sunlight is responsible for skin tanning, and the formation of *vitamin D from 7-dehydrocholesterol in the skin.

umami Name given to the special taste of *monosodium glutamate, *protein, certain *amino acids, and the *ribonucleotides (inosinate and guanylate). The Japanese name for a savoury flavour, now considered one of the five basic senses of *taste.

umbles Edible entrails of any animal (especially deer) which used to be made into umble or humble pie.

uncoupling proteins Proteins in muscle and brown adipose tissue (*see* ADIPOSE TISSUE, BROWN) that uncouple mitochondrial electron transport from oxidative phosphorylation, and so permit oxidation of metabolic fuels for heat production (*thermogenesis) without the normal control by the availability of ADP to be phosphorylated. The protein in brown adipose tissue is known as thermogenin.

unesterified fatty acids (UFA) *See* FATTY ACIDS, FREE.

UNICEF The United Nations Children's Fund (UNCF), originally the United Nations International Children's Emergency Fund.

(((⊕))) SEE WEB LINKS
• The UNICEF's homepage.

Unicum Trade name; Tyrolean *bitters, slightly sweet, an apéritif and *digestif.

universal product code Computer-readable bar code for labelling, first proposed for food labelling in 1973; the first supermarket checkout scanners to read them were installed in 1974.

unsaponifiable *See* SAPONIFICATION.

unsaturated fatty acids *See* FATTY ACIDS.

UNU United Nations University.

(⊕) SEE WEB LINKS
- The UNU's homepage.

upc *See* UNIVERSAL PRODUCT CODE.

uperization A method of sterilizing milk by injecting steam under pressure to raise the temperature to 150°C. The added water is evaporated off.

upside-down cake A cake or sponge pudding which is baked with a layer of fruit under the sponge mixture, then served upside down, with the fruit uppermost.

urd bean *See* GRAMS, INDIAN.

urea The end-product of nitrogen metabolism, excreted in the urine, $CO(NH_2)_2$. Synthesized in the liver from ammonia and the amino acid *aspartic acid; the major nitrogenous compound in urine, and the major component of the non-protein nitrogen in blood plasma.

urethane Ethyl carbamate, used as intermediate in organic syntheses, as a solubilizer, and as the precursor for polyurethane foam. Found in small amounts in liqueurs made from stone fruits, wines, and some distilled spirits where it is formed by reaction between alcohol and urea; a cause for concern since it is genotoxic.

uric acid The end-product of *purine metabolism in human beings and other apes; other mammals have the enzyme uricase, which converts the uric acid to allantoin, which is more soluble in water. *See also* GOUT.

urticaria Itchy skin irritation caused by the release of *histamine from mast cells, commonly in response to a food allergen. *See also* FOOD, ADVERSE REACTIONS.

urwaga *See* ORUBISI.

USDA US Department of Agriculture, created as an independent department in 1862.

(⊕) SEE WEB LINKS
- The USDA's homepage.

USRDA *Reference intakes used for nutritional labelling of foods in the USA before the introduction of *Daily Values.

uszka Polish; egg-flour dough stuffed with mushrooms, like ravioli.

UV *See* ULTRAVIOLET.

vacherin 1. Circular cakes of meringue and cream. 2. Range of French mild cheeses made from cow's milk; traditionally moulded in flat circles and wrapped in a border of bark.

vac-ice process Alternative name for freeze-drying. *See* DRYING, FREEZE.

vada Indian; spiced, deep-fried balls of legume flour that has been left overnight to undergo a lactic acid bacterial fermentation, together with *Leuconostoc mesenteroides*, which produces carbon dioxide as a leavening agent.

valerian Extracts and the essential oil (*see* OILS, ESSENTIAL) of the herbaceous perennial *Valeriana officianalis*, used as flavouring in many foods. The root has traditionally been used as a sedative and tranquillizer, with evidence of efficacy.

valine An essential *amino acid, rarely, if ever, limiting in foods, one of the branched-chain amino acids.

valzin (valzol) *See* DULCIN.

vanadium A *mineral known to be essential; it activates a number of enzymes. Sufficiently widespread for human dietary deficiency to be unknown, and there are no estimates of requirements.

vanaspati Indian; purified *hydrogenated vegetable oil; similar to *margarine and usually fortified with vitamins A and D. Also used to prepare ghee (vanaspati ghee; *see* BUTTER, CLARIFIED).

vanilla Extract of the vanilla bean, fruit of the tropical orchid *Vanilla planifolia* and related species. It was discovered in Mexico in 1571 and could not be grown elsewhere, because pollination could be effected only by a small Mexican bee, until artificial pollination was introduced in 1820. The main growing regions are now Central America, Indonesia, Madagascar, and Uganda.

The major flavouring principle is vanillin (methyl protocatechuic aldehyde), but other substances present add to the flavour. Ethyl vanillin is a synthetic substance which does not occur in the vanilla bean, patented by German chemist Ferdinand Tiemann, 1875; 3½ times as strong in flavour, and more stable to storage than vanillin, but does not have the true flavour.

vanilla sugar Sugar flavoured with *vanilla by storing the bean and sugar together.

vanillin *See* VANILLA.

vareniki Russian; rounds of noodle dough stuffed with meat, vegetables, curd cheese, etc. Similar to *ravioli.

vareschaga Russian; pork casseroled with beetroot juice and rye breadcrumbs.

vasoactive intestinal peptide (VIP) A small *peptide *hormone secreted by the gut, pancreas, and hypothalamus. It induces relaxation of smooth muscle, inhibits secretion of gastric juice, and increases secretion of water into *pancreatic juice and bile.

vasoconstriction Constriction of the blood vessels; the reverse of *vasodilatation.

vasodilatation (vasodilation) Dilation of the blood vessels; the reverse is *vasoconstriction. Caused by a rise in body temperature; serves to lose heat from the body.

vatana *See* PEAS.

vCJD Variant Creutzfeldt–Jakob disease. *See* CJD.

VDQS Vins délimités de qualité supérieure. *See* WINE CLASSIFICATION, FRANCE.

VDR *See* VITAMIN D RECEPTOR.

Vdt Vini di tavola. *See* WINE CLASSIFICATION, ITALY.

veal Meat of young calf (*Bos taurus*) 2½–3 months old. A 150-g portion is a rich *source of protein, niacin, iron, vitamin B_{12}, and selenium; a good source of vitamins B_1, B_2, and B_6, and zinc; a source of copper; contains about 15 g of fat of which one-third is saturated; supplies 350 kcal (1470 kJ).

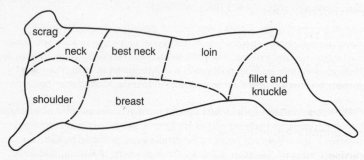

Veal. Cuts of veal

vegans Strict *vegetarians who consume no foods of animal origin.

vegeburger A *hamburger made from vegetable protein or vegetables; meat-free and so suitable for *vegetarians.

vegetable oyster *See* SALSIFY.

vegetable pepsin *See* PAPAIN.

vegetables Plants or parts of plants cultivated for food. Some foods that are botanically *fruits, such as tomatoes and cucumbers, and seeds, such as peas and beans, are included with the vegetables; some plants, such as rhubarb, are classed as fruit, although they are not botanically fruits. The distinction in popular usage depends on whether they are eaten as savoury (vegetables) or sweet (fruit) dishes.

As a source of nutrients most of the vegetables are useful sources of *vitamin C and *minerals, and the root vegetables supply carbohydrate. Green and yellow or orange vegetables and fruits are sources of *vitamin A as *carotene.

vegetable spaghetti *Spaghetti squash, a *gourd (vegetable marrow) with fibrous strands of flesh resembling spaghetti after cooking.

vegetarians Those who do not eat meat, either for ethical/religious reasons or because they believe that a meat-free diet confers health benefits. Apart from a risk of *vitamin B_{12} deficiency (vitamin B_{12} is found only in animal products), there are no adverse effects of a wholly meat-free diet, although vegetarian women are more at risk of *iron deficiency. Vitamin B_{12} supplements prepared by bacterial fermentation (and hence ethically acceptable to the strictest of vegetarians) are available.

The strictest vegetarians are vegans, who consume no products of animal origin at all; fruitarians eat only fruit, not other vegetables. Those who consume milk and milk products are termed lacto-vegetarians; those who also eat eggs, ovo-lacto-vegetarians. Some vegetarians (pescetarians) will eat fish but not meat, and the least strict will eat poultry, but not red meat.

veitchberry Variety of *loganberry.

velouté sauce Rich, white *sauce made with white stock (veal, chicken, or fish) stirred into a *roux; the basis of more elaborate sauces such as *allemande and *mousseline.

veltol *See* MALTOL.

vendace Freshwater fish, *Coregonus albula*.

vendemmia Italian; the vintage of a wine.

venison Meat of deer (*Odocoileus* spp.); traditionally *game, but now mainly farmed. A 150-g portion is a rich *source of protein, niacin, iron, vitamins B$_1$, B$_2$, B$_6$, and B$_{12}$, iron, copper, and zinc; contains 10g of fat, of which two-thirds is saturated; supplies 300kcal (1250kJ).

verbascose A pentasaccharide, galactosyl-galactosyl-galactosyl-glucosyl-fructose, found in legumes; not hydrolysed by intestinal enzymes, and a substrate for bacterial fermentation, leading to *flatulence.

verbena A herb of the Verbenaceae family. *See* VERVAIN.

verbena, lemon A lemon flavoured *herb, the leaves of *Lippia citriodora*.

verdelho *See* MADEIRA WINES.

verjuice Literally 'green juice'; sour juice of crab apples (and sometimes unripe grapes) formerly used in cooking meat, fish, and game dishes. Now normally replaced by lemon juice.

vermicelli *See* PASTA.

vermouth Fortified wine (about 16% *alcohol by volume) flavoured with herbs and *quinine. French vermouth is dry and colourless; Italian may be red or white and is sweet. Drunk as an apéritif, either with soda or with gin or vodka (a *martini). Name originally derived from German *Wermut* for wormwood, a toxic ingredient that was included in early vermouths (*see* ABSINTHE). Sweet or Italian vermouth, 15–17% alcohol (by volume), 12–20% sugar (by weight). Dry or French type, 18–20% alcohol, 3–5% sugar.

véronique Garnish of white grapes.

Versene Trade name for ethylene diamine tetra-acetic acid. *See* EDTA.

vert-pré A dish garnished with watercress and straw potatoes, often served with maître d'hôtel butter; also a dish served with green mayonnaise.

vervain Herb (*Verbena officinalis*) used to make *herb tea.

Verveine du Velay French; herb liqueur, strongly flavoured with verbena; there are two types, yellow and (stronger and sweetened with honey) green.

very low-density lipoprotein *See* VLDL.

vetch Old term applied generally to *legumes; originally *Vicia* spp., also called tares.

Ve-tsin Trade name for *monosodium glutamate.

***Vibrio* spp.** Infectious bacteria; seafood is the most common source of infection, although historically water is associated with *V. cholerae* (cholera). *V. cholerae* causes copious diarrhoea, with rapid loss of body fluids and mineral salts, especially potassium, resulting in dehydration, hypertension, and salt imbalance. *V. parahaemolyticus* causes diarrhoea, abdominal cramps, and nausea, with vomiting in 50% of cases. *V. vulnificus* is normally associated with raw oysters where there is faecal contamination of oyster beds. It causes profuse diarrhoea and *haemochromatosis and may lead to septicaemia.

Vichy, à la A dish prepared or garnished with carrots. Vichy carrots are young carrots, lightly scraped, cooked in water and butter until all the liquid has disappeared, and glazed with butter.

vichyssoise Cold leek and potato cream soup, invented by New York chef Louis Diat, 1916.

vicine A pyrimidine glycoside; together with its derivatives (divicine and convicine) the compounds present in fava beans that are responsible for the acute haemolytic anaemia of *favism.

viili Finnish; yoghurt made using *Streptococcus cremoris* as the main organism.

villi, intestinal Small, finger-like processes covering the surface of the small intestine in large numbers (20–40/mm^2), projecting some 0.5–1 mm into the lumen. They provide a large surface area (about 300 m^2) for absorption in the small intestine.

vinaigrette, à la With a dressing of oil, vinegar, and herbs (French dressing). *See* SALAD DRESSING.

vin classé *See* WINE CLASSIFICATION, LUXEMBOURG.

vindaloo Indian (especially south India and Sri Lanka); *curry, marinated and cooked in vinegar; highly spiced with chilli pepper and hence highly pungent.

vin délimité de qualité supérieure (VDQS) *See* WINE CLASSIFICATION, FRANCE.

vin de pays (vin de table) *See* WINE CLASSIFICATION, FRANCE.

vin de sable French; wines from grapes grown on sandy soil; especially the wines of the Languedoc.

vinegar A 4% solution of acetic acid; the product of two fermentations, first with yeast to convert sugars into alcohol, then this liquor, called gyle (6–9% alcohol), is fermented with *Acetobacter* spp. to form acetic acid. The film of bacteria in the mixture is known as mother of vinegar.

In most countries vinegar is made from grape juice (wine vinegar; may be from red, white, or rosé wine).

Malt vinegar is made from malted barley and may be distilled to a colourless liquid. Cider vinegar (simply known as vinegar in the USA) is made from apple juice; vinegars may be flavoured with a variety of herbs. Non-brewed condiment (once called non-brewed vinegar) is a solution of acetic acid, 4–8%, coloured with caramel. Balsamic vinegar is made from grape juice that has been concentrated over a low flame and fermented slowly in a series of wooden barrels; made in and around Modena, Italy.

vinho de mesa *See* WINE CLASSIFICATION, PORTUGAL.

vinho maduro *See* WINE CLASSIFICATION, PORTUGAL.

vinho verde Portuguese; literally 'green wine' (white and red) meaning that it is to be drunk when young, i.e. within three years of *vinification; light, effervescent wine of relatively low *alcohol content (less than 10%).

vini di tavola (con indicazione geografica) *See* WINE CLASSIFICATION, ITALY.

vinification The process of fermentation of sugars in grape juice to make wine.

vini tipici *See* WINE CLASSIFICATION, ITALY.

vino gasificado Spanish; sparkling wines produced by adding carbon dioxide.

vin ordinaire *See* WINE CLASSIFICATION, FRANCE.

vinos de la tierra *See* WINE CLASSIFICATION, SPAIN.

vintage The year of production of a wine, from the French *vendage*, for grape harvest. Used mainly for superior quality wines, when each year's production is matured separately. Ordinary and table wines (*see* WINE CLASSIFICATION) are not generally dated, and indeed the production from more than one year may be blended.

viognier A *grape variety widely used for *wine making, not one of the classic varieties.

violet The sweetly scented flowers of the wild violet (*Viola odorata*) are candied or crystallized and used as decorations in confectionery, or to make a sweet *soufflé. The flowers can be used to flavour syrups, and both flowers and leaves can be used in salads.

viosterol Irradiated ergosterol; *vitamin D_2.

VIP *See* VASOACTIVE INTESTINAL PEPTIDE.

Virginia date *See* PERSIMMON.

Virol Trade name for a vitamin preparation based on malt extract.

virpa *See* SOWANS.

virulence Capacity of pathogens to cause disease, indicated by the severity of infection in the host.

virus Sub-microscopic infectious agents, capable of reproduction only within a host cell; they consist of a core of nucleic acid (*DNA or *RNA) surrounded by a protein coat. They replicate by inserting their genetic material into the host cell's DNA.

viscera The organs within a body cavity, used especially for the abdominal viscera—*liver, *spleen, *gastro-intestinal tract, kidneys, etc.

viscogen Thickening agent for whipping *cream.

viscometer Instrument for measuring the *viscosity of liquids.

viscosity Of liquids, resistance to flow.

visfatin A *cytokine secreted by abdominal white *adipose tissue; it may have an insulin-like or insulin-potentiating action. Circulating concentrations may provide a useful marker of abdominal *obesity.

vision The process of vision is mediated by a pigment variously known as visual purple (because of its colour), rhodopsin (in the rod cells of the retina), and iodopsin (in the cone cells). This pigment is *vitamin A aldehyde bound to the protein opsin. The action of light causes a chemical change, with loss of the purple colour (known as bleaching), which results in the initiation of a nerve impulse from the retina to the brain. *See also* DARK ADAPTATION; NIGHT BLINDNESS.

visual pigments, visual purple *See* VISION.

vitafoods *See* FOODS, FUNCTIONAL.

vitamers Chemical compounds structurally related to a *vitamin, and converted to the same overall active metabolites in the body. They thus possess the same kind of biological activity, although sometimes with lower potency.

When there are several vitamers, the group of compounds exhibiting the biological activity of the vitamin is given a *generic descriptor (e.g. *vitamin A is the generic descriptor for retinol and its derivatives as well as several *carotenoids).

vitamin Thirteen organic substances are essential to human life in very small amounts. Eleven of these must be supplied in the diet (vitamins A, B_1, B_2, B_6, B_{12}, C, E, K, folate, biotin, and pantothenate); two (niacin and vitamin D) can be made in the body if there is sufficient of the *amino acid *tryptophan and exposure to sunlight respectively.

vitamin A Essential in the diet either as the preformed vitamin (retinol) found in animal foods or as a precursor, *carotene, found in plant foods; both are usually present in the diet. Required for control of growth, cell turnover and fetal development, maintenance of fertility, and maintenance of the epithelial tissues lining the mouth and respiratory and urinary tracts; essential in *vision.

Deficiency leads to slow adaptation to see in dim light (poor *dark adaptation), an early sign of deficiency, and later to night blindness; then drying of the tear ducts (*xerophthalmia) and ulceration of the cornea (keratomalacia) resulting in blindness.

Retinol occurs in animal products, especially liver, kidney, fish liver oils, milk, and butter. Carotene is found in green- and orange-coloured vegetables and fruits; especially rich in red *palm oil and *carrots. *See also* RETINOL ACTIVITY EQUIVALENT; RETINOL EQUIVALENT.

vitamin A toxicity Retinol in excess of requirements is stored in the liver, bound to proteins, and is a cumulative poison. When the storage capacity is exceeded, free retinol causes damage to cell membranes. *Carotene is not toxic in excess, since there is only a limited capacity to form retinol from carotene. The recommended upper limits of habitual daily intake of retinol are about 12.5 × *reference intake for adults, but only 2.5 × reference intake for infants. Retinol is also *teratogenic in excess, and for pregnant women the recommended upper limit of daily intake is 3000–3300 µg.

vitamin A$_2$ Old name for dehydroretinol, found in livers of freshwater fish; 40% of the biological activity of retinol.

vitamin B complex An old-fashioned term for the various B vitamins: *vitamin B$_1$ (thiamin), *vitamin B$_2$ (riboflavin), *niacin, *vitamin B$_6$, *vitamin B$_{12}$, *folate, *biotin, and *pantothenic acid. These vitamins occur together in cereal germ, liver, and yeast; they function as *coenzymes, and were discovered originally by separation from what was then known as vitamin B; hence, they are grouped together as the B complex.

vitamin B$_1$ Thiamin; essential in energy-yielding metabolism, especially of carbohydrates, and for nerve conduction. Deficiency results in the disease *beriberi—degeneration of the sensory nerves in the hands and feet, spreading through the limbs, with fluid retention and heart failure. Relatively acute deficiency, associated with alcohol abuse, results in central nervous system damage, the *Wernicke–Korsakoff syndrome.

Good sources are wholegrain and enriched bread and cereals, meat (especially liver, kidney, and heart, and pork), yeast, potatoes, and peas; cooking losses can be as much as 50%.

vitamin B$_1$ dependency syndromes A very small number of children have been reported with a variant form of *maple syrup urine disease which responds to supplements of large amounts of vitamin B$_1$.

vitamin B$_2$ Riboflavin; involved in a wide range of oxidation reactions, of fats, carbohydrates, and amino acids. Deficiency impairs energy-yielding metabolism and results in a set of symptoms known as ariboflavinosis:

cracking of the skin at the corners of the mouth (angular stomatitis), fissuring of the lips (cheilosis), and tongue changes (glossitis); seborrhoeic accumulations appear round the nose and eyes.

Occurs mainly in yeast, liver, milk, eggs, cheese, and pulses; milk and milk products are the main source in most diets.

vitamin B₃ Non-existent; term once used for *pantothenic acid and sometimes, wrongly, for *niacin.

vitamin B₄ Name given to what was later identified as a mixture of the *amino acids *arginine, *glycine, and *cystine.

vitamin B₅ Name given to a substance later presumed to be identical with vitamin B_6 or possibly nicotinic acid; also used sometimes for *pantothenic acid.

vitamin B₆ Generic descriptor for three compounds: the alcohol, pyridoxine (previously known as adermin and pyridoxol), the aldehyde, pyridoxal, and the amine, pyridoxamine, and their phosphates. All are equally active biologically.

Deficiency causes abnormalities of the metabolism of the amino acids *tryptophan and *methionine; in rats deficiency causes convulsions and skin lesions (acrodynia) and in dairy cows and dogs, anaemia with small, underpigmented red blood cells. Dietary deficiency leading to clinical signs is not known inhuman beings, apart from a single outbreak in babies fed a severely over heated preparation of formula milk in the 1950s; they showed abnormalities of amino acid metabolism and convulsions resembling epileptic seizures, which responded to supplements of the vitamin.

Rich sources include nuts, meat, fish, wholegrain cereals, and beans.

vitamin B₆ dependency syndromes A very small number of children suffer from genetic diseases affecting enzymes which require pyridoxal phosphate (*vitamin B_6) as coenzyme. The abnormality is corrected by the administration of large supplements of vitamin B_6.

vitamin B₆ toxicity Very high intakes of supplements of vitamin B_6, in excess of 200mg/day, far greater than could be obtained from food, lead to nerve damage.

vitamins B₇, B₈, and B₉ In the early days of nutrition research, when a new factor was discovered which was claimed to be essential for chick growth and feathering, the claimant stated that since nine factors were known the new factors should be called vitamins B_{10} and B_{11}. In fact, the B vitamins had been numbered only up to B_6, hence B_7, B_8, and B_9 have never existed. B_9 is sometimes (incorrectly) used for *folic acid.

vitamins B$_{10}$ and B$_{11}$ The names given to two factors claimed to be essential for chick growth and feathering; they were later shown to be a mixture of *vitamin B$_1$ and *folic acid.

vitamin B$_{12}$ A cobalt-containing compound, cobalamin, essential for normal metabolism of *folic acid, and hence for cell division. Deficiency leads to pernicious anaemia (*see* ANAEMIA, PERNICIOUS) when immature red blood cell precursors are released into the bloodstream, and there is degeneration of the spinal cord. The absorption of vitamin B$_{12}$ requires a specific protein (intrinsic factor) which is secreted in the gastric juice and it is failure of absorption, rather than dietary deficiency, that is the more usual cause of the problem. Vitamin B$_{12}$ is found only in animal foods, and strict *vegetarians require supplements prepared by bacterial fermentation. Meat, eggs, and dairy produce are rich sources and dietary deficiency is unlikely except among *vegans.

vitamin B$_{13}$ Orotic acid, an intermediate in *pyrimidine synthesis; there is no evidence that it is a dietary essential, and hence not a vitamin.

vitamin B$_{14}$ Not an established vitamin; name originally given to a substance found in human urine that increases the rate of cell proliferation in bone-marrow culture.

vitamin B$_{15}$ *Pangamic acid; no evidence that it has any physiological function in the body, so not a vitamin.

vitamin B$_{16}$ This term has never been used.

vitamin B$_{17}$ *Laetrile; no evidence that it has any physiological function in the body, so not a vitamin.

vitamin B$_c$ Obsolete name for *folic acid.

vitamin B$_p$ Called the antiperosis factor for chicks, but can be replaced by *manganese and *choline (which is not a dietary essential for human beings).

vitamin B$_T$ *Carnitine; an essential dietary factor for the mealworm, *Tenebrio molitor*, and certain related species, but not for human beings.

vitamin B$_w$ Or factor W; probably identical with *biotin.

vitamin B$_x$ Non-existent; has been used in the past for both *pantothenic acid and *p*-amino benzoic acid.

vitamin C *Ascorbic acid. Historically an inadequate intake of vitamin C led to *scurvy, especially common among sailors unable to obtain fruits and vegetables during long voyages. It has three main areas of function: i) as a general (non-enzymic) *antioxidant, including the reduction of oxidized *vitamin E in cell membranes; ii) as a coenzyme in the hydroxylation of *lysine and *proline in the synthesis of *collagen and *elastin, and hence essential for the normal formation of *connective tissue; iii) as a coenzyme in the formation of *noradrenaline.

Deficiency results in scurvy: seepage of blood from capillaries, subcutaneous bleeding, weakness of muscles, soft, spongy gums, and loss of dental cement leading to loss of teeth, and, in advanced cases, deep bone pain. A lesser degree of deficiency results in impaired healing of wounds. The requirement to prevent scurvy is less than 10 mg/day; reference intakes published by various authorities range between 40–90 mg/day. The different values can all be justified, depending on the criteria of adequacy adopted and the assumptions made in the interpretation of experimental data. At intakes above 100–120 mg/day the vitamin is excreted in the urine; there is little evidence of any adverse effects at intakes up to 4000 mg/day.

Losses from foods can be high as they stale; it is easily oxidized, especially in foods kept hot, and it is leached into cooking water. Fruits and vegetables are rich sources. It is also used in curing ham, and as an antioxidant and bread improver. *See also* ERYTHORBIC ACID; IRON.

vitamin D Vitamin D_3 is calciol or cholecalciferol; formed in the skin by the action of ultraviolet light on 7-dehydrocholesterol, and hence not strictly a vitamin. However, beyond about 45°N or S sunlight exposure may not be adequate to meet requirements, and a dietary source becomes essential. Vitamin D_2 (ercalciol or ergocalciferol) is a synthetic *vitamer produced by irradiation of ergosterol. The name vitamin D_1 was given originally to an impure mixture and is not used now.

The main metabolic function of vitamin D is to control *calcium metabolism. It stimulates the absorption of dietary calcium from the intestine and calcium turnover in bone. Deficiency causes *rickets in young children, *osteomalacia in adults. It is also important in regulation of gene expression and cell differentiation and turnover.

It is not widely distributed in foods, but is found in egg yolk, butter, oily fish, and enriched margarine. There are no *reference intakes for adults in the UK or the EU; the US/Canadian RDA for adults is 5 µg, increasing to 10 and 15 µg with increasing age. The obsolete *international unit of vitamin D = 25 ng calciol; 1 µg calciol = 40 iu.

vitamin D resistant rickets *See* RICKETS, REFRACTORY.

vitamin D toxicity Excessive intake of vitamin D results in disturbance of calcium metabolism, resulting in hypercalcaemia, i.e. dangerously raised blood calcium concentrations leading to *hypertension (raised *blood pressure), brain damage, and kidney damage. Excessive exposure to sunlight does not lead to excessive formation of vitamin D.

vitamin E Generic descriptor for a group of fat-soluble compounds essential for reproduction in animals. Essential for human beings (not for reproduction, so far as is known) but rarely, if ever, deficient in the diet. Two main groups of compounds have vitamin E activity: the tocopherols and the tocotrienols. There are 4 isomers of each: α-, β-, γ-, and δ-tocopherols and α-, β-, γ-, and δ-tocotrienols, with differing vitamin potencies.

Vitamin E functions primarily as an *antioxidant in cell membranes, protecting unsaturated fatty acids from oxidative damage.

The vitamin E content of foods is expressed as mg α-tocopherol equivalent (based on the different potencies of the vitamers). Vegetables, seeds, and most vegetable oils are good sources. In the UK and the EU an adequate intake is 0.4 mg/g dietary polyunsaturated fatty acid intake; the US/Canadian RDA is 15 mg/day. The obsolete *international unit of vitamin E activity was equal to 1 mg of synthetic α-tocopherol; on this basis natural-source α-tocopherol is 1.49 iu/mg.

vitamin F Sometimes used for the essential *fatty acids.

vitamin G Obsolete name for *vitamin B_2.

vitamin H *See* BIOTIN.

vitamin K Fat-soluble vitamin essential for the synthesis of *γ-carboxyglutamate in prothrombin and other proteins involved in the *blood clotting system, and bone proteins. Deficiency causes impaired blood coagulation and haemorrhage. Two groups of compounds have vitamin K activity: phylloquinones, found in green plants, and a variety of menaquinones synthesized by intestinal bacteria. Dietary deficiency is unknown, except when associated with general malabsorption diseases. However, some newborn infants are at risk of haemorrhage as a result of low vitamin K status (vitamin K deficiency bleeding), and it is general practice to give a single, relatively large dose of the vitamin shortly after birth.

vitamin L Factors extracted from yeast and thought at the time to be essential for lactation; they have not become established vitamins.

vitamin M Obsolete name for *folic acid.

vitamin P Name given to a group of plant *flavonoids (sometimes called bioflavonoids) which affect the strength of the walls of the blood capillaries: rutin (in buckwheat), hesperidin, eriodictin, and citrin (a mixture of hesperidin and eriodictin in the pith of citrus fruits). Although they are not dietary essentials they have *antioxidant activity and some are *phytoestrogens.

vitamin PP The *pellagra preventing vitamin, an old name for *niacin before it was identified.

vitamin Q *See* UBIQUINONE.

vitamin T Factor found in insect cuticle, mould mycelia, and yeast fermentation liquor, and claimed to accelerate maturation and promote protein synthesis. Also known as torulitine. Probably a mixture of *folic acid, *vitamin B$_{12}$, and *DNA.

vitaminoids Name given to compounds with 'vitamin-like' activity; considered by some to be vitamins or partially to replace vitamins. Includes *flavonoids, *inositol, *carnitine, *choline, *lipoic acid, and the essential *fatty acids. With the exception of the essential fatty acids, there is little evidence that any of them is a dietary essential.

vitamins, fat-soluble Vitamins A, D, E, and K, which are all soluble in lipids, but not in water.

vitamins, water-soluble Vitamin C and the B vitamins (including *pantothenic acid, *biotin, and *folate), which are all soluble in water, but not in lipids.

VKDB Vitamin K deficiency bleeding; *see* VITAMIN K.

VLDL Very low density *lipoprotein, assembled in the liver, containing both newly synthesized *triacylglycerol and that from *chylomicron remnants, as well as *phospholipids and *cholesterol (as cholesteryl esters), for transport to peripheral tissues.

VLED Very low *energy diet.

VOC Volatile organic compounds.

vodka Made from neutral spirit, i.e. alcohol distillate mainly from potatoes, with little or no acid, so that there is no ester formation and hence no flavour. Polish vodka is flavoured with a variety of herbs and fruits.

vodka, coconut *See* LAMBANOG.

vodkatini A *martini cocktail prepared with *vodka rather than *gin.

vol-au-vent Case of light puff *pastry filled with poultry, fish, vegetables, etc., in a flavoured sauce; may be served hot or cold.

vomiting A reflex action to expel the stomach contents through the mouth.

vomitoxin *See* TRICHOTHECENES.

vongole Italian; small clams.

V

wacholder *See* GIN.

wafer Very thin, crisp, sweet biscuit, served with ice cream etc. Wafer sandwich biscuits consist of several layers of wafer with a sweet or savoury cream filling.

waffle Crisp, golden-brown pancake with deep indentations made by baking batter in a waffle iron which cooks both sides simultaneously.

wähe Swiss; tarts made from yeast-leavened dough filled with fruit, vegetables, or cheese.

wahoo Marine fish, *Acanthocybium solandri.*

waist : hip ratio Simple method for estimating the distribution of subcutaneous and intra-abdominal *adipose tissue.

wakame Japanese; lobe leaf *seaweed *Undaria pinnatifida*. The flowering sprout is mekabu.

walewska Fish with a lobster sauce and garnish.

walnut The rough-shelled English walnut (so called because for centuries English ships carried it worldwide) is *Juglans regia*, black walnut is *J. nigra*; *hickory nut and *butternut are also walnuts. A 60-g portion (nine nuts) is a rich *source of vitamin E, copper, and selenium; a good source of protein, niacin, iron, and vitamin B$_1$; a source of calcium and zinc; contains 40g of fat, of which 10% is *saturated and 75% mono-unsaturated; provides 3g of dietary fibre; supplies 400kcal (1670kJ).

wappato *See* ARROWHEAD.

Warfarin A chemical that inhibits the metabolism of *vitamin K; used to reduce blood clotting in people at risk of *thrombosis and, at much higher doses, as a rodenticide. *See also* FETAL WARFARIN SYNDROME.

wari Indian, Pakistani; dried balls of legume and cereal flour that have undergone a yeast fermentation; can be stored for some months, then deep fried.

wasabi Japanese; pungent condiment from the root of the perennial Japanese horseradish *Wasabia japonica*. Commonly prepared together with *mustard.

wash, spent *See* SPENT WASH.

wassail 1. Spiced ale, drunk especially on festive occasions. 2. Salutation or toast drunk to a person's health.

wastel Medieval English; fine white bread made from sifted flour.

wasting Loss of *adipose tissue and *muscle in undernutrition.

water activity (a_w) Ratio between vapour pressure of water in the food and that of pure water at the same temperature. Most bacteria cannot grow at a_w below 0.9, yeasts below 0.85, and moulds below 0.7. So-called dehydrated foods have a_w lower than 0.6.

water balance The balance between intake and excretion of fluids. Average daily intakes are: as drinks, 1–1.5L; as aqueous part of food, 0.5L; and formed in the body by oxidation of foodstuffs (*see* WATER, METABOLIC), 300–500mL; total 2–3L. Losses from the lungs, 400–500mL; through the skin, 400–500mL; in faeces, 80–100mL; in urine, 1–1.8L.

Total body water is 40–44L, as: blood plasma, 2–3L; extracellular fluid (between cells), 10L; and intracellular fluid (within cells), 27–30L. The kidneys control the volume of extracellular water by excreting water. Ingestion of sodium chloride (*salt) raises the *osmotic pressure of the extracellular water, causing thirst.

water biscuit *See* CRACKERS.

watercress Leaves of *Nasturtium officinale* (green watercress, remains green in autumn and is susceptible to frost) and *N. microphyllum × officinale* (brown or winter watercress); eaten raw in salads. A 60-g portion is a rich *source of vitamin C; a good source of vitamin A (1300µg carotene); a source of calcium and iron; provides 1.6g of dietary fibre; supplies 10kcal (40kJ).

water, demineralized Water that has been purified by passage through a bed of *ion-exchange resin which removes mineral salts; as pure as distilled water.

water, double labelled Dual isotopically labelled water, containing the stable isotopes deuterium and ^{18}O (i.e. $^2H_2^{18}O$). Widely used as a means of estimating *energy expenditure over a period of 1–3 weeks. After drinking the labelled water, the labelled oxygen is lost from the body more rapidly than the deuterium, since ^2H is lost only in water, while ^{18}O is lost in both water and carbon dioxide because of the rapid equilibrium between carbon dioxide and bicarbonate. Determination of the relative amounts of both isotopes in urine or

w

saliva thus permits estimation of total carbon dioxide production, and hence oxygen consumption and energy expenditure.

water, electrolysed Salt water is passed through an *electrolysis unit to produce either acidic or alkaline electrolysed water. Acidic water has antibacterial activity, and is used to wash foods in preference to chlorinated water; alkaline water is used to clean food preparation surfaces.

water, extracellular; water, intracellular *See* WATER BALANCE.

water-glass Sodium silicate; used at one time to preserve eggs, by forming a layer of insoluble calcium silicate around the shell, so sealing the pores.

water-ice *See* SORBET.

water lemon *See* PASSION FRUIT.

Waterlow classification A system for classifying *protein-energy malnutrition in children based on wasting (the percentage of expected weight for height) and the degree of stunting (the percentage of expected height for age). *See also* GOMEZ CLASSIFICATION; WELLCOME CLASSIFICATION.

watermelon Fruit of *Citrullus vulgaris*. Also *C. lanatus, C.* and *Colocynthis citrullus* (known in West Africa as egusi), grown mainly for the seeds, which are added to rice and legume based dishes, or ground to flour. *See also* MELON.

water, metabolic Produced in the body by the oxidation of foods. 100g of fat produces 107.1g; 100g of starch 55.1g; and 100g of protein 41.3g of water. *See also* WATER BALANCE.

water, mineral Natural, untreated spring waters, some of which are naturally carbonated; may be slightly alkaline or salty. Numerous health claims have been made for the benefits arising from the traces of a large number of minerals found in solution. They are normally named after the town nearest the source. Examples are Apollinaris, Buxton, Evian, Malvern, Perrier, Vichy, Vittel.

Sparkling mineral water may either contain the gases naturally present at the source or may be artificially carbonated (*soda water, *Seltzer water, or *club soda). Carbonated beverages are sometimes called minerals.

waterzooi (waterzoei, waterzootje) Belgian; chicken or fish simmered in white wine with vegetables.

waxes *Esters of *fatty acids with long-chain monohydric alcohols (fats are esters of fatty acids with glycerol), e.g. beeswax, an ester of palmitic acid with myricyl alcohol; spermaceti, palmitic acid with cetyl alcohol. Animal waxes are often esters of the steroid alcohol *cholesterol.

waxing Coating fruits and vegetables with a thin layer of edible wax. In the case of apples and oranges this replaces the natural wax that is removed when the crop is washed; in the case of vegetables it is an addition; in both instances the waxing prevents loss of moisture, prolongs storage life, and improves the appearance.

wbc White *blood cells.

WCRF World Cancer Research Fund; leads a global network of charities dedicated to the prevention and control of cancer by means of healthy food and nutrition, physical activity, and weight management.

(⊕) SEE WEB LINKS
• The WCRF International's homepage.
• The WCRF UK's homepage.

weaning The process of introducing solid foods to an infant's diet, ideally after six months of breast- (or formula) feeding.

weaning foods Foods specially formulated for infants aged between three and nine months for the transition between breast- or bottle-feeding and normal intake of solid foods.

Weende analysis *See* ANALYSIS, PROXIMATE.

weenie American name for small sausages, abbreviation of wienerwurst.

weever Marine fish, species of the family *Trachinidae*.

weighed inventory method In dietary and nutritional surveys; subjects keep a record of the weight of all foods eaten, for analysis using *food composition tables. *See also* HOUSEHOLD MEASURES METHOD.

weight, desirable (ideal weight) Standardized tables of desirable (or ideal) weight for height for adults are based on life expectancy; both undernutrition and obesity are associated with increased risk of premature death. Desirable weight corresponds to a *body mass index (the ratio of weight in kg/height^2 in m) between 20–25. Tables of ideal weight based on actuarial data were first published by the Metropolitan Life Assurance Co. of New York in 1942.

weight for age An index of the adequacy of the child's nutrition to support growth. Standard weight for age is the 50th centile of the weight for age curves of well fed children. *See also* ANTHROPOMETRY; NCHS STANDARDS.

weight for height For children, can be used as an alternative to *weight for age as an index of nutritional adequacy; for adults it is the only acceptable way of expressing weight relative to ideal or desirable weight. *See also* ANTHROPOMETRY; NCHS STANDARDS; WEIGHT, DESIRABLE.

weight for height, desirable ranges of Calculated on the basis of body mass index = 20–25 (which is the desirable range for both men and women).

weight, metabolic *Energy expenditure and *basal metabolic rate depend on the amount of metabolically active tissue in the body, rather than total body weight; body weight$^{0.75}$ is generally used to calculate the weight of active tissue.

weighting oils *See* OILS, BROMINATED.

weisse *See* BEER.

weisswurst German; white sausages made with veal, cream, and eggs.

Wellcome classification A system for classifying *protein-energy malnutrition in children based on percentage of expected weight for age and the presence or absence of *oedema. Between 60 and 80% of expected weight is underweight in the absence of oedema, and kwashiorkor if oedema is present; under 60% of expected weight is marasmus in the absence of oedema, and marasmic kwashiorkor if oedema is present. *See also* GOMEZ CLASSIFICATION; WATERLOW CLASSIFICATION.

welschriesling A *grape variety widely used for *wine making, not one of the classic varieties. Also known as Italian riesling; the wines cannot legally be labelled simply *riesling.

Welsh onion *See* ONION, WELSH.

Welsh rarebit (originally Welsh rabbit) Melted cheese, mixed with mustard powder, pepper, and brown ale, served on toast. Buck rarebit is Welsh rarebit topped with a poached egg.

Wensleydale English hard cheese, originally made from sheep's or goat's milk, now cow's milk; may be blue veined.

Wernicke–Korsakoff syndrome The result of damage to the brain as a result of *vitamin B$_1$ deficiency, commonly associated with alcohol abuse. Affected subjects show clear signs of neurological damage (Wernicke's encephalopathy) with psychiatric changes (*Korsakoff's psychosis) characterized by loss of recent memory and confabulation (the invention of fabulous stories). *See also* BERIBERI.

Wesson oil Cottonseed oil deodorized by high temperature vacuum process developed by David Wesson in 1899.

wetzel grid Children are grouped by physique into five groups, ranging from tall and thin to short and thick-set. A healthy child will grow, as measured by height and weight, along one of these channels at a standard rate; if s/he deviates from the channel, malnutrition is suspected. *See also* ANTHROPOMETRY.

wey The measure of 48 bushels of oats or 40 bushels of salt or 'corn'.

WFA *Weight for age.

WFH *Weight for height.

whale Meat of *Baleanoptera* spp. A 150-g portion is a rich *source of protein, iron, and niacin; a source of vitamin B_2; contains 5g of fat, of which 25% is saturated, 35% mono-unsaturated; supplies 200kcal (840kJ).

wheat The most important of the cereals and one of the most widely grown crops. Many thousand varieties are known but there are three main types: *Triticum vulgare*, used mainly for *bread; *T. durum* (*T. turgidum* var. *durum*, durum wheat; *see also* KAMUT), largely used for *pasta; and *Triticum compactum* (club wheat), too soft for ordinary bread. The berry is composed of the outer, branny husk, 13% of the grain; the germ or embryo (rich in nutrients), 2%; and the central endosperm (mainly starch), 85%. Inca wheat is *Amaranthus* spp. *See also* FLOUR, EXTRACTION RATE.

wheatfeed Also called millers' offal and wheat offals; by-product from milling of *wheat, other than the *germ; bran of various particle sizes and varying amounts of attached endosperm.

wheat germ *See* GERM, WHEAT; FLOUR, EXTRACTION RATE.

whelks *Shellfish; several types of spiral-shelled marine *molluscs, *Buccinum* spp., *Fusus antiquus*. A 100-g portion of flesh (670g in the shell) is a rich *source of protein, niacin, vitamin B_{12}, and iron; supplies 100kcal (420kJ).

whey The residue from milk after removal of the *casein and most of the fat (as in cheese making); also known as lacto-serum. Contains about 1% protein (*see* WHEY PROTEINS) together with all the lactose and water-soluble vitamins and minerals; 92% water.

Whey cheese can be made by heat coagulation of the protein and whey butter from the small amount of fat (0.25%). Dried whey is added to processed cheese; most whey is fed in liquid form to pigs.

whey proteins The soluble proteins in milk, other than *casein: β-lactoglobulin (about 50% of the total), bovine serum albumin (BSA), α-lactalbumin, and immunoglobulins. There are also small amounts of β-microglobulin, *lactoferrin, transferrin, and acyl glycoproteins.

whim-wham Scottish; similar to *syllabub.

whisky (whiskey) A grain *spirit distilled from fermented *malted *barley, *rye, *maize, or sometimes other cereal. Most brands of whisky are a blend of malt whisky with spirit distilled from grain. The distilled spirit is diluted to about 62% alcohol and matured in wooden casks; Irish and Scotch whisky, made from malted barley, are matured for at least three years. Single malt whisky is from a single distillery; pure malt is blended malt whisky blended from several distilleries. Bourbon, made from malted maize, is matured for at least one year. Sour mash bourbon is made from mash that has yeast left in it from a previous fermentation. Other American and Canadian whiskies are made from rye. Diluted after maturation and generally around 40% *alcohol by volume, 220 kcal (920 kJ) per 100 mL.

Both spellings permitted but generally whisky is the Scotch variety and whiskey the Irish and American varieties. Name derived from the Gaelic *uisge beatha*, water of life. First recorded reference is an order from James IV of Scotland to give 8 bowls of malt to Friar John Cor to make whisky (1494).

white blood cells *See* LEUCOCYTES.

whitebait A mixture of young *herrings (*Clupea harengus*) and young *sprats (*Sprattus sprattus*); they are caught together and cannot readily be separated. Known as sild when canned.

white cell count *See* LEUCOCYTES.

whitecurrants *See* REDCURRANTS.

whitefish Oily freshwater fish, *Coregonus* spp.

white foots Fine, white precipitate of calcium and other salts deposited in jars of meat cured with rock salt.

white leaf beet *See* CHARD, SWISS.

white pudding Sausage made from white meat (chicken, rabbit, pork), cereal, and spices. The French *boudin blanc* includes eggs and onions. Irish white pudding is made from flake or leaf lard and oatmeal, spiced; served sliced and fried.

white spirits Distilled *spirits from fermented fruit; *eau-de-vie or *alcool blanc in French, *schnapps in German.

whiting Marine fish, *Merlangius merlangus*. Pacific whiting (or hake) is *Merluccius productus*, blue whiting is *Merlanguis poutassou*, southern blue whiting is *Micromesistius australis*.

WHO World Health Organization; headquarters in Geneva.

(((⊕))) SEE WEB LINKS

• The WHO's homepage.

wholefoods Foods that have been minimally refined or processed, and are eaten in their natural state. In general nothing is removed from, or added to, the foodstuffs in preparation. Wholegrain cereal products are made by milling the complete grain.

wholesome Description applied to food that is fit for human consumption as far as hygiene is concerned.

wholewheat meal Flour or meal prepared by milling the whole wheat grain, i.e. 100% extraction rate. *See* FLOUR, EXTRACTION RATE.

whortleberry *See* BILBERRY.

Wilson's disease *Copper intoxication due to failure of its excretion in *bile, and also impaired synthesis of the copper transport protein *ceruloplasmin, leading to liver disease (hepatolenticular degeneration), neurological signs, and corneal and kidney damage, as a result of inappropriate accumulation of copper in tissues.

WIN Weight-control Information Network of the National Institute of Diabetes and Digestive and Kidney Diseases.

(((⊕))) SEE WEB LINKS

• The WIN's homepage.

windberry *See* BILBERRY.

wine Fermented juice from *grapes (varieties of *Vitis vinifera*). Red wines are made by fermenting the juice together with the skins at 21–29°C; white wines normally from white grapes by fermenting the juice alone at 15–17°C; rosé by removing the skins after 12–36 hours, or by mixing red and white wines.

Beverages made by fermenting other fruit juices and sugar in the presence of vegetables, leaves, or roots are also called wines (elderberry, elderflower, parsnip, peapod, rhubarb, etc.), although the legal definition may be restricted to the fermented grape. *See also* ALCOHOLIC BEVERAGES.

White wines are graded as dry (0.6% sugars) to sweet (6% sugars), on a scale of 1 to 9. Red wines are graded from A (light and dry) to E (full-bodied and heavy). Wines generally contain 9–14% alcohol, dry wines 70 kcal (290 kJ), sweet wines 120 kcal (500 kJ), and about 1 mg of iron per 100 mL; there are only traces of vitamins.

wine, apéritif Slightly bitter-tasting fortified wines drunk before meals; types of *vermouth, including (trade names) Amer Picon, Bonal, Byrrh, Campari, Dubonnet, Fernet-Branca, Martini, Saint Raphaël. Made from red or white wine fortified with spirit and flavoured with herbs and quinine. They contain 15–25% alcohol by volume, 5–10% sugars, 75–130 kcal (320–550 kJ) per 100 mL.

wineberry Orange-coloured fruit of the Japanese and Chinese wild *raspberry, *Rubus phoenicolasius*, and now also hybrids with European cultivated raspberries.

wine, British Made in UK from imported grape juice or concentrated grape juice, as distinct from English wine, which is made from grapes grown in England.

wine classification May be on the basis either of the region in which the grapes are grown or quality, using grapes from a wide geographical area (e.g. in Australia and China). The first 'temporary' wine classification was introduced in France for the 1855 Paris exhibition of the Bordeaux vineyards. The German (and Austrian) system is based on both the geographical origin of the grapes and also their ripeness or natural sugar content.

National classifications are as follows (in increasing order of quality for each country):

wine classification, Austria As for Germany (*see* WINE CLASSIFICATION, GERMANY), with an additional class of QmP wines, ausbruch, intermediate in sweetness between beerenauslese and trockenbeerenauslese.

wine classification, Bulgaria Three grades: wines of declared variety of brand; wine of declared geographical origin (DGO); controliran, specific varieties grown in specific areas. The best of DGO and controliran wines can be offered as reserve, and in exceptional years as special reserve.

wine classification, Canada Wines from specified areas (three designated areas in Ontario and four in British Columbia) are labelled VQA (Vintners' Quality Alliance, Canada). Wines must be made from classic grape varieties or preferred hybrids, and the wine must contain at least 85% of the variety named on the label. Wines described as estate-bottled must be made only from grapes owned or controlled by the winery; if a particular vineyard designation is used, the site must be within a recognized viticultural area and all the grapes must come from the designated vineyard. Ice wine (*see* EISWEIN) made from grapes that have frozen on the vine, very sweet.

wine classification, France Vin de table (or vin ordinaire); vin de pays (subdivided into vin de pays de zone for wines from a single area; départementaux for wines from one département; régionaux for wines from more than one département); vin délimité de qualité supérieure (VDQS); appellation contrôlée (AC) or appellation d'origine contrôlée (AOC) for wines from a specified area, from specified grape varieties grown under controlled conditions.

wine classification, Germany (and Austria) Tafelwein (Deutscher tafelwein is of German origin; wine labelled simply as tafelwein may be of mixed origin); Landwein (dry or half-dry wines from one of fifteen designated areas); Qualitäwein bestimmer Anbaugebeite, QbA (from eleven designated areas and approved grape varieties; sugar may be added to increase sweetness; each bottle carries a batch number (Amtlicher Prüfungsnummer, AP), as proof that it complies with QbA status); Qualitäwein mit Präkat, QmP, with six quality gradings based on the level of natural sugar at harvest (extra sugar may not be added): kabinett, light, fruity, and delicate, usually dry; späese, late-picked grapes, dry to sweet; auslese, selected late-picked grapes, rich and sweet; beerenauslese, late-picked grapes affected by *noble rot, always sweet;

w

trockenbeerenauslese, late-picked grapes that have dried to raisins on the vine, strong and sweet; eiswein, rare, made from grapes that have frozen on the vine, very sweet.

wine classification, Italy Vini da tavola (Vdt); vini da tavola con indicazione geografica (from a particular area); vini tipici (equivalent to French vin de pays); denominazione di origine controllata (DOC, from specified areas and grape varieties); denominazione di origine controllata e garantita (DOCG, as DOC but with more stringent regulations and control).

wine classification, Luxembourg Appellation Controlée wines must carry a vintage; bottles carry a neck label awarded by the state-controlled Marque Nationale after tasting, according to the strength of the wine; in order of increasing alcohol content the grades are: non admis, marque nationale, vin classé premier cru, grand premier cru.

wine classification, Portugal Indicação de proveniencia regulamentada (IPR); região demarcada (RD, the same as AC). Table wines are vinho de mesa, wines aged more than 1 year are vinho maduro.

wine classification, South Africa Classification by variety of grape and area of production; coloured seals used: blue band indicates that origin is certified; red band guarantees vintage year; green band certifies grape varieties; 'estate' certifies that it is from one estate; 'superior' on gold seal indicates superior quality. Wines also carry identification numbers to testify that controls have been adhered to during production.

wine classification, Spain Vinos de la tierra (two-thirds of the grapes must come from the region named on the label); denominación de origen (DO).

wine classification, USA Each state has its own appellation of origin; in addition 'American wine' or 'vin de table' is blended wine from one area or more; multi-state appellation is wine from two or three neighbouring states (the percentage from each must be shown on the label); for State and County appellation at least 75% must come from the designated area. 'Approved viticultural areas' must have defined boundaries, specific characteristics, and a proven reputation for quality; 85% of the grapes used must come from the defined area; when an individual vineyard is named, 95% of the grapes must have been grown there.

For tax purposes a table wine must be between 10 and 14% alcohol; stronger wines are classified as dessert wines, even if dry; dessert wines between 17 and 21% alcohol are classified by alcoholic strength, not sweetness.

US wines may be sold by a generic classification (e.g. Chablis or Loire); such names are prohibited from export to the EU.

wine, fortified Made by adding *brandy or other *spirit to increase the *alcohol content of the wine to 15–18% and so prevent further fermentation (to acids) in warm climates; e.g. *Madeira, *marsala, *port, *sherry.

wine, sparkling Wine containing bubbles of carbon dioxide, bottled under pressure. There are three methods of production: i) the méthode champenoise in which the wine undergoes a second fermentation in the bottle; wine produced outside the Champagne region of France may not be called *champagne, even if made by this method; ii) the tank or bulk method, in which the wine is bottled while still fermenting slightly; iii) the addition of carbon dioxide gas while bottling.

   Lightly sparkling wines are known as pétillant or frizzante; they are often young wines, bottled while still fermenting (e.g. *lambrusco, *vinho verde).

wine stone *See* ARGOL.

wine sweetness The UK Wine Promotion Board classifies white and rosé wines from 1 for very dry wines (0.6% sugars) to 9 (very sweet, 6% sugars). For red wines the classification is from A (light and dry) to E (full-bodied heavy wines).

   German and Austrian labelling is trocken (dry), halbtrocken (half dry), halbsüss or lieben (medium sweet), and süss (very sweet).

winkle (periwinkle) *Shellfish; small, snail-like, marine *molluscs, *Littorina* spp.; common or edible periwinkle is *L. littorea*, smooth periwinkle is *L. obtusata*, gulf periwinkle is *L. irrorata*, and southern periwinkle is *L. angulifera*.

winter berry Fruit of the American evergreen shrub *Gaultheria procumbens*; red, with a spicy flavour; used mainly for pies and sauces.

winterization The removal of the more saturated glycerides from edible oil so that it remains clear at low temperatures. The oil is chilled and the solidified palmitates and stearates are filtered out.

wishbone Small, forked bone between the neck and breast of poultry, also known as merrythought.

witch Marine fish, *Glyptocephalus cynoglossus*, also known as Torbay sole.

witchetty grubs Edible grubs, species of longicorn beetle (*Xylentes* spp.); associated with Australian aborigines.

witloof *See* CHICORY.

wok Chinese vessel for *stir frying; a shallow, bowl-shaped pan in which food can be fried rapidly in a small amount of oil over a high heat.

wolfberry *See* GOJI BERRY.

wood alcohol *See* METHYL ALCOHOL.

wood blewits *See* BLEWITS.

wood-ears (Chinese black fungus) An edible wild fungus, *Auricuaria polytricha*; *see* MUSHROOMS.

wood grouse *See* CAPERCAILLIE.

woodruff A wild plant of woodlands on chalk or limestone (*Galium odoratum*); the leaves have the smell and flavour of new mown hay, and are used to flavour alcoholic or fruit drinks, or to make a *herb tea.

wood sugar *See* XYLOSE.

wool green S A green *colour, Green S.

worcester berry American species of *gooseberry, *Ribes divaricatum*.

Worcestershire sauce Characterized by spicy flavour, sediment, and thin supernatant liquid. Recipes are usually secret but basically soya, tamarinds, anchovies, garlic and spices, plus sugar, salt, and vinegar, matured 6 months in oak casks.

work *See* ENERGY.

World Food Programme Part of the Food and Agriculture Organization of the United Nations; intended to give international aid in the form of food from countries with a surplus.

wormseed *See* EPAZOTE.

wort *See* BEER.

WPC *Whey protein concentrate.

wraplings *See* WUNTUN.

wrasse Marine fish, all species of the family *Labridae*.

WTO World Trade Organization.

((⊕)) SEE WEB LINKS

• The WTO's homepage.

wuntun (wonton) Chinese; small dough parcels containing meat, boiled or deep fried, eaten as an accompaniment to a meal or in a soup. Also known as chiao-tzu or wraplings. Sweet wuntun is deep fried, served with sugar or syrup, and is stuffed with sweetened bean paste.

wurst German; sausage; würstchen are small sausages. Also used generally for salami.

w

xanthan gum A high molecular mass glycan produced by the aerobic fermentation of *Xanthomonas campestris*. Stable to wide range of *pH and temperature; used as thickening agent to form gels and increase viscosity in foods.

xanthelasma Yellow fatty plaques on the eyelids, due to *hypercholesterolaemia.

xanthia Cocktail made with equal amounts of yellow *Chartreuse, cherry brandy, and gin.

xanthine A *purine, intermediate in the metabolism of adenine and guanine to *uric acid. *Caffeine (in coffee and tea) is 1,3,7-trimethylxanthine; *theophylline (in tea) is 1,3-dimethylxanthine; *theobromine (in cocoa) is 3,7-dimethylxanthine.

xanthophylls Yellow-orange hydroxylated *carotene derivatives; occur in all green leaves together with the chlorophyll and carotene, also present in egg yolk, *Cape gooseberry, *rose hips, etc. Most have no *vitamin A activity. Include flavoxanthin, lutein, cryptoxanthin, which is converted into vitamin A, rubixanthin, rhodoxanthin, and canthaxanthin.

xanthosis Yellowing of the skin associated with high blood concentrations of *carotene.

Xenical *See* ORLISTAT.

xenobiotic Substances foreign to the body, including drugs and some food additives.

xerophilic *See* OSMOPHILES.

xerophthalmia Advanced *vitamin A deficiency in which the epithelium of the cornea and conjunctiva of the eye deteriorates because of impairment of the tear glands, resulting in dryness then ulceration, leading to blindness.

xerosis, conjunctival Keratinization of the epithelial cells of the conjunctiva, an early stage in the development of the *vitamin A deficiency disease *xerophthalmia.

xerostomia Dry mouth due to reduced secretion of *saliva, commonly a side-effect of medication, but there is a progressive loss of acinar tissue in *salivary glands with increasing age.

xocoatl See CHOCOLATE.

xylans A major constituent of *hemicellulose, consisting of D-xylose linked $\beta1{\rightarrow}4$, with glucuronic acid and arabinose esterified to carbon-2 and/or carbon-3 of xylose, and side-chains that contain varying amounts of xylose and arabinose. Especially abundant in *wheat *bran.

xylitol A five-carbon *sugar alcohol found in some fruits and vegetables; 80–100% of the sweetness of sucrose; used in sugar-free hard sweets and gelatine gums. Apart from being of low cariogenicity, xylitol is said to have an effect in suppressing the growth of some of the bacteria associated with dental *caries; see SWEETS, TOOTH-FRIENDLY.

xyloascorbic acid Alternative name for ascorbic acid (*vitamin C) to distinguish it from isoascorbic acid (*erythorbic acid, araboascorbic acid), which has only slight vitamin C activity.

xyloglucans A constituent of *hemicellulose, consisting of short chains of glucose polymers linked $\beta1{\rightarrow}4$ (as in *cellulose), with D-xylose or short chains of xylose, galactose, and fructose linked to carbon-6 of glucose.

xylose Pentose (five-carbon) sugar found in plant tissues as complex polysaccharide; 40% as sweet as sucrose. Also known as wood sugar.

x

yacon Tuber of the Andean perennial herbaceous plant *Smallanthus sonchifolius* (syn. *Polymnia sonchifolia*), usually eaten raw; rich in *inulin. Both the roots and leaves are used to prepare a medicinal tea.

yakhni Indian *bouillon or *stock made from meat and bones, sometimes with the addition of vegetables. Garhi yakhni is concentrated and sets to a jelly.

yakifu Japanese; cake made by mixing *gluten with starch or wheat flour and baking.

yakju Korean; rice wine.

Yakult Trade name for yoghurt containing live *Lactobacillus* spp. which are *probiotics. Originally Japanese name for yoghurt fermented with *L. casei*.

yam Tubers of perennial climbing plants of *Dioscorea* spp.; white yam is *D. rotundata*, yellow or Guinea yam is *D. cayenensis*, Chinese or lesser yam is *D. esculenta*, winged or water yam is *D. alata*, and potato yam or air potato is *D. bulbifera*. A major food in parts of Africa and the Far East. A 150-g portion is a *source of vitamins B$_1$ and C; provides 5 g of dietary fibre; supplies 200 kcal (840 kJ). In the USA sweet potatoes (*see* POTATO, SWEET) are sometimes called yams and the *oca is also known as New Zealand yam.

yam bean (jicama) 1. The edible tuber of a climbing vine (*Pacchyrhizus erosus*) originally native to Central America. 2. The African yam bean, *Sphenostylis stenocarpa*; the seeds are eaten.

yam, elephant Edible roots of *Amorphophallus* spp. *A. rivieri* (syn. *A. konjac*) is the source of *konjac; *A. campanulatus* is the Asian elephant yam.

yang *See* DIET, MACROBIOTIC.

Yarmouth bloater *See* HERRING, RED.

yarrow *See* MILFOIL.

yautia *See* TANNIA.

yeast Unicellular organisms, sometimes grouped with the *fungi; unlike *bacteria, they are eukaryotic. Some are of major importance in the food industry. *Saccharomyces cerevisiae* and *S. carlsbergensis* are used in brewing, wine making, and baking. Varieties such as *Candida utilis* (formerly *Torula* *utilis*) are grown on carbohydrate or hydrocarbon media as animal feed and potential human food, since they contain about 50% protein (dry weight) and are very rich in B vitamins.

Some yeasts are pathogenic (especially *Candida* spp., which cause thrush); many are used in biotechnology for production of *hormones and other proteins.

See also OSMOPHILES.

yeast extract A preparation of the water-soluble fraction of autolysed brewers' *yeast, valuable both as a source of the B vitamins and for its strong savoury flavour. Commercial preparations include Marmite, Yeastrel, Yeatex, and Vegemite, used as a drink or a bread spread. A 9-g portion (1 teaspoonful, or the amount spread on two slices of bread) is a rich *source of vitamin B_2, niacin, and folate; a good source of vitamin B_1; supplies 15 kcal (60 kJ).

yeast fermentation, bottom Or deep fermentation; fermentation during the manufacture of *beer with a yeast that sinks to the bottom of the tank. Most beers are produced this way; ale, porter, and stout being the principal beers produced by top fermentation.

yeheb A nut, fruit of *Cordeauxia edulis*, originally from the Horn of Africa.

yellow fats *See* FAT SPREAD.

yellowtail Various marine fish, *Seriola* spp. *S. quinqueradiata* is farmed in Japan and elsewhere.

yerba dulce The leaves of the Paraguayan shrub, *Stevia rebaudiana*, the source of *stevioside and *rebaudioside.

yerba maté *See* MATÉ.

Yersinia enterocolitica Food-borne pathogen that causes abdominal pain and diarrhoea, with mild fever, possibly lasting 2–3 weeks. In 2–3% of cases there are long-term health effects. Infection is mainly through pork products. The organism can grow at temperatures as low as 0 °C.

Yersiniosis Infection with *Yersinia enterocolitica*.

yield Weight of food after processing as a percentage of the unprocessed material.

yin *See* DIET, MACROBIOTIC.

yiu tiao Chinese; fried dough sticks, generally eaten for breakfast.

ylang-ylang oil Aromatic oil from flowers of Filipino tree *Cananga odorata* used as a flavouring in soft drinks, confectionery, and baked goods.

yoghurt Milk (from a variety of animals, but usually cows) coagulated and fermented with two bacteria, *Streptococcus thermophilus* and *Lactobacillus bulgaricus*. May be pasteurized, when most of the bacteria are destroyed; otherwise termed live yoghurt. Bioyoghurts also contain *Lactobacillus acidophilus* (*see* MILK, ACIDOPHILUS) and *Bifidobacterium bifidum* (*see* PROBIOTICS). Soft frozen yoghurt, as a low fat alternative to *ice cream, was first introduced in 1972.

Stirred yoghurt is prepared in bulk; set yoghurt is fermented in the plastic containers in which it will be sold. Strained yoghurt (Greek style yoghurt) is prepared by removing some of the whey either by straining through a cloth or by centrifugation.

yókan Japanese; confectionery made with *agar, sugar, and adzuki bean paste (*see* BEAN, ADZUKI).

yolk index Index of freshness of an egg; ratio between height and diameter of yolk under defined conditions. As the egg deteriorates, the yolk index decreases.

Yorkshire pudding *Batter cake, traditionally eaten with roast beef.

youngberry A cross between *blackberry and *dewberry.

yuan hsiaos Chinese festival sweet; a small piece of crystallized fruit or ground walnut mixed with sugar, rolled in ground glutinous rice, then boiled and served in the cooking water (which forms a bland soup).

yuba Made by drying the skin that forms on the surface of soya milk during heating. Used in meat substitutes, wrapped round other foods, or eaten alone after deep frying. Sometimes called tofu skin or bean curd skin.

yukwa Korean; snack food made by deep-frying dried dough prepared by steeping waxy rice for 1-2 weeks.

Yusho disease Caused by leakage of polychlorinated biphenyls which contaminated edible oil on the Japanese island of Kyushu in 1968.

y

za'atar **1.** The herb, *Thymbra spicata*. **2.** A blend of ground *sumac, *sesame seeds and za'atar, and other herbs, used to season meat and fish, or mixed with *olive oil and used as a spread for *pitta.

zabaglione (zabaione) Italian; frothy dessert made from egg yolks, sugar, and wine (usually marsala) whisked over gentle heat until thick. French sabayon is similar.

ZAG Zinc α2 glycoprotein, secreted by various tumours; activates lipolysis and hence contributes to loss of adipose tissue in *cachexia.

zakuska Russian appetizer; *caviar, *blinis, smoked sausages, cold meats, pickled fish, and tvoroinki (cheese dumplings).

zampone Italian; pork sausage where meat is stuffed in boned pig's trotter instead of casing.

zander Freshwater fish, *Stizostedion lucioperca*, also known as pike-perch.

zarzuela Spanish (Catalan); spiced seafood and fish stew served with sauces on a bed of rice.

zather A blend of *sumac and *thyme use to flavour labni, a cream cheese made from yoghurt.

zearalenone *Mycotoxin produced by *Fusarium* spp. growing on maize; it has oestrogenic activity, but low acute toxicity, and may have similar beneficial effects to *phytoestrogens with respect to bone health and hormone-dependent cancer.

zeaxanthin One of the *carotenoid pigments in maize, egg yolk, and *Physalis* (*Cape gooseberry); not vitamin A active. *See also* LUTEIN.

zébrine Variety of *aubergine with purple and white stripes.

zedoary Root of the Indian plant *Curcuma zedoaria* (round zedoary) or *C. zerumbet* (long zedoary), a member of the ginger family. Used fresh or pickled in Indian cuisine, and as dried spice in Indonesian. Also known as wild turmeric and shoti.

zeer Sudanese; earthenware vessel used for preparation of *kawal.

zeera *See* KALONJI.

zein The major protein of *maize (*Zea mays*), very poor in lysine and tryptophan.

Z-enzyme *Enzyme found associated with *amylases, that attacks the few β-1,3-links present in *amylose. Pure, crystalline β-amylase will convert only 70% of amylose to maltose; it requires the presence of the Z-enzyme for complete conversion.

zest Outer skin of citrus fruits. *See* FLAVEDO.

zinc An essential mineral which forms the *prosthetic group of a large number of enzymes, and the receptor proteins for *steroid and *thyroid hormones and *vitamins A and D. Deficiency results in hypogonadism and delayed puberty, small stature, and mild anaemia; it occurs mainly in subtropical regions where a great deal of zinc is lost in sweat, and the diet is largely based on unleavened wholemeal bread, in which much of the zinc is unavailable because of the high content of *phytate. Marginal deficiency is widespread.

Meat, fish (especially shellfish), legumes, and (leavened) wholegrain cereals are rich sources. Synergistic zinc is a trade name for *zinc supplement that also contains *copper and *vitamin A, which are claimed to aid its absorption.

zinfandel Red grape variety especially grown in California for *wine making. Zinfandel wines may be blush (rosé) or red. White zinfandel wines are really rosé. The wines have a characteristically fruity flavour.

zireh *See* KALONJI.

zitoni *See* PASTA.

zizanie *See* RICE, WILD.

Zollinger–Ellison syndrome Excessive secretion of *gastric acid and increased gastro-intestinal motility as a result of secretion of *gastrin by tumours of G-cells of the *pancreas (gastrinoma).

zoonotic transmission Animal to person transmission of organisms associated with *food-borne diseases, commonly by animal faecal contamination of water or fields growing salad and other crops.

zooplankton *See* PLANKTON.

zubrowka Polish; *vodka flavoured with a single sprig of bison grass in each bottle; known in English as bison grass vodka.

zucchini Italian; variety of *marrow developed to be harvested when small, including courgettes. American and Australian name for *courgette.

z

zuppa inglese Italian; rich cake or *trifle.

Z-score In statistics, a way of expressing values relative to the population or group mean as the number of standard deviations away from the mean.

zwetschgenwasser (zwetschenwasser) *See* QUETSCH.

zwieback German name for twice-baked bread or rusk. Ordinary dough plus eggs and butter, baked, sliced, baked again to a rusk, and sometimes sugar-coated.

Zygosaccharomyces Yeasts that grow in high concentrations of sugar (osmophilic) that cause spoilage of honey, jams, and syrups.

zymase The mixture of *enzymes in *yeast which is responsible for *fermentation.

zymogens The inactive form in which some enzymes, especially the *protein digestive enzymes, are secreted, being activated after secretion. Also called pro-enzymes, or enzyme precursors.

Multiples and submultiples of units

submultiple	prefix	symbol	multiple	prefix	symbol
10^{-1}	deci	d	10^{1}	deca	da
10^{-2}	centi	c	10^{2}	hecta	h
10^{-3}	milli	m	10^{3}	kilo	k
10^{-6}	micro	μ	10^{6}	mega	M
10^{-9}	nano	n	10^{9}	giga	G
10^{-12}	pico	p	10^{12}	tera	T
10^{-15}	femto	f	10^{15}	peta	P
10^{-18}	atto	a	10^{18}	exa	E

Equivalence of Imperial and metric units

Imperial	metric	metric	Imperial
1 oz	28.35 g (approx 30 g)	100 g	3½ oz
1 lb	454 g (approx 450 g)	1 kg	2.18 lb (35 oz)
1 fl oz	28.35 mL (approx 30 mL)	1 mL	0. 035 fl oz
1 pint (20 fl oz)	568 mL (approx 570 mL)	1 L	35 fl oz = 1.75 pints
1 gal	4.5 L		
1 in	2.54 cm	1 cm	0.39 in
1 ft	30.48 cm	1 m	39 in

Appendix II: Estimated average requirements for energy

age	males		females	
	kcal	MJ	kcal	MJ
0–3m	545	2.28	515	2.16
4–6m	690	2.89	645	2.69
7–9m	825	3.44	765	3.20
10–12m	920	3.85	865	3.61
1–3y	1230	5.15	1165	4.86
4–6y	1715	7.16	1545	6.46
7–10y	1970	8.24	1740	7.28
11–14y	2220	9.27	1845	7.92
15–18y	2755	11.51	2110	8.83
19–50y	2550	10.60	1940	8.10
51–59y	2550	10.60	1900	8.00
60–64y	2380	9.93	1900	7.99
65–74y	2330	9.71	1900	7.96
75+ y	2100	8.77	1810	7.61
pregnant			+200	+0.8
lactating 1m			+450	+1.9
lactating 2m			+530	+2.2
lactating 3m			+570	+2.4

These figures assume an average level of physical activity; people with a high level of activity have higher requirements, and those with a very sedentary life-style have lower requirements.

1 kcal = 4.184 kJ, rounded off to 4.2;
1000 kcal = 4200 kJ = 4.2 MJ

vitamin		functions	deficiency disease
A	retinol β-carotene	visual pigments in the retina; regulation of gene expression and cell differentiation (β-carotene is an antioxidant)	night blindness, xerophthalmia; keratinization of skin.
D	calciferol	maintenance of calcium balance; enhances intestinal absorption of Ca^{2+} and mobilizes bone mineral; regulation of gene expression and cell differentiation	rickets = poor mineralization of bone; osteomalacia = bone demineralization
E	tocopherols tocotrienols	antioxidant, especially in cell membranes; roles in cell signalling	extremely rare—serious neurological dysfunction
K	phylloquinone menaquinones	coenzyme in formation of γ-carboxy-glutamate in enzymes of blood clotting and bone matrix	impaired blood clotting, haemorrhagic disease
B_1	thiamin	coenzyme in pyruvate and 2-oxo-glutarate dehydrogenases, and transketolase; regulates Cl^- channel in nerve conduction	peripheral nerve damage (beriberi) or central nervous system lesions (Wernicke–Korsakoff syndrome)
B_2	riboflavin	coenzyme in oxidation and reduction reactions; prosthetic group of flavoproteins	lesions of corner of mouth, lips and tongue, sebhorroeic dermatitis
niacin	nicotinic acid nicotinamide	coenzyme in oxidation and reduction reactions, functional part of NAD and NADP; role in intracellular calcium regulation and cell signalling	pellagra—photosensitive dermatitis, depressive psychosis
B_6	pyridoxine pyridoxal pyridoxamine	coenzyme in transamination and decarboxylation of amino acids and glycogen phosphorylase; modulation of steroid hormone action	disorders of amino acid metabolism, convulsions

	folic acid	coenzyme in transfer of one-carbon fragments	megaloblastic anaemia
B_{12}	cobalamin	coenzyme in transfer of one-carbon fragments and metabolism of folic acid	pernicious anaemia = megaloblastic anaemia with degeneration of the spinal cord
	pantothenic acid	functional part of CoA and acyl carrier protein: fatty acid synthesis and metabolism	peripheral nerve damage (nutritional melalgia or 'burning foot syndrome')
H	biotin	coenzyme in carboxylation reactions in gluconeogenesis and fatty acid synthesis; role in regulation of cell cycle	impaired fat and carbohydrate metabolism, dermatitis
C	ascorbic acid	coenzyme in hydroxylation of proline and lysine in collagen synthesis; antioxidant; enhances absorption of iron	scurvy—impaired wound healing, loss of dental cement, subcutaneous haemorrhage

Appendix IV: US/Canadian Recommended Dietary Allowances and Acceptable Intakes, 1997–2001

age	vit A µg	vit D µg	vit E mg	vit K µg	vit B$_1$ mg	vit B$_2$ mg	niacin mg	vit B$_6$ mg	folate µg	vit B$_{12}$ µg	vit C mg	Ca mg	P mg	Mg mg	Fe mg	Zn mg	Cu µg	Se µg	I µg	Cr µg	Mn mg	Mo µg
0–6 m	400	5	4	2.0	0.2	0.3	2	0.1	65	0.4	40	210	100	30	–	2	200	15	110	0.2	–	2
7–12 m	500	5	5	2.5	0.3	0.4	4	0.3	80	0.5	50	270	275	75	11	3	220	20	130	5.5	0.6	3
1–3 y	300	5	6	30	0.5	0.5	6	0.5	150	0.9	15	500	460	80	7	3	340	20	90	11	1.2	17
4–8 y	400	5	7	55	0.5	0.6	8	0.6	200	1.2	25	800	500	130	10	5	440	30	90	15	1.5	22
males																						
9–13 y	600	5	11	60	0.9	0.9	12	1.0	300	1.8	45	1300	1250	240	8	8	700	40	120	25	1.9	34
14–18 y	900	5	15	75	1.2	1.3	16	1.3	400	2.4	75	1300	1250	410	11	11	890	55	150	35	2.2	43
19–30 y	900	5	15	120	1.2	1.3	16	1.3	400	2.4	90	1000	700	400	8	11	900	55	150	35	2.3	45
31–50 y	900	5	15	120	1.2	1.3	16	1.3	400	2.4	90	1000	700	420	8	11	900	55	150	35	2.3	45
51–70 y	900	10	15	120	1.2	1.3	16	1.7	400	2.4	90	1200	700	420	8	11	900	55	150	30	2.3	45
>70 y	900	15	15	120	1.2	1.3	16	1.7	400	2.4	90	1200	700	420	8	11	900	55	150	30	2.3	45
females																						
9–13 y	600	5	11	60	0.9	0.9	12	1.0	300	1.8	45	1300	1250	240	8	8	700	40	120	21	1.6	34
14–18 y	700	5	15	75	1.0	1.0	14	1.2	400	2.4	65	1300	1250	360	15	9	890	55	150	24	1.6	43
19–30 y	700	5	15	90	1.1	1.1	14	1.3	400	2.4	75	1000	700	310	18	8	900	55	150	25	1.8	45
31–50 y	700	5	15	90	1.1	1.1	14	1.3	400	2.4	75	1000	700	320	18	8	900	55	150	25	1.8	45
51–70 y	700	10	15	90	1.1	1.1	14	1.5	400	2.4	75	1200	700	320	8	8	900	55	150	20	1.8	45
>70 y	700	15	15	90	1.1	1.1	14	1.5	400	2.4	75	1200	700	320	8	8	900	55	150	20	1.8	45
pregnant	770	5	15	90	1.4	1.4	18	1.9	600	2.6	85	1000	700	350	27	11	1000	60	220	30	2.0	50
lactating	900	5	16	90	1.4	1.6	17	2.0	500	2.8	120	1000	700	310	9	12	1300	70	290	45	2.6	50

Figures for infants under 12months are Adequate Intakes, based on the observed mean intake of infants fed principally on breast milk; for nutrients other than vitamin K figures are RDA, based on estimated average requirement + 2 sd; figures for vitamin K are Adequate Intakes, based on observed average intakes. Figures for calcium, chromium, manganese are AI.

Appendix V: EU Population Reference Intakes of nutrients, 1993

age	protein g	vit A µg	vit B₁ mg	vit B₂ mg	niacin mg	vit B₆ mg	folate µg	vit B₁₂ µg	vit C mg	Ca mg	P mg	Fe mg	Zn mg	Cu mg	Se µg	I µg
6–12 m	15	350	0.3	0.4	5	0.4	50	0.5	20	400	300	6	4	0.3	8	50
1–3 y	15	400	0.5	0.8	9	0.7	100	0.7	25	400	300	4	4	0.4	10	70
4–6 y	20	400	0.7	1.0	11	0.9	130	0.9	25	450	350	4	6	0.6	15	90
7–10 y	29	500	0.8	1.2	13	1.1	150	1.0	30	550	450	6	7	0.7	25	100
males																
11–14 y	44	600	1.0	1.4	15	1.3	180	1.3	35	1000	775	10	9	0.8	35	120
15–17 y	55	700	1.2	1.6	18	1.5	200	1.4	40	1000	775	13	9	1.0	45	130
18+ y	56	700	1.1	1.6	18	1.5	200	1.4	45	700	550	9	9.5	1.1	55	130
females																
11–14 y	42	600	0.9	1.2	14	1.1	180	1.3	35	800	625	18	9	0.8	35	120
15–17 y	46	600	0.9	1.3	14	1.1	200	1.4	40	800	625	17	7	1.0	45	130
18+ y	47	600	0.9	1.3	14	1.1	200	1.4	45	700	550	16*	7	1.1	55	130
pregnant	57	700	1.0	1.6	14	1.3	400	1.6	55	700	550	*	7	1.1	55	130
lactating	63	950	1.1	1.7	16	1.4	350	1.9	70	1200	950	16	12	1.4	70	160

* 8mg iron post-menopausally; supplements required in latter half of pregnancy.

Appendix VI: UK Reference Nutrient Intakes, 1991

age	vit B$_1$	vit B$_2$	niacin	vit B$_6$	vit B$_{12}$	folate	vit C	vit A	vit D	Ca	P	Mg	Na	Fe	Zn	Cu	Se	I
	mg	mg	mg	mg	μg	μg	mg	μg	μg	mg	mg	mg	mg	mg	mg	mg	μg	μg
0–3 m	0.2	0.4	3	0.2	0.3	50	25	350	8.5	525	400	55	210	1.7	4.0	0.2	10	50
4–6 m	0.2	0.4	3	0.2	0.3	50	25	350	8.5	525	400	60	280	4.3	4.0	0.3	13	60
7–9 m	0.2	0.4	4	0.3	0.4	50	25	350	7.0	525	400	75	320	7.8	5.0	0.3	10	60
10–12 m	0.3	0.4	5	0.4	0.4	50	25	350	7.0	525	400	80	350	7.8	5.0	0.3	10	60
1–3 y	0.5	0.6	8	0.7	0.5	70	30	400	7.0	350	270	85	500	6.9	5.0	0.4	15	70
4–6 y	0.7	0.8	11	0.9	0.8	100	30	500		450	350	120	700	6.1	6.5	0.6	20	100
7–10 y	0.7	1.0	12	1.0	1.0	150	30	500		550	450	200	1200	8.7	7.0	0.7	30	110
males																		
11–14 y	0.9	1.2	15	1.2	1.2	200	35	600		1000	775	280	1600	11.3	9.0	0.8	45	130
15–18 y	1.1	1.3	18	1.5	1.5	200	40	700		1000	775	300	1600	11.3	9.5	1.0	70	140
19–50 y	1.0	1.3	17	1.4	1.5	200	40	700		700	550	300	1600	8.7	9.5	1.2	75	140
50+ y	0.9	1.3	16	1.4	1.5	200	40	700	10.0	700	550	300	1600	8.7	9.5	1.2	75	140
females																		
11–14 y	0.7	1.1	12	1.0	1.2	200	35	600		800	625	280	1600	14.8	9.0	0.8	45	130
15–18 y	0.8	1.1	14	1.2	1.5	200	40	600		800	625	300	1600	14.8	7.0	1.0	60	140
19–50 y	0.8	1.1	13	1.2	1.5	200	40	600		700	550	270	1600	14.8	7.0	1.2	60	140
50+ y	0.8	1.1	12	1.2	1.5	200	40	600	10.0	700	550	270	1600	8.7	7.0	1.2	60	140
pregnant	+0.1	+0.3				+100	+10	+100	10.0									
lactating	+0.1	+0.5	+2		+0.5	+60	+30	+350	10.0	+550	+440	+50			+6.0	+0.3	+15	

Appendix VII: Recommended Nutrient Intakes for vitamins, FAO 2001

age	vit A µg	vit D µg	vit K µg	vit B$_1$ mg	vit B$_2$ mg	niacin mg	vit B$_6$ mg	folate µg	vit B$_{12}$ µg	vit C mg	panto mg	biotin µg
0-6 m	375	5	5	0.2	0.3	2	0.1	80	0.4	25	1.7	5
7-12 m	400	5	10	0.3	0.4	4	0.3	80	0.5	30	1.8	6
1-3 y	400	5	15	0.5	0.5	6	0.5	160	0.9	30	2.0	8
4-6 y	450	5	20	0.6	0.6	8	0.6	200	1.2	30	3.0	12
7-9 y	500	5	25	0.9	0.9	12	1.0	300	1.8	35	4.0	20
males												
10-18y	600	5	35-55	1.2	1.3	16	1.3	400	2.4	40	5.0	30
19-50y	600	5	65	1.2	1.3	16	1.3	400	2.4	45	5.0	30
50-65y	600	10	65	1.2	1.3	16	1.7	400	2.4	45	5.0	30
> 65y	600	15	65	1.2	1.3	16	1.7	400	2.4	45	5.0	30
female												
10-18y	600	5	35-55	1.1	1.0	16	1.2	400	2.4	40	5.0	25
19-50y	600	5	55	1.1	1.1	14	1.3	400	2.4	45	5.0	30
50-65y	600	10	55	1.1	1.1	14	1.5	400	2.4	45	5.0	30
> 65y	600	15	55	1.1	1.1	14	1.5	400	2.4	45	5.0	30
pregnant	800	5	55	1.4	1.4	18	1.9	600	2.6	55	6.0	30
lactating	850	5	55	1.5	1.6	17	2.0	500	2.8	70	7.0	35

Appendix VIII: Food additives permitted in the EU

Colours

Yellow and orange colours

E100	Curcumin
E101	(i) Riboflavin, (ii) Riboflavin-5'-phosphate (vitamin B_2)
E102	Tartrazine (=FD&C Yellow no 6)
E104	Quinoline yellow
E110	Sunset Yellow FCF; Orange Yellow S (=FD&C Yellow no 6)

Red colours

E120	Cochineal; Carminic acid; Carmines
E122	Azorubine; Carmoisine
E123	Amaranth
E124	Ponceau 4R; Cochineal Red A
E127	Erythrosine (=FD&C Red no 3)
E129	Allura Red AC (=FD&C Red no 40)

Blue colours

E131	Patent Blue V
E132	Indigotine; Indigo Carmine (=FD&C Blue no 2)
E133	Brilliant Blue FCF (=FD&C Blue no 1)

Green colours

E140	Chlorophylls and chlorophyllins (the natural green colour of leaves)
E141	Copper complexes of chlorophyll and chlorophyllins
E142	Green S

Brown and black colours

E150a	Plain caramel
E150b	Caustic sulphite caramel
E150c	Ammonia caramel
E150d	Sulphite ammonia caramel
E151	Brilliant Black BN; Black PN
E153	Vegetable carbon
E154	Brown FK
E155	Brown HT

Derivatives of carotene

E160a	Carotenes
E160b	Annatto; Bixin; Norbixin
E160c	Paprika extract; Capsanthian; Capsorubin
E160d	Lycopene
E160e	Beta-apo-8'-carotenal (C30)
E160f	Ethyl ester of beta-apo-8'-carotenoic acid (C30)

Other plant colours

E161b	Lutein
E161g	Canthaxanthin
E162	Beetroot Red; Betanin
E163	Anthocyanins

Inorganic compounds used as colours

E170	Calcium carbonate
E171	Titanium dioxide
E172	Iron oxides and hydroxides
E173	Aluminium
E174	Silver
E175	Gold
E180	Litholrubine BK

Preservatives

Sorbic acid and its salts

E200	Sorbic acid
E202	Potassium sorbate
E203	Calcium sorbate

Benzoic acid and its salts

E210	Benzoic acid
E211	Sodium benzoate
E212	Potassium benzoate
E213	Calcium benzoate
E214	Ethyl *p*-hydroxybenzoate
E215	Sodium ethyl *p*-hydroxybenzoate
E218	Methyl *p*-hydroxybenzoate
E219	Sodium methyl *p*-hydroxybenzoate

Sulphur dioxide and its salts

E220	Sulphur dioxide
E221	Sodium sulphite
E222	Sodium hydrogen sulphite
E223	Sodium metabisulphite
E224	Potassium metabisulphite
E226	Calcium sulphite
E227	Calcium hydrogen sulphite
E228	Potassium hydrogen sulphite

Biphenyl and its derivatives

E230	Biphenyl; diphenyl (for surface treatment of citrus fruits)
E231	Orthophenyl phenol (for surface treatment of citrus fruits)
E232	Sodium orthophenyl phenol (sodium biphenyl-2-yl oxide)

Other preservatives

E234	Nisin
E235	Natamycin (NATA, for surface treatment of cheeses and dried cured sausages)
E239	Hexamethylene tetramine (hexamine)
E242	Dimethyl dicarbonate
E1105	Lysozyme (an antibacterial enzyme found in tears)

Pickling salts

E249	Potassium nitrite
E250	Sodium nitrite
E251	Sodium nitrate
E252	Potassium nitrate (saltpetre)

Acids and their salts

E280	Propionic acid
E281	Sodium propionate
E282	Calcium propionate
E283	Potassium propionate
E284	Boric acid
E285	Sodium tetraborate; borax

Antioxidants

Vitamin C

E300	Ascorbic acid
E301	Sodium ascorbate
E302	Calcium ascorbate
E304	Fatty acid esters of ascorbic acid (a lipid-soluble derivative of the vitamin)

Vitamin E

E306	Tocopherols (natural source, mixed isomers)
E307	Alpha-tocopherol
E308	Gamma-tocopherol
E309	Delta-tocopherol

Other antioxidants

E310	Propyl gallate
E311	Octyl gallate
E312	Dodecyl gallate
E315	Erythorbic acid (the D-isomer of vitamin C, little vitamin activity)
E316	Sodium erythorbate
E319	Tertiary butyl hydroquinone (TBHQ)
E320	Butylated hydroxyanisole (BHA)
E321	Butylated hydroxytoluene (BHT)
E586	4-Hexylresorcinol

Sweeteners

(Sugar alcohols used as bulk sweeteners)

E420	(i) Sorbitol, (ii) Sorbitol syrup
E421	Mannitol
E953	Isomalt
E955	Sucralose
E962	Salts of aspartame-acesulfame
E965	(i) Maltitol, (ii) Maltitol syrup
E966	Lactitol
E967	Xylitol

Intense (synthetic) sweeteners

E950	Acesulfame K
E951	Aspartame
E952	Cyclamic acid and its Na and Ca salts
E954	Saccharin and its Na, K, and Ca salts
E957	Thaumatin
E959	Neohesperidine DC

Emulsifiers, stabilizers, thickeners, and gelling agents

E322	Lecithins (found especially in egg yolk and soya bean)

Alginates

E400	Alginic acid
E401	Sodium alginate
E402	Potassium alginate
E403	Ammonium alginate
E404	Calcium alginate
E405	Propane-1,2-diol alginate

Plant gums (soluble fibre)

E406	Agar
E407	Carrageenan
E407a	Processed eucheuma seaweed
E410	Locust bean gum; carob gum
E412	Guar gum
E413	Tragacanth
E414	Acacia gum; gum arabic
E415	Xanthan gum
E416	Karaya gum
E417	Tara gum
E418	Gellan gum
E425	Konjac
E462	Soybean hemicellulose

Polysorbates

E432	Polyoxyethylene sorbitan monolaurate; Polysorbate 20
E433	Polyoxyethylene sorbitan mono-oleate; Polysorbate 80
E434	Polyoxyethylene sorbitan monopalmitate; Polysorbate 40
E435	Polyoxyethylene sorbitan monostearate; Polysorbate 60
E436	Polyoxyethylene sorbitan tristearate; Polysorbate 65

Cellulose derivatives

E460	Cellulose
E461	Methyl cellulose
E463	Hydroxypropyl cellulose
E464	Hydroxypropyl methyl cellulose
E465	Ethyl methyl cellulose
E466	Carboxy methyl cellulose, sodium carboxy methyl cellulose
E468	Cross-linked sodium carboxy methyl cellulose
E469	Enzymatically hydrolysed carboxy methyl cellulose

Fatty acid derivatives and modified fats

E470a	Sodium, potassium, and calcium salts of fatty acids
E470b	Magnesium salts of fatty acids
E471	Mono- and diglycerides of fatty acids

E472a	Acetic acid esters of mono- and diglycerides of fatty acids
E472b	Lactic acid esters of mono- and diglycerides of fatty acids
E472c	Citric acid esters of mono- and diglycerides of fatty acids
E472d	Tartaric acid esters of mono- and diglycerides of fatty acids
E472e	Mono- and diacetyltartaric acid esters of mono- and diglycerides of fatty acids
E472f	Mixed acetic and tartaric acid esters of mono- and diglycerides of fatty acids
E473	Sucrose esters of fatty acids
E474	Sucroglycerides
E475	Polyglycerol esters of fatty acids
E476	Polyglycerol polyricinoleate
E477	Propane-1,2-diol esters of fatty acids
E479b	Thermally oxidized soya bean oil interacted with mono-and diglycerides of fatty acids
E481	Sodium stearoyl-2-lactylate
E482	Calcium stearoyl-2-lactylate
E483	Stearyl tartrate
E491	Sorbitan monostearate
E492	Sorbitan tristearate
E493	Sorbitan monolaurate
E494	Sorbitan mono-oleate
E495	Sorbitan monopalmitate

Other compounds

E440	Pectins (found naturally in fruit, especially apples)
E442	Ammonium phosphatides
E444	Sucrose acetate isobutyrate
E445	Glycerol esters of wood rosins
E1103	Invertase

Other additives

Acid, acidity regulators, anti-caking agents, antifoaming agents, bulking agents, carriers and carrier solvents, emulsifying salts, firming agents, flavour enhancers, flour treatment agents, foaming agents, glazing agents, humectants, modified starches, packaging gases, propellants, raising agents, and sequestrants.

Acidity regulators

Carbon dioxide and carbonates

E170	Calcium carbonates
E290	Carbon dioxide
E500	Sodium carbonates
E501	Potassium carbonates
E503	Ammonium carbonates
E504	Magnesium carbonates

Acetic acid and its salts

E260	Acetic acid (vinegar is dilute acetic acid)
E261	Potassium acetate
E262	Sodium acetate
E263	Calcium acetate

Lactic acid and its salts

E270	Lactic acid (the acid of sour milk)
E325	Sodium lactate
E326	Potassium lactate
E327	Calcium lactate

Citric acid and its salts

E330	Citric acid
E331	Sodium citrates
E332	Potassium citrates
E333	Calcium citrates
E380	Triammonium citrate

Tartaric acid and its salts

E334	Tartaric acid (L-(+))
E335	Sodium tartrates

E336	Potassium tartrates (cream of tartar)
E337	Sodium potassium tartrate
E353	Metatartaric acid
E354	Calcium tartrate

Phosphoric acid and its salts

E338	Phosphoric acid
E339	Sodium phosphates
E340	Potassium phosphates
E341	Calcium phosphates
E343	Magnesium phosphates
E450	Diphosphates
E451	Triphosphates
E452	Polyphosphates
E541	Sodium aluminium phosphate

Malic acid and its salts

E296	Malic acid
E350	Sodium malates
E351	Potassium malate
E352	Calcium malates

Adipic acid and its salts

E355	Adipic acid
E356	Sodium adipate
E357	Potassium adipate

Hydrochloric acid and its salts

E507	Hydrochloric acid
E508	Potassium chloride
E509	Calcium chloride
E511	Magnesium chloride
E512	Stannous chloride

Sulphuric acid and its salts

E513	Sulphuric acid
E514	Sodium sulphates
E515	Potassium sulphates
E516	Calcium sulphate
E517	Ammonium sulphate
E520	Aluminium sulphate
E521	Aluminium sodium sulphate
E522	Aluminium potassium sulphate
E523	Aluminium ammonium sulphate

Other acids and their salts

E297	Fumaric acid
E363	Succinic acid
E385	Calcium disodium ethylene diamine tetra-acetate; calcium disodium EDTA

Alkalis

E524	Sodium hydroxide
E525	Potassium hydroxide
E526	Calcium hydroxide
E527	Ammonium hydroxide
E528	Magnesium hydroxide
E529	Calcium oxide
E530	Magnesium oxide

Other salts

E535	Sodium ferrocyanide
E536	Potassium ferrocyanide
E538	Calcium ferrocyanide

Compounds used as anti-caking agents and other uses

E422	Glycerol (used as a humectant, also for its sweetness)
E431	Polyoxyethylene (40) stearate
E459	Beta-cyclodextrin

Silicon salts

E551	Silicon dioxide
E552	Calcium silicate
E553a	(i) Magnesium silicate, (ii) Magnesium trisilicate
E553b	Talc
E554	Sodium aluminium silicate
E555	Potassium aluminium silicate
E556	Aluminium calcium silicate

Other compounds

E558	Bentonite
E559	Aluminium silicate; Kaolin
E570	Fatty acids
E574	Gluconic acid
E575	Glucono delta-lactone
E576	Sodium gluconate
E577	Potassium gluconate
E578	Calcium gluconate
E579	Ferrous gluconate
E585	Ferrous lactate

Compounds used as flavour enhancers

Amino acids

E620	Glutamic acid
E621	Monosodium glutamate
E622	Monopotassium glutamate
E623	Calcium diglutamate
E624	Monoammonium glutamate
E625	Magnesium diglutamate
E640	Glycine and its sodium salt

Nucleotides

E626	Guanylic acid
E627	Disodium guanylate
E628	Dipotassium guanylate
E629	Calcium guanylate
E630	Inosinic acid
E631	Disodium inosinate
E632	Dipotassium inosinate
E633	Calcium inosinate
E634	Calcium 5'-ribonucleotides
E635	Disodium 5'-ribonucleotides

Other compounds

E650	Zinc acetate

Compounds used as glazing agents

E900	Dimethylpolysiloxane
E901	Beeswax, white and yellow
E902	Candelilla wax
E903	Carnauba wax
E904	Shellac
E905	Microcrystalline wax
E912	Montan acid esters (for surface treatment of citrus fruits)
E914	Oxidized polyethylene wax

Compounds used to treat flour

E920	L-Cysteine (an amino acid)
E927b	Carbamide

Propellant gases

E938	Argon
E939	Helium
E941	Nitrogen
E942	Nitrous oxide
E943a	Butane
E943b	Iso-butane
E944	Propane
E948	Oxygen
E949	Hydrogen

Modified starches (used as thickening and gelling agents)

E1404	Oxidized starch
E1410	Monostarch phosphate
E1412	Distarch phosphate
E1413	Phosphated distarch phosphate
E1414	Acetylated distarch phosphate
E1420	Acetylated starch
E1422	Acetylated distarch adipate
E1440	Hydroxy propyl starch
E1442	Hydroxy propyl distarch phosphate
E1450	Starch sodium octanoyl succinate
E1451	Acetylated oxidized starch
E1452	Starch aluminium octenyl succinate, polyethylene glycol 6000

Miscellaneous compounds

E999	Quillaia extract
E1200	Polydextrose
E1201	Polyvinylpyrrolidone
E1202	Polyvinylpolypyrrolidone
E1204	Pullulan
E1505	Triethyl citrate
E1518	Glyceryl triacetate; triacetin
E1520	Propan-1,2-diol; propylene glycol

Oxford Paperback Reference

A Dictionary of Chemistry

Over 4,200 entries covering all aspects of chemistry, including physical chemistry and biochemistry.

'It should be in every classroom and library ... the reader is drawn inevitably from one entry to the next merely to satisfy curiosity.'

School Science Review

A Dictionary of Physics

Ranging from crystal defects to the solar system, 3,500 clear and concise entries cover all commonly encountered terms and concepts of physics.

A Dictionary of Biology

The perfect guide for those studying biology – with over 4,700 entries on key terms from biology, biochemistry, medicine, and palaeontology.

'lives up to its expectations; the entries are concise, but explanatory'

Biologist

'ideally suited to students of biology, at either secondary or university level, or as a general reference source for anyone with an interest in the life sciences'

Journal of Anatomy

Oxford Paperback Reference

Concise Medical Dictionary

Over 10,000 clear entries covering all the major medical and surgical specialities make this one of our best-selling dictionaries.

'"No home should be without one" certainly applies to this splendid medical dictionary'

Journal of the Institute of Health Education

'An extraordinary bargain'

New Scientist

'Excellent layout and jargon-free style'

Nursing Times

A Dictionary of Nursing

Comprehensive coverage of the ever-expanding vocabulary of the nursing professions. Features over 10,000 entries written by medical and nursing specialists.

An A-Z of Medicinal Drugs

Over 4,000 entries cover the full range of over-the-counter and prescription medicines available today. An ideal reference source for both the patient and the medical professional.

OXFORD

Oxford Paperback Reference

The Concise Oxford Companion to English Literature
Margaret Drabble and Jenny Stringer

Based on the best-selling *Oxford Companion to English Literature*, this is an indispensable guide to all aspects of English literature.

Review of the parent volume
'a magisterial and monumental achievement'

Literary Review

The Concise Oxford Companion to Irish Literature
Robert Welch

From the ogam alphabet developed in the 4th century to Roddy Doyle, this is a comprehensive guide to writers, works, topics, folklore, and historical and cultural events.

Review of the parent volume
'Heroic volume ... It surpasses previous exercises of similar nature in the richness of its detail and the ecumenism of its approach.'

Times Literary Supplement

A Dictionary of Shakespeare
Stanley Wells

Compiled by one of the best-known international authorities on the playwright's works, this dictionary offers up-to-date information on all aspects of Shakespeare, both in his own time and in later ages.

Oxford Paperback Reference

The Kings of Queens of Britain
John Cannon and Anne Hargreaves

A detailed, fully-illustrated history ranging from mythical and pre-conquest rulers to the present House of Windsor, featuring regional maps and genealogies.

A Dictionary of Dates
Cyril Leslie Beeching

Births and deaths of the famous, significant and unusual dates in history – this is an entertaining guide to each day of the year.

'a dipper's blissful paradise ... Every single day of the year, plus an index of birthdays and chronologies of scientific developments and world events.'

Observer

A Dictionary of British History
Edited by John Cannon

An invaluable source of information covering the history of Britain over the past two millennia. Over 3,600 entries written by more than 100 specialist contributors.

Review of the parent volume
'the range is impressive ... truly (almost) all of human life is here'
Kenneth Morgan, *Observer*

OXFORD